ELECTROMAGNETISM
Volume 2
Applications
Magnetic Diffusion and Electromagnetic Waves

ASHUTOSH PRAMANIK

Professor Emeritus, College of Engineering, Pune
Formerly of Corporate Research and Development Division, BHEL
(Senior Dy. General Manager)
and
The Universities of Birmingham and Leeds
(Research Engineer and Lecturer)
and
D.J. Gandhi Distinguished Visiting Professor, IIT Bombay

PHI Learning Private Limited

Delhi-110092
2014

₹ 525.00

ELECTROMAGNETISM VOLUME 2 (APPLICATIONS)
Magnetic Diffusion and Electromagnetic Waves
Ashutosh Pramanik

ISBN-978-81-203-4901-8

The export rights of this book are vested solely with the publisher.

Published by Asoke K. Ghosh, PHI Learning Private Limited, Rimjhim House, 111, Patparganj Industrial Estate, Delhi-110092 and Printed by Rajkamal Electric Press, Plot No. 2, Phase IV, HSIDC, Kundli-131028, Sonepat, Haryana.

To the revered memory of my parents
Tarapada Pramanik and **Renubala Pramanik**
whose encouragement and support for my professional career
made this book possible
and
to my grandson
Om S. Advant
for his love and affection

Contents

8. Magnetic Field of Steady Currents in Presence of Magnetic Materials...255–279

Plates

VOLUME 2
APPLICATIONS
Magnetic Diffusion and Electromagnetic Waves

Preface

The continuing good response to this book from various institutes and universities has encouraged me further to make some substantial additions and extrapolations which has made this book voluminous, so that it has now become necessary to divide the book *Electromagnetism: Theory and Applications*, Second Edition into two parts: *Electromagnetism (Theory)—Volume 1* and *Electromagnetism (Applications: Magnetic Diffusion and Electromagnetic Waves)—Volume 2*, even though there has been no break in the continuity of the underlying philosophy of this book as a whole.

The additions to the material contents of the book have been of two types; i.e. one type which is essential to maintain the continuity of the theme of presentation even when new material is being added; and the second type which elaborates some of the critical aspects of a topic, but such elaborations can be studied separately and might hamper the continuity of the main theme of presenting the subject in a logical manner. The first type of additions have been incorporated at suitable points in the main part of the text, and the second type of additions have been presented as additional appendices in the book. However, such selections have been very much a matter of personal choice, and not all readers have to necessarily agree on the choices made by the author.

An example of the first type of addition in the main text is shown by the "geometrical representation of the transformation equations of the vectors from one coordinate system to another system". Though the idea of geometrical representation of vectors is not a completely new idea as such presentations were used by masters like Prof. R.S. Elliot in 1960's and by Prof. Balanis in 1980's, they had fallen into disuse for quite some time. With the elimination of rigorous teaching of both Euclidean and coordinate geometry at the school level, it has become necessary to remind both students as well as teachers, the advantages offered by geometrical approach to the study of vectors and phaser (i.e. quantities defined by two parameters as against the scalars which are defined by one parameter only), as this technique enables easier pictorial visualization of the vectors as used in the study of electromagnetic phenomena, thus making the appreciation of the inside-physics of such problems simpler with greater clarity. Hence it can be justifiably argued that such diagrammatic explanation of vector representation can be considered as an integral part of teaching this topic right from the beginning. Similarly the additional material in the chapter on vector potentials which deals with new types of potentials can also be taken as necessary tools to be used for further study of applications of electromagnetic waves as well as magnetic diffusion.

An earlier omission of the concept of complex permittivity has now been corrected and amplified by including not only this topic but also complex permeability as well as the methods of including the effects of all the constitutive parameters in anisotropic media which would also include problems in the area of nanotechnology. The consideration of conductivity has also been extended to the concepts of surface resistivity (useful in evaluating the wall-losses in wave-guides) and finally to the derivation of the surface current (i.e. current sheet) from both the wave equation as well as the diffusion equation (eddy current approach). All types of currents have been explained, including the space-charge limited current.

Furthermore with increasing research on permanent magnet machines, a more detailed study of B–H loops of Ferromagnetic materials has been provided. Methods of designing and analysing permanent magnets for various applications using even classical methods, viz. Fröhlich equation, Evershed criterion etc. have also been described in reasonable details. With the advent of computers, these methods had been considered to be outdated and eliminated from modern books of electromagnetism (and to be found in old classical books). But with the revival of new types of machines, such methods are again coming into prominence. There has also been a relook at Faraday's law of electromagnetic induction as an effect of relative motion of the observer with reference to magnetic field and the coil. The concept of 'moving field'—its mathematical interpretation and physical meaning, and its correlation with 'pulsating field'—usually dealt with superficially—has now been explained using practical examples. Also the distinction between mechanical forces of magnetic origin as well as of electromagnetic origin, has been explained by using experimental techniques. The new developments, with increasing applications, like 'Halbach magnets' with one-sided flux, and also some others have been discussed and explained in reasonable depth.

On the high frequency aspects of electromagnetism, the topics like wave polarization, mechanism of radiation, concept of aperture in receiving antennae, etc.—topics which are usually glossed over, have been now explained in sufficient details in separate appendices (usually meant for serious readers). The method of images has also been extended to problems of discrete conduction currents along with displacement currents—used usually in antennae problems. The topics of electromechanical energy conversion and Maxwell's stresses have now been supplemented by their tensor formalisms.

Regarding the study of numerical methods, the functionals used in F.E.M. for various operating equations, including those of axi-symmetric problems of both scalar and vector potentials have now been described. The methods for treating open-boundary problems by F.E.M. have also been indicated.

I would like to express my sincere thanks to Prof. S.C. Mehrotra of the Department of Computer Science (and originally of physics) of Marathwada University, for bringing to my notice the omission of the concept of complex permittivity in the previous edition of my book— an omission which has now been adequately covered. I also acknowledge most gratefully, the detailed discussions on various topics of Electromagnetism I had with my colleague Mr. Srinivas Baka, which have helped me in reformulating a number of ideas in this edition. Three of my postgraduate students whose discussions and questions have stimulated me significantly about the presentation of the topics have been Meenal Kulkarni, Md. Moti-ur-Reza and Priyanka Bastawade and I acknowledge their contributions and help.

My thanks are also due to Prof. S.S. Dambare, Head of the Department and Prof. B.N. Chaudhari, for providing the necessary facilities in the department, I acknowledge hereby the help and support of Mr. Darshan Kumar, Senior Editor (Retd.) and subsequently Ms. Shivani Garg, Senior Editor and Mr. Sachin Jadhav, Regional Marketing Officer of PHI Learning for their help and support in preparing this edition.

Last but not the least, I acknowledge with love, the unstinting encouragement and support from my daughter Mrinmayee, along with my son-in-law Sreekant Advant and my grandson Om, and the silent and patient forbearance of my wife Lalita in spite of her ill-health during this period.

There has been continuous and sincere effort on my part to eliminate printing errors and omissions as far as possible, but it is very likely that there are some which have been overlooked. I shall be most grateful to all readers who would kindly bring to my notice all such omissions and missed out errors which can then be eliminated in subsequent editions.

ASHUTOSH PRAMANIK

Preface to the Second Edition

The good response received by this book from various institutes and universities, has encouraged me to make some additions and a few minor changes in this edition. The basic structure of the book and the philosophy of presentation of the subject matter, of course, have remained unchanged. A substantial amount of additional material, mostly dealing with applications, has been incorporated.

To start with, the vector transformations in different coordinate systems, have now been included. The topics of Electrostatics and Magnetostatics had already been dealt with, fairly adequately, and hence remain unaltered. Some historical comments have been introduced at various places in the book, in order to enhance the understanding of the process of development of the subject. A proof for the independent boundary conditions as derived from the integral form of the Maxwell's equations has now been presented in a separate appendix. Since the Bessel functions and the Legendre functions are widely used in waveguides and antennae, an appendix dealing with the properties of these functions, has now been provided. The chapter on the vector potential has been significantly expanded as the need for a clearer understanding of the properties of the vector potentials, has now become increasingly important because more and more three-dimensional electromagnetic problems (not merely static problems) are being solved numerically. The simplicity of the vector potential for two-dimensional problems is no longer there, as in three-dimensional problems, the magnetic vector potential ($\mathbf{A}$) would have more than one component. In this context, Carpenter's electric vector potential ($\mathbf{T}$) might be of some help in some of the eddy current problems, but there are quite a number of problems where the $\mathbf{A}$ vector might be a preferred choice. A device which has not been much exploited in the numerical solutions is the Hertz vector ($\mathbf{Z}_e$ or $\mathbf{Z}_m$). Hence a section dealing with its derivation and interpretation has been included in this chapter. One of the great attractions of the Hertz vector has been that it combines in itself the capabilities of the vector potential as well as the scalar potential and thus eliminates the need for using the two potentials for the complete solution. Though the Hertz vector has been used mostly for wave problems so far, this is not an essential restriction for this vector, as its general definition does include the conducting region parameter (σ) and hence can be used for solving the eddy current problems where required.

A practical problem on induction heating has now been added to the chapter on Magnetic Diffusion as an illustration of the analysis of a practical device. Though the topic of wave propagation had been dealt with adequately and comprehensively, the topics of wave guidance and radiation have now been expanded with emphasis on the practical aspects. This requirement has come up due to new development like optical fibres, and I have used the present opportunity to make suitable additions to both in waveguides and antennae. I have also included the theory of Bicylindrical coordinate system as a separate appendix to provide the physical basis of the circuit approach to the cylindrical transmission line systems. The characteristics of antennae and arrays have now been considered in some detail, so that the mathematical basis has now been better balanced by practical details. The chapter on special relativity now includes the effects of Lorentz transformation on both forces and energy. Originally the chapter on 'Numerical Analysis' dealt with the variational basis of the FEM. This has now been supplemented by a simple description of the procedural details of the method so as to enable the reader to use the method without going into the heavy mathematics underlying the method. A short description of the FDTD (finite difference in time domain) has been added because this method is now being used to analyse microstrip antennae. However a short description of the method of moments (MOM) has been put in a separate appendix because even though it is being used numerically, it is basically an integral method. The inclusion of this method is justified because quite a large range of problems relating to antennae are being solved by MOM. A new chapter on 'Modern Topics and Applications' has now been added which covers both the high-frequency and the low-frequency applications. This chapter contains brief descriptions of topics ranging from microwaves and satellite communications to maglev systems for transportations. Finally the Appendix 6 which dealt with non-conservative fields, has now been expanded further to have a relook at the concept of self-inductance.

I would like to express my sincere thanks to Prof. S.V. Kulkarni of the Department of Electrical Engineering, IIT Bombay, who was instrumental in organizing my stay as a visiting faculty member in his department, and also for his interest in the subject of Electromagnetism. I had many stimulating discussions with him which have helped me in selecting the material for this edition. My sincere thanks are also due to Prof. R.K. Shevgaonkar, then head of the department, who very kindly asked me to act as a referee for his NPTEL course on 'Electromagnetic Waves'. His refreshing and lucid approach to the topic along with his book on *Electromagnetic Waves* have been the source of inspiration for me to make the necessary additions to the topics of Electromagnetic Waves described here. I am indebted to Prof. R.P. Aiyer of the Advanced Centre for Research in Electronics (ACRE) for the section on FDTD and for his general interest in the electromagnetic problems. It was Prof. Agashe's interest in the Relativistic aspects that encouraged me to incorporate the additional material in the chapter dealing with that topic. I take this opportunity to thank him for his interest and for the discussions I had with him.

I would also like to express my thanks to all the members of the 'Field Computation Lab' for their interest in the electromagnetic problems. The discussions I had with them have resulted in some of the additions to this book. Though I cannot name all of them, I must mention the help and interest of Messrs Avinash Bhangaonkar, Ravindra Bhide and K. Kaushik. I am also indebted to Mr. E. Ramaswamy of Crompton Greaves, Mumbai for his interest and stimulating discussions on various aspects of electromagnetism, particularly on topics related to non-conservative fields of Appendix VI in this book. I would take this opportunity to thank my old friend Mr. T.K. Mukherjee, originally of BHEL, then Crompton Greaves and now Executive Director, C.G. Core-El, who introduced me to Prof. S.V. Kulkarni and thus started this whole sequence of events.

My thanks are also due to Mr. S. Ramaswamy, Regional Sales Manager, Mr. Darshan Kumar, Senior Editor, and Ms. Pushpita Ghosh, Managing Editor of Prentice-Hall of India for their interest and support in bringing out this edition successfully. Last but not the least, my thanks are due to my daughter Mrinmayee for her constant encouragement and support for completing this job and my wife Lalita for her patience and forbearance during this period.

I have tried to eliminate the printing errors and omissions as far as possible, but it is likely that some would have been missed out. I shall be grateful to all the readers who would kindly bring to my notice any such missed-out errors, which can then be eliminated in subsequent printruns and editions.

ASHUTOSH PRAMANIK

Preface to the First Edition

This book is the culmination of a long experience in both industrial research as well as teaching in academic and professional world in more than one country, dealing with mostly electromagnetic problems in engineering. There are, of course, a number of good books on electromagnetism for students and engineers and scientists in industries and research institutes. But most of these books have a strong bias towards wave problems and high frequency engineering. There has been, in general, a tendency to gloss over in-depth exposition of eddy current problems in most of these books, with a few minor exceptions. Even there, mostly simple and highly idealized problems, away from real-life situations, have only been considered. While working in industrial research in the UK and India, in the area of applied electromagnetism dealing with problems of eddy current effects and associated loss and force calculations in generating and allied equipment, a need for a book on electromagnetism dealing comprehensively with eddy current aspects was strongly felt. The feeling for this need was further enhanced while teaching electromagnetism to engineering students in the UK (to both power engineering as well as high frequency electronics) at undergraduate and postgraduate levels as well as to design and development engineers in industry in India.

Most of the present textbooks and reference books on electromagnetism have dealt in great details the problems of wave propagation, transmission, reflection and refraction in different media, while paying relatively scant attention to magnetic diffusion and current distributions in conducting media. The present book has tried to correct this imbalance without in any way sacrificing the details of the study of electromagnetic waves. Any book on electromagnetism would require a certain minimum level of mathematical knowledge on the part of the readers, though the necessary mathematical knowledge has been kept to a minimum. The book assumes a knowledge of basic differential and integral calculus and elementary differential equations, and an introductory chapter on applications of vector calculus has been added to help and remind the readers about those aspects of vectors which are necessary and are used in the study of the subject. However it must be reminded that though a certain minimum amount of elementary mathematics has to be used in a textbook on electromagnetics, the main emphasis in this book has been on the "physics" (or "inside physics") of the various phenomena discussed herein. From this point of view, the students of applied mathematics and theoretical physics may find a certain lack of mathematical rigour and elegance at some places in the book, but this has been found necessary in order to keep in mind the need for explaining the physical aspects. Advanced mathematical concepts, wherever they have been used, been usually explained before showing their usage in applications. Use of tensor calculus has been avoided in the most of the text, till the last but one chapter which deals with the relativistic aspects of electromagnetism, necessary for explaining the behaviour of homopolar machines.

This book follows a quasi-historical approach to the subject starting with the presentation of electrostatics, even though the fundamental basis of electromagnetism is "Maxwell's electromagnetic field equations". The reason for this approach has been that a knowledge of the historical progress of the development of the subject enables the learner to appreciate the logical progress that took place in the development of the subject. However in a textbook for students, it is not possible to adhere to strict historical sequence, because of certain conceptual difficulties that arise during the learning of various topics. Hence after starting with electrostatics followed by electric current and then magnetostatics, it has been necessary to bring in quasi-static magnetic fields before completing the study of magnetostatics. One of the main reasons for such a break-up is that a topic like inductance cannot be explained completely on the basis of magnetostatics only and hence quasi-static magnetism and electromagnetic induction have to be brought in before completing static magnetism. Another such topic which has to be brought in earlier is the concept of magnetic vector potential, which logically follows from Maxwell's equations. In this context, this book presents, for the first time (in the history of electromagnetism), the concept of electric vector potential, as developed by C.J. Carpenter, because of its wide applicability in solving eddy current problems. Also, while discussing the energy transfer process, the energy vectors other than Poynting vector have been described in some detail, as for example Slepian vectors. This has been done because in spite of the simplicity, elegance and wide acceptance of the Poynting vector, it does not explain fully the inside mechanism of the energy transfer process and some of the Slepian vectors seem to offer a more acceptable explanation of the processes. There are other topics, such as mechanical forces due to time-varying currents, magnetic field analysis of electro-mechanical energy transfer and a variety of eddy current problems that have been overlooked in books on electromagnetics, which have been now included here. Finally, the approach to electromagnetism via special relativity has now assumed greater importance from practical viewpoint. This is because it (this approach) clears up a lot of ambiguity and confusion in explaining of number of examples of electromagnetic induction, including the homopolar device of Faraday's disc type motor which is assuming greater practical importance with the applications of superconducting dc machines.

This book provides a comprehensive treatment of the subject for the students. Even though the present move in teaching is for shorter courses on electromagnetism, the need for a comprehensive book with latest developments included becomes greater because the student has to do a greater amount of self-study to complement the shorter teaching hours.

A book like this can only be produced with plenty of assistance from the author's colleagues during his professional life. First and foremost I would like to thank very sincerely and deeply my guide and friend Mr. J.G. Henderson of the department of Electronic and Electrical Engineering, the University of Birmingham, who first introduced me to electromagnetic problems and then guided and helped me during my research in academic world as well as in industry. I also wish to record my thanks to Mr. J.M. Layton and Dr. T.S.M. MacClean (Reader in Electromagnetism) of the same department for stimulating and interesting discussions I had with them during my stay in the department. I acknowledge gratefully the help I received regarding the presentation of guided waves. My thanks are also due to Mr. A.B.J. Reece who headed the Electromagnetics Lab of Nelson Research Laboratories of English Electric Co. (now part of G.E.C., U.K.) for his help and guidance on end-winding problems of hydrogenerators and turbogenerators, while I was working with him. I would like to express my thanks and gratefulness to Late Prof. G.W. Carter of the department of Electrical and Electronic Engineering, the University of Leeds, for his help and discussions in collecting my material for this book. I freely acknowledge his contributions to the chapter "Relativity and Electromagnetism". In fact on his day of retirement Prof. Carter presented me with all his notes and papers on relativity as well as electromagnetism (including some of the early edition of papers by his late father, Dr. F.W. Carter) which are my treasured possessions now. I have borrowed-freely and copiously in preparing the Chapter 20 of this book. My sincere thanks are also due to Prof. P.J. Lawrenson, F.R.S. of the same department for many discussions and for his work and help on conformal transformation problems, as well as for the finite difference analysis of various electromagnetic problems. Some of the other colleagues whose help and discussions I would like to acknowledge are Dr. J.M. Stephenson, Mr. M. McDermott, Dr. J.R. Richardson and Mr. D. Dring.

I would also like to thank my ex-colleagues in the Electromagnetic Phenomena Laboratory of Bharat Heavy Electricals Ltd. Corporate Research and Development, at Hyderabad for the various stimulating discussions and arguments I had with them, during my stewardship of the Laboratory. I would like to mention particularly Mr. M.M. Bhaway, Mr. C. Prem Kumar and Dr. S.C. Bhargava of the Laboratory for their queries and discussions on various projects and topics. For the field plots of Chapter 21, I am thankful to Mr. Bhaway and Dr. Parthasarathy of my laboratory. I would also like to acknowledge the discussions I had with Dr. K. Eswaran and Mr. R.V.S. Krishna Dutt of Applied Analysis Laboratory of the same organization. Finally, I would like to thank and acknowledge the help of Dr. M.V.K. Chari, Director of Research, General Electric, Schenectady for the sections on Finite Element method. Dr. Chari delivered a 4-week course on FEM at BHEL–R&D, during his visit to our laboratories and I have borrowed heavily and freely from his material, which I do acknowledge.

Prof. S.C. Dutta Roy of IIT Delhi deserves my sincere thanks for his encouragement in writing this book and also for his help during the process of publication.

Last but not the least, my thanks are due to both my daughter Mrinmayee and my wife Lalita for their help and patience during the preparation of this book. My daughter has helped me with numerous discussions as a physicist during the writing of the book and without her help as a computer expert it would have been impossible to computerize the book. My wife's patience, forbearance and tolerance has seen me through the preparation of the manuscript and also during this long process of printing. I also would like to record my thanks to editorial and production departments of Prentice-Hall of India (particularly to editor Mr. Darshan Kumar) for their patience and their bearing with me during the printing of this book, and Mr. S. Ramaswamy, Marketing Executive, Prentice-Hall of India for his help to expedite the process of publishing.

ASHUTOSH PRAMANIK

15 Time-Varying Fields in Conductors (Magnetic Diffusion)

15.1 INTRODUCTION

During our study of the Maxwell's equations in Chapter 12, we found that these equations could be combined together to produce an operating equation in terms of a single field vector (i.e. the vector Helmholtz equation), which could be further reduced to two limiting equations. In the present chapter, we shall consider one of those two limiting cases, i.e. in the conducting media and at relatively low frequencies, the displacement current term can be neglected, so that the operating equation of our interest is

$$\nabla^2 \mathbf{H} - j\omega\mu\sigma\mathbf{H} = 0 \tag{12.39a}$$

$$\nabla^2 \mathbf{E} - j\omega\mu\sigma\mathbf{E} = 0 \tag{12.39b}$$

(assuming sinusoidal time-harmonic variations of the field vectors—though we shall consider some non-sinusoidal transient problems as well). These problems fall under the general category of eddy currents and skin effect types. In most of these problems, we can use the above equations as the starting point, though for the initial few problems, we shall derive the specific operating equation starting from the Maxwell's equations for the sake of clarity and a proper insight into the physics of the problems. In general, we shall evaluate the current distributions as well as the magnetic field distributions in the conducting bodies, followed by the energy dissipations or the losses and the energy transfers by both the Poynting vector as well as the current density distributions in the structures.

15.2 ALTERNATING CURRENT DISTRIBUTION IN A SEMI-INFINITE CONDUCTING BLOCK (SIMPLEST EXAMPLE OF THE VECTOR DIFFUSION-TYPE EQUATION)

Alternating current (ac) phenomena at a fixed frequency $f = \omega/2\pi$ are being investigated by the phasor method, in which we can write

$$\mathbf{J} = \text{Re}\{\mathbf{J}\} \exp(j\omega t) \tag{15.1}$$

Here $\{\mathbf{J}\}$ stands for a set of three complex numbers, just as $\mathbf{J}$ is a set of three time-varying components. The fourth Maxwell's equation [i.e. Eq. (12.18)] then takes the form

$$\operatorname{curl} \{\mathbf{H}\} = \nabla \times \{\mathbf{H}\} = \{\mathbf{J}\} + j\omega\{\mathbf{D}\} \tag{15.2}$$

[i.e. Eq. (12.22)].

Let us consider the relative magnitudes of the last two terms in a region filled with a material of conductivity σ and permittivity $\varepsilon/\varepsilon_0$.

Let $\mathbf{E}$ have a maximum value $\hat{E}$ in a certain direction, then $\mathbf{J}$ has the maximum value of $\sigma\hat{E}$ and $\mathbf{D}$ has the maximum value of $\varepsilon\hat{E}$ in the same direction.

$$\therefore \qquad \left|\frac{\text{Displacement current density}}{\text{Conduction current density}}\right| = \frac{\omega\varepsilon\hat{E}}{\sigma\hat{E}} = \omega\varepsilon\rho \tag{15.3}$$

where $\rho = 1/\sigma$.

For copper, $\rho = 1.7 \times 10^{-8}$ Ω-m and $\varepsilon = \varepsilon_0 = 8.854 \times 10^{-12}$.

The above ratio $\rightarrow 1$, when $f \rightarrow 10^{18}$ Hz (X-rays).

$\therefore$ For communication frequencies $< 10^6$ Hz, it is negligible in copper.

$\therefore$ For such problems, the displacement current can reasonably be neglected.

We now consider a semi-infinite block of resistivity ρ and permeability μ/μ_0 with one plane face taken as $x = 0$ (Figure 15.1). An alternating magnetizing force $\mathbf{H}_0$ is applied at this

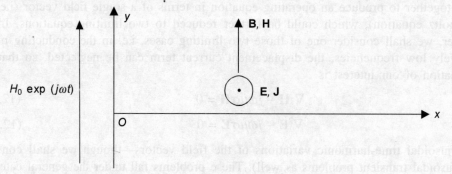

Figure 15.1 Semi-infinite conducting block subjected to an alternating magnetic field.

surface in the direction Oy, setting up $\mathbf{B}$ in the same direction in the material. The variations in $\mathbf{B}$ set up the electric fields and the consequent induced currents in the perpendicular Oz direction (i.e. normal to the plane of the paper). All the quantities will be phasors, so the notation $\{\mathbf{J}\}$ is not needed. For simplicity we write $\mathbf{B}, \mathbf{H}, \mathbf{J}, \mathbf{E}$ which are all assumed to be complex numbers, with the real quantity $\mathbf{H}_0$ acting as the reference phasor.

The relevant equations are:

$$\operatorname{div} \mathbf{B} = \nabla \cdot \mathbf{B} = 0 \tag{15.4a}$$

$$\operatorname{curl} \mathbf{E} = \nabla \times \mathbf{E} = -\frac{\partial \mathbf{B}}{\partial t} \tag{15.4b}$$

$$\operatorname{curl} \mathbf{H} = \nabla \times \mathbf{H} = \mathbf{J} \tag{15.4c}$$

$$\mathbf{E} = \rho\mathbf{J} \tag{15.4d}$$

$$\mathbf{B} = \mu\mathbf{H} \tag{15.4e}$$

with $\mathbf{B} = \mathbf{i}_x 0 + \mathbf{i}_y B_y + \mathbf{i}_z 0$ where $\mathbf{B}$ varies with x only, the zero divergence of $\mathbf{B}$ is automatically satisfied. Inserting the components into the other equations, and treating all the quantities as phasors so that the $\partial/\partial t$ operator becomes $j\omega$,

$$\frac{dE_z}{dx} = j\omega B_y \tag{15.5a}$$

$$\frac{dH_y}{dx} = J_z \tag{15.5b}$$

$$E_z = \rho J_z \tag{15.5c}$$

$$B_y = \mu H_y \tag{15.5d}$$

$$\therefore \qquad j\omega B_y = \frac{dE_z}{dx} = \rho\left(\frac{dJ_z}{dx}\right) = \rho\left(\frac{d^2 H_y}{dx^2}\right) = \left(\frac{\rho}{\mu}\right)\left(\frac{d^2 B_y}{dx^2}\right)$$

or

$$\frac{d^2 B_y}{dx^2} - j\left(\frac{\omega\mu}{\rho}\right) B_y = 0 \tag{15.6}$$

The other quantities H_y, E_z, J_z all obey equations of the same form. The dimensions of Eq. (15.6) show that the quantity $(\omega\mu/\rho)$ must have the dimensions of $(1/\text{length}^2)$; we thus write

$$\left(\frac{\rho}{\omega\mu}\right)^{1/2} = d \tag{15.7}$$

and obtain

$$\left(\frac{d^2 B_y}{dx^2}\right) - \left(\frac{j}{d^2}\right) B_y = 0 \tag{15.8}$$

The general solution of this equation is

$$B_y = B_1 \exp\left(\frac{x\sqrt{j}}{d}\right) + B_2 \exp\left(\frac{-x\sqrt{j}}{d}\right) \tag{15.9}$$

where B_1 and B_2 are unknown constants of integration to be determined.

Boundary conditions to evaluate the unknowns B_1 and B_2.   For a semi-infinite block, B_1 must be zero to keep the value of B_y finite as $x \to \infty$; also at $x = 0$, $B_y = B_0 = \mu H_0 = B_2$.
     Thus

$$B_y = B_0 \exp\left(\frac{-x\sqrt{j}}{d}\right) \tag{15.10}$$

But

$$\sqrt{j} = \frac{1+j}{\sqrt{2}}$$

So

$$B_y = B_0 \exp\left(\frac{-x(1+j)}{d\sqrt{2}}\right)$$

or

$$B_y = B_0 \exp\left(\frac{-x}{d\sqrt{2}}\right)\left[\cos\left(\frac{x}{d\sqrt{2}}\right) - j \sin\left(\frac{x}{d\sqrt{2}}\right)\right] \qquad (15.11)$$

In fact, if we include the time-variation term explicitly in the above expression,

$$B_y = B_0 \exp\left[\frac{-x(1+j)}{d\sqrt{2}}\right] \exp(j\omega t)$$

or

$$B_y = B_0 \exp\left(\frac{-x}{d\sqrt{2}}\right)\left[\cos\left(\frac{x}{d\sqrt{2}} - \omega t\right) - j \sin\left(\frac{x}{d\sqrt{2}} - \omega t\right)\right] \qquad (15.12)$$

The first term $B_0 \exp\{-x/(d\sqrt{2})\}$ represents the amplitude of B_y as we penetrate into the block normal to the $x = 0$ surface, and the term in the bracket indicates the phase of B_y at each point x and at the instant of time t. The above expression shows that the vector **B** is a wave penetrating into the block moving forward in the x-direction, but as the wave penetrates further in, the amplitude of the wave is continually getting attenuated (Figure 15.2). Such a phenomenon is

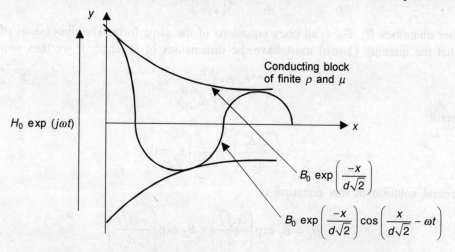

Figure 15.2 B_y wave diffusing into the conducting block.

called 'diffusion'. It will be seen that the magnetic field vector **B** (as all other field vectors) have the maximum value at the surface $x = 0$, and the magnitude decreases exponentially as x increases, the damping term (factor) being exp $\{-x/(d\sqrt{2})\}$.

At a depth $x = d\sqrt{2}$, known as the 'depth of penetration', $B_y = (1/e)B_0$, i.e. B is $(1/e) = 0.368$ or 36.8% of the surface value of B (i.e. B_0 or B_S). The flux is thus mainly confined to the surface layers of the material. Next we calculate the total flux in the material, i.e. the total flux per unit length measured perpendicular to the plane of the diagram ($= \Phi$) is given by

$$\Phi = \int_{x=0}^{x \to \infty} B_0 \exp\left(\frac{-x\sqrt{j}}{d}\right) dx = \frac{B_0 d}{\sqrt{j}}\left[- \exp\left(\frac{-x\sqrt{j}}{d}\right)\right]\Bigg|_0^\infty$$

$$= -\left(\frac{B_0 d\sqrt{2}}{1+j}\right)\left(\frac{1}{\infty}-1\right) = \frac{B_0 d(1-j)}{\sqrt{2}} \tag{15.13}$$

The term $(1-j)/\sqrt{2}$ has the modulus unity, and shows that the total flux Φ lags the surface flux density by 45°. The multiplying term of B_0 in the above equation shows that the magnitude of the total flux Φ is the same as if the flux density at the surface ($= B_0$) had the constant value over the depth d. Thus d gives a measure of the effectiveness of the material as a carrier of the magnetic flux (or of current). On this basis, Professor Carter in his book, calls 'd' as the depth of penetration. But the more accepted definition of the depth of penetration is now $d\sqrt{2}$ which we also have accepted in our present discussion.

In copper, at 50 Hz, $\rho = 1.7 \times 10^{-8}$ Ω-m, $d\sqrt{2}$ = 0.93 cm. In iron, at the same frequency, taking $\rho = 10^{-7}$ Ω-m and $\mu = 10^3\mu_0$, $d\sqrt{2}$ = 0.071 cm. Thus there is no point in making the diameter of the wires, or the thickness of the transformer laminations, greater than about twice the depth of penetration at the operating frequency. This tendency for the alternating flux or current to crowd towards the surface of the material is called the 'skin effect'.

The other vectors may be derived from Eq. (15.10) via Eq. (15.5). Thus,

$$J_z = \frac{dH_y}{dx} = \left(\frac{1}{\mu}\right)\left(\frac{dB_y}{dx}\right) = -\left(\frac{B_0\sqrt{j}}{\mu d}\right)\exp\left(\frac{-x\sqrt{j}}{d}\right)$$

and

$$E_z = \rho J_z = -\left(B_0 \omega d\sqrt{j}\right)\exp\left(\frac{-x\sqrt{j}}{d}\right) \tag{15.14}$$

since $\omega\mu/\rho = 1/d^2$ and $\omega d = \rho/(\mu d)$.

Just as we have plotted B_y as a function of x in the metal block (Figure 15.2), we shall now plot J_z (in the metal block) in the complex plane, to show the variations of the current density vector J_z, both in magnitude and phase (Figure 15.3), i.e.

$$J_z = -\left(\frac{B_0\sqrt{j}}{\mu d}\right)\exp\left(\frac{-x\sqrt{j}}{d}\right) = J_0 \exp\left(\frac{-x}{d\sqrt{2}}\right)\exp\left(\frac{-jx}{d\sqrt{2}}\right)$$

$$= J_0 \exp\left(\frac{-x}{d\sqrt{2}}\right) \angle -\theta$$

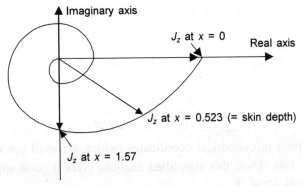

Figure 15.3   Complex plane diagram for J_z at various distances x from the surface of the semi-infinite metal block.

where

J_0 = the surface current density

$\theta = x/(d\sqrt{2})$.

In a circular wire of diameter $2a \gg (d\sqrt{2})$, the current-carrying skin can be treated as a plane. (This, of course, is an approximation, which is justifiable.) Its width is $2\pi a$. Therefore, by analogy with Eq. (15.13), (Figure 15.4), the total current I is given by

$$I = 2\pi a J_0 d\left(\frac{1-j}{\sqrt{2}}\right) \tag{15.15}$$

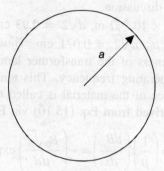

Figure 15.4   A metal wire of circular cross-section of radius $a \gg d\sqrt{2}$.

where J_0 is the surface current density $= -\left(\dfrac{B_0\sqrt{j}}{\mu d}\right)$

or

$$I = 2\pi a d J_0\left(\frac{1-j}{\sqrt{2}}\right)$$

∴   The voltage drop V per unit length of the conductor is

$$V = \rho J_0 = \frac{\rho I}{2\pi a d}\left(\frac{1+j}{\sqrt{2}}\right) \tag{15.16}$$

We may thus write

$$V = (R + j\omega L)I, \qquad \text{where } R = \omega L = \frac{\rho}{2\sqrt{2}\pi a d} \tag{15.17}$$

The skin effect thus increases the resistance of the wire, and in addition causes it to have inductance. The resistance R_0 per unit length, at very low frequencies (and for dc at $f = 0$) is $\rho/(\pi a^2)$.

∴

$$\frac{R_{ac}}{R_0} = \frac{\omega L}{R_0} = \frac{a}{2\sqrt{2}d} \tag{15.18}$$

A more accurate analysis in cylindrical coordinates (which we shall see subsequently) gives this ratio as $[a/(2\sqrt{2}\,d) + 1/4]$. Thus, this simplified analysis gives a good approximation to the ratio R/R_0, when a/d exceeds about 3.

15.2.1 Power Loss Calculation (Using Poynting Vector)

We use the complex Poynting vector:

$$\mathbf{S}' = \mathbf{E}_c \times \mathbf{H}_c^*$$

At the surface $x = 0$, $H_y = H_0$, and $E_z = -E_0 = -B_0\omega d\sqrt{j}$ [from Eq. (15.14)]. See Figure 15.5. Thus $(\mathbf{E} \times \mathbf{H})_0$ is normally inwards, with no corresponding outward vector at $x \to \infty$. The power

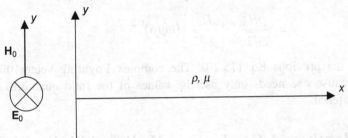

Figure 15.5 Surface field values of the semi-infinite block.

denoted by $(\mathbf{E} \times \mathbf{H}_0)$ is the ohmic loss associated with the eddy currents. In this case

$$\mathbf{H}^* = \mathbf{H} = \mathbf{H}_0 = \mathbf{i}_y H_0$$

and

$$\mathbf{E} = \mathbf{E}_0 = \mathbf{i}_z \mu H_0 \omega d\sqrt{j} = \mathbf{i}_z \mu H_0 \omega d\left(\frac{1+j}{\sqrt{2}}\right)$$

$\therefore$ The complex Poynting vector $\mathbf{S}'$ is

$$\mathbf{S}' = \mathbf{E} \times \mathbf{H}^* = \mathbf{i}_x H_0^2 \omega \mu d\left(\frac{1+j}{\sqrt{2}}\right)$$

and the average value is

$$\bar{S} = \frac{1}{2}\,\text{Re}(\mathbf{S}') = H_0^2\,\frac{\omega\mu d}{2\sqrt{2}}\ \text{watts/metre}^2 \tag{15.19}$$

Substituting for $d = \sqrt{\rho/(\omega\mu)}$,

$$\bar{S} = \left(\frac{H_0^2}{2\sqrt{2}}\right)\sqrt{\omega\mu\rho}\ \text{watts/metre}^2 \tag{15.20}$$

To evaluate this without recourse to the Poynting vector, we consider the induced current density $\mathbf{J}$,

$$\mathbf{J} = -\mathbf{i}_z\left(H_0\,\frac{\sqrt{j}}{d}\right)\exp\left(\frac{-x\sqrt{j}}{d}\right)$$

which has the magnitude

$$|\mathbf{J}| = \left(\frac{H_0}{d}\right)\exp\left(\frac{-x}{d\sqrt{2}}\right)$$

The loss is then

$$= \int_0^\infty \left(\frac{1}{2}\right)\rho\,|\mathbf{J}|^2\,dx \tag{15.21}$$

(where the factor (1/2) comes in because the peak values are assumed).

$$= \frac{1}{2}\rho\left(\frac{H_0^2}{d^2}\right)\int_0^\infty \exp\left(\frac{-x\sqrt{2}}{d}\right) dx$$

$$= \frac{1}{2}\rho\left(\frac{H_0^2}{d^2}\right)\left(\frac{d}{\sqrt{2}}\right)\left[-\exp\left(\frac{-x\sqrt{2}}{d}\right)\right]_0^\infty$$

$$= \frac{\rho H_0^2}{2\sqrt{2}d} = \left(\frac{H_0^2}{2\sqrt{2}}\right)(\omega\mu\rho)^{1/2}$$

which is same as the previous Eq. (15.20). The complex Poynting vector thus gives a quicker solution, partly because one needs only use the values of the field quantities at the surface, not all through the material.

15.2.2 Skin-depth and Conducting Media of Finite Dimensions

Thus, the study of the phenomenon of flow of an alternating current in a conducting medium, shows that this current does **not** distribute itself uniformly in the medium, as happens when a direct current {time-invariant} flows in it. The alternating current, on the other hand, re-distributes itself such that there is a stronger concentration of the current near the surface of the medium and as one goes toward inside {normal to the direction of current-flow}, the magnitude of the current {to be rigorous, it is the 'current density'} decreases continually, in an exponential manner. Thus phenomenon is known as 'skin-effect', and from a rigorous study of this aspect in

Section 15.2, the concept of depth of penetration {= $d\sqrt{2}$, where $d = (\sqrt{\omega\mu\sigma})^{-1}$, ω = frequency of the alternating current, μ = permeability of the medium, σ = conductivity of the medium = $1/\rho$, ρ = resistivity of the medium} was derived. This appears as a characteristic property of the conducting medium which depends on its permeability and resistivity and is not a function of its geometrical dimensions. However, before going into the behaviour of this parameter, it would be helpful to our understanding, if we have a re-look at its derivation.

A semi-infinite block of conducting medium was considered and on its surface {$x = 0$ plane in the co-ordinate system considered} on alternating magnetic field sheet was imposed over the whole surface $x = 0$. This field was uniform over the whole plane, and there was no space variation, the field being directed along the y-axis. {This incident field sheet could have been **J** (current density sheet) of same frequency (= ω), which would produce similar results.} It should be carefully noted that the incident field {$\mathbf{H}_y$ or $\mathbf{J}_z$} is a stationary sheet imposed on the surface $x = 0$ of the semi-infinite conducting block. The incident field is **NOT** a travelling wave. The effect of this incident field, applied at the surface, on the inside region ($x > 0$) of the conducting medium is somewhat unexpected. The analysis of Section 15.2 shows that in the region under consideration, a travelling wave (of **B** and **J**) has been generated which is propagating in +x direction, but as the wave progresses inside (with x increasing), the amplitude of this wave is continually decreasing in an exponential manner. Such a process in which a wave is propagating with continually decreasing amplitude {and eventually dying out as $x \to \infty$} is called 'diffusion' {in this case 'magnetic diffusion'} and such a dying wave {or decreasing wave} is called an 'evanescent wave'.

Next, coming to the geometrical dimensions of the conducting medium, so far what has been considered is a semi-infinite region which has simplified the problem to a one-dimensional one, and the rate of decrement of the wave amplitude to be $e^{-x/(d\sqrt{2})}$ which is the attenuating factor of the wave, dependant only on the physical parameter of the medium, independent of its geometrical dimensions. Furthermore, in this one-dimensional problem, all the lines of current-flow are parallel to z-axis {and **B** lines are parallel to y-axis}, though they flow in ± z-direction (**B** in ± y-direction). This means that the current-flow lines turn through 180° at infinity. However, this is an idealized situation, since in reality, in most of the devices, the geometrical dimensions are finite and the attenuating factor then becomes dependent on the geometrical dimensions as well. Also whilst the frequency of the diffusing wave is same as that of the incident signal (which is not a wave), the effect of the skin-depth is to introduce a space-phase-lag, in the diffusing wave, such that the phase lag is a function of both the point under consideration as well as the depth of penetration $(= d\sqrt{2})$ of the medium.

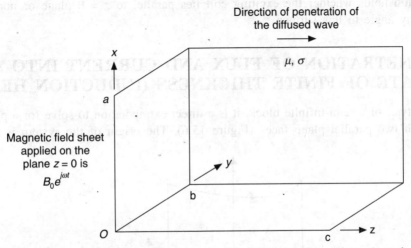

Figure 15.5(a) A three-dimensional conducting block of dimensions (a × b × c). Incident magnetic field is on the plane z = 0 and the direction of penetration of the diffused wave is +z →.

In a conducting block of dimensions ($a \times b \times c$) as shown in Figure 15.5(a). The incident field is applied on the plane $z = 0$ and the evanescent wave generated in the block as a consequence, penetrates the block in +z direction {and not in +x direction as in Section 15.2 and Section 15.2.1}, the exponent of the attenuating factor is given by

$$k_{zr} = \frac{1}{\sqrt{2}}\left(\sqrt{k_{mn}^4 + \alpha^4} - k_{mn}^2\right)^{1/2}, \text{ where}$$

$$k_{mn}^2 = \left(\frac{m\pi}{a}\right)^2 + \left(\frac{n\pi}{b}\right)^2$$

$$\alpha^2 = (\omega\mu_0\mu_r\sigma) = \frac{1}{d^2}$$

m, n being harmonic orders in x- and y-directions respectively. The space-phase-shift term will be controlled by the coefficient k_{zi} instead of just $d\sqrt{2}$, where

$$k_{zi} = \frac{1}{\sqrt{2}} \left\{ \sqrt{k_{mn}^4 + \alpha^4} + k_{mn}^2 \right\}^{1/2}$$

These factors have been derived by rigorous mathematical analysis which is not presented here.

The presence or absence of harmonic orders would depend on the nature of the incident field patterns. Also, in blocks of finite dimensions, since both $\mathbf{J}$ lines and $\mathbf{B}$ lines must form closed loops, i.e. close on themselves (and mutually orthogonal to each other), they will change directions in the finite region. On the plane $z = 0$, $\mathbf{J}$ loops will lie on that plane, i.e. J_x and J_y will exist, but $J_z = 0$ for $z = 0$ surface.

A further remarkable property of eddy current distribution in the conducting block of finite dimensions as shown in the adjoining figure is that whatever may be the shape and orientation of the exciting coil in front of the surface $z = 0$, the eddy current loops inside the block will all lie in planes parallel to the $z = 0$ plane, i.e. there will be no component of eddy currents in the z-direction. The eddy currents behave as if the block is laminated parallel to the surface. The above condition holds whether the exciting coil lies parallel to $z = 0$ plane or normal to it or inclined at any angle to this surface.

15.3   PENETRATION OF FLUX AND CURRENT INTO A PLATE OF FINITE THICKNESS (INDUCTION HEATING)

From the analysis of a semi-infinite block, it is a direct extrapolation to solve for a plate of finite thickness with two parallel plane faces (Figure 15.6). The origin of the system is taken at the

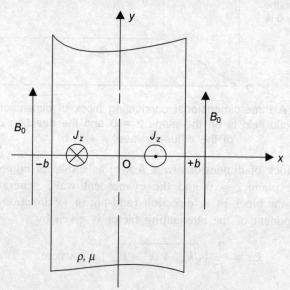

Figure 15.6   Plane faced metal block.

centre of the plate, so that the plane faces are given by $x = \pm b$. The same field is applied on both the faces, i.e. $B = B_0$ at $x = \pm b$.

The initial steps of the analysis are similar to those of the semi-infinite block, and the general solution comes out of the form

$$B_y = B = B_1 \exp\left(\frac{x\sqrt{j}}{d}\right) + B_2 \exp\left(\frac{-x\sqrt{j}}{d}\right)$$

corresponding to Eq. (15.9). The constants B_1 and B_2 have to be evaluated using the conditions that $B_y = B_0$ at $x = \pm b$. This gives

$$B_y = B_0 \left[\frac{\exp\left(\dfrac{x\sqrt{j}}{d}\right) + \exp\left(\dfrac{-x\sqrt{j}}{d}\right)}{\exp\left(\dfrac{b\sqrt{j}}{d}\right) + \exp\left(\dfrac{-b\sqrt{j}}{d}\right)}\right]$$

which can be expressed as

$$B_y = B_0 \left[\frac{\cosh\left(\dfrac{x\sqrt{j}}{d}\right)}{\cosh\left(\dfrac{b\sqrt{j}}{d}\right)}\right] = B_0 \frac{\cosh\left[\left(\dfrac{x}{d}\right)\left(\dfrac{1+j}{\sqrt{2}}\right)\right]}{\cosh\left[\left(\dfrac{b}{d}\right)\left(\dfrac{1+j}{\sqrt{2}}\right)\right]} \tag{15.22}$$

If such a plate is to be used as a lamination in a transformer core, then the deciding factor would be the total amount of magnetic flux, which would be carried by the unit depth of the lamination. This would be the basis for deciding the minimum thickness of each lamination so that its central layers are optimally used.

The value of the total flux per unit length ($= \Phi$) is given by

$$\Phi = \int_{x=-b}^{x=+b} B_y \, dx$$

$$= \frac{B_0}{\cosh\left[\left(\dfrac{b}{d}\right)\left(\dfrac{1+j}{\sqrt{2}}\right)\right]} \int_{x=-b}^{x=+b} \cosh\left[\left(\dfrac{x}{d}\right)\left(\dfrac{1+j}{\sqrt{2}}\right)\right] dx$$

$$= \frac{2B_0 d\left(\dfrac{\sqrt{2}}{1+j}\right) \sinh\left[\left(\dfrac{b}{d}\right)\left(\dfrac{1+j}{\sqrt{2}}\right)\right]}{\cosh\left[\left(\dfrac{b}{d}\right)\left(\dfrac{1+j}{\sqrt{2}}\right)\right]}$$

$$= 2B_0 d\left(\frac{1-j}{\sqrt{2}}\right) \times \frac{\sinh \alpha \cos \alpha + j \cosh \alpha \sin \alpha}{\cosh \alpha \cos \alpha + j \sinh \alpha \sin \alpha} \tag{13.23}$$

where

$$a = \frac{b}{d\sqrt{2}} \tag{15.23}$$

The magnitude of this flux is $|\Phi|$, which is

$$|\Phi| = 2B_0 d \times \sqrt{\frac{\sinh^2\alpha\cos^2\alpha + \cosh^2\alpha\sin^2\alpha}{\cosh^2\alpha\cos^2\alpha + \sinh^2\alpha\sin^2\alpha}}$$

$$= 2B_0 d \times \sqrt{\frac{\cosh 2\alpha - \cos 2\alpha}{\cosh 2\alpha + \cos 2\alpha}}$$

If the flux penetration were complete, then the flux would be

$$2B_0 b = \Phi_0$$

$$\therefore \quad |\Phi| = \left(\frac{\Phi_0}{\alpha\sqrt{2}}\right) \times \sqrt{\frac{\cosh 2\alpha - \cos 2\alpha}{\cosh 2\alpha + \cos 2\alpha}} \tag{15.24}$$

The ratio $|\Phi/\Phi_0|$ is a measure of the reduction in the effective permeability of the lamination material due to the presence of the eddy currents in it. This is plotted as a function of (b/d) in Figure 15.7. The next parameter important from the designer's point of view is the eddy current

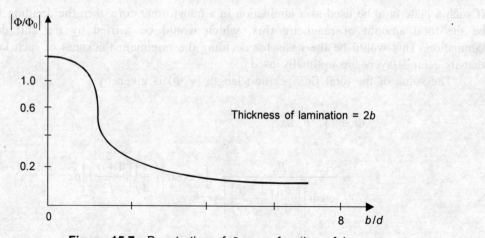

Figure 15.7 Penetration of Φ as a function of b.

loss in the laminations, and so we now calculate the eddy current loss. So we need to evaluate the current density vector $\mathbf{J}$, i.e.

$$J_z = -\frac{dH_y}{dx} = -\left(\frac{1}{\mu_0\mu_r}\right)\left(\frac{dB_y}{dx}\right)$$

and using the value of B_y obtained in Eq. (15.22), we get

$$J_z = \left(\frac{B_0}{\mu_0\mu_r d}\right)\left(\frac{1+j}{\sqrt{2}}\right) \times \frac{\sinh\left[\left(\dfrac{x}{d}\right)\left(\dfrac{1+j}{\sqrt{2}}\right)\right]}{\cosh\left[\left(\dfrac{b}{d}\right)\left(\dfrac{1+j}{\sqrt{2}}\right)\right]}$$

which can be expressed as

$$J_z = -\left(\frac{B_0}{\mu_0 \mu_r d}\right)\left(\frac{1+j}{\sqrt{2}}\right) \times \frac{\sinh\left(\frac{x}{d\sqrt{2}}\right)\cos\left(\frac{x}{d\sqrt{2}}\right) + j\cosh\left(\frac{x}{d\sqrt{2}}\right)\sin\left(\frac{x}{d\sqrt{2}}\right)}{\cosh\alpha\cos\alpha + j\sinh\alpha\sin\alpha}$$

and hence the magnitude of J_z is

$$J_z = \left(\frac{B_0}{\mu_0 \mu_r d}\right) \times \sqrt{\frac{\sinh^2\left(\frac{x}{d\sqrt{2}}\right)\cos^2\left(\frac{x}{d\sqrt{2}}\right) + \cosh^2\left(\frac{x}{d\sqrt{2}}\right)\sin^2\left(\frac{x}{d\sqrt{2}}\right)}{\cosh^2\alpha\cos^2\alpha + \sinh^2\alpha\sin^2\alpha}}$$

$$= \left(\frac{B_0}{\mu_0 \mu_r d}\right) \times \left[\frac{\cosh\left(\frac{x\sqrt{2}}{d}\right) - \cos\left(\frac{x\sqrt{2}}{d}\right)}{\cosh 2\alpha + \cos 2\alpha}\right]$$

∴ The eddy current loss ($= W_e$) is

$$W_e = \int_{-b}^{+b} \rho |J_z|^2 \, dx$$

$$= \left(\frac{\rho B_0^2 \sqrt{2}}{\mu_0 \mu_r d}\right)\left(\frac{\sinh 2\alpha - \sin 2\alpha}{\cosh 2\alpha + \cos 2\alpha}\right) \tag{15.25}$$

It will be seen that the second term is the square of the term for the flux-linkage as obtained in Eq. (15.24).

A second application of the results of this problem is in the design and use of induction furnaces. The term, $[(\sinh 2\alpha - \sin 2\alpha)/(\cosh 2\alpha + \cos 2\alpha)]$ is the important parameter for the users of induction furnaces. The above quantity is a function of α or $b/(d\sqrt{2})$, say $F(\alpha)$ or $F\{b/(d\sqrt{2})\}$. If this function is plotted for a range of $b/(d\sqrt{2})$ or α, it will be seen that for maximum heating, the sheets should have a thickness $2b \simeq 2.25(d\sqrt{2})$, i.e. b should be slightly greater than the skin-depth $(d\sqrt{2})$ $(=\delta)$. If the sheets are thicker, the eddy currents will not penetrate far enough; and if the sheets are thinner, the eddy currents will be smaller.

15.4 ALTERNATING CURRENT FLOW IN A FLAT SHEET

We now look at the problem of an alternating current flowing in a sheet of finite thickness ($2b$) (Figure 15.8). In this case, the current flows in the y-direction and hence the current density vector will have only the y-component, and the magnetic flux density **B** will have only the z-component. These field vectors will vary only with x, i.e. $\partial/\partial y = 0$ and $\partial/\partial z = 0$.

∴ curl **H** = **J** equation will reduce to

$$-\frac{\partial H_z}{\partial x} = J_y \tag{15.26}$$

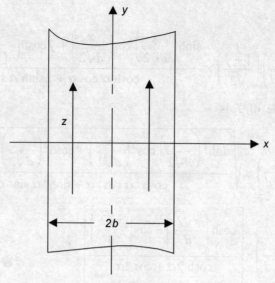

Figure 15.8 Current flow in a flat sheet.

and curl $\mathbf{E} = -\dfrac{\partial \mathbf{B}}{\partial t}$ reduces to

$$\frac{\partial E_y}{\partial x} = -\frac{\partial B_z}{\partial t} \tag{15.27}$$

Using the constituent relations

$$\mathbf{B} = \mu \mathbf{H} \text{ and } \mathbf{J} = \sigma \mathbf{E} \tag{15.28}$$

we get

$$J_y = -\left(\frac{1}{\mu_0}\right)\left(\frac{\partial B_z}{\partial x}\right) \quad \text{and} \quad \left(\frac{\partial B_z}{\partial t}\right) = \left(\frac{1}{\sigma}\right)\left(\frac{\partial J_y}{\partial x}\right)$$

$$\therefore \quad \frac{\partial J_y}{\partial t} = -\left(\frac{1}{\mu_0}\right)\left(\frac{\partial^2 B_z}{\partial x \partial t}\right) = +\left(\frac{1}{\mu_0 \sigma}\right)\left(\frac{\partial^2 J_y}{\partial x^2}\right) \tag{15.29}$$

Since the current through the block is alternating, we write it as

$$J_y = \hat{J} \exp\left(j \omega t\right) \tag{15.30}$$

$\therefore$ Equation (15.29) becomes

$$\frac{\partial^2 \hat{J}}{\partial x^2} = j \omega \mu_0 \sigma \hat{J} \tag{15.31}$$

Since all the quantities are phasors, we simplify our writing by omitting the peak notation, and as before

$$\frac{1}{\omega \mu_0 \sigma} = d^2 \tag{15.32}$$

the equation for the current density vector becomes

$$\frac{\partial^2 J_y}{\partial x^2} - \left(\frac{j}{d^2}\right) J_y = 0 \tag{15.33}$$

Its general solution is (i.e. the space variation of J),

$$J_y = J_1 \exp\left(\frac{x\sqrt{j}}{d}\right) + J_2 \exp\left(\frac{-x\sqrt{j}}{d}\right) \tag{15.34}$$

where J_1 and J_2 are unknown constants to be determined from the boundary conditions which are:

(1) at $x = 0$, $J_y = J_0$ (say); and
(2) $x = 0$ is the axis of symmetry.

Hence, from these conditions, the two equations are

$$J_0 = J_1 + J_2 \quad \text{and} \quad J_1 = J_2$$

∴   The solution becomes

$$J_y = \left(\frac{J_0}{2}\right)\left[\exp\left\{\frac{(1+j)x}{d\sqrt{2}}\right\} + \exp\left\{\frac{-(1+j)x}{d\sqrt{2}}\right\}\right]$$

$$= J_0 \cosh\left[\frac{(1+j)x}{d\sqrt{2}}\right] \tag{15.35}$$

On the surface $x = \pm b$,

$$J_y = J_S = J_0 \cosh\left[\frac{(1+j)b}{d\sqrt{2}}\right]$$

∴   Expressing the current density vector in terms of the surface value,

$$J_y = J_S \left[\frac{\cosh\left\{\frac{(1+j)x}{d\sqrt{2}}\right\}}{\cosh\left\{\frac{(1+j)b}{d\sqrt{2}}\right\}}\right] \tag{15.36}$$

The total current per unit width of the sheet is

$$I = \int_{-b}^{+b} J_y\, dx = \left(\frac{2\sqrt{2}J_S d}{1+j}\right)\tanh\left(\frac{(1+j)b}{d\sqrt{2}}\right) \tag{15.37}$$

If $b/(d\sqrt{2})$ is large, then $\tanh\left[(1+j)b/(d\sqrt{2})\right] \to 1$. This is true within 1% if $b/(d\sqrt{2}) > 2.64$. Thus in a sheet of this thickness,

$$I = \frac{2\sqrt{2}J_S d}{1+j} \tag{15.38}$$

We now calculate the impedance of the sheet, which would also give us the loss in an alternative way. The voltage applied to the sheet can be obtained from the surface electric field. The voltage per unit length in the y-direction is

$$V = \frac{J_S}{\sigma} \tag{15.39}$$

$\therefore$ The complex impedance per unit area of y- and z-directions is

$$Z = \frac{V}{I} = \left(\frac{1+j}{2\sqrt{2}d\sigma} \right) \coth \left[\frac{(1+j)b}{d\sqrt{2}} \right] \tag{15.40}$$

Separating the real and the imaginary parts,

$$Z = R + jX = \left(\frac{1+j}{2\sqrt{2}d\sigma} \right) \times \frac{\cosh \alpha \cos \alpha + j \sinh \alpha \sin \alpha}{\sinh \alpha \cos \alpha + j \cosh \alpha \sin \alpha}$$

where

$$\alpha = \frac{b}{d\sqrt{2}} \tag{15.41}$$

After further manipulations,

$$R = \left(\frac{1}{2\sqrt{2}d\sigma} \right) \left(\frac{\sinh 2\alpha + \sin 2\alpha}{\cosh 2\alpha - \cos 2\alpha} \right)$$

$$X = \left(\frac{1}{2\sqrt{2}d\sigma} \right) \left(\frac{\sinh 2\alpha - \sin 2\alpha}{\cosh 2\alpha - \cos 2\alpha} \right) \tag{15.42}$$

This reactance is due to the redistribution of the current inside the sheet, and hence is due to the 'internal inductance' of the sheet. The resistance in Eq. (15.42) is due to the alternating current. The direct current resistance of the sheet is

$$R_{dc} = \frac{1}{2b\sigma} \tag{15.43}$$

$\therefore$ The ratio of ac to dc resistance is

$$\frac{R_{ac}}{R_{dc}} = \frac{b}{d\sqrt{2}} \frac{\sinh 2\alpha + \sin 2\alpha}{\cosh 2\alpha - \cos 2\alpha} \tag{15.44}$$

When this ratio is plotted as a function of $b/(d\sqrt{2})$, then for large values of $\alpha = b/(d\sqrt{2})$, it tends to $b/(d\sqrt{2})$ (Figure 15.9), because the current tends to concentrate in the surface layers of $b/(d\sqrt{2})$. At low values of $b/(d\sqrt{2})$, the expression can be expanded in the ascending powers of α, i.e.

$$\frac{R_{ac}}{R_{dc}} = 1 + \left(\frac{4}{45} \right) \alpha^4 \tag{15.45}$$

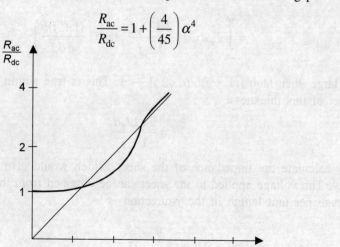

Figure 15.9   AC resistance of a flat sheet.

When we consider thin sheets, it is seen that the above expression still holds, i.e. the ac loss for thin sheets can be evaluated without considering the effects of the magnetic field of the eddy currents. If the effects of the field of eddy currents are negligible, then the behaviour is said to be 'resistance-limited'. For thick sheets, in which the current is confined in the surface layers, the behaviour is said to be 'inductance-limited'.

15.5   SKIN EFFECT (OR EDDY CURRENTS) IN AN ISOLATED CIRCULAR CONDUCTOR

We consider a long conductor, of circular cross-section, carrying an alternating current I, the current density at any radius r being $\mathbf{J}$, the direction of the current being normal to the plane of the paper into it (Figure 15.10).

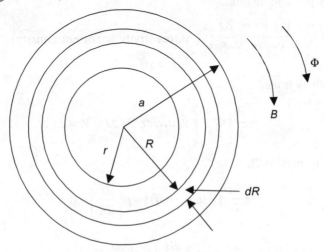

Figure 15.10   A circular conductor of radius a, carrying an alternating current.

The total current $= I$; the current density $= \mathbf{J}$; the applied voltage $= V$; the induced voltage $= e$; the frequency of the current $= f$; or angular frequency $= \omega = 2\pi f$; the external flux linked per unit length $= \Phi$.

The current density is a function of the radius only. The alternating current gives rise to the magnetic flux; and from the Maxwell's equation,

$$\oint_C H_r \, dl = \text{current enclosed by the contour,}$$

$$2\pi R H(R) = \int_{r=0}^{r=R} 2\pi r\, dr\, J(r) \tag{15.46}$$

This equation is true at any instant of time, since all are functions of time.

Differentiating with respect to R,

$$\frac{\partial}{\partial R}(RH) = RJ \tag{15.47}$$

[At the centre $(r \to 0)$, $H \times 2\pi r = \pi r^2 J_0$ $\therefore$ $H = (J_0/2)r \to$ as $r \to 0$.]

Let Φ = the flux linking the conductor externally per unit length. Then the total flux linking with the core of radius R is given by

$$\text{External flux } \Phi + \int\limits_{R}^{r=a} \mu_0 \mu_r H \, 1 \cdot dr$$

$\therefore$ Induced voltage per unit length at radius r is

$$\equiv e = -\frac{\partial}{\partial t}\left[\Phi + \int\limits_{R}^{a} \mu_0 \mu_r H dr \right] \tag{15.48}$$

This creates a certain current density, in addition to the applied voltage. We know that V = applied voltage per unit length.

$$\therefore \qquad \underbrace{V + e}_{\text{Total voltage}} = \underbrace{\rho J}_{\text{Gradient}} \quad \text{(i.e. resistivity} \times \text{current density)}$$

$$\therefore \quad e = \rho J - V$$

Let us assume that Φ is finite.

$$\therefore \qquad -\frac{\partial}{\partial t}\left[\Phi + \int\limits_{R}^{a} \mu_0 \mu_r H dr \right] = \rho J - V = e \tag{15.49}$$

Differentiating with respect to R,

$$-\frac{\partial}{\partial t}\left[-\mu_0 \mu_r H(R) \right] = \rho \left(\frac{dJ}{dR} \right) - 0$$

or

$$\mu_0 \mu_r \left(\frac{\partial H}{\partial t} \right) = \rho \left(\frac{dJ}{dR} \right) \tag{15.50}$$

Since the current flowing through the conductor is assumed to be sinusoidal, $\partial/\partial t = j\omega$ and Eq. (15.50) becomes

$$\left(\frac{j\omega \mu_0 \mu_r}{\rho} \right) H = \frac{dJ}{dR}$$

or

$$j\lambda^2 H = \frac{dJ}{dR}$$

where

$$\lambda^2 = \frac{\omega \mu_0 \mu_r}{\rho} = \frac{1}{d^2} \tag{15.51}$$

$\therefore$ From Eqs. (15.47) and (15.51),

$$j\lambda^2 H = \frac{d}{dR}\left[\left(\frac{1}{R} \right) \frac{\partial}{\partial R} (RH) \right] = \frac{d}{dR}\left(\frac{dH}{dR} + \frac{H}{R} \right)$$

or

$$R^2 \left(\frac{d^2 H}{dR^2} \right) + R \left(\frac{dH}{dR} \right) - \left(j\lambda^2 R^2 + 1 \right) H = 0$$

Compare this equation with the Bessel's equation of the order n, which is

$$x^2\left(\frac{d^2y}{dx^2}\right) + x\left(\frac{dy}{dx}\right) + \left(x^2 - n^2\right)y = 0 \qquad (15.52)$$

so that the equation for H can be rewritten as

$$R^2\left(\frac{d^2H}{dR^2}\right) + R\left(\frac{dH}{dR}\right) + \left(j^3\lambda^2R^2 - 1\right)H = 0 \qquad (15.53)$$

∴ The solution of this equation is

$$H = AJ_1(j^{3/2}\lambda R) + BY_1(j^{3/2}\lambda R) \qquad (15.54)$$

where $J_1(j^{3/2}\lambda R)$ and $Y_1(j^{3/2}\lambda R)$ are Bessel's functions (of first order) of first and second kind respectively. It should be noted that the arguments of these Bessel's functions are complex and hence they can be expressed as Kelvin functions, i.e. Ber and Bei functions. However we shall use them as they are and convert them later to polar form. (Note that A and B are unknown constants of integration, and can be complex.)

From Eq. (15.47), the current density J can now be expressed as

$$J = \left(\frac{1}{R}\right)\left[\frac{d}{dR}(RH)\right]$$

$$= \left(\frac{1}{R}\right)\left[\frac{d}{dR}\left\{RAJ_1\left(j^{3/2}\lambda R\right) + RBY_1\left(j^{3/2}\lambda R\right)\right\}\right]$$

$$= \left(\frac{1}{R}\right) \times \frac{d}{d\left(j^{3/2}\lambda R\right)}\left[\left(j^{3/2}\lambda R\right)AJ_1\left(j^{3/2}\lambda R\right) + \left(j^{3/2}\lambda R\right)BY_1\left(j^{3/2}\lambda R\right)\right]$$

$$= \left(\frac{1}{R}\right)\left[\left(j^{3/2}\lambda R\right)AJ_0\left(j^{3/2}\lambda R\right) + \left(j^{3/2}\lambda R\right)BY_0\left(j^{3/2}\lambda R\right)\right]$$

$$\therefore \quad J = \left[\left(j^{3/2}\lambda\right)AJ_0\left(j^{3/2}\lambda R\right) + \left(j^{3/2}\lambda\right)BY_0\left(j^{3/2}\lambda R\right)\right]$$

Note that $j^{3/2}$ implies a phase shift.

The Bessel's function of the second kind $Y_n(x) \to \infty$ as $x \to 0$.

But $H \to 0$ as $R \to 0$. ∴ $B = 0$.

$$\therefore \quad H = AJ_1(j^{3/2}\lambda R), \qquad J = (j^{3/2}\lambda)\, AJ_0(j^{3/2}\lambda R)$$

However in tubular conductors, the general solution for the finite value of B is valid.

Now, to evaluate A, if the total current is I, then at $R = a$, $\oint H dr = I$; or

$$2\pi a H_a = I = 2\pi a A J_1(j^{3/2}\lambda a)$$

$$\therefore \quad A = \frac{I}{2\pi a J_1\left(j^{3/2}\lambda a\right)}$$

$$\therefore \qquad H = \left(\frac{I}{2\pi a}\right)\frac{J_1\left(j^{3/2}\lambda R\right)}{J_1\left(j^{3/2}\lambda a\right)}, \quad \text{and} \quad J = \frac{\left(j^{3/2}\lambda\right)I}{2\pi a}\frac{J_0\left(j^{3/2}\lambda R\right)}{J_1\left(j^{3/2}\lambda a\right)} \qquad (15.55)$$

Expressing the Bessel's functions in polar form

$$H = \left(\frac{I}{2\pi a}\right)\left[\frac{M_1(\lambda R)\exp\{j\theta_1(\lambda R)\}}{M_1(\lambda a)\exp\{j\theta_1(\lambda a)\}}\right]$$

$$J = \left[\frac{\left(j^{3/2}\lambda\right)I}{2\pi a}\right]\left[\frac{M_0(\lambda R)\exp\{j\theta_0(\lambda R)\}}{M_1(\lambda a)\exp\{j\theta_1(\lambda a)\}}\right] \qquad (15.56)$$

We now plot the amplitude $M_0(\lambda R)$ as a function of $(\lambda R) = x$ (Figure 15.11). From the curve, it will be seen that for sufficiently high λ (i.e. the reciprocal of skin-depth/$\sqrt{2}$), at the outer radii, the current density increases.

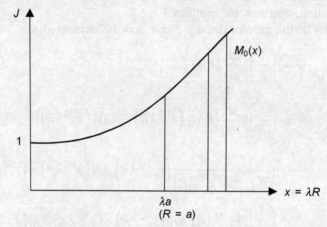

Figure 15.11 Current density amplitude as a function of radius R of the conductor.

$\therefore$ At higher frequencies (f), most of the current will be located in the outermost shells. The current density at the centre of the wire is minimum, and increases monotonically with radius. Furthermore, if '(λa)' is increased, the discrepancy of the current density at the centre and the outer radius increases and vice versa.

Next, we consider the phase of the current density vector. The terms affecting the phase are (Figure 15.12)

$$j^{3/2} \to \left(\frac{3\pi}{4}\right) + \theta_0(\lambda R) - \theta_1(\lambda a) = \text{phase of } J - \text{phase of } I \qquad (15.57)$$

Note: For large values of $x(= \lambda R)$, $x > 45$

$$\theta_0(x) = 40 \cdots x - 5.06/x - 22\tfrac{1}{2}°; \qquad \theta_1(x) = 40 \cdots x + 15.19/x + 67\tfrac{1}{2}°.$$

When $\lambda \to 0$ ($\lambda = \omega\mu_0\mu_r/\rho$), i.e. at low frequencies, all the current densities (at different radii) are in phase. At sufficiently high frequencies, in the current density at any radius, there are different phase reversals.

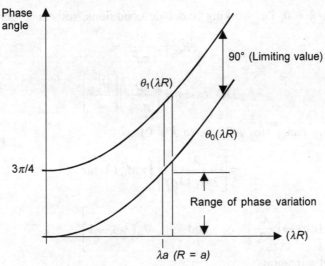

Figure 15.12 Phase variations in J as a function of R.

(*Note:* We have already seen that the skin current density leads the resultant total current by 45°—true for high frequencies as well.) Note further that at high frequencies, a (very very) small change in r is sufficient to cause the phase change by 45° between two shells.

15.5.1 Loss Calculation and the Effective Resistance in the Circular Conductor

We now calculate the effective resistances for various values of λ.

$$J = \left[\frac{(j^{3/2}\lambda)I}{2\pi a} \right] \left[\frac{M_0(\lambda R)\exp\{j\theta_0(\lambda R)\}}{M_1(\lambda a)\exp\{j\theta_1(\lambda a)\}} \right] \quad \text{at radius } R \qquad (15.58)$$

$\therefore$

$$|J| = \left[\frac{\lambda|I|}{2\pi a} \right] \left[\frac{M_0(\lambda R)}{M_1(\lambda a)} \right]$$

where

$$|I| = \text{amplitude of the current} \qquad (15.59)$$

$\therefore$ The total ohmic loss per unit length =

$$\underbrace{\left[\frac{\rho 1}{2\pi r dr} \right]}_{\substack{\text{resistance} \\ \text{per unit length}}} \underbrace{\left[\frac{(2\pi r dr)^2}{2} \right]}_{(\text{area})^2} \underbrace{\left[\frac{\lambda^2 |I|^2}{4\pi^2 a^2} \right] \left[\frac{M_0^2(\lambda R)}{M_1^2(\lambda a)} \right]}_{(\text{current density})^2}$$

$$(15.60)$$

i.e. the loss is proportional to the (rms current)^2.

This is to be integrated within the limits 0 to a, thus, the loss

$$= \frac{\rho \lambda^2 |I|^2}{(4\pi a^2) M_1^2(\lambda a)} \int_0^a r M_0^2(\lambda r) dr \qquad (15.61)$$

We note that, when $\lambda = 0$, i.e. working under dc conditions, resistance per unit length

$$R_{dc} = \frac{\rho}{\pi a^2}$$

$\therefore$ DC losses $= \left(\frac{\rho}{\pi a^2} \right) \left(\frac{|I|^2}{2} \right)$ (15.62)

$\therefore$ Multiplying factor (for AC due to $\lambda \neq 0$)

$$= \left[\frac{\lambda^2}{2M_1^2(\lambda a)} \right] \int_0^a r\, M_0^2(\lambda r)\, dr$$ (15.63)

$$\left[\text{at } \lambda = 0,\ M_1^2(\lambda a) \rightarrow \left(\frac{\lambda a}{2} \right)^2 \quad \text{and} \quad M_0(\lambda r) \rightarrow 1 \right]$$

We refer to Lommel's integral,

$$\int_0^a r J_0(kr) J_0(lr)\, dr = \left(\frac{a}{k^2 - l^2} \right) [(k J_0(la) J_1(ka) - l J_0(ka) J_1(la)]$$ (15.64)

In this expression, let $k = j^{3/2}\lambda$, $l = (-j)^{-3/2}\lambda = j^{-3/2}\lambda$.

On substituting and expressing the integral in the polar form:

$$\int_0^a M_0(\lambda r) \exp\{-j\theta_0(\lambda r)\} M_0(\lambda r) \exp\{-j\theta_0(\lambda r)\} r\, dr = \left(\frac{a}{j^3\lambda^2 - j^{-3}\lambda^2} \right) \times$$

$$[(j^{3/2}\lambda) M_0(\lambda a) \exp\{-j\theta_0(\lambda a)\} M_1(\lambda a) \exp\{j\theta_1(\lambda a)\}$$

$$- (j^{-3/2}\lambda) M_0(\lambda a) \exp\{j\theta_0(\lambda a)\} M_1(\lambda a) \exp\{-j\theta_1(\lambda a)\}]$$

noting that $j^3 = -j$ and $j^{-3} = j$.

$$\int_0^a r M_0^2(\lambda r)\, dr$$

$$= -\left(\frac{a}{2j\lambda} \right) [\exp j\{(3\pi/4) + \theta_1(\lambda a) - \theta_0(\lambda a)\}] - \exp[-j\{(3\pi/4) + \theta_1(\lambda a) - \theta_0(\lambda a)\}] \times [M_0(\lambda a) M_1(\lambda a)]$$

noting that $j^{3/2} = \exp\{j(3\pi/4)\}$ and $j^{-3/2} = \exp\{-j(3\pi/4)\}$

$$= -\left(\frac{a}{\lambda} \right) [\sin\{(3\pi/4) + \theta_1(\lambda a) - \theta_0(\lambda a)\}][M_0(\lambda a) M_1(\lambda a)]$$

$$= -\left(\frac{a}{\lambda} \right) [\sin\{-(\pi/4) + \theta_1(\lambda a) - \theta_0(\lambda a)\}][M_0(\lambda a) M_1(\lambda a)]$$

$\therefore$ From Eq. (15.63), the multiplying factor

$$= \left(\frac{a\lambda}{2} \right) \left[\frac{M_0(\lambda a)}{M_1(\lambda a)} \right] [\sin\{(-\pi/4) + \theta_1(\lambda a) - \theta_0(\lambda a)\}] \quad \text{and} \quad \lambda a = a \left(\frac{\omega\mu_0\mu_r}{\rho} \right)^{1/2}$$ (15.65)

The multiplying factor increases with resistance.

15.6 SKIN EFFECT IN PLATED CONDUCTORS

In radio frequency and higher frequency transmissions, the resonant cavities and waveguides are often silver-plated to utilize the low resistivity of silver, and thus reduce the ohmic losses in these devices. It is of interest to determine the variation of the loss with the thickness of the plated coating. Another type of practical application is that of tinned copper wires. We can study the effects of such coatings on the resistance of such wires.

So once again, we consider a semi-infinite block of metal of resistivity ρ_2, coated with a second metal layer of resistivity ρ_1 and thickness a (Figure 15.13). The flow of an alternating

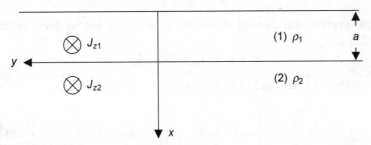

Figure 15.13   Semi-infinite metal block with a surface coating of thickness a.

current of frequency $\omega = 2\pi f$ is in the z-direction, and is uniform in the y-direction, i.e. the only variation is in the x-direction. The flow of the current would induce a magnetic field, which would be directed in the y-direction, and also be a function of x. Let the current densities be J_{z1} and J_{z2} in the two media respectively, and as derived in Section 15.2, the equations satisfied by these current density vectors come out to be

$$\frac{d^2 J_{z1}}{dx^2} - \left(\frac{j}{d_1^2}\right) J_{z1} = 0 \quad \text{and} \quad \frac{d^2 J_{z2}}{dx^2} - \left(\frac{j}{d_2^2}\right) J_{z2} = 0 \tag{15.66}$$

where

$$d_1 = \left(\frac{\rho_1}{\omega\mu_1}\right)^{1/2} \quad \text{and} \quad d_2 = \left(\frac{\rho_2}{\omega\mu_2}\right)^{1/2} \tag{15.67}$$

The general solutions will be

$$J_{z1} = A_1 \exp\left(\frac{x\sqrt{j}}{d_1}\right) + B_1 \exp\left(\frac{-x\sqrt{j}}{d_1}\right) \quad \text{and} \quad J_{z2} = A_2 \exp\left(\frac{x\sqrt{j}}{d_2}\right) + B_2 \exp\left(\frac{-x\sqrt{j}}{d_2}\right)$$

remembering that J_{z1} and J_{z2} are both phasors (i.e. complex vectors with only one component i.e. in the z-direction only).

Since the current density cannot become infinite as $x \to \infty$,

$$J_{z2} = B_2 \exp\left(\frac{-x\sqrt{j}}{d_2}\right) \quad \text{and} \quad J_{z1} = A_1 \exp\left(\frac{x\sqrt{j}}{d_1}\right) + B_1 \exp\left(\frac{-x\sqrt{j}}{d_1}\right) \tag{15.68}$$

The other boundary conditions are at $x = 0$,

$$E_{z1} = E_{z2} \quad \text{and} \quad H_{y1} = H_{y2}$$

$\therefore$ From Eq. (15.48)

$$E_{z1} = \rho_1 J_{z1} = \rho_1(A_1 + B_1) = \rho_2 B_2 = (\rho_2 J_{z2} = E_{z2}) \tag{15.69}$$

and

$$H_{y1} = \left(\frac{1}{j\omega\mu_1}\right)\left(\frac{dE_{z1}}{dx}\right) = \left(\frac{\rho_1}{j\omega\mu_1}\right)\left(\frac{dJ_{z1}}{dx}\right) = \left(\frac{\rho_1}{j\omega\mu_1}\right)\frac{\sqrt{j}}{d_1}$$

$$= \frac{d_1}{\sqrt{j}}(A_1 - B_1) = \left(\frac{\rho_2}{j\omega\mu_2}\right)\frac{\sqrt{j}}{d_2}(-B_2) = \frac{d_2}{\sqrt{j}}(-B_2) \tag{15.70}$$

We shall now express the current densities in terms of the surface value of J_{z2} on the surface plane $x = 0$, i.e.

$$\text{at } x = 0, \; J_{z2} = B_2 = J_{02} \tag{15.71}$$

Hence from Eqs. (15.69), (15.70), and (15.71), we get

$$J_{z1} = J_{02}\left(\frac{d_2}{\mu_1 d_1^2}\right) \times \left[\left\{\mu_2 d_2 \cosh\left(\frac{x}{d_1\sqrt{2}}\right) - \mu_1 d_1 \sinh\left(\frac{x}{d_1\sqrt{2}}\right)\right\}\cos\left(\frac{x}{d_1\sqrt{2}}\right)\right.$$

$$\left. - j\left\{\mu_1 d_1 \cosh\left(\frac{x}{d_1\sqrt{2}}\right) - \mu_2 d_2 \sinh\left(\frac{x}{d_1\sqrt{2}}\right)\right\}\sin\left(\frac{x}{d_1\sqrt{2}}\right)\right]$$

$$J_{z2} = J_{02}\exp\left(\frac{-x}{d_2\sqrt{2}}\right)\left[\cos\left(\frac{x}{d_2\sqrt{2}}\right) - j\sin\left(\frac{x}{d_2\sqrt{2}}\right)\right] \tag{15.72}$$

It should be noted that there is now a discontinuity in current density at the interface plane between the two metals. So if say a brass bar is coated with silver, then the silver part would carry a larger share of current than if it had been brass in its place.

So now we calculate the total current in each of the two metals for a width, say, W,

$$\therefore \qquad I_2 = W\int_0^\infty J_{z2}\, dx = J_{02}W\int_0^\infty \exp\left[\frac{-(1+j)x}{d_2\sqrt{2}}\right]dx = \left(\frac{J_{02}Wd_2}{\sqrt{2}}\right)(1 - j)$$

and

$$I_1 = W\int_0^\infty J_{z1}\, dx = \frac{J_{02}Wd_2}{\sqrt{2}\mu_1 d_1}\left[\left(P - \mu_1 d_1\sqrt{2}\right) - j\left(Q - \mu_1 d_1\sqrt{2}\right)\right]$$

where

$$P = \left(\mu_2 d_2\sqrt{2}\right) \times \left[\sinh\left(\frac{a}{d_1\sqrt{2}}\right)\cos\left(\frac{a}{d_1\sqrt{2}}\right) + \cosh\left(\frac{a}{d_1\sqrt{2}}\right)\sin\left(\frac{a}{d_1\sqrt{2}}\right)\right]$$

$$+ \left(\mu_1 d_1\sqrt{2}\right) \times \left[\cosh\left(\frac{a}{d_1\sqrt{2}}\right)\cos\left(\frac{a}{d_1\sqrt{2}}\right) + \sinh\left(\frac{a}{d_1\sqrt{2}}\right)\sin\left(\frac{a}{d_1\sqrt{2}}\right)\right]$$

$$Q = \left(\mu_2 d_2 \sqrt{2}\right) \times \left[\sinh\left(\frac{a}{d_1\sqrt{2}}\right)\cos\left(\frac{a}{d_1\sqrt{2}}\right) - \cosh\left(\frac{a}{d_1\sqrt{2}}\right)\sin\left(\frac{a}{d_1\sqrt{2}}\right)\right]$$

$$+ \left(\mu_1 d_1 \sqrt{2}\right) \times \left[\cosh\left(\frac{a}{d_1\sqrt{2}}\right)\cos\left(\frac{a}{d_1\sqrt{2}}\right) - \sinh\left(\frac{a}{d_1\sqrt{2}}\right)\sin\left(\frac{a}{d_1\sqrt{2}}\right)\right]$$

$\therefore$ The total current, $I = I_1 + I_2$

$$= \left(\frac{J_{02}Wd_2}{\sqrt{2}\mu_1 d_1}\right)(P - jQ) = \left(\frac{J_{02}Wd_2}{\sqrt{2}\mu_1 d_1}\right)\left(P^2 + Q^2\right)^{1/2} \angle - \alpha$$

where

$$\alpha = \tan^{-1}\left(\frac{Q}{P}\right) \tag{15.73}$$

We now calculate the power loss in a rectangular section of the plated conductor, of width W in the y-direction and l in the z-direction.

$\therefore$ The loss in the metal 2, for the rectangular section:

$$P_2 = \rho_2 Wl \int_{x=0}^{x \to \infty} |J_{z2}|^2 \, dx = \rho_2 WlJ_{02}^2 \int_0^\infty \exp\left(\frac{x\sqrt{2}}{d_2}\right) dx$$

$$= \frac{\rho_2 Wl d_2 J_{02}^2}{\sqrt{2}} \tag{15.74}$$

And for the conductor 1,

$$P_1 = \rho_1 Wl \int_{x=0}^{x \to \infty} |J_{z1}|^2 \, dx$$

$$= \left(\frac{\rho_1 WlJ_{02}^2 d_2^2}{2\sqrt{2}\mu_1^2 d_1^3}\right) \times \left[\left(\mu_2 d_2 \sqrt{2}\right)^2 + \left(\mu_1 d_1 \sqrt{2}\right)^2\right]\sinh\left(\frac{a}{d_1\sqrt{2}}\right)\cosh\left(\frac{a}{d_1\sqrt{2}}\right)$$

$$+ \left[\left(\mu_2 d_2 \sqrt{2}\right)^2 - \left(\mu_1 d_1 \sqrt{2}\right)^2\right]\sin\left(\frac{a}{d_1\sqrt{2}}\right)\cos\left(\frac{a}{d_1\sqrt{2}}\right) + \mu_1\mu_2 d_1 d_2 \sinh^2\left(\frac{a}{d_1\sqrt{2}}\right) \tag{15.75}$$

$\therefore$ The total power $P_T = P_1 + P_2$

$$= \left[\frac{\rho_1 WlJ_{02}^2 d_2^2}{\left(2\sqrt{2}\mu_1^2 d_1^3\right)}\right] U$$

where

$$U = \left(\frac{1}{2}\right)\left[\left\{\left(\mu_2 d_2 \sqrt{2}\right)^2 + \left(\mu_1 d_1 \sqrt{2}\right)^2\right\}\sinh\left(\frac{a}{d_1\sqrt{2}}\right)\right.$$

$$\left. + \left\{\left(\mu_2 d_2 \sqrt{2}\right)^2 - \left(\mu_1 d_1 \sqrt{2}\right)^2\right\}\sin\left(\frac{a}{d_1\sqrt{2}}\right) + \mu_1\mu_2 d_1 d_2 \cosh\left(\frac{a}{d_1\sqrt{2}}\right)\right] \tag{15.76}$$

∴   The equivalent resistance of the composite bar is

$$R_{eq} = \frac{P_T}{|I|^2} = \left(\frac{\rho_1 l}{W d_1 \sqrt{2}} \right) \left(\frac{U}{P^2 + Q^2} \right) \tag{15.77}$$

We now express this equivalent resistance in terms of the resistance of a homogeneous bar of the plating metal, i.e. metal 1,

$$\therefore \qquad R_1 = \frac{\rho_1 l}{W d_1 \sqrt{2}} \qquad \text{and} \qquad \frac{R_{eq}}{R_1} = \frac{U}{P^2 + Q^2} \tag{15.78}$$

And, if we do a similar comparison with the metal 2, then

$$\frac{R_{eq}}{R_2} = \left(\frac{\mu_1 d_1}{\mu_2 d_2} \right) \left(\frac{U}{P^2 + Q^2} \right) \tag{15.79}$$

We now compare the resistance of a silver-plated brass bar with that of a solid bar of the same dimensions, as shown in the Figure 15.14. It is seen that if the silver plate thickness

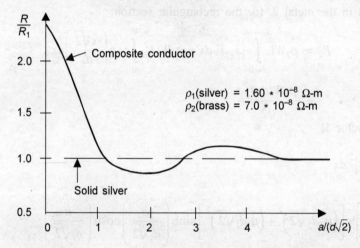

Figure 15.14   Resistance ratio for a silver-plated brass block.

exceeds 1.2 times the skin-depth ($d_1 \sqrt{2}$), then the resistance of the composite bar is nearly the same as that of pure silver. The surprising point to be noted is that, there is a dip in this curve from $[a/(d_1 \sqrt{2})] = 1.2$ to 2.6, when for this thickness, the total resistance of the composite bar and hence its $I^2 R$ current loss as well, are *less than those for a pure silver bar*.

We can similarly analyze other composite metal bars, such as copper–lead, and so on.

15.7   MAGNETIC DIFFUSION AS AN ELECTRICAL TRANSIENT

So far all the problems we have considered are of the type in which the currents have been induced in the conducting media as a consequence of imposing a steady sinusoidally varying (with time, i.e. time-harmonic) magnetic field on it, or by forcing a similar alternating current on the medium. Also in the present problem under consideration, the material medium is at rest, and we study the diffusion of the magnetic field and the associated induced eddy currents in the conducting medium, when the forcing magnetic field is suddenly switched on as a step-function of time. We devise a model such that we have simplified the geometry with only one component of the magnetic field existing, and one orthogonal component of the electric field and hence the current as well are present in the model, so that the analysis is a simple one (from the mathematical viewpoint). Thus we have an electromagnet of an infinitely permeable, non-conducting magnetic material with an air-gap of length w (Figure 15.15), excited through an N-turn winding by a constant-current source of current I, which can be turned on or off by the switch S. In the gap is a slab of non-magnetic conducting material of dimensions $l \times w \times b$ (l being the length, w the width, and b the thickness) as shown in Figure 15.15, with constant conductivity σ (or resistivity $\rho = 1/\sigma$). The dimensions w and l are large compared with the thickness b, and hence the edge effects (i.e. fringing) can be neglected. The coordinate system for the problem is as defined in Figure 15.15(b). Initially it is assumed that the switch S is

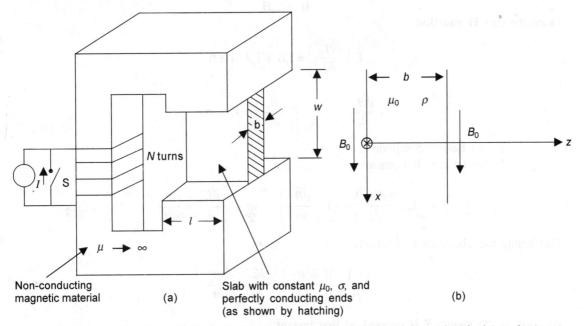

Non-conducting
magnetic material   (a)

Slab with constant μ_0, σ, and
perfectly conducting ends   (b)
(as shown by hatching)

Figure 15.15   (a) System devised to study magnetic diffusion as an electrical transient;
(b) coordinate system for the one-dimensional diffusion model.

closed, and hence there is no current in the winding and hence no magnetic flux in the magnet. At the instant $t = 0$, the switch S is opened, and now we shall study the time variations of the flux.

The boundary conditions on opening the switch are:
Outside the block, in the gap of the magnet, for $t > 0$, $z < 0$, $z > b$,

$$\mathbf{B} = \mathbf{i}_x B_0$$

where

$$B_0 = \frac{\mu_0 NI}{w} \tag{15.80}$$

It should be noted that only the x-component of $\mathbf{B}$ exists in the air-gap of the magnet, and it varies with z only.

Inside the block (of thickness b), the displacement currents can be neglected. The relevant Maxwell's equations are

$$\text{curl } \mathbf{H} = \nabla \times \mathbf{H} = \mathbf{J}$$

and

$$\text{curl } \mathbf{E} = \nabla \times \mathbf{E} = -\frac{\partial \mathbf{B}}{\partial t}$$

Since $\mathbf{B}$ has x-component only and is a function of z only,

$$\text{div } \mathbf{B} = \nabla \cdot \mathbf{B} = 0$$

is automatically satisfied.

The constituent relations are:

$$\mathbf{E} = \rho \mathbf{J} \qquad \text{or} \qquad \mathbf{J} = \sigma \mathbf{E}$$

and

$$\mathbf{B} = \mu_0 \mathbf{H}$$

From the curl $\mathbf{H}$ equation,

$$\mathbf{i}_y \left(\frac{\partial H_x}{\partial z} \right) = \mathbf{i}_x 0 + \mathbf{i}_y J_y + \mathbf{i}_z 0$$

or

$$\left(\frac{\partial H_x}{\partial z} \right) = \left(\frac{1}{\mu_0} \right)\left(\frac{\partial B_x}{\partial z} \right) = J_y = \sigma E_y$$

$\therefore$ $\mathbf{E}$ can have y-component only.

$\therefore$ From the curl $\mathbf{E}$ equation,

$$\mathbf{i}_x \left(-\frac{\partial E_y}{\partial z} \right) = -\mathbf{i}_x \left(\frac{\partial B_x}{\partial t} \right) \qquad \text{or} \qquad \frac{\partial E_y}{\partial z} = \frac{\partial B_x}{\partial t}$$

Combining the above two equations,

$$\left(\frac{1}{\mu_0 \sigma} \right)\left(\frac{\partial^2 B_x}{\partial z^2} \right) = \frac{\partial E_y}{\partial z} = \frac{\partial B_x}{\partial t} \tag{15.81}$$

As soon as the switch S is opened, at that instant,

$$\text{at } t = 0^+, \ B_x = 0 \qquad \text{(inside the conducting block).} \tag{15.82}$$

The distribution of B_x at $t = 0^+$ is shown diagrammatically in the air-gap of the magnet in Figure 15.16.

This condition follows from the equation: $\nabla \times \mathbf{E} = -\dfrac{\partial \mathbf{B}}{\partial t}$

or

$$\oint_C \mathbf{E} \cdot d\mathbf{l} = -\left(\frac{\partial}{\partial t} \right) \iint_S \mathbf{B} \cdot d\mathbf{S} = \frac{1}{\sigma} \oint_C \mathbf{J} \cdot d\mathbf{l} \tag{15.83}$$

which is essentially the Stokes' theorem.

The implication of the ideal B_x distribution as shown by Eq. (15.82) and as shown in Figure 15.16 is that the external flux density in the air-gap (i.e. external to the conducting

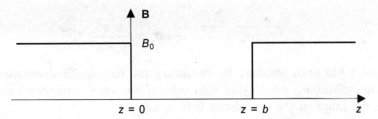

Figure 15.16   Distribution of B_x at $t = 0^+$ in the conducting slab.

block) is established in zero time. This mathematical simplification implies that at this instant, the time-derivative of **B** will be infinite. In the contour C of the Stokes' theorem equation, if C includes $z = 0$ or $z = b$, then it indicates an infinite current density, but actually a finite surface current is necessary to terminate the B_0 field. In a real situation, the flux density B_0 is established rapidly but in a finite time. This idealization will be better understood when we discuss the solution at the completion of this problem.

It should also be understood that after a sufficient long time, all transient currents in the slab will die out, and then B_x will become uniform throughout the block, i.e.

$$\{\text{as } t \to \infty, B_x \to B_0 \text{ and then } (\partial B_x/\partial t) = 0 \text{ for the steady-state conditions.}\} \qquad (15.84)$$

So to solve Eq. (15.81), we use the method of separation of variables, and assume a solution of the form

$$B_x = B(z) B(t) + C_0 \qquad (15.85)$$

Substituting in Eq. (15.81),

$$\left[\frac{1}{\mu_0 \sigma B(z)}\right]\left[\frac{d^2 B(z)}{dz^2}\right] = \left[\frac{1}{B(t)}\right]\left[\frac{dB(t)}{dt}\right] = -\alpha$$

(α being an arbitrary constant at this stage).

$$\therefore \qquad B(z) = C_1 \sin\left(\sqrt{\mu_0 \sigma \alpha}\, z\right) + C_2 \cos\left(\sqrt{\mu_0 \sigma \alpha}\, z\right)$$

and

$$B(t) = \exp\left(-\alpha t\right)$$

$\therefore$ The solution will have the general form

$$B_x = \left[C_1 \sin\left(\sqrt{\mu_0 \sigma \alpha}\, z\right) + C_2 \cos\left(\sqrt{\mu_0 \sigma \alpha}\, z\right)\right]\exp\left(-\alpha t\right) + C_0 \qquad (15.86)$$

where C_1, C_2, C_0, and α are constants to be determined from the boundary conditions.

For the necessary initial condition of B_x at $t = 0^+$, from $z = 0$, $C_2 = 0$, and $C_0 = B_0$.

$$\therefore \qquad B_x = C_1 \exp\left(-\alpha t\right) \sin\left(\sqrt{\mu_0 \sigma \alpha}\, z\right) + B_0 \qquad (15.87)$$

This equation must satisfy the initial conditions of B_x over the range $z = 0$ to $z = b$, as shown in the rectangular distribution represented diagrammatically in Figure 15.16, i.e.

$$\text{for } 0 < z < b, \quad 0 = \sum_{n=1}^{\infty} a_n \sin\left(\frac{n\pi z}{b}\right) + B_0 \tag{15.88}$$

$$\therefore \quad \sqrt{\mu_0 \sigma \alpha_n} = \frac{n\pi}{b} \quad \text{or} \quad \alpha_n = \frac{n^2 \pi^2}{\mu_0 \sigma b^2} \tag{15.89}$$

The above equation has been obtained by expanding the rectangular distribution in a 'Fourier sine series'. So to evaluate a_n, multiplying both sides of the series expansion by $\sin(m\pi z/b)$, and integrating over the limits of the periodicity 0 to b, i.e.

$$\int_0^b B_0 \sin\left(\frac{m\pi z}{b}\right) dz = \int_0^\infty \sum_{n=1}^{\infty} a_n \sin\left(\frac{n\pi z}{b}\right) \sin\left(\frac{m\pi z}{b}\right) dz \tag{15.90}$$

All the right-hand terms for which $m \neq n$ vanish, leaving:

$$\int_0^b a_n \sin^2\left(\frac{n\pi z}{b}\right) dz = -B_0 \int_0^b \sin\left(\frac{n\pi z}{b}\right) dz$$

$$\therefore \quad a_n = -\left(\frac{4}{n\pi}\right) B_0 \quad \text{for } n = 1, 3, 5, \dots$$

$$= 0 \quad \text{for } n = 2, 4, 6, \dots \tag{15.91}$$

$$\therefore \quad B_x = B_0 \left[1 - \sum_{n=1,3,5,\dots}^{\infty} \left(\frac{4}{n\pi}\right) \{\exp(-\alpha_n t)\} \sin\left(\frac{n\pi z}{b}\right) \right] \tag{15.92}$$

Note that each space harmonic damps at different rate, the higher harmonics damping faster.

We now define the fundamental time constant τ as

$$\tau = \frac{1}{\alpha_1} = \frac{\mu_0 \sigma b^2}{\pi^2}, \quad n = 1 \tag{15.93}$$

$$\therefore \quad B_x = B_0 \left[1 - \sum_{n=1,3,5,\dots}^{\infty} \left(\frac{4}{n\pi}\right) \left\{ \exp\left(\frac{-n^2 t}{\tau}\right) \right\} \sin\left(\frac{n\pi z}{b}\right) \right] \tag{15.94}$$

The fundamental time constant, which is the longest time-constant of the series, is called the 'diffusion time-constant' of the system.

We now plot the flux density distribution as a function of z in the thickness of the block b at different instants of time (Figure 15.17). It will be noted that, at $t = 0$, the flux is completely eliminated from the slab. With the progress of time, the flux diffuses into the slab. Because the higher harmonics damp out faster,

at $t = 0.1\tau$, only 3 terms are needed for B_x calculation;
at $t = 0.3\tau$, only 2 terms are required; and
for $t > \tau$, only the fundamental term is significant.

This shows why the fundamental diffusion time τ is the controlling time constant in the diffusion process. Also, the field is nearly completely diffused in the material in time, $t > 3\tau$.

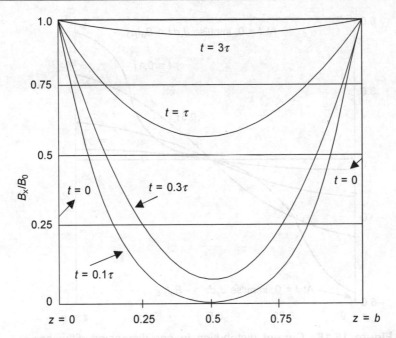

Figure 15.17 B_x as a function of z, with the time t as a parameter.

Next, we consider the behaviour of the current density inside the slab during the transient diffusion process. The current density is given by

$$J_y = \left(\frac{1}{\mu_0}\right)\left(\frac{\partial B_x}{\partial z}\right) = -\left(\frac{B_0}{\mu_0 b}\right)\sum_{n=1,3,5,\cdots}^{\infty}\left[4\left\{\exp\left(\frac{-n^2 t}{\tau}\right)\right\}\cos\left(\frac{n\pi z}{b}\right)\right] \qquad (15.95)$$

The space distribution of current density J_y is shown in the Figure 15.18. Note from this equation, that at $t = 0$, this series does not converge at $z = 0$ and $z = b$. This shows that at $t = 0$, the magnetic field is completely excluded from the slab, and to terminate the external magnetic field, a surface current density is required—which implies an infinite volume current density— thus at $t = 0$, there are impulses of J_y at $z = 0$ and $z = b$. As the time progresses, the currents diffuse in the slab and decay. At the surface of the slab (i.e. $z = 0$ and $z = b$) the current density decays continually, but at an interior point, the current density increases from zero to some maximum value and then decays back to zero.

Conservation of current requires that the current flows down one side of the block and return on the opposite side. Hence in Figure 15.18, the current distribution graphs show an odd symmetry (or skew symmetry) about $z = b/2$. Note also that a one-dimensional solution implies perfectly conducting end-plates on the slab to provide a return path for the currents.

Notes:

1.   It is a point to be noted that for such electromagnetic phenomena, occurring outside the slab, which have characteristic times much shorter than the diffusion time τ, the properties of the slab can be approximated by assuming its $\sigma \to \infty$. This is a valid assumption, used in calculating the sub-transient component of the end-winding reactances in large turbogenerators, i.e. the time-duration is so short that only the air-

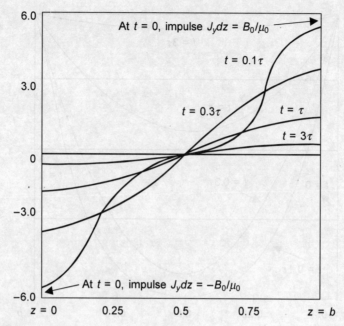

Figure 15.18 Current distribution in one-dimension diffusion.

region flux has been established and the flux has been excluded from the interior of the block (which in the case of the turbogenerator end-region is the clamping plate on the core-end-surface).

2. On the other hand, for those phenomena which have characteristic times much longer than the diffusion time τ, the perturbations due to the diffusion effects can be neglected for field calculations. These two limiting cases are analogous to the constant current and the constant flux conditions of the lumped parameter systems.

Some examples of diffusion time constants ($\tau = \mu_0 \mu_r \sigma b^2 / \pi^2$) are:

1. A slab of copper 1 cm thick, $\sigma = 5.9 \times 10^7$ mhos/m; $\tau = 1$ ms
2. Seeded combustion gas, 1 metre thick, $\sigma = 40$ mhos/m; $\tau = 10$ μs
3. Silicon-iron (4%), 1 cm thick, $\sigma = 1.7 \times 10^6$ mhos/m, $\mu_r = 5000$, $\tau = 100$ ms

We see that even though the conductivity of Si-Fe is much lower than that of copper, its diffusion time is much higher because of high relative permeability. This high diffusion time constant of Si–Fe makes the laminations of the iron cores necessary in all alternating current equipment, such as generators, motors, and transformers.

15.7.1 Diffusion Time-constant and Skin-depth

So far, the magnetic diffusion process in any conducting medium has been observed to take place, when the incident magnetic field is a function of time, i.e. if the diffusion process is due to the term $\left(\dfrac{\partial B}{\partial t}\right)$ having a non-zero value. This has happened in two different ways:

1. When **B** is a time-harmonic function which is $\mathbf{B}_0 e^{j\omega t}$ {or $\mathbf{B}_0$ [(sin/cos) ωt]}, ω being the angular frequency of the time variation). The first illustration of such behaviour is elaborated in the example of Section 15.2, with further examples of the same basic nature being explained in Section 15.3 to Section 15.6.

2. When the time-dependence of B is not of time-harmonic type (i.e. not a repeatable oscillatory function of time), but of a transient nature, e.g., a step-function or a single pulse, etc. In such cases, as explained in the problem of Section 15.7, the diffusion process produces, in the conducting medium, a decaying distribution of the magnetic field which is a function of both the distance from the incident field surface as well as time.

The space decaying pattern as shown in Eq. (15.92) is of form $\left[1 - \displaystyle\sum_{n \text{ odd int}} \frac{4}{n\pi} \sin \frac{n\pi z}{b} \right]$

and on the second term is superimposed an exponentially time-decaying term $\exp\{-\alpha_n t\}$ where the exponent α_n is a function of the conducting regions's magnetic permeability and electrical conductivity. The consequence of this type of time variation is that with increasing time (i.e. $t \to \infty$) the magnetic field in the conductor tends to become uniform as shown in Figure 15.17. With this time-varying magnetic field, the associated transient current is a surface current-sheet initially at $t = 0$, which then decays with time and tends to uniform distribution in the conductor with zero value as $t \to \infty$, the time-constant of the variation being the fundamental value of α_n {$n = 1$}. This behaviour of current is due to the fact that the conductor is a lossy dissipative medium. The surface current density at $t = 0$ implies an infinite volume current-density at $t = 0$ and zero flux penetration in the medium at that instant of time, with the progress of time the currents diffuse in the slab. On the surface of the slab, the current density decays continuously, but at any interior point, the current density increases from zero to some maximum value and then decays back to zero (Figure 15.18).

So far, we have considered the diffusion process due to time-variation of the incident magnetic field, of different types, but not considered any relative motion between the magnetic field and the conducting medium. When the time-variation of the magnetic field is of time-harmonic type, the diffusion process is controlled by the 'depth of penetration', and when the time-variation of **B** is of transient nature, the diffusion process is controlled by the 'diffusion time-constant'.

15.8   MAGNETIC DIFFUSION AS A RESULT OF RELATIVE MOTION OF THE CONDUCTING MEDIUM

So far we have considered the phenomenon of the magnetic diffusion caused by changes in the magnetic field with time, i.e. either due to a transient change in the field or due to a change in the field in a regular periodic manner with time (time-harmonic fields). In all these cases, it has been assumed that there has been no relative motion between the conducting body and the source field. However, it is also possible to produce the diffusion effect by a relative displacement between the source field and the conducting body (taking place in a finite time). Such continuous displacements can be produced either by a moving conducting body or by a travelling magnetic field pattern or by a combination of both. Before we study specific examples of such a phenomenon, we shall extend the operating equation [i.e. Eq. (12.39)] to include the effects of the relative motion. This can be done by either of the two ways.

Maxwell's equation of electromagnetic induction (or Faraday's law of induction) which has been used to derive Eq. (12.39), does not include the effects of the moving media, even though we have generalized this equation [i.e. Eq. (12.10) in integral form, or Eq. (12.17) in differential form] to include such effects in Chapter 10, Sections 10.3 to 10.4. So now we use this generalized equation along with other relevant equations to derive the generalized diffusion equation. For this purpose, our relevant Maxwell's equations are

$$\nabla \cdot \mathbf{B} = 0 \tag{12.16}$$

$$\nabla \times \mathbf{H} = \mathbf{J} \tag{12.18'}$$

$$\nabla \times \mathbf{E} = -\left(\frac{\partial \mathbf{B}}{\partial t}\right) + \nabla \times (\mathbf{v} \times \mathbf{B}) \tag{10.29'}$$

Here Eq. (12.18') is the Ampere's law Eq. (12.18) in which the displacement current term ($\partial \mathbf{D}/\partial t$) has been neglected; and Eq. (10.29') is the differential form of the generalized electromagnetic induction Eq. (10.29), which was written in the integral form. (And $\mathbf{v}$ is the velocity of the moving medium.)

The relevant constituent relations for this phenomenon are

$$\mathbf{B} = \mu \mathbf{H} \tag{12.13}$$

$$\mathbf{E} = \rho \mathbf{J} \quad \text{or} \quad \mathbf{J} = \sigma \mathbf{E} \tag{12.14}$$

Rewriting Eq. (12.17') with Eq. (12.14), we get

$$\nabla \times \mathbf{H} = \sigma \mathbf{E}$$

and doing a curl operation on this equation, we get

$$\left(\frac{1}{\sigma}\right) \nabla \times \nabla \times \mathbf{H} = \nabla \times \mathbf{E} = -\left(\frac{\partial \mathbf{B}}{\partial t}\right) + \nabla \times (\mathbf{v} \times \mathbf{B})$$

from Eq. (10.29').

Converting this equation to a single variable (i.e. $\mathbf{B}$) equation by using Eq. (12.13), we get

$$\left(\frac{1}{\mu\sigma}\right) \nabla \times \nabla \times \mathbf{B} = -\left(\frac{\partial \mathbf{B}}{\partial t}\right) + \nabla \times (\mathbf{v} \times \mathbf{B}) \tag{15.96}$$

The left-hand side of this equation can be expressed as

$$-\left(\frac{1}{\mu\sigma}\right) \nabla \times \nabla \times \mathbf{B} = -\left(\frac{1}{\mu\sigma}\right)\left[\nabla(\nabla \cdot \mathbf{B}) - \nabla^2 \mathbf{B}\right] \text{—vector identity}$$

and using Eq. (12.16) which makes the first term of this equation to vanish, we get

$$-\left(\frac{1}{\mu\sigma}\right) \nabla^2 \mathbf{B} + \left(\frac{\partial \mathbf{B}}{\partial t}\right) = \nabla \times (\mathbf{v} \times \mathbf{B}) \tag{15.97}$$

This equation describes the distribution of the magnetic field in the conducting medium. It includes both the effects of the time-varying magnetic field and the material motion, and can be used for solving a variety of practical engineering problems. This equation is also of great importance in determining the magnetic field origins in the liquid core of the earth, and in this context it is sometimes referred to as the 'Bullard's equation'. This equation can also be derived in an alternative manner, using the restricted equation for the electromagnetic induction, i.e. Eq. (12.18) and then replacing the constituent relation (12.14) by a more general form in which the effects of relative motion are included. We shall see later in Chapter 20, when we deal with moving coordinate systems (Electromagnetism and Special Relativity), that the current density vector $\mathbf{J}$ can be expressed as

$$\mathbf{J} = \sigma(\mathbf{E} + \mathbf{v} \times \mathbf{B}) \qquad (15.98)$$

This equation along with the other constituent relation

$$\mathbf{B} = \mu\mathbf{H} \qquad (12.13)$$

and the relevant Maxwell's equations

$$\nabla \cdot \mathbf{B} = 0 \qquad (12.16)$$

$$\nabla \times \mathbf{H} = \mathbf{J} \qquad (12.18')$$

$$\nabla \times \mathbf{E} = -\left(\frac{\partial \mathbf{B}}{\partial t}\right) \qquad (12.17)$$

would give us the same result (as we have seen in the earlier part of this section).

We now start with Eq. (12.17), and obtain

$$\nabla \times \mathbf{E} = \nabla \times \left[\left(\frac{1}{\sigma}\right)\mathbf{J} - \mathbf{v} \times \mathbf{B}\right] = -\left(\frac{\partial \mathbf{B}}{\partial t}\right)$$

by using Eq. (15.98).

Or

$$\left(\frac{1}{\sigma}\right)\nabla \times \mathbf{J} + \frac{\partial \mathbf{B}}{\partial t} = \nabla \times (\mathbf{v} \times \mathbf{B})$$

or

$$\left(\frac{1}{\mu\sigma}\right)\nabla \times \nabla \times \mathbf{B} + \frac{\partial \mathbf{B}}{\partial t} = \nabla \times (\mathbf{v} \times \mathbf{B})$$

by using Eq. (12.18').

And, as before, the operator identity gives us

$$\nabla \times \nabla \times \mathbf{B} = [\nabla(\nabla \cdot \mathbf{B}) - \nabla^2\mathbf{B}] = -\nabla^2\mathbf{B} \text{ [from Eq. (12.16)]}.$$

∴ The above equation reduces to

$$-\left(\frac{1}{\mu\sigma}\right)\nabla^2\mathbf{B} + \frac{\partial \mathbf{B}}{\partial t} = \nabla \times (\mathbf{v} \times \mathbf{B}) \qquad (15.97')$$

which is same as Eq. (15.97), i.e. the 'general equation for magnetic diffusion' which includes both the effects of time-varying magnetic fields as well as material motion.

There are again two limiting cases:

1. When the material motion is absent, the equation simplifies to

$$\left(\frac{1}{\mu\sigma}\right)\nabla^2 \mathbf{B} = \frac{\partial \mathbf{B}}{\partial t} \tag{15.99}$$

which is really the vector diffusion equation of (12.39) in which the time-variation operator $(\partial/\partial t)$ has been kept in the general form, and not restricted to the time-harmonic variation. In fact, it is this equation, which we have been solving in the problems discussed in Sections 15.2 to 15.6.

2. The second limiting case, which is also of considerable importance, is also obtained when there is only motion under steady-state conditions, i.e. the magnetic field vector is not time-varying. We shall look at some situations consistent with this condition. The equation for this limiting condition is

$$-\left(\frac{1}{\mu\sigma}\right)\nabla^2 \mathbf{B} = \nabla \times (\mathbf{v} \times \mathbf{B}) \tag{15.99'}$$

However some of the most important engineering examples are those of the time-varying excitation in presence of material motion. The induction motors are examples of interaction of this type. Now we shall have a look at some of these problems in a simplified manner.

15.9 STEADY-STATE MAGNETIC FIELD IN A FIXED FRAME

This type of steady-state (non-time-varying) diffusion problem is relevant to magneto-hydrodynamic (MHD) generators. The system consists of a continuous strip of material of constants, σ, ε_0, μ_0, sliding with constant velocity $\mathbf{v}$ between a parallel pair of highly conducting electrodes. The dimensions and the coordinate system are as shown in Figure 15.19.

The sliding strip is assumed to make perfect contacts with the electrodes. The system is excited by current sources at the end $z = l$, so that the total current to the electrodes is I amps.

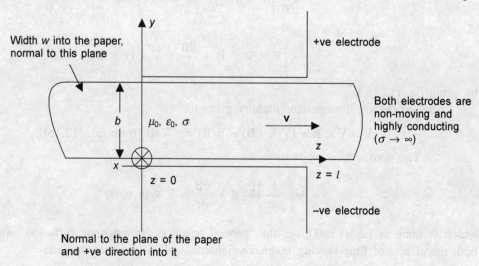

Figure 15.19 Geometry for diffusion in presence of steady motion only.

We intend to determine the **B** distribution in the system, and the effects of the system parameters on this distribution.

Once again, l/b and w/b are assumed to be large enough so that the edge and the end effects can be neglected. The flux density **B** can be taken to be one-dimensional, i.e. only B_x exists, since the current flow is in the y-direction:

$$\mathbf{B} = \mathbf{i}_x B_x, \quad \mathbf{J} = \mathbf{i}_y J_y, \quad \text{and hence } \mathbf{E} = \mathbf{i}_y E_y \tag{15.100}$$

and hence the field quantities vary as a function of z only, and there is no variation with respect to x or y.

Also, the constant velocity of the strip is

$$\mathbf{v} = \mathbf{i}_z \mathbf{v}_z \tag{15.101}$$

From the $\nabla \times \mathbf{E}$ Eq. (10.29′), which now simplifies to $\nabla \times \mathbf{E} = \nabla \times (\mathbf{v} \times \mathbf{B})$, we get

$$\mathbf{i}_x \left(-\frac{\partial E_y}{\partial z} \right) = \mathbf{i}_x \left[-\frac{\partial}{\partial z} \left(\mathbf{v}_z B_x \right) \right]$$

or

$$\left(\frac{1}{\sigma} \right) \left(\frac{\partial J_y}{\partial z} \right) = \mathbf{v}_z \left(\frac{\partial B_x}{\partial z} \right) \tag{15.102}$$

And from the $\nabla \times \mathbf{H}$ Eq. (12.18′):

$$\mathbf{i}_y \left(+\frac{\partial H_x}{\partial z} \right) = \mathbf{i}_y J_y \quad \text{or} \quad \left(\frac{1}{\mu_0} \right) \left(\frac{\partial B_x}{\partial z} \right) = J_y \tag{15.103}$$

From Eq. (15.103),

$$\left(\frac{1}{\mu_0} \right) \left(\frac{\partial^2 B_x}{\partial z^2} \right) = \frac{\partial J_y}{\partial z} = \mathbf{v}_z \sigma \left(\frac{\partial B_x}{\partial z} \right)$$

or

$$\left(\frac{d^2 B_x}{dz^2} \right) - \mu_0 \sigma \mathbf{v}_z \left(\frac{dB_x}{dz} \right) = 0 \tag{15.104}$$

The total derivative has replaced the partial derivative, since B_x is a function of z only. Thus the above Eq. (15.104) is the equivalent of Eq. (15.99) for this problem.

The relevant boundary conditions for the problem are:

At $\qquad z = 0, B_x = 0;$ $\qquad$ and $\qquad$ at $z = l, B_x = \dfrac{\mu_0 I}{w}$ $\qquad$ (15.105)

When the velocity $\mathbf{v}_z$ is a finite constant, the solution of B_x is of the form

$$B_x = C \exp(\alpha z) \tag{15.106}$$

Substituting in Eq. (15.104), we get

$$\alpha^2 - \mu_0 \sigma \mathbf{v}_z \alpha = 0$$

The solutions of this equation are

$$\alpha = \mu_0 \sigma \mathbf{v}_z \text{ and } \alpha = 0$$

∴ The general solution for B_x is

$$B_x = C_0 + C_1 \exp(\mu_0 \sigma v_z z)$$

Using the boundary conditions of (15.105),

$$0 = C_0 + C_1, \text{ from the } z = 0 \text{ condition} \rightarrow C_0 = -C_1, \text{ and } \frac{\mu_0 I}{w} = C_0 + C_1 \exp(\mu_0 \sigma v_z l)$$

∴

$$C_1 = \left(\frac{\mu_0 I}{w}\right)\left[\exp(\mu_0 \sigma v_z l) - 1\right]^{-1}$$

We write

$$\mu_0 \sigma v_z l = R_m \tag{15.107}$$

which is dimensionless and defined as the 'magnetic Reynold's number'.

∴

$$B_x = \left(\frac{\mu_0 I}{w}\right) \frac{\exp\left(\frac{R_m z}{l}\right) - 1}{\exp(R_m) - 1} \tag{15.108}$$

and the current density distribution is

$$J_y = \left(\frac{1}{\mu_0}\right)\left(\frac{dB_x}{dz}\right) = \frac{I}{wl} \frac{R_m \exp\left(\frac{R_m z}{l}\right)}{\exp(R_m) - 1} \tag{15.109}$$

When $R_m \rightarrow 0$, i.e. the velocity v_z is made zero, these two distributions become

$$B_x = \left(\frac{\mu_0 I}{w}\right)\left(\frac{z}{l}\right) \quad \text{and} \quad J_y = \frac{I}{wl}$$

which can also be obtained by directly putting $v_z = 0$ in the equations (15.104).

We now plot B_x and J_y as functions of position z in the slab for different values of the magnetic Reynold's number R_m (Figure 15.20). It is seen that at $v_z = 0$, the distributions of **B** and **J** in the slab are linear, and as R_m keeps on increasing these distributions become more and more nonlinear due to the higher exponential variations with R_m and velocity. It should also be noted that the direction of motion and the direction of diffusion (of **B** and **J**) are opposite. The magnitude of R_m is an indicator of the relative effectiveness of the two processes. A large R_m produces a slow diffusion. The magnetic Reynold's number can be taken as proportional to the ratio of the 'diffusion time constant' [defined earlier in the Section 15.7, Eq. (15.93)] to the time taken by a sample of the material to traverse the length of the electrodes.

Remembering

$$\tau \text{ or } \tau_d = \frac{\mu_0 \sigma l^2}{\pi^2} \tag{15.93}$$

and the time required by a sample of material to traverse the length l with a velocity v_z is

$$\tau_t = \frac{l}{v_z}$$

∴

$$\frac{\tau_d}{\tau_t} = \frac{\mu_0 \sigma v_z l}{\pi^2} = \frac{R_m}{\pi^2} \tag{15.110}$$

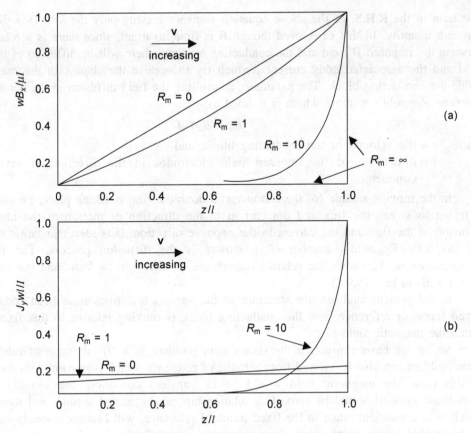

Figure 15.20 B and J distributions in the system of Figure 15.19 as functions of z and R_m:
(a) B_x distribution and (b) J_y distribution.

It should be noted that there are other ways of defining R_m as well, which we shall use in other problems.

15.9.1 Magnetic Diffusion and Steady Motion (Magnetic Reynolds' Number)

So far, in Sections 15.2 to 15.7, the magnetic diffusion has been shown to be due to time-variation of the incident magnetic field on the conducting medium. However, looking at the general equation for magnetic diffusion {i.e. Eq (15.97)} is written in a slightly different form:

$$\frac{1}{\mu\sigma}\nabla^2\mathbf{B} = \frac{\partial\mathbf{B}}{\partial t} - \nabla\times(\mathbf{v}\times\mathbf{B}) \qquad (15.97'')$$

where $\mathbf{v}$ is the velocity of the moving medium.

As already mentioned is Section 15.8, there are two limiting cases of the above general diffusion equation. The first limiting equation has been explained and illustrated by the examples discussed in Sections 15.2 to 15.7 where the imposed magnetic field $\mathbf{B}$ has time-variation and the conducting medium is fixed, i.e. $\mathbf{v} = 0$.

The second limiting case is one which has been illustrated in Section 15.9 when $\mathbf{B}$ is time-invariant and the conducting medium is moving with a constant velocity $\mathbf{v}$ in which case, the first term in the R.H.S. of the above equation vanishes leaving only the $\nabla \times (\mathbf{v} \times \mathbf{B})$ term as a non-zero quantity. In this case, even though $\mathbf{B}$ is time-invariant, since there is a relative motion between the imposed $\mathbf{B}$ field and the conducting medium, there will be diffusion of the magnetic field and the associated eddy currents, which try to oppose the change in the magnetic field inside the conducting block. The parameter controlling the field diffusion in the conductor is the magnetic Reynold's number which is defined as

$$R_m = \mu_0 \sigma v l$$

where   v = the velocity of the conducting block, and

       l = dimension of the imposed field electrodes in the direction of motion of the conductor.

In the moving sample (of the conductor) a double action is taking place, i.e. the conductor is trying to sweep the flux and the current in the direction of motion of the block and the diffusion of the flux and the current in the opposite direction. It is seen that larger the value of the magnetic Reynold's number (R_m), slower is the diffusion process. The fundamental interpretation of R_m shows the relative importance of diffusion ($= \nabla^2 \mathbf{B}$) and the velocity term ($\nabla \times \mathbf{v} \times \mathbf{B}$) in Eq. (15.99′).

In the present analysis, the structure of the various quantities have been considered in a 'fixed frame of reference' and the conducting block is moving relative to this fixed frame, in which the magnetic field lies.

So far we have considered the steady-state problem in a 'fixed frame of reference'. The same problem can also be viewed from a frame of reference which is moving with the conductor. In this case, the magnetic field would be in transient condition, the velocity (v_z in our co-ordinate system) would be zero. This relationship can be turned around, and then a problem which is in a transient state in the fixed frame of reference, will become a steady-state problem in the moving frame of reference. Such an example gives further insight into the significance of the magnetic Reynolds' number.

Such analyses have been used for designing mechanisms for mechanical amplification of magnetic flux density, which are used with chemical explosives and other plasma devices for controlled thermonuclear reactions.

15.10   SINUSOIDALLY TIME-VARYING MAGNETIC FIELD IN PRESENCE OF MOTION

Now we consider a problem in which we introduce both the characteristic dynamical times into a single system, i.e. a sheet of conducting metal of conductivity σ is moving to the right with a constant velocity $\mathbf{v}$ in the z-direction (Figure 15.21). The sheet is assumed to move in the air-gap of an infinitely permeable magnetic circuit, so that the problem can be considered as a one-dimensional problem. $\mathbf{B}$ is uniform in the x- and y-directions, with variations in the z-direction, and has only one component, i.e.

$$\mathbf{B} = \mathbf{i}_y \, \text{Re}\left[\hat{B}_0 \, \exp\left(j\omega t \right) \right] \qquad \text{at } z = 0 \qquad (15.111)$$

We consider an ideal distribution of this type, without going into the device of its generation, just as we had assumed ideal field distributions in the problems described in Sections 15.2 and 15.3. Since there are no variations in the x- and the y-directions, the operators

$$\frac{\partial}{\partial x} = \frac{\partial}{\partial y} = 0$$

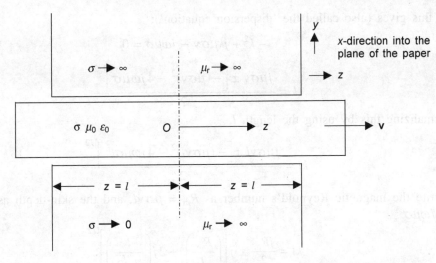

Figure 15.21 A thin slab of conductor moving in the +z-direction in the air-gap of a magnetic circuit.

and the one-dimensional magnetic field in the moving sheet then satisfies Eq. (15.97), which in this case simplifies from

$$-\left(\frac{1}{\mu\sigma}\right)\nabla^2\mathbf{B}+\left(\frac{\partial\mathbf{B}}{\partial t}\right)=\nabla\times(\mathbf{v}\times\mathbf{B}) \qquad (15.97)$$

to

$$\left(\frac{1}{\mu\sigma}\right)\left(\frac{\partial^2 B_y}{\partial z^2}\right)=\left(\frac{\partial B_y}{\partial t}\right)+\mathbf{v}\left(\frac{\partial B_y}{\partial z}\right) \qquad (15.112)$$

and the currents in the slab would flow in the x-direction, which would be given by the curl $\mathbf{H}=\mathbf{J}$ equation, which in this case simplifies to

$$J_x=-\left(\frac{1}{\mu}\right)\left(\frac{\partial B_y}{\partial z}\right) \qquad (15.113)$$

It should be noted that the direction of $\mathbf{B}$ (the y-direction) is at right angles to the direction of motion (the z-direction), which is also the direction in which the variations take place.

Since the excitation is sinusoidal with time, we can assume the solution of the equation to be of the form

$$B_y=\text{Re}\left[\hat{B}_y(z)\exp(j\omega t)\right] \qquad (15.114)$$

where ω the angular frequency is the same as that of the source excitation. Substituting this expression in Eq. (15.112), we get

$$\frac{\partial^2\hat{B}_y}{\partial z^2}-\mu\sigma\mathbf{v}\left(\frac{\partial\hat{B}y}{\partial z}\right)-j\omega\mu\sigma\hat{B}_y=0 \qquad (15.115)$$

The solution of this equation will be of the form

$$\hat{B}_y(z)=\exp(-jkz)$$

Then, this gives (also called the 'dispersion equation'):

$$-k^2 + jk\mu\sigma v - j\omega\mu\sigma = 0 \tag{15.116}$$

$$\therefore \qquad k = \frac{j\mu\sigma v \pm \left[-(\mu\sigma v)^2 - 4j\omega\mu\sigma\right]^{1/2}}{2}$$

or normalizing this by using the length l,

$$kl = \frac{j\mu\sigma vl \pm \left[-(\mu\sigma vl)^2 - 4j\omega\mu\sigma l^2\right]^{1/2}}{2}$$

We write the magnetic Reynold's number as $R_m = \mu\sigma vl$, and the skin-depth as $d\sqrt{2}$, where $d^2 = 1/\omega\mu\sigma$.

$$\therefore \qquad kl = \frac{jR_m}{2} \pm j\left[\left(\frac{R_m}{2}\right)^2 + 2j\left(\frac{l}{d\sqrt{2}}\right)\right]^{1/2} \tag{15.117}$$

so that the solution (15.114) takes the form

$$B_y(z, t) = \text{Re}\left[\hat{B}_0 \exp\{j(\omega t - kz)\}\right] \tag{15.118}$$

which is that of a travelling waveform in which the wave number k is complex (in the complex variable sense). Since k is complex, it means that there is a real part of the exponent $\exp(-jkz) = \exp(-k_i z)\exp(-jk_r z)$, where k can be expressed as $k = k_r + jk_i \rightarrow \exp(-k_i z)$ shows the attenuating nature of the wave as it progresses in the z-direction—similar to what we have seen in the problem dealt with in Section 15.2 (when R_m is made zero, or $v = 0$, such that $R_m = 0$). The attenuation of the dispersion wave (as it is called), then depends wholly on the skin-depth $(= d\sqrt{2})$. In the present problem, the attenuation of the wave is a function of both the skin-depth as well as the magnetic Reynold's number R_m. We shall now have a look at the complex nature of k (the wave number) in the present problem. Equation (15.117) shows that k has two values, which we denote by k^+ and k^-, then both these can be expressed as

$$k^+ = k_r^+ + jk_i^+ \qquad \text{and} \qquad k^- = k_r^- + jk_i^-$$

On separating the real and the imaginary parts of k^+ and k^-, we find that:

$$\text{for } z > 0, \ B_y = \text{Re}\left[\hat{B}_0 \exp\left(-\left|k_i^+\right|z\right) \cdot \exp\left(j\omega t - \left|k_r^+\right|z\right)\right]$$

and

$$\text{for } z < 0, \ B_y = \text{Re}\left[\hat{B}_0 \exp\left(-\left|k_i^-\right|z\right) \cdot \exp\left(j\omega t + \left|k_r^-\right|z\right)\right] \tag{15.119}$$

There are two diffusion waves propagating respectively in the $+z$ and $-z$ directions starting from $z = 0$, with phase velocities ω/k_r^+ and ω/k_r^- respectively, both of which are modified by the material motion. It should be noted that on separating the real and the imaginary parts of k^+ and k^-, we get

$$k_r^- = -k_r^+ \qquad \text{and} \qquad k_i^- > 0 > k_i^+ \tag{15.120}$$

Thus the spatial rate of attenuation of the wave travelling (or dispersing) to the right is lessened due to the motion of the slab also to the right, whereas the wave travelling to the left gets attenuated faster as a consequence of the slab motion in the opposite direction.

A practical application of the magnetic diffusion phenomenon discussed in this section, is that the device shown in Figure 15.21 can be used to measure the velocity of the material. A mechanism based on this phenomenon, for measuring the velocity of the material, has the advantage that it (the mechanism) does not require any mechanical or electrical contact with the moving medium.

15.10.1   Diffusion in Moving Conducting Medium due to Incident Alternating (Time-harmonic) Magnetic Field

In the problem discussed in Section 15.10, the diffusion process in the conducting medium is due to relative motion between the conducting block and the incident magnetic field which is alternating with time. The analysis has been done in a fixed frame of reference with respect to which the magnetic field is not moving (though alternating with time) and the conducting medium is moving in the +ve z-direction at constant velocity **v**. The incident magnetic field **B**, is a uniform pattern with no space variation in the plane normal to the direction of motion (z-direction). It is not a space wave. But since it is alternating with time, the diffused pattern, in the moving conducting block, is that of travelling wave-form which has been mathematically expressed as

$$\mathrm{Re}\{B_0 \exp(j(\omega t - kz))\}$$

in Eq. (15.118), k is a complex number as shown in Eq. (15.117), i.e. $k = k_r + jk_i$ and has two values k^+ and k^- as shown from the solution of the dispersion equation [Eq. (15.116)]. Thus the diffused wave is an evanescent wave which is getting attenuated as it propagates further. In fact, the dispersion wave is made of two components, one propagating in $+z$ direction and the other one in $-z$ direction. For both these waves, the attenuating factors are functions of both the magnetic Reynold's number as well as the skin-depth (i.e. depth of penetration) of the conducting block because the incident magnetic field is now of the harmonically time-varying type and from the values of k_r^+, k_i^+, k_r^- and k_i^-, it will be obvious that the spatial rate of attenuation of the diffused wave traversing in the direction of motion of the conducting block is lesser than the attenuation rate of the diffused wave traversing against the direction of motion of the conductor. When the two are travelling is opposite directions, naturally the attenuation is faster than when they are moving in the same direction as the relative displacement between the two is smaller. The values of the components of k^+ and k^- are given below:

$$k_i^- = \frac{R_m}{2l} + \frac{1}{\sqrt{2}} \sqrt{\sqrt{\left(\frac{R_m}{2l}\right)^4 + 4\left(\frac{1}{d\sqrt{2}}\right)^4} + \left(\frac{R_m}{2l}\right)^2}$$

$$k_i^+ = \frac{R_m}{2l} - \frac{1}{\sqrt{2}} \sqrt{\sqrt{\left(\frac{R_m}{2l}\right)^4 + 4\left(\frac{1}{d\sqrt{2}}\right)^4} + \left(\frac{R_m}{2l}\right)^2}$$

$$k_r^+ = -k_r^- = -\frac{1}{\sqrt{2}} \sqrt{\sqrt{\left(\frac{R_m}{2l}\right)^4 + 4\left(\frac{1}{d\sqrt{2}}\right)^4} - \left(\frac{R_m}{2l}\right)^2}$$

It is to be noted that apart from the attenuating factor, the space phase of these diffused waves is also a function of both the magnetic Reynold's number as well as the depth of penetration of the conducting block.

15.11   TRAVELLING WAVE DIFFUSION IN MOVING MEDIUM

This problem and the next two are of great practical importance in solving both the operational as well as the design problems of electrical machines (i.e. large induction motors and turbo-generators). However we shall solve here the basic idealized problems (which have closed-form solutions), which can then be extrapolated to match the detailed boundary conditions of the actual practical problems.

The first problem we consider is that of a travelling wave of a surface current sheet (which in an alternating current machine is produced by a uniformly distributed three-phase winding), imposed on a semi-infinite conducting medium (which represents in developed Cartesian geometry, a solid rotor of large ac machines). It (the medium) is subjected to a travelling mmf wave, or preferably a travelling current sheet wave $[A \exp \{j(\omega_S t - ky)\}]$, the direction of the current flow being in the z-direction, and the sheet lying in the y-z plane on the $x = 0$ surface of the conducting block (Figure 15.22).

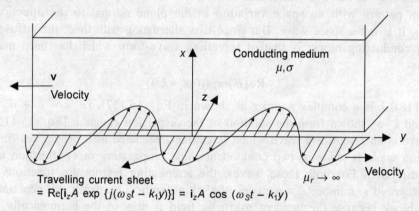

Figure 15.22   Moving conducting medium, subjected to a travelling current sheet.

The practical problem from which this simplified system has been derived, is from the solid rotor surface of a large turbogenerator in which the three-phase currents of the distributed stator winding produce the travelling (or the rotating) current sheet which travels at the synchronous speed of $\omega_S = 2\pi f$ or $\omega_S = 2\pi n_S$ revs/sec for a two-pole machine, or more generally $\omega_S = 2\pi n_S p$ for a $(2p)$-pole machine (n_S, being the number of rotations per second). Hence the current sheet can be expressed as

$$\text{the travelling current sheet} = \mathbf{i}_z \text{Re}[A \exp \{j(\omega_S t - k_1 y)\}], \text{ A real,} \qquad (15.121a)$$

where the wave number $k_1 = (2\pi/\lambda)$, λ being $= \pi D_R$, where D_R is the diameter of the rotor of the machine. The conducting block is moving at the speed $v = n_S \pi D_R$, in the direction $(-y)$, opposite to that of the travelling current sheet; i.e.

$$\mathbf{v} = -\mathbf{i}_y v = -\mathbf{i}_y (n_S \pi D_R) \qquad (15.121b)$$

This model now simulates (in a highly simplified and idealized manner in Cartesian geometry), the problem of a turbogenerator rotor travelling at synchronous speed in one direction, and the negative sequence current sheet travelling at the same synchronous speed in the opposite direction. (In our present analysis, we have taken the current sheet to travel in the forward (or positive) direction, and the rotor block to travel in the opposite (negative or backward) direction; though in an actual turbogenerator, the two travel in the opposite senses. However the final results in loss calculations are not affected by either convention.)

In this case, it will be seen that the components of the magnetic field vector **B** as well as the induced current density vector **J** in the rotor material, would satisfy the same operating equation, which we have derived earlier as

$$\nabla^2 \mathbf{B} = \mu\sigma \left[\left(\frac{\partial \mathbf{B}}{\partial t} \right) - \nabla \times (\mathbf{v} \times \mathbf{B}) \right] \tag{15.97}$$

It will also be seen that this problem is no longer a simple one-dimensional problem of the types, which we have been discussing so far in this chapter. The field vectors vary with more than one space variable, as well as the magnetic field vector (i.e. one of the dependent variable vectors) has more than one component. Hence, this being the first problem of relatively more complex nature, we shall, instead of substituting and using directly Eq. (15.97), derive the scalar components of this equation directly from the first principles, i.e. the generalized relevant equations of Maxwell, which for this problem are

$$\nabla \times \mathbf{H} = \mathbf{J} \tag{15.122a}$$

$$\nabla \times \mathbf{E} = - \left(\frac{\partial \mathbf{B}}{\partial t} \right) + \nabla \times (\mathbf{v} \times \mathbf{B}) \tag{15.122b}$$

$$\nabla \cdot \mathbf{B} = 0 \tag{15.122c}$$

and the relevant constituent relations are

$$\sigma \mathbf{E} = \mathbf{J} \tag{15.123a}$$

$$\mathbf{B} = \mu \mathbf{H} \tag{15.123b}$$

and the velocity of the moving block is

$$\mathbf{v} = \mathbf{i}_y(-\mathrm{v}) \tag{15.124}$$

In the medium under consideration, only J_z exists, and there is no variation in the z-direction, i.e. $\partial/\partial z = 0$.

∴ From Eq. (15.123a),

$$\mathbf{J} = \mathbf{i}_z J_z = \sigma \mathbf{E} = \mathbf{i}_z \sigma E_z \qquad \text{or} \qquad J_z = \sigma E_z \tag{15.125}$$

and from Eq. (15.122a),

$$\nabla \times \mathbf{H} = \mathbf{i}_x 0 + \mathbf{i}_y 0 + \mathbf{i}_z \left(\frac{\partial H_y}{\partial x} - \frac{\partial H_x}{\partial y} \right) = \mathbf{i}_z J_z$$

$$\therefore \qquad \frac{\partial H_y}{\partial x} - \frac{\partial H_x}{\partial y} = J_z$$

or

$$\frac{\partial B_y}{\partial x} - \frac{\partial B_x}{\partial y} = \mu\sigma E_z \tag{15.126}$$

and hence from Eq. (15.122b),

$$\mathbf{B} = \mathbf{i}_x B_x + \mathbf{i}_y B_y = \mu(\mathbf{i}_x H_x + \mathbf{i}_y H_y), \qquad H_z = 0$$

$$\therefore \qquad (\mathbf{v} \times \mathbf{B}) = - \mathbf{i}_z[(- \mathrm{v})(B_x)] = \mathbf{i}_z \mathrm{v} B_x \tag{15.127}$$

∴ From Eq. (15.122b),

$$\nabla \times \mathbf{E} = \mathbf{i}_x \left(\frac{\partial E_z}{\partial y} \right) + \mathbf{i}_y \left(-\frac{\partial E_z}{\partial x} \right)$$

$$= -\left[\mathbf{i}_x \left(\frac{\partial B_x}{\partial t} \right) + \mathbf{i}_y \left(\frac{\partial B_y}{\partial t} \right) \right] + \mathbf{i}_x \left[\frac{\partial}{\partial y} (vB_x) \right] + \mathbf{i}_y \left[-\frac{\partial}{\partial x} (vB_x) \right]$$

This equation gives the following two scalar equations:

$$\frac{\partial E_z}{\partial y} = -\left(\frac{\partial B_x}{\partial t} \right) + v \left(\frac{\partial B_x}{\partial y} \right)$$

and

$$-\left(\frac{\partial E_z}{\partial x} \right) = -\left(\frac{\partial B_y}{\partial t} \right) - v \left(\frac{\partial B_x}{\partial x} \right) \tag{15.128}$$

On substituting from Eq. (15.126), these equations become:

$$\left(\frac{1}{\mu\sigma} \right) \left(\frac{\partial^2 B_y}{\partial x \partial y} - \frac{\partial^2 B_x}{\partial y^2} \right) = -\left(\frac{\partial B_x}{\partial t} \right) + v \left(\frac{\partial B_x}{\partial y} \right)$$

and

$$\left(\frac{1}{\mu\sigma} \right) \left(-\frac{\partial^2 B_y}{\partial x^2} + \frac{\partial^2 B_x}{\partial x \partial y} \right) = -\left(\frac{\partial B_y}{\partial t} \right) - v \left(\frac{\partial B_x}{\partial x} \right)$$

Equation (15.122c) becomes

$$\frac{\partial B_x}{\partial x} + \frac{\partial B_y}{\partial y} = 0 \tag{15.129}$$

which combined with the previous equations gives

$$\frac{\partial^2 B_x}{\partial x^2} + \frac{\partial^2 B_x}{\partial y^2} = \mu\sigma \left(\frac{\partial B_x}{\partial t} \right) - \mu\sigma v \left(\frac{\partial B_x}{\partial y} \right)$$

and

$$\frac{\partial^2 B_y}{\partial x^2} + \frac{\partial^2 B_y}{\partial y^2} = \mu\sigma \left(\frac{\partial B_y}{\partial t} \right) - \mu\sigma v \left(\frac{\partial B_y}{\partial y} \right) \tag{15.130}$$

To obtain a similar equation in E_z and/or J_z, we differentiate the first equation of (15.128) partially with respect to y, and the second one (again partially) with respect to x, and get

$$\frac{\partial^2 E_z}{\partial y^2} = -\left(\frac{\partial^2 B_x}{\partial y \partial t} \right) + v \left(\frac{\partial^2 B_x}{\partial y^2} \right),$$

and

$$-\left(\frac{\partial^2 B_z}{\partial x^2} \right) = -\left(\frac{\partial^2 B_y}{\partial x \partial t} \right) - v \left(\frac{\partial^2 B_x}{\partial x^2} \right)$$

Subtracting the second equation from the first,

$$\frac{\partial^2 E_z}{\partial x^2} + \frac{\partial^2 E_z}{\partial y^2} = -\left(\frac{\partial}{\partial t}\right)\left(\frac{\partial B_x}{\partial y} - \frac{\partial B_y}{\partial x}\right) + v\left[\frac{\partial^2 B_x}{\partial y^2} + \left(\frac{\partial}{\partial x}\right)\left(-\frac{\partial B_y}{\partial y}\right)\right]$$

$$= -\left(\frac{\partial}{\partial t}\right)(-\mu\sigma E_z) + v\left(\frac{\partial}{\partial y}\right)\left(\frac{\partial B_x}{\partial y} - \frac{\partial B_y}{\partial x}\right)$$

$$= +\mu\sigma\left(\frac{\partial E_z}{\partial t}\right) + v\left(\frac{\partial}{\partial y}\right)(-\mu\sigma E_z)$$

or

$$\left(\frac{\partial^2 E_z}{\partial x^2}\right) + \left(\frac{\partial^2 E_z}{\partial y^2}\right) = \mu\sigma\left(\frac{\partial E_z}{\partial t}\right) - \mu\sigma v\left(\frac{\partial E_z}{\partial y}\right) \tag{15.131}$$

and hence for J_z,

$$\left(\frac{\partial^2 J_z}{\partial x^2}\right) + \left(\frac{\partial^2 J_z}{\partial y^2}\right) = \mu\sigma\left(\frac{\partial J_z}{\partial t}\right) - \mu\sigma v\left(\frac{\partial J_z}{\partial y}\right) \tag{15.132}$$

Since the induced fields in the block are due to a travelling field source, the solutions for the magnetic field and the current density vectors would take the form:

$$\mathbf{B} = \text{Re}\left[\mathbf{i}_x\hat{B}_x(x) + \mathbf{i}_y\hat{B}_y(x)\right]\exp\left[j(\omega_S t - k_1 y)\right]$$

$$\mathbf{J} = \text{Re}\left[\mathbf{i}_z\hat{J}_z(x)\right]\exp\left[j(\omega_S t - k_1 y)\right] \tag{15.133}$$

Substituting for B_x in Eq. (15.130),

$$\frac{d^2\hat{B}_x}{dx^2} - \alpha_1^2\hat{B}_x = 0 \tag{15.134}$$

where

$$\alpha_1 = k_1\sqrt{1 + j\left(\frac{\mu\sigma}{k_1^2}\right)(\omega_S + vk_1)} = k_1\sqrt{1 + jS}$$

$$S = \left(\frac{\mu\sigma}{k_1^2}\right)(\omega_S + vk_1) \tag{15.135}$$

The solution of Eq. (15.134) is

$$\hat{B}_x = \hat{B}_1\exp(-\alpha_1 x) + \hat{B}_2\exp(+\alpha_1 x) \tag{15.136}$$

where α_1 has been defined to have a positive real part. The x-dimension of the block is assumed to be quite large compared to the wavelength of the travelling current sheet, (i.e. $2\pi/k_1$), and hence for the first boundary condition:

1. As $x \to \infty$, $B_x \to 0$ $\therefore$ $B_2 = 0$, and hence:

$$\hat{B}_x = \hat{B}_1\exp(-\alpha_1 x) \tag{15.137}$$

2. The second boundary condition is: on $x = 0$, $\hat{B}_y = \mu_0 A$

where A will be determined by the amplitude of the imposed current sheet. We also assume that the air-gap between the applied current sheet and the surface of the conducting block is quite small, and the lower surface of the current sheet is bounded by a highly permeable region. Hence to apply this boundary condition, we use Eq. (15.129) from which we get

$$\hat{B}_y = \left(\frac{1}{jk_1}\right)\left(\frac{\partial \hat{B}_x}{\partial x}\right) = -\left(\frac{\alpha_1}{jk_1}\right)\hat{B}_1$$

$\therefore$ On $x = 0$, $\hat{B}_y = \mu_0 A$, and hence:

$$\hat{B}_1 = -\left(\frac{jk_1}{\alpha_1}\right)\mu_0 A$$

$\therefore$
$$\mathbf{B} = \mathrm{Re}\left[-\mathbf{i}_x\left(\frac{jk_1}{\alpha_1}\right)\mu_0 A + \mathbf{i}_y \mu_0 A\right]\exp\left(-\alpha_1 x\right)\exp\left[(j\omega_S t - k_1 y)\right] \qquad (15.138)$$

The induced currents in the moving block are obtained by using Eq. (15.122a), i.e.

$$\mathbf{J} = \mathbf{i}_z J_z = \mathbf{i}_z \hat{J}_z \exp\left[j(\omega_S t - k_1 y)\right] = \mathbf{i}_z\left(\frac{1}{\mu_0}\right)\left(\frac{\partial B_y}{\partial x} - \frac{\partial B_x}{\partial y}\right)$$

$$= \mathbf{i}_z\left(-\alpha_1 A + \frac{k_1^2}{\alpha_1}\right)\exp\left(-\alpha_1 x\right)\exp\left[j(\omega_S t - k_1 y)\right]$$

$$= \mathbf{i}_z j\left(\frac{\mu\sigma}{\alpha_1}\right)(\omega_S + vk_1)\,A\,\exp\left(-\alpha_1 x\right)\exp\left[j(\omega_S t - k_1 y)\right] \qquad (15.139)$$

$\mathbf{J}$ is, in fact, the real part of the above expression.

If α_1 is expressed as a complex number of the form

$$\alpha_1 = C + jD = k_1\sqrt{\left[1 + j\left(\frac{\mu\sigma}{k_1^2}\right)(\omega_S + vk_1)\right]} = k_1\sqrt{(1 + jS)}$$

then

$$C = \left(\frac{k_1}{\sqrt{2}}\right)\left(\sqrt{1 + S^2} + 1\right)^{1/2}, \qquad D = \left(\frac{k_1}{\sqrt{2}}\right)\left(\sqrt{1 + S^2} - 1\right)^{1/2} \qquad (15.140)$$

This shows that the term $\exp(-\alpha_1 x)$ can be expressed as $\exp(-Cx)\cdot\exp(-Dx)$, which implies that these $\mathbf{B}_x$, $\mathbf{B}_y$, $\mathbf{J}_z$ vectors, apart from travelling in the $+y$-direction in the conducting block, they also diffuse (i.e. or disperse or travel with attenuation) in the $+x$-direction, which means that the wavelength of the diffusing pattern in the x-direction is $(2\pi/D)$ and the pattern is being attenuated by a damping factor which is $\exp(-Cx)$, where C and D are given by Eq. (15.140). It will be noticed that both C and D are functions of S, i.e. $(\mu\sigma/k_1^2)(\omega_S + vk_1)$, and the magnetic diffusion time will be a function of the wavelength of the diffusion wave which is a function of $(\mu\sigma/k_1^2)$; whereas the rate of change with respect to time of B_x for an observer moving with the velocity v of the slab (or the block) is

$$\left(\frac{\partial}{\partial t} - v\frac{\partial}{\partial y}\right)B_x \to j(\omega_S + vk_1)\hat{B}_x \qquad (15.141)$$

i.e. $(\omega_S + vk_1)$ is the frequency of the magnetic flux density for an observer moving with the conducting block.

$$\therefore \qquad S \propto \frac{\text{magnetic diffusion time}}{\text{period of excitation in the frame of the moving medium}}$$

i.e.
$$S \propto \left(\frac{\mu\sigma}{k_1^2}\right)(\omega_S + vk_1) \qquad (15.142)$$

The phase velocity of the travelling wave is ω/k, and S is zero when $v = \omega_S/k_1$ and *is in the direction of travelling current sheet* (*i.e. the +ve y-direction*). Under this condition, there is no interaction between the conducting block and the travelling current sheet, which means that no currents are induced and the magnetic flux density completely penetrates the medium. When $v = 0$, the situation is similar to that of the skin effect described in Section 15.2. However we are, at present, considering the situation when the conducting block is moving in the direction opposite to that of the exciting (travelling) current sheet.

Now if the velocity of the current sheet is $= \omega_S/k_1$ in the +y-direction and the conducting block is moving in the −y-direction with the velocity v whose magnitude is same as that of the exciting current sheet, i.e. $v = \omega_S/k_1$, then the equations for the magnetic flux density **B** (15.138) and the current density **J** (15.139) in the block reduce to the form

$$\mathbf{B} = \left[-\mathbf{i}_x \frac{jk_1}{\alpha} + \mathbf{i}_y\right]\mu_0 A \exp(-\alpha x) \exp[j(\omega_S t - k_1 y)]$$

$$\mathbf{J} = \mathbf{i}_z j\left(\frac{2\omega_S \mu\sigma}{\alpha}\right) A \exp(-\alpha x) \exp[j(\omega_S t - k_1 y)]$$

where

$$\alpha = k_1\left(1 + j\frac{2\omega_S \mu\sigma}{k_1^2}\right)^{1/2} \qquad (15.143)$$

These expressions will be considered in the subsequent sections of this chapter where they will be used as the basis for the equivalence of different approaches of loss calculations in turbogenerator rotors.

The results of the analysis of the present system (with some modifications, i.e. the conducting block and the travelling current sheet both travelling in the same +y-direction) are also usable in other important practical applications, such as tracked transportation schemes with levitation. This is because the induced currents in the conducting block produce time average forces in the x- and y-directions. The force in the x-direction makes it possible to levitate the block on the magnetic field, and the force in the y-direction can be used for accelerating the propulsion of the slab in that direction.

Note further that when ω_S is zero, then S becomes proportional to v [Eq. (15.142)], and in this limit S is a magnetic Reynold's number based on the wavelength of the current sheet. This indicates that a large magnetic Reynold's number implies that the induced field effects are significant.

15.12 TRAVELLING CURRENT SHEET IMPOSED ON A STATIONARY CONDUCTING MEDIUM

The geometry of the present problem is same as that of the problem discussed in the previous Section 15.11, the only differences being that the conducting block is now stationary (as shown in Figure 15.23), and the velocity of the travelling current sheet is twice that of its velocity in the previous problem. The travelling current sheet is

$$= \mathrm{Re}[\mathbf{i}_z A \exp \{j(\omega_2 t - k_2 y)\}]$$

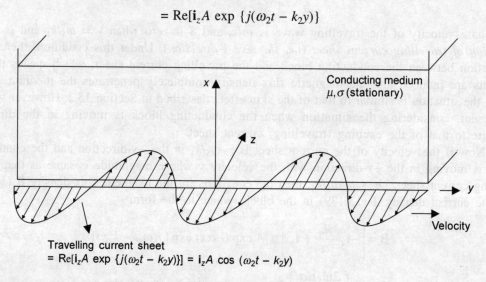

Travelling current sheet
$$= \mathrm{Re}[\mathbf{i}_z A \exp \{j(\omega_2 t - k_2 y)\}] = \mathbf{i}_z A \cos (\omega_2 t - k_2 y)$$

Figure 15.23 Stationary conducting medium, subjected to a travelling current sheet.

In the present problem, $\omega_2 = 2\omega_S$, of the previous problem and the wavelengths of both the current sheets are the same. Since the conducting block is not moving, i.e. v = 0, the operating equation which would be satisfied by the magnetic flux density **B** and the induced current density **J** would be of the form

$$\nabla^2 \mathbf{B} = \mu\sigma\left(\frac{\partial \mathbf{B}}{\partial t}\right) \tag{15.144}$$

As in the previous case, **J** will have only one component, i.e. J_z, and **B** will have the components B_x and B_y; and there will be no variations in the z-direction, i.e. $\partial/\partial z = 0$. Hence, we can derive by a process similar to that of the previous section (Section 15.11), that the equations satisfied by B_x, B_y, and J_z would be:

$$\frac{\partial^2 B_x}{\partial x^2} + \frac{\partial^2 B_x}{\partial y^2} = \mu\sigma\left(\frac{\partial B_x}{\partial t}\right) \tag{15.145a}$$

$$\frac{\partial^2 B_y}{\partial x^2} + \frac{\partial^2 B_y}{\partial y^2} = \mu\sigma\left(\frac{\partial B_y}{\partial t}\right) \tag{15.145b}$$

$$\frac{\partial^2 J_z}{\partial x^2} + \frac{\partial^2 J_z}{\partial y^2} = \mu\sigma\left(\frac{\partial J_z}{\partial t}\right) \tag{15.145c}$$

The solutions of **B** and **J** can be written in the form:

$$\mathbf{B} = \mathrm{Re}\,[\mathbf{i}_x \hat{B}_x(x) + \mathbf{i}_y \hat{B}_y(x)]\exp[j(\omega_2 t - k_2 y)]$$

$$\mathbf{J} = \mathrm{Re}\,[\mathbf{i}_z \hat{J}_z(x)]\exp[j(\omega_2 t - k_2 y)] \tag{15.146}$$

B also satisfies the equation

$$\frac{\partial B_x}{\partial x} + \frac{\partial B_y}{\partial y} = 0 \tag{15.147}$$

As before, substituting from Eq. (15.146) in Eq. (15.145), we get

$$\frac{\partial^2 \hat{B}_x}{\partial x^2} - \alpha_2^2 \hat{B}_x = 0$$

where

$$\alpha_2 = k_2 \left(1 + j\frac{\omega_2 \mu \sigma}{k_2^2}\right)^{1/2} = k_2 \left(1 + jS_2\right)^{1/2}$$

$$S_2 = \frac{\omega_2 \mu \sigma}{k_2^2} \tag{15.148}$$

The solution of the above equation is of the form

$$\hat{B}_x = \hat{B}_3 \exp(\alpha_2 x) + \hat{B}_4 \exp(-\alpha_2 x) \tag{15.149}$$

The relevant boundary conditions in this problem are:

1. On $x = 0$, $\hat{B}_y = \mu_0 A$, neglecting the air-gap dimensions; and
2. as $x \to \infty$, $\mathbf{B} \to 0$.

$$\therefore \qquad \hat{B}_3 = 0 \qquad \text{and} \qquad \hat{B}_x = \hat{B}_4 \exp(-\alpha_2 x) \tag{15.150}$$

From Eq. (15.147),

$$\hat{B}_y = \left(\frac{1}{jk_2}\right)\left(\frac{\partial B_x}{\partial x}\right) = -\left(\frac{\alpha_2}{jk_2}\right)\hat{B}_x$$

using Eq. (15.150).

And using B_y at $x = 0$ as $= \mu_0 A$, we get

$$\mathbf{B} = \left[-\mathbf{i}_x \left(\frac{jk_2}{\alpha_2}\right)\mu_0 A + \mathbf{i}_y \mu_0 A\right]\exp(-\alpha_2 x)\exp\left[j(\omega_2 t - k_2 y)\right] \tag{15.151}$$

$$\mathbf{J} = \mathbf{i}_z J_z = \mathbf{i}_z \hat{J}_z \exp[j(\omega_2 t - k_2 y)]$$

$$= \mathbf{i}_z\left[\left(\frac{\partial H_y}{\partial x}\right) - \left(\frac{\partial H_x}{\partial y}\right)\right] = \left(\frac{\mathbf{i}_z}{\mu}\right)\left[\left(\frac{\partial B_y}{\partial x}\right) - \left(\frac{\partial B_x}{\partial y}\right)\right]$$

$$= \mathbf{i}_z\left[-\alpha_2 A + \left(\frac{k_2^2}{\alpha_2}\right)A\right]\exp(-\alpha_2 x)\exp[j(\omega_2 t - k_2 y)]$$

$$= -\mathbf{i}_z j\left(\frac{\omega_2 \sigma \mu}{\alpha_2}\right)A \exp(-\alpha_2 x)\exp[j(\omega_2 t - k_2 y)] \tag{15.152}$$

In this case, $\omega_2 = 2\omega_S$, and $k_2 = k_1 = k$, then the expressions for the magnetic flux density and the eddy current density distributions in the conducting block become

$$\mathbf{B} = \left[-\mathbf{i}_x \left(\frac{jk}{\alpha_2} \right) + \mathbf{i}_y \right] \mu_0 A \exp(-\alpha_2 x) \exp[j(2\omega_S t - ky)] \tag{15.153a}$$

$$\mathbf{J} = -\mathbf{i}_z j \left(\frac{2\omega_S \sigma \mu}{\alpha_2} \right) A \exp(-\alpha_2 x) \exp[j(2\omega_S t - ky)] \tag{15.153b}$$

where

$$\alpha_2 = k \left[1 + j \left(\frac{2\omega_S \mu \sigma}{k_2} \right) \right]^{1/2} = k \left(1 + jS_2 \right)^{1/2} \tag{15.153c}$$

Note: For the current sheets of these two problems, $\omega_2 = 2\omega_S$ but $k_2 = k_1 = k$ (i.e. the same wave number), because the wavelength λ is same for both the current sheet waves.

It should be further noted that Eqs. (15.153) are same as Eqs. (15.143) except that these wave patterns are travelling at a speed $2\omega_S$ with respect to a stationary conducting block; whereas in the problem of Eqs. (15.143), the wave patterns of these field distributions were travelling in the forward (i.e. $+y$-direction) direction with a speed ω_S with respect to a fixed frame of reference, and the conducting block was also travelling at the same speed but in the opposite direction (i.e. $-y$-direction) with respect to the same fixed frame of reference. Furthermore, since α_2 of this equation is same as the α of Eq. (15.143), the diffusion (or the dispersion) of these field distributions in the x-direction (i.e. in the direction normal to the plane of the applied current sheet) in the conducting block, would be identical with that of the previous problem. So, since the variations with respect to x- and y-variables are same for both the sets of equations, the induced current and the magnetic field distributions are identical and hence the eddy current losses (as will be shown later) and also the forces come out to be the same.

15.13   STATIONARY, PULSATING, SINUSOIDALLY DISTRIBUTED CURRENT SHEET IMPOSED ON STATIONARY CONDUCTING BLOCK

The geometry of this problem is also the same as the two problems discussed in Sections 15.11 and 15.12, i.e. a semi-infinite conducting block of permeability μ and conductivity σ is subjected to a current sheet on the surface $x = 0$ (Figure 15.24). This current sheet is not a

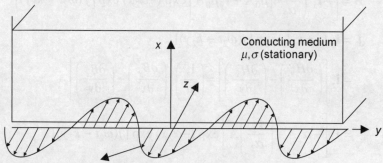

Pulsating current sheet = $\mathbf{i}_z A (\cos k_3 y) \exp(j\omega_3 t)$—not travelling

Figure 15.24   Stationary conducting block, subjected to a pulsating current sheet.

travelling current sheet as in the previous two problems, but is a stationary, pulsating (i.e. alternating and fixed spatially) sheet extending over the $x = 0$ surface. The wavelength of this current sheet is same as the wavelength of the travelling current sheets of those problems ($k_3 = k_2 = k_1 = k$).

Once again, **B** and **J** in the conducting block will be of similar form to what was derived in Section 15.10 or 15.11, and hence we shall not go into the derivation of the operating equations starting from the fundamental Maxwell's equations. These field vectors satisfy the vector diffusion equation of the form

$$\nabla^2 \mathbf{B} = \mu\sigma \left(\frac{\partial \mathbf{B}}{\partial t} \right) \tag{15.144}$$

as $v = 0$ in this case as well.

And the pulsating current sheet is $= \mathbf{i}_z A \cos k_3 y \exp(j\omega_3 t)$. $\tag{15.144'}$

The frequency of this current sheet is same as that of Section 15.12, i.e. $\omega_3 = \omega_2 = 2\omega_S$.

As before, the current density vector **J** will have only the z-component J_z, and the magnetic flux density vector will have only B_x and B_y components, and these will have no variations in the z-direction [i.e. $(\partial/\partial z) = 0$]. The equations satisfied by these components would be same as the equations in (15.145) which we rewrite here for convenience:

$$\frac{\partial^2 B_x}{\partial x^2} + \frac{\partial^2 B_x}{\partial y^2} = \mu\sigma \left(\frac{\partial B_x}{\partial t} \right) \tag{15.145a}$$

$$\frac{\partial^2 B_y}{\partial x^2} + \frac{\partial^2 B_y}{\partial y^2} = \mu\sigma \left(\frac{\partial B_y}{\partial t} \right) \tag{15.145b}$$

$$\frac{\partial^2 J_z}{\partial x^2} + \frac{\partial^2 J_z}{\partial y^2} = \mu\sigma \left(\frac{\partial J_z}{\partial t} \right) \tag{15.145c}$$

The solutions for **B** and **J** for this problem would be of similar form to those of Section 15.12, but not the same, as the source is now a pulsating current sheet. Hence,

$$\mathbf{B} = [\mathbf{i}_x \hat{B}_x(x) \sin k_3 y + \mathbf{i}_y \hat{B}_y(x) \cos k_3 y] \exp(j\omega_3 t)$$

$$\mathbf{J} = [\mathbf{i}_z \hat{J}_x(x) \cos k_3 y] \exp(j\omega_3 t) \tag{15.154}$$

B in this problem also satisfies the same zero divergence equation, i.e.

$$\frac{\partial B_x}{\partial x} + \frac{\partial B_y}{\partial y} = 0 \tag{15.147}$$

Hence substituting for B_x from Eq. (15.154) into the equation of (15.145), we get

$$\frac{d^2 \hat{B}_x}{dx^2} - \alpha_3^2 \hat{B}_x = 0$$

where

$$\alpha_3 = k_3 \left(1 + j \frac{\omega_3 \mu\sigma}{k_3^2} \right)^{1/2} = k_3 \left(1 + j S_3 \right)^{1/2}$$

$$\tag{15.155}$$

$$S_3 = \frac{\omega_3 \mu\sigma}{k_3^2}$$

The expression for $\hat{B}_x$ will take the form

$$\hat{B}_x = \hat{B}_5 \exp(\alpha_3 x) + \hat{B}_6 \exp(-\alpha_3 x)$$

The boundary conditions at $x = 0$ and $x \to \infty$ are also same as before, i.e.

1. On $x = 0$, $\hat{B}_y = \mu_0 A$, neglecting the air-gap dimensions; and
2. as $x \to \infty$, $\mathbf{B} \to 0$.

$$\therefore \qquad \hat{B}_5 = 0 \qquad \text{and} \qquad \hat{B}_x = \hat{B}_6 \exp(-\alpha_3 x) \tag{15.156}$$

And from Eq. (15.147),

$$\hat{B}_y = \left(\frac{1}{jk_3}\right)\left(\frac{\partial \hat{B}_x}{\partial x}\right) = -\left(\frac{\alpha_3}{jk_3}\right)\hat{B}_x$$

and from the boundary condition (1), B_y at $x = 0$ as $= \mu_0 A$.

$$\therefore \qquad \mathbf{B} = \left[-\mathbf{i}_x\left(\frac{\mu_0 k_3}{\alpha_3}\right)A \sin k_3 y + \mathbf{i}_y \mu_0 A \cos k_3 y\right]\exp(-\alpha_3 x)\exp(j\omega_3 t)$$

and

$$\mathbf{J} = -\mathbf{i}_z j\left(\frac{\omega_3 \mu_0 \sigma}{\alpha_3}\right)A \cos k_3 y \exp(-\alpha_3 x)\exp(j\omega_3 t) \tag{15.157}$$

When $k_3 = k$, and $\omega_3 = 2\omega_S$, and since we are considering a conducting block, $\mu = \mu_0$, then $\alpha_3 = \alpha_2 = \alpha_1 = \alpha$.

So Eq. (15.157) become

$$\mathbf{B} = \left[-\mathbf{i}_x\left(\frac{k}{\alpha}\right)\sin ky + \mathbf{i}_y \cos ky\right]\mu_0 A \exp(-\alpha x)\exp(j2\omega_S t)$$

$$\mathbf{J} = -\mathbf{i}_z j\left(\frac{2\omega_S \mu_0 \sigma}{\alpha}\right)A \cos ky \exp(-\alpha x)\exp(j2\omega_S t)$$

and

$$\alpha = k\left(1 + j\frac{2\omega_S \sigma \mu}{k^2}\right)^{1/2} = k\left(1 + jS_3\right)^{1/2} \tag{15.158}$$

Since the exp $(-\alpha x)$ term is same as in the previous problem (of Section 15.12), the dispersion of the field vectors in the x-direction (i.e. the radial direction in the turbogenerator rotor) is similar to those of the last problem.

15.14 LOSS CALCULATIONS IN THE CONDUCTING BLOCK

The three configurations, which we have considered in Sections 15.11 to 15.13, have given us the magnetic flux density $\mathbf{B}$ and the induced (eddy) current density $\mathbf{J}$ in the conducting block, under three different excitation systems. We shall now look into the losses in the block due to these excitations. The losses can be calculated by using the complex Poynting vector or the loss distribution using the formula $(\mathbf{J} \cdot \mathbf{J}^*/\sigma)$. Since in the practical problem (which occurs in the turbogenerator rotors and some other large ac rotating machines), the loss distribution patterns are as important as the total losses, we shall, in the present analysis, use the (relatively more cumbersome) loss distribution formula, instead of the Poynting vector which calculates the total loss from the knowledge of the surface values of the field vectors.

So, for convenience, we rewrite the **B** and the **J** expressions from the three analyses, which we have completed just now. From Section 15.11, where the excitation is due to a travelling current sheet wave which is moving in the $+y$-direction at a velocity (ω_S/k) and the conducting block moving in the $-y$-direction with a velocity of same magnitude, we get from Eq. (15.143).

$$\mathbf{B} = \left[-\mathbf{i}_x \left(\frac{jk}{\alpha} \right) + \mathbf{i}_y \right] \mu_0 A \exp[(-\alpha x) \exp (j\omega_S t - ky)]$$

$$\mathbf{J} = -\mathbf{i}_z j \left(\frac{2\omega_S \mu \sigma}{\alpha} \right) A \exp[(-\alpha x) \exp (j\omega_S t - ky)]$$

where

$$\alpha = k \left(1 + j \frac{2\omega_S \sigma \mu}{k^2} \right)^{1/2} = k(1 + jS_1)^{1/2} \tag{15.143}$$

From Section 15.12, where the excitation is due to a travelling current sheet wave moving with a velocity $(2\omega_S/k)$ in the $+y$-direction and a stationary conducting block, we get from Eqs. (15.153),

$$\mathbf{B} = \left[-\mathbf{i}_x \left(\frac{jk}{\alpha_2} \right) + \mathbf{i}_y \right] \mu_0 A \exp(-\alpha_2 x) \exp j(2\omega_S t - ky) \tag{15.153a}$$

$$\mathbf{J} = -\mathbf{i}_z j \left(\frac{2\omega_S \sigma \mu}{\alpha_2} \right) A \exp(-\alpha_2 x) \exp j(2\omega_S t - ky) \tag{15.153b}$$

where

$$\alpha_2 = k \left(1 + j \frac{2\omega_S \mu \sigma}{k^2} \right)^{1/2} = k(1 + jS_2)^{1/2} \tag{15.153c}$$

From Section 15.13, where the excitation is due to a pulsating current sheet which is alternating with an angular frequency $(2\omega_S)$ and has the same wavelength as $(1/k)$ as that of the travelling waves of the current sheets of the earlier two sections, and a stationary conducting block, we have the expressions for the field vectors as given in Eq. (15.158) as

$$\mathbf{B} = \left[-\mathbf{i}_x \left(\frac{k}{\alpha} \right) \sin ky + \mathbf{i}_y \cos ky \right] \mu_0 A \exp(-\alpha x) \exp (j2\omega_S t)$$

$$\mathbf{J} = -\mathbf{i}_z j \left(\frac{2\omega_S \mu_0 \sigma}{\alpha} \right) A \cos ky \exp (-\alpha x) \exp (j2\omega_S t)$$

and

$$\alpha = k \left(1 + j \frac{2\omega_S \mu \sigma}{k^2} \right)^{1/2} = k (1 + jS_3)^{1/2} \tag{15.158}$$

Loss calculations. Since the time-averaging over one time-period of a sinusoidal wave pattern introduces merely a factor of ½ in both the travelling as well as the pulsating current sheet wave problems, we need to consider only the amplitude parts of these expressions for the induced (or eddy) current distribution vectors. It is also seen that both the current distributions due to the travelling current sheets as obtained in the two sets of equations (15.143) and (15.153) have the same amplitudes, and hence it follows that the total losses as well as the loss distributions would be same in either of these two cases. So now, for comparison, we need to consider only two cases instead of the three, i.e. one due to a travelling current sheet and the other due to a pulsating current sheet. So we shall now use the suffix 'tr' (i.e. $\mathbf{J}_{tr}$) to indicate the induced current density obtained either from Eqs. (15.143) or (15.153), and 'pl' (i.e. $\mathbf{J}_{pl}$) to indicate the induced current density produced by the pulsating current sheet of Eqs. (15.158). So we have got the following two expressions:

$$\hat{\mathbf{J}}_{tr} = -\mathbf{i}_z j \left(\frac{2\omega_S \mu_0 \sigma}{\alpha} \right) A \exp(-\alpha x) \exp(-jky) \qquad (15.159)$$

$$\hat{\mathbf{J}}_{pl} = -\mathbf{i}_z j \left(\frac{2\omega_S \mu_0 \sigma}{\alpha} \right) A \exp(-\alpha x) \cos ky \qquad (15.160)$$

Since α is complex, we have

$$\alpha = k \left(1 + j \frac{2\omega_S \mu_0 \sigma}{k^2} \right)^{1/2} = k(1 + jS)^{1/2} = a + jb, \qquad \text{then}$$

$$a = \frac{1}{\sqrt{2}} \left[\left(k^4 + 4\omega_S^2 \mu_0^2 \sigma^2 \right)^{1/2} + k^2 \right]^{1/2}$$

$$b = \frac{1}{\sqrt{2}} \left[\left(k^4 + 4\omega_S^2 \mu_0^2 \sigma^2 \right)^{1/2} - k^2 \right]^{1/2}$$

$$\mathbf{J}_{tr} = -\mathbf{i}_z j \left[\frac{2\omega_S \mu_0 \sigma A}{\left(k^4 + 4\omega_S^2 \mu_0^2 \sigma^2 \right)^{1/2}} \right] \exp(-ax)(b + ja) \exp[-j(bx + ky)] \qquad (15.161a)$$

$$\mathbf{J}_{pl} = -\mathbf{i}_z j \left[\frac{2\omega_S \mu_0 \sigma A}{\left(k^4 + 4\omega_S^2 \mu_0^2 \sigma^2 \right)^{1/2}} \right] \exp(-ax)(b + ja) [\exp\{(-jbx)\} \cos ky] \qquad (15.161b)$$

∴ The loss density at any point is given by

$$\delta W_{tr} = \frac{\left(\hat{\mathbf{J}}_{tr} \cdot \hat{\mathbf{J}}_{tr}^* \right)}{\sigma} \qquad (15.162a)$$

$$\delta W_{pl} = \frac{\left(\hat{\mathbf{J}}_{pl} \cdot \hat{\mathbf{J}}_{pl}^* \right)}{\sigma} \qquad (15.162b)$$

where the asterisk (*) denotes the complex conjugate of the quantity. Let us also denote

$$\frac{2\omega_S \mu_0 \sigma A}{\left(k^4 + 4\omega_S^2 \mu_0^2 \sigma^2 \right)^{1/2}} = C \qquad (15.163)$$

then

$$\delta W_{tr} = \left(\frac{C^2}{\sigma} \right) (a^2 + b^2) \exp(-2ax) \tag{15.164a}$$

$$\delta W_{pl} = \left(\frac{C^2}{\sigma} \right) (a^2 + b^2) \exp(-2ax) \cos^2 ky \tag{15.164b}$$

When we consider our model in these three problems to represent an idealized and simplified section of a turbogenerator rotor (under the specified operating conditions), the y-direction corresponds to the peripheral direction of the rotor, the z-direction corresponds to the axial direction of the machine, and the x-direction as the radial direction. So we shall now calculate the time-averaged loss over one pole-pitch length in the peripheral direction, i.e. in the y-direction from $y = 0$ to $y = \pi D_R/2$ [D_R being the rotor diameter of (say) a two-pole machine].

$$\therefore \quad k = \frac{2\pi}{\lambda} = \frac{2\pi}{\pi D_R} = \frac{2}{D_R}$$

In the axial direction, we shall take unit length (as there is no z-variation, and the rotor is long enough to justify the neglect of the end effects and which have to be considered separately), and as the z-directed currents penetrate the rotor radially (i.e. the x-direction), we are justified in integrating over the radial distance from $x = 0$ (the rotor surface) to $x \to \infty$ (i.e. towards the shaft centre-line).

$$\bar{W}_{tr} = \frac{1}{2} \int\limits_{x=0}^{x \to \infty} \int\limits_{y=0}^{y = \pi D_R/2} \delta W_{tr} \, dx \, dy \cdot 1$$

$$= \left[\frac{C^2(a^2 + b^2)}{2\sigma} \right] \left(\frac{\pi D_R}{2} \right) \int\limits_0^\infty \exp(-2ax) \, dx$$

$$= \left[\frac{C^2(a^2 + b^2) \pi D_R}{4\sigma} \right] \left(\frac{1}{-2a} \right) (0 - 1) = \frac{C^2(a^2 + b^2) \pi D_R}{8a\sigma} \tag{15.165}$$

$$\bar{W}_{pl} = \frac{1}{2} \int\limits_{x=0}^{x \to \infty} \int\limits_{y=0}^{y = \pi D_R/2} \delta W_{pl} \, dx \, dy \cdot 1$$

$$= \left[\frac{C^2(a^2 + b^2)}{2\sigma} \right] \int\limits_0^{\pi D_R/2} \cos^2 ky \, dy \int\limits_0^\infty \exp(-2ax) \, dx$$

$$= \left[\frac{C^2(a^2 + b^2)}{2\sigma} \right] \left(\frac{1}{2} \right) \left(\frac{\pi D_R}{2} \right) \left(\frac{1}{2a} \right) = \frac{C^2(a^2 + b^2) \pi D_R}{16a\sigma} \tag{15.166}$$

The bar "−" indicates the time-averaged value of the losses per time-period which introduces the factor of (½) in each of the above expressions. We find that:

$$\overline{W}_{tr} = 2\overline{W}_{pt} \left[\frac{\omega_s^2 \mu_0^2 \sigma \pi D_R A^2}{2a(k^4 + 4\omega_s^2 \mu_0^2 \sigma^2)} \right] \tag{15.167}$$

The above expression shows the equivalence relationship between the results due to these two (different) excitations imposed on the same system, and thus provides the mathematical and physical justifications for using the stationary current sheet approach to solve the problems with travelling current sheet excitations as well as with moving conducting media.

15.14.1   Counter–Revolving Field Theory and Its Application to the Analysis of 1-phase Induction Machine)

So far in the Sections 15.10 to 15.14, the concepts of the revolving magnetic fields and the pulsating magnetic fields have been discussed, and the loss calculations show that a pulsating wave of flux can be considered to be equivalent to two counter-revolving flux wave, each having half the amplitude of pulsating flux pattern. This theory is often used to explain and analyse the behaviour of single-phase induction machine in which it is argued that the air-gap flux is a pulsating wave. Whilst the theory of a pulsating wave equivalent to the counter-revolving fields of half amplitude, is perfectly correct by itself, the analogy is often wrongly made thereby producing incorrect and absurd results. The following discussion is an attempt to point out the sources of the errors and the method of correcting them. The usual explanations with its errors and subsequent corrections are as indicated below.

A single coil carrying an alternating current produces a pulsating field of the form $b = B_m \sin \omega t$. This may be represented as a pair of rotating fields, each of magnitude $B_m/2$, revolving in opposite directions as shown in Figure 15.24(a).

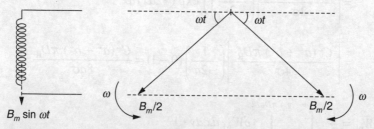

Figure 15.24(a)   Pulsating wave resolved into two counter-revolving fields.

From the figure, it is obvious that the resultant horizontal component of the counter-rotating fields is always zero, and the vertical components will always add up to $B_m \sin \omega t$. It is based on this point that the theory of the single-phase induction motor is developed, and this is as if two separate poly-phase induction motors (i.e. 3-phase motors of identical rating and nature) were connected to a common shaft, and had their stator winding connected for opposite rotation and each winding connected to a common source of supply (3-phase), i.e. the stator windings of the two machines are in parallel. The torque from each machine is then plotted as a function of speed, and the ordinates of the two curves are subtracted to obtain the resultant torque of the single-phase machines. Though it has not been stated explicitly so far, by rotating field, it is implied that the fields under consideration are the 'air-gap flux-density fields'. By using this method, most of the properties of the single-phase induction motor can be deduced **'qualitatively'**, and appear to agree with practical experience. But it should be carefully noted that this agreement is only qualitative and **'not quantitative'**. The fact that there has been a qualitative agreement of results is purely fortuitous as the method of analogy used is totally incorrect from the beginning.

It should be clearly understood that the equivalence between the pulsating field and the two counter-rotating fields producing the pulsating field is quite correct. The fallacy (and hence the source of error) lies in the assumption that the magnetic flux in the air-gap of a single-phase induction machine in which the rotor is revolving, is purely pulsating. In reality, the air-gap flux of a revolving single-phase machine, is a combination of a pulsating component and a rotating component. So the counter-rotating theory of the machine would be correct, if the quantity which is resolved into two components is the m.m.f. (magnetomotive force) or the stator currents (or the stator current-sheet), and not the magnetic flux in the air-gap of the machine. This is because (like the situation of the air-gap of any other machine) the air-gap flux is due to the m.m.fs of both the stator and the rotor windings when the rotor is revolving.

Therefore, core has to be taken when the word 'field' is being used as there should be no ambiguity in it, i.e. the word can be interpreted as either m.m.f. or flux whichever appears convenient. Another example of such loose usage of words is when the speed/torque curve is plotted and its shape is discussed in terms of the Resistance/Reactance (= R/X) ratio without specifying which reactance-leakage or magnetizing (i.e. X_l or X_{mag}) is meant. The fact is that the field under consideration is the m.m.f. field, and it is the magnetizing reactance which gives the correct result. Thus there is no justification for any vagueness or ambiguity in the explaining theory.

The correct interpretation of the **counter-rotating m.m.f. approach** is that the single-phase induction machine is equivalent to two identical polyphase machines (3-phase) of equal rating and nature, the stators being mounted on a common shaft, connected for opposite rotation and connected **in series**. From this starting argument, it follows that the machine shall be capable of running, once given the start, is that for the condition that the speed/force curve at the constant current, has a peak to the right of the origin is that $X_m/R_2 > 1$ (i.e. magnetizing reactance/rotor resistance).

On the other hand, by using the fallacious argument of counter-rotating fluxes, i.e. machines connected in parallel, produces the result that the machines can run only if $X_2/R_2 > 1$ (i.e. leakage reactance/rotor resistance). This implies that a poor machine, which will not run, can be made to run by increasing the leakage flux, i.e. by making it more imperfect, which means that 'cover the rotor conductor with a cylinder of steel or increase the air gap'. Thus the fundamental error becomes more and more obvious.

15.14.2   Magnetic Wave (Travelling and Stationary—Pulsating) Diffusion in Conducting Medium (with and without Motion)

Though the title of this discussion is comprehensive enough to include all possible combinations of the various situations, it should be understood that if problem of an incident travelling time-harmonic magnetic wave on a moving conducting medium is properly discussed and understood, all the remaining situations could be automatically taken care of by making various velocities (i.e. velocity of the travelling magnetic wave, and the velocity of the conducting block) equal to zero. Hence the main emphasis of this discussion is on the problem stated above.

The first point to be noted is that in earlier problems in this chapter, it has been possible to simplify the majority of problems to one-dimensional problems by suitable idealizations regarding their geometrical dimensions, the present series of problems are two-dimensional in their simplest form. Thus, the direction of motion, of both the travelling magnetic field wave and that of the conducting block, is along the $\pm$ y-axis, whereas the field diffusion in the conducting block is in the x-direction. Also, since there are two velocities of two different parts, the equivalent of the magnetic Reynold's number will be somewhat more complicated. This problem is neither of the two limiting types discussed so far, as now in this problem, there exist both harmonically time-varying magnetic field wave as well as the conducting block with motion. The analysis produces parameter like α and S which are defined in Eq. (15.135) and are functions of permeability ($= \mu$) and conductivity ($= \sigma$) of the conducting block, its velocity ($= v$), angular frequency ($= \omega_s$) of the travelling magnetic field wave, its wave number ($= k_1$). Also since this problem contains two motions (i.e. travelling magnetic field wave and the moving conducting block), one must be careful about the frames of reference that is being used [e.g. ($\omega_s + vk_1$) is the frequency of the magnetic flux density for an observer who is moving with the conducting block].

The parameter S is zero when the velocity of the conducting block $v = \omega_s/k$, which is also the phase velocity of the magnetic travelling wave, provided both are moving in the same direction. In this synchronous condition, there is zero interaction between the conducting block and the travelling current sheet, and hence no currents are induced in the block. So there is complete magnetic flux penetration of the block when $v = 0$. This is the case of skin effect as described in Section 15.2.

The force in the z-direction (direction of motion of the travelling magnetic field or the current sheet) can be calculated from

$$F_z = \frac{1}{2} \text{Re}\{\hat{J}_x \hat{B}_y^*\}$$

The time-average force per unit x-z area is

$$<T_z> = \int_0^\infty <F_z> \, dy$$

$$= \frac{1}{4} \frac{S[\hat{B}_z(0)]^2/\mu_0}{\sqrt{1+S^2}\ \text{Re}\ \sqrt{1+jS}}$$

When no currents are induced in the slab ($S = 0$), there is no force in the z-direction basis for a distributed linear induction M/c.

15.15 EDDY CURRENT LOSSES AND SATURATION EFFECTS IN IRON

The eddy current losses (or the induced current losses) calculated on the basis of the constant relative permeability in ferromagnetic media have been found to be too small when they are compared with the measured values. This is quite a complicated problem, which has been investigated by a number of workers like MacLean, McConnel, and Agarwal. When the iron is in the form of thin sheets, i.e. laminations in transformers and ac rotating machines, the domain structure becomes one of the most important factors. This aspect plays an important role in the anisotropic, cold-rolled, and grain-oriented (CRGO) steel laminations used in power transformers. The anomaly between the calculated eddy current losses (under assumed constant μ) and the measured losses was found to be (by Brailsford) ranging between 3 to 10 times. This loss was named as the 'anomalous eddy current loss', and the anomaly factor was found to be a function of the domain size, frequency and B_{max}.

Whilst the domain effects are important in thin sheets, in solid iron and steel the deciding factor is the shape of the $B-H$ relationship. In the present discussion, we shall emphasize the underlying principle of how to deal with the saturation effects of B, rather than the detailed results. First we consider a semi-infinite slab of iron (Figure 15.25), on whose $x = 0$ surface an alternating magnetizing force $H_s \sin \omega t$ is applied (directed in the +ve y-direction). At this stage we make a drastic simplifying assumption regarding the $B-H$ characteristic of the saturated material, i.e. that the $B-H$ curve is a step-function as indicated in Figure 15.26. Hence under the steady-state conditions, the flux density then can have only two values, i.e. either $+B_s$ or $-B_s$. When a sinusoidally time-varying magnetizing field $H_s \sin \omega t$ is imposed on the surface of the block, then during the positive half-cycle, the influence of the positive magnetic field penetrates into the material. Thus a wave of magnetic flux moves into the medium, and at the wave-front there is a change from $+B_s$ to $-B_s$. And this wave is followed by one of opposite sign, and such a process keeps on repeating with the time-period of the alternating field.

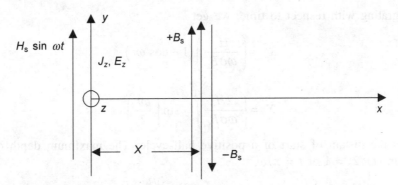

Figure 15.25   Penetration of flux in a semi-infinite iron block.

In the semi-infinite block under consideration, at an instant of time t, let the distance of the wavefront from the surface of the material be X, and hence its velocity is (dX/dt). This transition surface where the flux density changes from B_s to $-B_s$ has been called the 'separating surface' by Agarwal in his analysis. Now the rate of change of flux ($= \Phi$) per unit width in the z-direction is

$$\frac{d\Phi}{dt} = 2B_s \left(\frac{dX}{dt} \right) \tag{15.168}$$

Beyond this distance X, at this moment, there are no time-varying effects, because the wave has not penetrated so far. Hence there are no induced currents for $x > X$. Hence applying the Faraday's law (Maxwell's curl **E** equation) to a rectangular circuit, which encloses the wavefront, we have

$$E_z = -2B_s \left(\frac{dX}{dt} \right) \quad \text{and} \quad J_z = -2\sigma B_s \left(\frac{dX}{dt} \right) \tag{15.169}$$

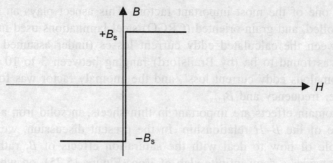

Figure 15.26   Step-function B–H characteristic of the material.

∴   The total current per unit width in the y-direction is

$$I = -H_s \sin \omega t = \int_0^X J_z \cdot dx \cdot l = -2\sigma B_s X \left(\frac{dX}{dt} \right) \tag{15.170}$$

or

$$\sigma B_s \left(\frac{d(X)^2}{dt} \right) = H_s \sin \omega t$$

∴   Integrating with respect to time, we get

$$X^2 = \left(\frac{H_s}{\omega \sigma B_s} \right) \left(1 - \cos \omega t \right)$$

and hence

$$X = \left(\frac{2H_s}{\omega \sigma B_s} \right)^{1/2} \sin \left(\frac{\omega t}{2} \right) \tag{15.171}$$

where $t = 0$ is the instant of start of a positive half-cycle. The maximum depth of penetration occurs when $\sin (\omega t/2) = 1$ or $t = \pi/\omega$.

∴ $$\delta_s = \left(\frac{2H_s}{\omega \sigma B_s} \right)^{1/2} = X_{max} \tag{15.172}$$

Comparing this with the skin-depth of the linear theory, i.e.

$$\delta_1 = d\sqrt{2} = \left(\frac{2}{\omega \mu_0 \mu_r \sigma} \right)^{1/2} \tag{15.173}$$

it should be noted that in the nonlinear case, the permeability $\mu_0 \mu_r$ has been replaced by the ratio B_s/H_s.

The velocity of the wavefront is [from Eq. (15.171)]:

$$\frac{dX}{dt} = \left(\frac{1}{2} \right) \omega \sqrt{\frac{2H_s}{\omega \sigma B_s}} \cos \left(\frac{\omega t}{2} \right) \tag{15.174}$$

It is also observed that the current density throughout the depth X is independent of the variable x.

∴ The instantaneous power loss per unit surface area is $= J_z^2 \dfrac{X}{\sigma}$.

∴ The energy lost per half-cycle $= W_1 = \dfrac{1}{\sigma} \displaystyle\int_{t=0}^{t=\pi/\omega} J_z^2 \, X dt$

Substituting from Eqs. (15.169), (15.171), and (15.174),

$$W_1 = \left(\omega^2 \sigma \delta_s^3 B_s^2\right) \int_{t=0}^{t=\pi/\omega} \cos^2\left(\frac{\omega t}{2}\right) \sin\left(\frac{\omega t}{2}\right) dt$$

$$= \left(\frac{2}{3}\right)\left(\omega^2 \sigma \delta_s^3 B_s^2\right) \tag{15.175}$$

We now plot $E(t)$ [or $J(t)$], $X(t)$, and $H(t)$ as a function of t (Figure 15.27).

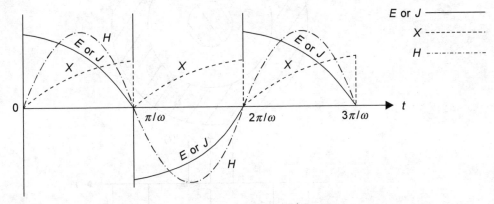

Figure 15.27 Plots of wave-shapes of E (or J), X and H in a thick saturated block of iron.

By a Fourier series analysis of H and E wave-shapes, the fundamental components come out to be

$$H_{1s} = -jH_s \qquad \text{and} \qquad E_{1s} = \left(\frac{8H_s}{3\pi \delta_s \sigma}\right)(\cos \omega t + 2 \sin \omega t) \tag{15.176}$$

Comparing this with the loss calculated on the basis of constant μ it is seen that this loss is 70% higher than the linear B–H characteristic. This analysis holds for sheets whose half-thickness d (the thickness being $2d$) is $> \delta_s$. For a detailed analysis of the losses in thin sheets, interested readers are recommended to read the papers by Agarwal, and by Lim & Hammond.

15.16 PROXIMITY LOSS

The non-uniform distribution of current in an isolated conductor caused by the passage of an alternating current in the medium has been called the 'skin effect' due to the tendency of the current to concentrate near the surface layers of the conducting body. If a second conductor is present in the vicinity of the first conductor, both carrying alternating currents of same frequency, then the alternating current in the second conductor causes a further change in the current distribution in the first conductor. This phenomenon is known as the 'proximity effect'. Essentially both are electromagnetic induction phenomenon, and the distinction between them is, though clear, rather artificial. Since the proximity effect and the skin effect are really two facets of the same phenomenon, it is not always possible to analyze the two effects separately. Also the analysis of the combined proximity and skin effects is often quite complicated. For example, an analytical solution does exist for determining the proximity effects in a circular coaxial cable in which the inner and the outer conductors are carrying currents in the opposite directions (Figure 15.28). But the solution is quite involved, and is obtained as a function of

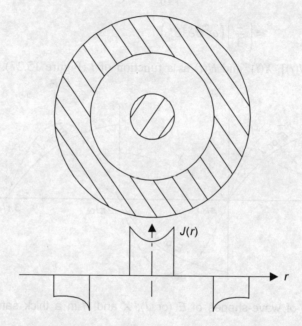

Figure 15.28 Proximity effect in a coaxial cable.

complex Bessel's functions or Ber and Bei functions. However, in general, the influence of the proximity effect is small compared with the skin effect. We shall, however, consider a highly idealized problem to illustrate this effect so as to gain some insight into this problem. We consider two conducting sheets of conductivity σ, permeability μ, and thickness b. The currents in the two sheets are equal in magnitude but opposite in direction, and their frequency is $\omega = 2\pi f$; and the sheets are so large that their finite size effects can be neglected. Since these sheets are large in size, we can assume them to be of infinite size, and hence the magnetic field on either side of each sheet is independent of the distance from the sheet (Figure 15.29). This follows from the problem discussed in the Chapter 7, Section 7.10.9.

Because of the symmetry of the problem, **J** and **H** would vary in the y-direction only (inside the sheets). Since the coordinate axes are as shown in Figure 15.29, the operational equation for **J** and **H** inside either sheet is obtained as

$$\frac{d^2 J_z}{dy^2} - j\omega\mu\sigma J_z = 0$$

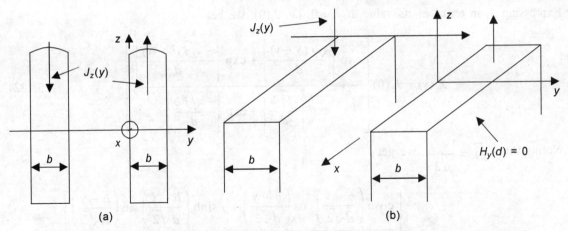

Figure 15.29 Two parallel strip conductors of thickness b carrying the same alternating current in opposite directions: (a) sectional view in the plane $x = 0$ and (b) isometric view.

and using the skin-depth notation $d^2 = (\omega\mu\sigma)^{-1}$, the equation for J_z becomes:

$$\frac{d^2 J_z}{dy^2} - \left(\frac{j}{d^2}\right) J_z = 0 \tag{15.177}$$

It should be noted that **J** would have only the z-component, and **H** only the x-component.

Its solution is of the form

$$J_z(y) = J_1 \exp\left[\frac{\sqrt{j}\,y}{d}\right] + J_2 \exp\left[\frac{-\sqrt{j}\,y}{d}\right] \tag{15.178}$$

Also, because of the symmetry of the problem, we need consider the current distribution in one of the two sheets. Let us consider the sheet with the current in the $+z$-direction. The **H** field in the sheet is given by the equation

$$j\omega\mu\sigma H_x = -\frac{dJ_z}{dy}$$

$$\therefore \qquad H_x(y) = -\left(\frac{1}{j\omega\mu\sigma}\right)\left(\frac{\sqrt{j}}{d}\right)\left\{J_1 \exp\left(\frac{\sqrt{j}\,y}{d}\right) - J_2 \exp\left(\frac{-\sqrt{j}y}{d}\right)\right\} \tag{15.179}$$

On $y = b$, $H_x(b) = 0$ [see Section 7.10.9, Eq. (7.68)].

$$\therefore \quad \text{This condition gives: } J_2 = J_1 \exp\left(\frac{2\sqrt{j}\,b}{d}\right) \tag{15.180}$$

$$\therefore \qquad J_z(y) = J_1 \exp\left(\frac{\sqrt{j}\,b}{d}\right)\left[\exp\left\{\frac{\sqrt{j}\,(b-y)}{d}\right\} + \exp\left\{\frac{-\sqrt{j}\,(b-y)}{d}\right\}\right] \tag{15.181}$$

Expressing J_1 in terms of its value at $y = 0$, i.e. $J_z(0)$, we get

$$J_z(y) = J_z(0) \left[\frac{\exp\left\{ \frac{\sqrt{j}\,(b - y)}{d} \right\} + \exp\left\{ \frac{-\sqrt{j}\,(b - y)}{d} \right\}}{\exp\left\{ \frac{\sqrt{j}\,b}{d} \right\} + \exp\left\{ \frac{-\sqrt{j}\,b}{d} \right\}} \right] \tag{15.182}$$

Noting that $\sqrt{j} = \dfrac{1 + j}{\sqrt{2}}$, we get

$$J_z(y) = J_z(0) \times \left[\frac{\cosh\left(\frac{b - y}{d\sqrt{2}} \right) \cos\left(\frac{b - y}{d\sqrt{2}} \right) + j \sinh\left(\frac{b - y}{d\sqrt{2}} \right) \sin\left(\frac{b - y}{d\sqrt{2}} \right)}{\cosh\left(\frac{b}{d\sqrt{2}} \right) \cos\left(\frac{b}{d\sqrt{2}} \right) + j \sinh\left(\frac{b}{d\sqrt{2}} \right) \sin\left(\frac{b}{d\sqrt{2}} \right)} \right]$$

$$\therefore \quad \left| \frac{J_z(y)}{J_z(0)} \right| = \left[\frac{\cosh^2\left(\frac{b - y}{d\sqrt{2}} \right) - \sin^2\left(\frac{b - y}{d\sqrt{2}} \right)}{\cosh^2\left(\frac{b}{d\sqrt{2}} \right) - \sin^2\left(\frac{b}{d\sqrt{2}} \right)} \right]^{1/2} \tag{15.183}$$

This above ratio has been plotted as a function of (y/b), in Figure 15.30. It should be noted that if the second strip were not present, the current distribution would have been symmetrical about

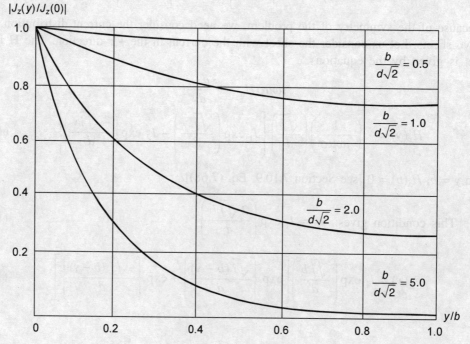

Figure 15.30 Current distribution in the strips of Figure 15.29.

the line $y = b/2$. This analysis is based on the assumption of infinitely large sheets. If the finite dimensions of the sheets are taken into account, then the proximity effects become more pronounced when the sheets are nearer to each other. In general, the proximity effect tends to increase the resistance of the conductors and decrease the internal inductance.

15.17   UNILATERAL AND BILATERAL INDUCTION HEATING OF FLAT PLATES

Induction heating of flat metal plates is an industrial problem. There are other shapes of objects which are also heated by the method of induction, but most of possible shapes of objects can be reduced in theoretical and technical consideration to flat or cylindrical shape. The problem of heat treatment and induction heating has to be solved in the best possible way, which means optimizing the heating parameters for the electrothermal process, i.e. the three points for consideration are: (i) high heating rate, (ii) minimum electrical energy consumption, and (iii) requisite temperature distribution in the plate or medium. The frequency range used is usually 50 Hz to 3 MHz.

In industry, the objects are heated by induction either unilaterally or bilaterally, i.e. the suitably shaped heating inductor is applied to one side of the heated plate or object, or two inductors are applied to both the sides of the plate. The inductors are the source of the electromagnetic energy and can be represented (for the purpose of analysis) by a suitably directed current-sheet or its associated electric field (= **E**) or the magnetic field (= **H**). The induced field so generated in the heated plate is characterized by three vectors, i.e. the electric field **E** (or the induced current-density vector **J**), the associated magnetic field **H** (or **B**), and the Poynting vector (as a basis for the energy transfer from the inducing source).

In the present analysis, the object is a flat metal plate extending to infinity (for the purpose of analysis) both along its length and width (in the y- and z- directions respectively) and of finite thickness b (in the x-direction) The material characteristics of the plate are its electrical

conductivity σ $\left(\text{or resistivity } \rho = \dfrac{1}{\sigma}\right)$ and magnetic permeability $\mu = \mu_0\,\mu_r$ (μ_r being the relative permeability), both being assumed constants. Three different types of heating arrangements are considered here. First, the object is heated unilaterally (i.e. from one side only) by the inductor placed parallel to one of the faces. In the other two cases, the plate is heated bilaterally by means of two inductors placed on two sides of the plate. The two inductors are so positioned that the induced currents on the two faces of the plate are in the same direction and have the same phase. This is the case of bilateral heating with compatible currents. In the final arrangement, the current in one of the inductors is reversed so that the induced currents on the two faces of the plate are in opposite directions. In this case we have bilateral heating with inverse currents. The three arrangements are shown in Figure 15.31 (a), (b) and (c).

The currents fed into the inductors are $I_0 e^{j\omega t}$, in the y-direction, so that the exciting **E** field on the surface of the plate is $\mathbf{i}_y E_0 e^{j\omega t}$, $\omega = 2\pi f$, f being the frequency of the supply current within the range of the frequency used for induction heating (i.e. 50 Hz to 3 MHz). The associated magnetic field on the surface would be $\mathbf{i}_z H_0 e^{j\omega t}$. For the simplicity of analysis, the problem is reduced to a one-dimensional one so that the uniform current sheet extends to infinity in y- and z-directions, and the only variation of the fields is in the x-direction. So we shall now discuss the behaviour of these field vectors **E**, **H** and **S** (the Poynting vector = **E** × **H**) for these three systems,

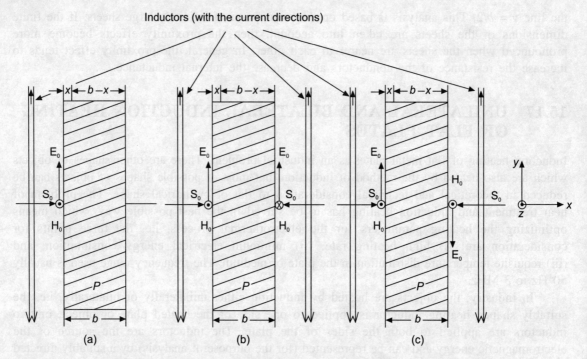

Figure 15.31 Induction heating systems of flat plate: (a) unilateral heating, (b) bilateral heating with compatible currents, and (c) bilateral heating with inverse currents.

starting first with the unilateral heating system, because the other two arrangements can be considered as due to suitably modified superposition of the unilateral system applied to both the sides of the heated plate of finite thickness.

15.17.1 Unilateral Induction Heating of a Plate [Figure 15.31(a)]

The characteristics of a heated flat metal plate of finite thickness would be known by determining the distribution of the electromagnetic field inside it, i.e. **E**, **J**, **H** and **S** in the plate. The geometry and the physics of the problem have been defined in Section 15.17. From Section 15.2, we know that when such an alternating magnetic or electric field is applied on the flat face of a semi-infinite metal block, the induced field in it is a travelling field, with its amplitude in the same direction as the inducing field, diffusing in the metal block in a direction normal to the plane on which the inducing field has been applied. By diffusion, we mean that the amplitude of the induced field gets attenuated as the field progresses inside [as seen in Eq. (15.12)]. In the present problem, the situation is somewhat different because now the conducting metal plate has finite thickness and it does not extend to infinity. So when the diffused field reaches the end surface of the plate (i.e. $x = b$), the field re-enters the air-space which has zero conductivity and the field in this region will become a plane uniform wave travelling with constant amplitude in this region and the fields on the two sides of this plane of discontinuity $x = b$ would satisfy the continuity conditions of **B** and **E** (or **H** and **J**). In this sense, this problem is more complex than that of the semi-infinite metal block as it is now a composite problem involving diffusion as well as uniform plane wave. (As such it should be studied after Chapter 17, though of course we have been briefly introduced to uniform plane waves in Chapter 12, Section 12.6.) So for a proper rigorous analysis of this problem, we start with Maxwell's equations though we could have written down the diffusion equation directly.

As mentioned earlier this is a simplified one-dimensional problem with variations in the x-direction only.

Hence $\dfrac{\partial}{\partial y} = 0$ and $\dfrac{\partial}{\partial z} = 0.$ The relevant Maxwell's equations are

$$\text{curl } \mathbf{E} = \nabla \times \mathbf{E} = -\frac{\partial \mathbf{B}}{\partial t} \tag{15.4b}$$

$$\text{curl } \mathbf{H} = \nabla \times \mathbf{H} = \mathbf{J} \tag{15.4c}$$

and the constitutive relations are

$$\mathbf{B} = \mu\mathbf{H}, \qquad \mathbf{D} = \varepsilon\mathbf{E} \qquad \text{and} \qquad \mathbf{J} = \sigma\mathbf{E} \quad (\sigma = 1/\rho) \tag{15.4f}$$

The inductor current sheet is assumed to be in the y-direction, i.e.

$$\mathbf{J}_S = \mathbf{i}_y J_{So} e^{j\omega t} \tag{15.184a}$$

where

J_{So} = surface current density (per unit width)

ω = the angular frequency of the alternating current = $2\pi f$

Hence the inducing **E** field will be

$$\mathbf{E}_i = \mathbf{i}_y E_0 e^{j\omega t} \tag{15.184b}$$

and the associated magnetic field on the surface of the plate will be

$$\mathbf{H}_i = \mathbf{i}_z H_0 e^{j\omega t} \tag{15.184c}$$

Hence, Eqs. (15.4b) and (15.4c) reduce to

$$\mathbf{i}_x 0 + \mathbf{i}_y 0 + \mathbf{i}_z \frac{\partial E_y}{\partial x} = -\mathbf{i}_z \frac{\partial B_z}{\partial t}$$

and

$$\mathbf{i}_x 0 + \mathbf{i}_y \left(-\frac{\partial H_z}{\partial x}\right) + \mathbf{i}_z 0 = \mathbf{i}_y J_y$$

inside the plate.

Differentiating these equations w.r.t. x (which in this case is equivalent to taking curl again),

$$\frac{\partial^2 E_y}{\partial x^2} = -j\omega \frac{\partial B_z}{\partial x} = -j\omega\mu \frac{\partial H_z}{\partial x} = +j\omega\mu J_y = +j\omega\mu\sigma E_y$$

and

$$-\frac{\partial^2 H_z}{\partial x^2} = \sigma \frac{\partial E_y}{\partial x} = -j\omega\sigma B_z = -j\omega\mu\sigma H_z$$

from the constitutive relations (15.4f) and $\dfrac{\partial}{\partial t} = j\omega$

Now, $\omega\mu\sigma = \dfrac{1}{d^2}$, $d\sqrt{2}$ being the depth of penetration of the metal.

We substitute $j\omega\mu\sigma = k^2$ (or β^2)

$$\therefore \qquad k = \frac{1+j}{d\sqrt{2}} \qquad\qquad (18.184d)$$

$\therefore$ The equations for E and H become:

$$\frac{\partial^2 E_y}{\partial x^2} + k^2 E_y = 0 \qquad \text{and} \qquad \frac{\partial^2 H_z}{\partial x^2} k^2 H_z = 0 \qquad\qquad (15.185)$$

In the air-space beyond the thickness of the plate (thickness $= b$ and so the air-space is $x > b$), Eq. (15.4b) is replaced by

$$\nabla \times \mathbf{H} = \frac{\partial \mathbf{D}}{\partial t} \qquad\qquad (15.4b')$$

and so the operating equation for $\mathbf{H}$ or $\mathbf{E}$ in this region will be

$$\frac{\partial^2 H_z}{\partial x^2} = j^2 \omega^2 \mu\varepsilon\, H_z \qquad \text{and} \qquad \frac{\partial^2 E_y}{\partial x^2} = j^2 \omega^2 \mu\varepsilon\, E_y$$

Substituting $\qquad -k_1^2 = j^2 \omega^2 \mu\varepsilon$, we get

$$\frac{\partial^2 E_y}{\partial x^2} + k_1^2 E_y = 0 \qquad \text{and} \qquad \frac{\partial^2 H_z}{\partial x^2} + k_1^2 H_z = 0 \qquad\qquad (15.186)$$

Since both $\mathbf{E}$ and $\mathbf{H}$ have one component only, we drop the suffices y and z and use the suffix 1 for the air-space to differentiate it from the plate.

So, the solutions for Eqs. (15.185) are

$$H = A \exp(-kx) + B \exp(kx)$$

and

$$\mathbf{E} = \frac{1}{\sigma} (\nabla \times \mathbf{H}) = -\frac{1}{\sigma} \frac{\partial H}{\partial x} \qquad\qquad (15.187)$$

$$= \frac{k}{\sigma} \{A \exp(-kx) - B \exp(kx)\}$$

in the metal plate (i.e. $0 < x < b$).

In the air-space behind the metal plate (i.e. $x > b$)

$$\left.\begin{array}{l} H_1 = C \exp(-k_1 x) + D \exp(k_1 x) \qquad x > b \\[2mm] E_1 = -\dfrac{1}{j\omega\varepsilon} \dfrac{\partial H_1}{\partial x} \\[2mm] \quad\ = \dfrac{k_1}{j\omega\varepsilon} \{C \exp(-k_1 x) - D \exp(k_1 x)\} \end{array}\right\} \qquad (15.188)$$

Here A, B, C, D are the constants of integration to be determined from the boundary conditions and the interface continuity conditions:

(i) for $x \to \infty$, $\mathbf{H}_1$, $\mathbf{E}_1 \to 0$;

(ii) for $x = 0$, $H = H_0$;

(iii) for $x = b$, $\quad H_{b-} = H_{1_{b+}}$ $\quad$ and $\quad E_{b-} = E_{1_{b+}}$

From the boundary condition (i), $D = 0$. It should be noted that the term containing D, in fact, represents the reflected wave which cannot exist in this case as the air-space extends to infinity. From (ii),

$$H_0 = A + B \tag{15.189}$$

From (iii),

$$A \exp(-kb) + B \exp(kb) = C \exp(-k_1 b) \tag{15.190a}$$

and

$$\frac{k}{\sigma}\{A \exp(-kb) - B \exp(kb)\} = \frac{k_1}{j\omega\varepsilon} C \exp(-k_1 b) \tag{15.190b}$$

From Eqs. (15.190a) and (15.190b),

$$\frac{A \exp(-kb) + B \exp(kb)}{A \exp(-kb) - B \exp(kb)} = \frac{k}{\sigma}\frac{j\omega\varepsilon}{k_1} \tag{15.191}$$

R.H.S of this equation
$$= \frac{j\omega\varepsilon k}{\sigma k_1} = \frac{j\omega\varepsilon}{\sigma} \frac{\sqrt{j\omega\mu\sigma}}{j\omega\sqrt{\mu\varepsilon}}$$

$$= \sqrt{j\omega} \sqrt{\frac{\varepsilon}{\sigma}} = \frac{1+j}{\sqrt{2}} \sqrt{2\pi f} \sqrt{\varepsilon\rho}$$

Since the frequency range of induction heating is 50 Hz to 3 MHz, and for metals $\varepsilon = \varepsilon_0 = 8.854 \times 10^{12}$ and ρ ranges from 1.75×10^{-6} Ω-cm for copper to approximately 140×10^{-6} Ω-cm for molten cost-iron,

the R.H.S. of Eq. (15.191) $\simeq 10^{-10} \simeq 0$

$\therefore$ $\qquad\qquad\qquad B = -A \exp(-2kb)$

and hence

$$A = H_0 \frac{1}{1 - \exp(-2kb)}, \quad B = -H_0 \frac{\exp(-2kb)}{1 - \exp(-2kb)} \tag{15.192}$$

and from Eq. (15.190b) $\qquad\qquad C = 0$

Hence the intensity of the magnetic field behind the metal plate is zero, i.e. the magnetic field (and the associated electric field) does not penetrate through the metal plate for the range of industrial frequencies and the types of metals used in induction heating processes. The metal plate behaves like a magnetic screen.

By substituting for A and B in Eqs. (15.187), the field parameters inside the metal plate come out to be

$$H = H_0 \frac{\exp(-kx) - \exp(kx)\exp(-2kb)}{1 - \exp(-2kb)}$$

$$= H_0 \frac{\sinh\{k(b - x)\}}{\sinh(kb)} \tag{15.193a}$$

$$E = H_0 \frac{k}{\sigma} \frac{\cosh\{k(b - x)\}}{\sinh(kb)} \tag{15.193b}$$

$$J = H_0 k \frac{\cosh\{k(b - x)\}}{\sinh(kb)} \tag{15.193c}$$

J being the current density inside the plate.

The power density inside the plate would be

$$P = \frac{1}{2} \rho J^2$$

$$= \frac{1}{2} \frac{H_0^2 k^2}{\sigma} \frac{\cosh^2\{k(b - x)\}}{\sinh^2(kb)} \tag{15.193d}$$

For graphical representation of these quantities, we normalize them with respect to the surface values and take their moduli, remembering that k is complex, i.e. $= (1 + j)/(d\sqrt{2})$. So, we get

$$\frac{|H|}{|H_0|} = \sqrt{\left[\frac{\cosh\left\{\dfrac{2(b - x)}{d\sqrt{2}}\right\} - \cos\left\{\dfrac{2(b - x)}{d\sqrt{2}}\right\}}{\cosh\left(\dfrac{2b}{d\sqrt{2}}\right) - \cos\left(\dfrac{2b}{d\sqrt{2}}\right)} \right]} \tag{15.194a}$$

$$\frac{|E|}{|E_0|} = \frac{|J|}{|J_0|} \sqrt{\left[\frac{\cosh\left\{\dfrac{2(b - x)}{d\sqrt{2}}\right\} + \cos\left\{\dfrac{2(b - x)}{d\sqrt{2}}\right\}}{\cosh\left(\dfrac{2b}{d\sqrt{2}}\right) - \cos\left(\dfrac{2b}{d\sqrt{2}}\right)} \right]} \tag{15.194b}$$

and

$$\frac{|P|}{|P_0|} = \frac{\cosh\left\{\dfrac{2(b - x)}{d\sqrt{2}}\right\} + \cos\left\{\dfrac{2(b - x)}{d\sqrt{2}}\right\}}{\cosh\left(\dfrac{2b}{d\sqrt{2}}\right) - \cos\left(\dfrac{2b}{d\sqrt{2}}\right)} \tag{15.194c}$$

From the above expression, we can calculate total power per unit cross-sectional area along the total width b of the plate, i.e.

$$P_T = \int_0^b P\,dx = \frac{1}{\sigma}\left(\frac{H_0}{d\sqrt{2}}\right)^2 \int_0^b \frac{\cosh\left\{\dfrac{2(b - x)}{d\sqrt{2}}\right\} + \cos\left\{\dfrac{2(b - x)}{d\sqrt{2}}\right\}}{\cosh\left(\dfrac{2b}{d\sqrt{2}}\right) - \cos\left(\dfrac{2b}{d\sqrt{2}}\right)}\,dx$$

$$= \frac{H_0^2}{\sigma d\sqrt{2}} \frac{\sinh\left(\dfrac{2b}{d\sqrt{2}}\right) + \sin\left(\dfrac{2b}{d\sqrt{2}}\right)}{\cosh\left(\dfrac{2b}{d\sqrt{2}}\right) - \cos\left(\dfrac{2b}{d\sqrt{2}}\right)} \qquad (15.195)$$

From this expression, it is seen that the total heating power of the plate is a function of H_0, the electrical parameters of the plate (i.e. σ), and also the ratio $\left(\dfrac{b}{d\sqrt{2}}\right)$, i.e. (thickness of the plate)/ (depth of penetration of the eddy currents). The following quantity reduces to

$$\frac{\sinh\left(\dfrac{2b}{d\sqrt{2}}\right) + \sin\left(\dfrac{2b}{d\sqrt{2}}\right)}{\cosh\left(\dfrac{2b}{d\sqrt{2}}\right) - \cos\left(\dfrac{2b}{d\sqrt{2}}\right)} = \lambda = f\left\{\frac{b}{(d\sqrt{2})}\right\}. \qquad (15.195a)$$

When the thickness of the plate b becomes infinite (i.e. much larger) relative to the depth of penetration $(= d\sqrt{2})$, then $\lambda \rightarrow 1$, and

$$\text{the heating power in the plate } = \frac{H_0^2}{\sigma d\sqrt{2}} \qquad (15.196)$$

The variations of the heating power produced in the plate can be seen by studying the changes in λ as a function of the ratio of the thickness of the plate $(= b)$ to its depth of penetration $(= d\sqrt{2})$. The function λ is near minimum when $\dfrac{b}{d\sqrt{2}} = \dfrac{\pi}{2}$, i.e. $\lambda \approx 0.92$ and the heating power also reaches its minimum value which is 92% of the power defined by Eq. (15.196).

When we are considering the heating of a thick plate, we can let $b \rightarrow \infty$ (at least theoretically). The expressions for **H** and **E** simplify considerably, and the expressions become

$$\left.\begin{array}{l} H = H_0 \exp(-kx), \\[2mm] E = \dfrac{k}{\sigma} H_0 \exp(-kx), \qquad J = kH_0 \exp(-kx) \end{array}\right\} \qquad (15.197)$$

where k is now

$$= \frac{1}{d\sqrt{2}}.$$

This is the case of the semi-infinite block which is discussed in detail in Section 15.2.

For the plate of finite thickness b, when $\left|\dfrac{H}{H_0}\right|$, $\left|\dfrac{E}{E_0}\right|$ and $\left|\dfrac{P}{P_0}\right|$ are plotted as functions of

$\left|\dfrac{x}{b}\right|$ using $\dfrac{b}{d\sqrt{2}}$ as the parameter, it will be seen that H for all values of $\dfrac{b}{d\sqrt{2}}$, become zero when $x = b$, i.e. the plate acts as a screen preventing the leakage of magnetic field beyond its thickness. The magnetic field inside the plate is not uniform and has an exponential decay. The other quantities **E** and **P** decay near exponentially but have finite values at the other surface $(x = b)$ of the plate.

15.17.2 Bilateral Induction Heating of the Flat Plate

The flat plate can be heated bilaterally in two different ways as shown in Figures 15.31(b) and (c), i.e. by means of currents induced on both the sides of a plate, in the same direction (= compatibly), or in opposite directions (= inversely). First we consider the case of compatible currents as shown in Figure 15.31(b). In that case the induced E fields on the two surfaces of the plate E_0' and E_0'' are equal in amplitude, phase and direction. But their associated magnetic fields H_0' and H_0'' will have opposite directions and equal amplitude and phase (why ?).

Inside the plate, the induced current will have the same direction as the electric field. At a point (say) x from the left surface of the plate [Figure 15.31b], the electric field intensities will be E' and E'', and the magnetic field intensities H' and H'', so that the resulting fields will be

$$H = H' - H'' \qquad \text{and} \qquad E = E' + E''$$

Each field can be evaluated as in the previous section (Section 15.17.1), and hence

$$H' = H_0 \frac{\sinh\{k(b-x)\}}{\sinh(kb)}, \qquad H'' = H_0 \frac{\sinh(kx)}{\sinh(kb)}$$

$\therefore$ The magnetic field at a point A ($= x$) will be

$$H = H_0 \frac{\sinh\{k(b-x)\} - \sinh(kx)}{\sinh(kb)}$$

$$= H_0 \frac{\sinh\{k(b/2 - x)\}}{\sinh(kb/2)} \tag{15.198}$$

Similarly the electric field

$$E = H_0 \frac{k}{\sigma} \frac{\cosh\{k(b/2 - x)\}}{\sinh(kb/2)} \tag{15.199}$$

and the current density

$$J = H_0 k \frac{\cosh\{k(b/2 - x)\}}{\sinh(kb/2)} \tag{15.200}$$

Heating power density inside the plate is also given by

$$P = \frac{1}{2\sigma} J^2 = \frac{1}{2\sigma} (H_0 k)^2 \frac{\cosh^2\{k(b/2 - x)\}}{\sinh^2(k\,b/2)} \tag{15.201}$$

As in Section (15.17.1), we normalize these quantities with respect to the surface values and take their moduli (k being complex as before),

$$\frac{|H|}{|H_0|} = \sqrt{\left[\frac{\cosh\left(\dfrac{b-2x}{d\sqrt{2}}\right) - \cos\left(\dfrac{b-2x}{d\sqrt{2}}\right)}{\cosh\left(\dfrac{b}{d\sqrt{2}}\right) - \cos\left(\dfrac{b}{d\sqrt{2}}\right)} \right]}, \tag{15.202a}$$

$$\frac{|E|}{|E_0|} = \frac{|J|}{|J_0|} = \sqrt{\left[\frac{\cosh\left(\dfrac{b-2x}{d\sqrt{2}}\right) + \cos\left(\dfrac{b-2x}{d\sqrt{2}}\right)}{\cosh\left(\dfrac{b}{d\sqrt{2}}\right) - \cos\left(\dfrac{b}{d\sqrt{2}}\right)}\right]},$$ (15.202b)

and

$$\frac{|P|}{|P_0|} = \frac{\cosh\left(\dfrac{b-2x}{d\sqrt{2}}\right) + \cos\left(\dfrac{b-2x}{d\sqrt{2}}\right)}{\cosh\left(\dfrac{b}{d\sqrt{2}}\right) - \cos\left(\dfrac{b}{d\sqrt{2}}\right)}$$ (15.202c)

The fields have the maximum value on the two surfaces and decrease exponentially inside from both the surfaces, so that each component has a minimum at $x = b/2$. The magnetic inensity $H = 0$ at $x = b/2$.

The total heating power per unit cross-sectional area and along the whole width b is

$$P_T = \int_0^b P dx = \frac{1}{2\sigma}(H_0 k)^2 \int_0^b \frac{\cosh^2\{k(b/2 - x)\}}{\sinh^2(kb/2)} dx$$

$$= \frac{H_0^2}{4\sigma d^2} \int_0^b \frac{\cosh\left\{\dfrac{b-2x}{d\sqrt{2}}\right\} + \cos\left\{\dfrac{b-2x}{d\sqrt{2}}\right\}}{\cosh\left(\dfrac{b}{d\sqrt{2}}\right) - \cos\left(\dfrac{b}{d\sqrt{2}}\right)} dx$$

$$= \frac{H_0^2}{2\sigma d\sqrt{2}} \frac{\sinh\left(\dfrac{b}{d\sqrt{2}}\right) + \sinh\left(\dfrac{b}{d\sqrt{2}}\right)}{\cosh\left(\dfrac{b}{d\sqrt{2}}\right) - \cos\left(\dfrac{b}{d\sqrt{2}}\right)}$$ (15.203)

So, now the equivalent λ is:

$$\lambda = \frac{\sinh\left(\dfrac{b}{d\sqrt{2}}\right) + \sin\left(\dfrac{b}{d\sqrt{2}}\right)}{\cosh\left(\dfrac{b}{d\sqrt{2}}\right) - \cos\left(\dfrac{b}{d\sqrt{2}}\right)}$$ (15.204)

Next we consider a flat plate being heated inductively by two current sheets on two sides, the currents flowing in opposite directions [i.e. inversely, as shown in Figure [15.31(c)]. In this case the electric field intensities E_0' and E_0'' on the surfaces, will be of equal magnitude but of opposite directions whereas the magnetic field intensities H_0' and H_0'' will have the same magnitude and direction. So at any point inside the plate, the resultant field intensities will be

$$H = H' + H'' \quad \text{and} \quad E = E' - E''$$

As before,

$$H' = H_0 \frac{\sinh\{k(b-x)\}}{\sinh(kb)} \quad \text{and} \quad H'' = H_0 \frac{\sinh(kx)}{\sinh(kb)}$$

Hence the magnetic field at any point $A(=x)$ in the plate is

$$H = H_0 \frac{\sinh\{k(b-x)\} + \sinh(kx)}{\sinh(kb)}$$

$$= H_0 \frac{\cosh\{k(b/2 - x)\}}{\cosh(kb/2)} \tag{15.205}$$

And similarly the electric field

$$E = H_0 \frac{k}{\sigma} \frac{\sinh\{k(b/2 - x)\}}{\cosh(kb/2)} \tag{15.206}$$

and the current density

$$J = H_0 k \frac{\sinh\{k(b/2 - x)\}}{\cosh(kb/2)} \tag{15.207}$$

In this arrangement, the heating power density in the plate

$$P = \frac{1}{2\sigma}(H_0 k)^2 \frac{\sinh^2\{k(b/2 - x)\}}{\cosh^2(kb/2)} \tag{15.208}$$

As for the previous bilateral heating arrangement, normalizing these quantities with respect to their surface values and taking their moduli,

$$\frac{|H|}{|H_0|} = \sqrt{\left[\frac{\cosh\left(\dfrac{b-2x}{d\sqrt{2}}\right) + \cos\left(\dfrac{b-2x}{d\sqrt{2}}\right)}{\cosh\left(\dfrac{b}{d\sqrt{2}}\right) + \cos\left(\dfrac{b}{d\sqrt{2}}\right)}\right]} \tag{15.209a}$$

$$\frac{|E|}{|E_0|} = \frac{|J|}{|J_0|} = \sqrt{\left[\frac{\cosh\left(\dfrac{b-2x}{d\sqrt{2}}\right) - \cos\left(\dfrac{b-2x}{d\sqrt{2}}\right)}{\cosh\left(\dfrac{b}{d\sqrt{2}}\right) + \cos\left(\dfrac{b}{d\sqrt{2}}\right)}\right]} \tag{15.209b}$$

and

$$\frac{|P|}{|P_0|} = \frac{\cosh\left(\dfrac{b-2x}{d\sqrt{2}}\right) - \cos\left(\dfrac{b-2x}{d\sqrt{2}}\right)}{\cosh\left(\dfrac{b}{d\sqrt{2}}\right) + \cos\left(\dfrac{b}{d\sqrt{2}}\right)} \tag{15.209c}$$

As before, the fields have maximum values on the two surfaces of the plate, and decrease exponentially inside from both the surfaces, so that each component has a minimum at the centre $x = b/2$. The electric field intensity E and the current density J are zero at $x = b/2$.

Again, the total heating power per unit cross-sectional area and along the whole width b is

$$P_T = \int_0^b P\,dx = \frac{1}{2\sigma}(H_0 k)^2 \int_0^b \frac{\sinh^2\{k(b/2 - x)\}}{\cosh^2(kb/2)}\,dx$$

$$= \frac{H_0^2}{4\sigma d^2} \int_0^b \frac{\cosh\left\{\dfrac{b-2x}{d\sqrt{2}}\right\} - \cos\left\{\dfrac{b-2x}{d\sqrt{2}}\right\}}{\cosh\left(\dfrac{b}{d\sqrt{2}}\right) + \cos\left(\dfrac{b}{d\sqrt{2}}\right)} \, dx$$

$$= \frac{H_0^2}{2\sigma d\sqrt{2}} \frac{\sinh\left(\dfrac{b}{d\sqrt{2}}\right) - \sin\left(\dfrac{b}{d\sqrt{2}}\right)}{\cosh\left(\dfrac{b}{d\sqrt{2}}\right) + \cos\left(\dfrac{b}{d\sqrt{2}}\right)} \qquad (15.210)$$

And the corresponding λ in this case is

$$\lambda = \frac{\sinh\left(\dfrac{b}{d\sqrt{2}}\right) - \sin\left(\dfrac{b}{d\sqrt{2}}\right)}{\cosh\left(\dfrac{b}{d\sqrt{2}}\right) + \cos\left(\dfrac{b}{d\sqrt{2}}\right)} \qquad (15.211)$$

In all the three cases, i.e. (15.195a), (15.204) and (15.211), λ can be plotted as a function of $\left(\dfrac{b}{d\sqrt{2}}\right)$, to find the optimum value for the heating power in the plate, i.e. to maximize the eddy current losses in the plate. It should be noted that for these two types of bilateral induction heating, the magnetic field distribution in the plate with compatible currents [Eq. (15.198)], and the electric field or current density distribution [Eq. (15.206), Eq. (15.207)] for inverse currents are similar or nearly the same, both fields becoming zero at the central line (= $x = b/2$) of the plate. Similarly the electric field or current density distribution for compatible excitation current and the magnetic field distribution for inverse currents are same. However the loss distribution patterns for the two cases are significantly different. For the inverse current system, the concentration of eddy currents nearer the two surfaces is much greater and the penetration into the depth is much less compared with the compatible current arrangement. So when the heating is to be restricted nearer the surfaces of the plate, the inverse current arrangement would be preferable.

Note: The inverse current system is the one which has been discussed is detail in Section 15.3, where the problem has been defined in terms of the applied magnetic fields on the two surfaces of the plate and the direction of this field is along the y-axis. In the present problem the magnetic field is directed along the z-axis.

15.18 EDDY CURRENTS AND SKIN EFFECT IN TUBULAR CONDUCTORS

It has been shown in Section 15.2 that when the depth of penetration is small compared with the curvature of the conducting surface, i.e. Eqs. (15.15) to (15.18) in Section 15.2, then the analysis for the plane surface can be applied to that of a tubular conductor. This is in general true for high frequency currents in tubular conductors. But if this is not true, then the problem has to be solved by using the cylindrical polar coordinate system. Before starting to solve the problem in this coordinate system, it is worth recapitulating the main points of the results for circular conductors (i.e. of circular cross-section) as derived in Section 15.2 in the equations mentioned above.

When the radius of a of the circular conductor, or the radial thickness (i.e. $a - b$) of a tubular conductor (of outer radius a and inner radius b) is much greater than the depth of penetration $d\sqrt{2}$ [$d = (\omega\mu\sigma)^{-1/2}$], then the ac resistance and the reactance of the conductor come out to be

$$R_{ac} = \omega L = \frac{1}{2\sqrt{2}\pi\, a\sigma\, d} \tag{15.212}$$

per unit axial length and the complete circumferential width ($= 2\pi a$). Hence if a unit square is considered in the ϕ–z plane, then the ac resistance and reactance will be

$$R_{ac1} = \omega L_1 = \frac{1}{\sigma\, d\sqrt{2}} \tag{15.213}$$

It should be noted that the reactance (or the inductance) is due to the circumferential flux lying in the inside skin of the conductor where the alternating magnetic flux has penetrated starting from the outer surface.

Now, we consider the problem of the tabular conductor. In passing, it is mentioned that the problem of the isolated circular conductor has been solved in Section 15.5. The present problem does reduce to the problem of the circular conductor, when the inner radius b of the tube reduces to zero (i.e. $b \to 0$). Without going through all the intermediate steps, we can write down the equation for the current density $\mathbf{J}\,(= \mathbf{i}_z J_z$ or $\mathbf{i}_z J$ to simplify the notations since only the z-component of the current in the axial direction of the conductor exists) as:

$$\mu\sigma\frac{d\mathbf{J}}{dt} = \nabla^2\mathbf{J} \tag{15.214}$$

Since we are considering the steady state alternating current of angular frequency ω, i.e. $\mathbf{J}e^{j\omega t}$, the above equation further simplifies to

$$j\omega\mu\sigma J = \frac{d^2 J}{dr^2} + \frac{1}{r}\frac{dJ}{dr} \tag{15.215}$$

as there is variation only in the r-direction and no variation in ϕ-direction due to symmetry about the axis of the conductors as well as in the z-direction ($=$ the direction of current flow). Substituting $d^2 = \dfrac{1}{\omega\mu\sigma}$, the above equation is nothing but the modified Bessel's equation of zero order [cf. Eq. (4.44)]

i.e.

$$\frac{d^2 J}{dr^2} + \frac{1}{r}\frac{dJ}{dr} + \left(\frac{j}{d}\right)^2 J = 0 \tag{15.215a}$$

and its solution is of the form

$$J = C\, I_0\left\{\left(\frac{j}{d^2}\right)^{1/2} r\right\} + D\, K_0\left\{\left(\frac{j}{d^2}\right)^{1/2} r\right\} \tag{15.216}$$

To evaluate C and D, the relevant boundary conditions are:

(i) On the outer boundary $r = a$, the current density J is equal to the surface current density J_0. Hence

$$J_0 = C\, I_0 \left\{ \sqrt{j}\, \frac{a}{d} \right\} + D\, K_0 \left\{ \sqrt{j}\, \frac{a}{d} \right\} \tag{15.217}$$

(ii) On the inner boundary $r = b$, there can be no magnetic field inside the cavity. This follows from the solution of the problem discussed in Section 7.10.3 [i.e. Eq. (7.58)]. There it is seen that the magnetic field in a circular cavity of a current-carrying circular conductor is uniform and is a function of the distance between the axis of the conductor and the axis of the circular cavity. Hence it follows that if the cavity is co-axial with the conductor, the magnetic field inside the cavity will be zero. Hence, at $r = b$, $\mathbf{B} = 0$

or

$$\frac{1}{\sigma} (\nabla \times \mathbf{J}) = -\frac{dB}{dt} = 0$$

or

$$\frac{dJ}{dr} = 0$$

$$\therefore \qquad C\, I_1 \left\{ \sqrt{j}\, \frac{b}{d} \right\} + D\, K_1 \left\{ \sqrt{j}\, \frac{b}{d} \right\} = 0 \tag{15.218}$$

$$\therefore \qquad C_1 = \frac{K_1 \left\{ \sqrt{j}\, \dfrac{b}{d} \right\} J_0}{J_0 \left\{ \sqrt{j}\, \dfrac{a}{d} \right\} K_1 \left\{ \sqrt{j}\, \dfrac{b}{d} \right\} + I_1 \left\{ \sqrt{j}\, \dfrac{b}{d} \right\} K_0 \left\{ \sqrt{j}\, \dfrac{a}{d} \right\}} \tag{15.219}$$

$$D_1 = \frac{I_1 \left\{ \sqrt{j}\, \dfrac{b}{d} \right\}}{I_0 \left\{ \sqrt{j}\, \dfrac{a}{d} \right\} K_1 \left\{ \sqrt{j}\, \dfrac{b}{d} \right\} + I_1 \left\{ \sqrt{j}\, \dfrac{b}{d} \right\} K_0 \left\{ \sqrt{j}\, \dfrac{a}{d} \right\}} \tag{15.220}$$

15.18.1 Skin Effect in Solid Cylindrical Conductors

If the conductor is a solid cylinder instead of a tube, then $b \to 0$ and $D = 0$ because

$K_0 \left\{ \sqrt{j}\, \dfrac{r}{d} \right\} \to \infty$ as $r \to 0$. Hence the current distribution in the conductor is obtained as:

$$J = \frac{I_0 \left\{ \sqrt{j}\, \dfrac{r}{d} \right\}}{I_0 \left\{ \sqrt{j}\, \dfrac{a}{d} \right\}} J_0 \tag{15.221}$$

Since these modified Bessel's functions have complex arguments, they can be expressed as Kelvin's ber, bei, ker and kei functions (for the purpose of computations).

Thus,

$$I_0\left\{\sqrt{j}\ x\right\} = \text{ber}_0\ x + j\ \text{bei}_0\ x \qquad (15.222a)$$

and

$$K_0\left\{\sqrt{j}\ x\right\} = \text{ker}_0\ x + j\ \text{kei}_0\ x \qquad (15.222b)$$

This problem has been solved in detail in Section 15.5, where the Bessel functions with complex arguments have been expressed in polar form, and hence any further discussion of the above solution is not repeated here.

15.18.2 Internal Self-inductance of Cylindrical and Tubular Conductors due to Skin Effect While Carrying Alternating Currents

The analysis of the flux distribution in a cylindrical conductor (as well as in a tubular conductor with radial thickness greater than the "depth of penetration") carrying an alternating current has been discussed in Sections 15.2 and 15.18, and it is obvious that the magnetic flux loops are in the circumferential direction and inside the outer surface of the cylindrical as well as the tubular conductor. Hence the inductance caused by this alternating flux (as well as the effective ac resistance) can be considered as the "internal self-inductance" of the conductor (and also the internal resistance).

The ac inductance of the cylindrical (as well as tubular) wire as derived in Eq. (15.213) of Section 15.18 [deduced from Eq. (15.212) or Eq. (15.17) of Section 15.2] is effectively the inductance per unit axial length and the unit circumferential width, and can be denoted as L_{i1} and R_{i1}. These will now be expressed as:

$$L_{i1} = \frac{1}{\omega\sigma d\sqrt{2}} = \frac{R_{i1}}{\omega} \qquad (15.223)$$

It should be noted that at high frequencies L_{i1} is negligible, compared with the external inductance of the wire (i.e. the inductance L being $L \gg L_i$).

To evaluate the total L_i and R_i in practical problems such as cylindrical conductors in parallel wire transmission line problems, it is preferable to use energy expressions instead of using the flux linkage concept. The reason is that the presence of a second conductor in the vicinity of the first conductor produces a proximity effect which destroys the axial symmetry of the magnetic flux about the axis of each conductor. On the other hand the total current in the skin of the cylindrical conductor can be evaluated, with comparative ease. The expressions to be used are:

$$R_i I^2 = R_{i1} \oint J_s^2 ds \quad \text{and} \quad L_i I^2 = L_{i1} \oint J_s^2 ds \qquad (15.224)$$

where J_s is the current across the unit arc length in the cylindrical skin of the conductor. The above expressions can be used for each of the two conductors, whatever may be the radius of each conductor. If the conductors are of equal diameter, the total inductance and resistance will be twice that obtained from the above formula. When the conductors are of equal diameter, the total inductance and resistance will be twice that obtained from the above formula. When the conductors are of unequal radii, R_i and L_i have to be evaluated separately by taking into account the relevant limits of integration. For such two-dimensional problems, the solution is most conveniently obtained by using conjugate functions and the method has been discussed in detail in Sections 4.4–4.4.3 and Section 17.18. A brief description of the important aspects of the results follows.

Since the equipotentials and the lines of force (or current flow lines) are orthogonal. We use the complex potential function W, and write

$$W = U + jV \quad \text{and} \quad W = f(z),\ z = x + jy \tag{15.225}$$

$$U = U(x, y), \qquad V = V(x, y) \tag{15.225a}$$

so that

$$U + jV = f(x + jy) \tag{15.226a}$$

and

$$V - jU = jf(x + jy) = F(x + jy) \tag{15.226b}$$

$\therefore$ Differentiating W with respect to x and y respectively

$$\frac{\partial W}{\partial x} = \frac{\partial U}{\partial x} + j\frac{\partial V}{\partial x} = f'(z)\frac{\partial z}{\partial x} = f'(z) \tag{15.227a}$$

$$\frac{\partial W}{\partial y} = \frac{\partial U}{\partial y} + j\frac{\partial V}{\partial y} = f'(z)\frac{\partial z}{\partial y} = jf'(z) \tag{15.227b}$$

and hence,

$$\frac{\partial V}{\partial x} = -\frac{\partial U}{\partial y} \quad \text{and} \quad \frac{\partial V}{\partial y} = \frac{\partial U}{\partial x} \tag{15.228}$$

Thus, the two families of curves $U(x, y) = $ constant and $V(x, y) = $ constant intersect each other orthogonally. In such a case either set can be chosen to represent equipotentials in which case the chosen function becomes the potential function. The other set which is orthogonal to this then represents the lines of force (i.e. also called the stream function).

$$\therefore \quad \frac{dW}{dz} = \frac{\partial V}{\partial y} + j\frac{\partial V}{\partial x} = \frac{\partial U}{\partial x} - j\frac{\partial U}{\partial y} \left(\text{from } z = \frac{dW + jdV}{dx + jdy} \right) \tag{15.229}$$

Regardless of whether U or V is the potential function, the absolute value of $\dfrac{dW}{dz}$ at any point gives the magnitude of the electric field intensity at that point. From Eq. (15.229), it follows that

$$\left|\frac{dW}{dz}\right| = \frac{\partial U}{\partial n} = \frac{\partial V}{\partial s} \quad \text{or} \quad \left|\frac{dW}{dz}\right| = \frac{\partial V}{\partial n} = -\frac{\partial U}{\partial s} \tag{15.230}$$

(where dn is an element of length in the direction of maximum increase of potential, and ds the element of length obtained by rotating dn through $\pi/2$ radians in the counterclockwise sense), according as U or V is the potential function.

For example, if V is the potential function, then the flux through any section of an equipotential surface between the curves U_1 and U_2 is given by

$$\text{Flux} = -\varepsilon \int_{U_1}^{U_2} \frac{\partial V}{\partial n}\, ds = \varepsilon \int_{U_1}^{U_2} \frac{\partial U}{\partial s}\, ds = \varepsilon(U_2 - U_1) \tag{15.231}$$

Thus the capacitance of two closed equipotential surfaces at V_1 and V_2 can be expressed as

$$C = \frac{|Q|}{|V_2 - V_1|} = \frac{\varepsilon[U]}{|V_1 - V_2|} \tag{15.231a}$$

where the increment in U is expressed as $[U]$. The inductance can then the evaluated using the relationship.

$$LC = \mu\varepsilon \tag{15.232}$$

To evaluate the internal inductance due to eddy current skin effect, the integral in Eq. (15.224) has to be evaluated. From Section 17.18, Eq. (17.236) the tangential component of **B** on the $U = U_1$ cylinder is $\dfrac{\partial V}{\partial s}$. The mmf applied to a surface element gives $\mu J_S = B$. Hence,

$$\oint J_S^2 ds = \frac{1}{\mu^2} \oint \left[\frac{\partial V}{\partial s}\right]^2 ds = \frac{1}{\mu^2} \oint \frac{\partial V}{\partial s} dV \tag{15.233}$$

$\dfrac{\partial V}{\partial s}$ is known (for a given configuration) from the conjugate function relationship stated in Eq. (15.230), and hence the above integral can be suitably evaluated.

PROBLEMS

15.1 A pair of perfectly conducting plates holds a conducting block of rectangular cross-section, as shown in the figure below. The metal block and the plates extend a long way to the right. A current excitation $i(t) = \text{Re}\{I \exp(j\omega t)\}$ is applied uniformly to the plates along their left edge. Find the magnetic flux density in the region between the plates and the current density in the block.

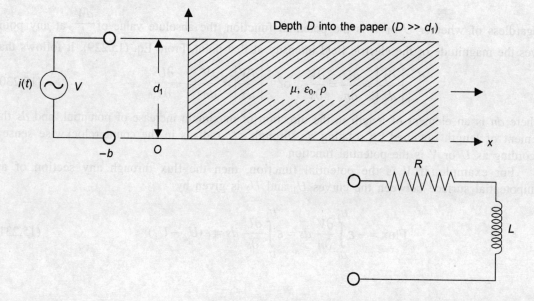

Find the equivalent reactance as seen at the current source. Using the equivalent circuit shown here, find the values of L and R.

Hint: Solve as a one-dimensional problem in x dimension.

Ans.: $\quad B_z = - \operatorname{Re} \dfrac{\mu \hat{I}}{D} \exp\left(\dfrac{-x}{d\sqrt{2}}\right) \exp j\left(\omega t - \dfrac{x}{d\sqrt{2}}\right)$

$$J_y = - \operatorname{Re} \dfrac{\hat{I}}{D} \dfrac{1+j}{d\sqrt{2}} \exp\left(\dfrac{x}{d\sqrt{2}}\right) \exp j\left(\omega t - \dfrac{x}{d\sqrt{2}}\right)$$

$$R = \dfrac{d_1}{D} \dfrac{\rho}{d\sqrt{2}}, \quad \omega L = \omega\left(\dfrac{\mu_0 b d_1}{D} + \dfrac{d_1}{D} \dfrac{\rho}{\omega d\sqrt{2}}\right),$$

where $d = \left(\dfrac{\rho}{\omega \mu}\right)^{1/2}$.

15.2 What will be the magnetic flux density and the current density in the above block if it extends over a length l in the x-direction?

Ans.: $\quad B_z = \dfrac{\mu \hat{I}}{D} \dfrac{\sinh \dfrac{(x-l)\sqrt{j}}{d}}{\sinh \dfrac{l\sqrt{j}}{d}}$

$$J_y = \dfrac{\hat{I}}{D} \dfrac{\sqrt{j}}{d} \dfrac{\cosh (x-l)\dfrac{\sqrt{j}}{d}}{\sinh l\sqrt{\dfrac{j}{d}}}$$

Note: $\exp(j\omega t)$ is implicit in these expressions.

15.3 A copper conductor of strip form has a length and breadth which are both much greater than its thickness $2b$. A coordinate system is taken with its centre at the origin at the centre of all three dimensions of the strip, the axes of x, y and z being in the direction of the thickness, the breadth and the length respectively. The strip carries a current in the z-direction, the density being represented by a phasor J. Neglecting edge effects, prove that (by solving the equation for H or B),

$$H = H_y = J_0 d \left(\dfrac{1-j}{\sqrt{2}}\right) \sinh \dfrac{(1+j)x}{d\sqrt{2}}$$

where J_0 is the value of the current at the centre, and d is the skin-depth.

15.4 An alternating current flows longitudinally in a copper conductor of thickness $2b$ and resistivity ρ, the length and the width of the conductor being great compared with b. Prove that the ratio of the maximum to the minimum current density is

$$\left[\frac{1}{2} \left(\cosh \frac{b\sqrt{2}}{d} + \cos \frac{b\sqrt{2}}{d} \right) \right]^{1/2}$$

where $d = \left(\dfrac{\rho}{\mu_0 \omega} \right)^{1/2}$.

15.5   From the analysis of the current distribution in a semi-infinite conducting block, at radio frequencies, prove that the ratio of ac resistance to the zero-frequency resistance (i.e. dc resistance or R_{dc}) of conductors of any shape of cross-section is equal to the inverse ratio of the areas. Derive this expression for (i) a conductor of circular cross-section of radius a, (ii) a rectangular bar $a \times b$.

Hint: Use the one-dimensional skin-depth d.

15.6   An iron plate is bounded by the parallel planes $x = \pm b$. The plate extends to $+\infty$ in the z-direction and is wide enough in the $\pm y$-directions so that the edge effects can be ignored (which simplifies it to a one-dimensional problem). Wire is wound uniformly round the plate such that the layers of wire are parallel to the y-axis. An alternating current is sent through the wire, thus producing a magnetizing intensity $\mathbf{i}_z H_0 \cos \omega t$ on the surfaces of the plate (i.e. $\mathbf{H}$ has only z-component on the two surfaces). Show that the $\mathbf{H}$ field inside the plate at a distance x from its centre is given by:

$$\mathbf{H} = \mathbf{i}_z H_0 \sqrt{\frac{\cosh 2mx + \cos 2mx}{\cosh 2mb + \cos 2mb}} \cdot \cos (\omega t + \beta)$$

$$\tan \beta = \frac{- \sinh m(b + x) \sin m(b - x) - \sinh m(b - x) \sin m(b + x)}{\cosh m(b + x) \cos m(b - x) + \cosh m(b - x) \cos m(b + x)}$$

where $m^2 = \dfrac{\omega \mu \sigma}{2} = \dfrac{1}{2d^2}$, i.e. $m = \dfrac{1}{d\sqrt{2}}$, d being the depth of penetration of iron of permeability $\mu (= \mu_0 \mu_r)$ and conductivity σ. Discuss the limiting cases of mb small and mb large.

15.7   When there are time-varying currents in a conducting medium, the magnetic vector potential $\mathbf{A}$ satisfies the equation

$$\mathbf{E} = -\frac{\partial \mathbf{A}}{\partial t}$$

Show, hence, that $\mathbf{A}$ satisfies the equation $\nabla^2 \mathbf{A} = \mu \sigma \dfrac{\partial \mathbf{A}}{\partial t}$ (a)

Show, now, the solution of $\mathbf{A}$ is of the form given by Eq. (13.7.2) of Problem 13.7, i.e.

$$\mathbf{A} = \nabla \times \mathbf{W} = \nabla \times (\mathbf{u} W_1 + \mathbf{u} \times \nabla W_2)$$

is such that $\mathbf{W}$, W_1 and W_2 all satisfy the above equation (a). Also show that now W_1 and W_2 both contribute to the $\mathbf{B}$ field.

16 Charge Relaxation

16.1 INTRODUCTION

The relaxation of charge (in good or slightly conducting media) is the mechanism by which the motion has an effect on the electric field distributions in electric field systems. We shall discuss this phenomenon in this chapter by considering a number of examples. Initially we shall consider systems in which the conducting medium is at rest. In such problems, the relaxation time is of fundamental importance for determining the volume and the surface charge densities, which result from the initial conditions and excitations. Subsequently we shall look at the effect of steady motion on the relaxation of the free charges, and study the effects of the 'electric Reynold's number', based on the material velocity.

The field equations of relevance for the charge relaxation are

$$\text{curl } \mathbf{E} = \nabla \times \mathbf{E} = 0 \tag{16.1}$$

$$\text{div } \mathbf{D} = \nabla \cdot \mathbf{D} = \rho_{\text{fc}} \tag{16.2}$$

$$\text{div } \mathbf{J} + \frac{\partial \rho_{\text{fc}}}{\partial t} = \nabla \cdot \mathbf{J} + \frac{\partial \rho_{\text{fc}}}{\partial t} = 0 \tag{16.3}$$

Thus we consider two of the Maxwell's Eqs. (16.1) and (16.2). Equation (16.1) is the restricted form of the Faraday's law because here we are considering the electric field of *free charges* with which there is *no* associated time-varying magnetic field. The third equation (16.3) is the continuity equation (based on the conservation of charge) which is a consequence of the Maxwell's equations. The relevant constituent relations are

$$\mathbf{D} = \varepsilon \mathbf{E} \tag{16.4}$$

and we restrict ourselves to the situations in which the conduction of free charge can be accounted for by a constitutive law of the form

$$\mathbf{J} = \sigma \mathbf{E} + \rho_{\text{fc}} \mathbf{v} \tag{16.5}$$

in which we have combined the 'Ohm's law' with the field transformation arising out of motion. This law describes the conduction process in a wide range of solids, liquids and gases, but does not apply for all general situations.

As we analyze and study the subject of charge relaxation, we shall notice that this subject has some significant similarity with the magnetic diffusion, which we studied in Chapter 15. We now start with the equation of continuity [i.e. Eq. (16.3)] and the constituent relation given by Eq. (16.5)

$$\nabla \cdot (\sigma \mathbf{E} + \rho_{\text{fc}} \mathbf{v}) + \frac{\partial \rho_{\text{fc}}}{\partial t} = 0 \tag{16.6}$$

Expressing ρ_{fc} in terms of $\mathbf{E}$ by using Eqs. (16.2) and (16.4), we get

$$\nabla \cdot (\sigma \mathbf{E}) + \nabla \cdot [\mathbf{v}\nabla \cdot (\varepsilon \mathbf{E})] + \left(\frac{\partial}{\partial t}\right)[\nabla \cdot (\varepsilon \mathbf{E})] = 0 \tag{16.7}$$

When the velocity $\mathbf{v}$ is given, Eq. (16.7) involves only the electric field intensity $\mathbf{E}$. Also, it is a scalar equation and hence, in general, it will not uniquely define the three components of $\mathbf{E}$. However from Eq. (16.1), we can define a scalar potential ϕ such that

$$\mathbf{E} = - \text{grad } \phi = - \nabla\phi \tag{16.8}$$

Then Eq. (16.7) becomes

$$\nabla \cdot (\sigma \nabla \phi) + \nabla \cdot [\mathbf{v}\nabla \cdot (\varepsilon \nabla \phi)] = -\left(\frac{\partial}{\partial t}\right)[\nabla \cdot (\varepsilon \nabla \phi)] \tag{16.9}$$

Physically this equation is an account of the conservation of the free charge in the system. The first term represents the flow of free charges into a small volume due to conduction. The second term is a consequence of the convection of the medium giving rise to the transport of the free charges into a given region. The term on the right-hand-side of the equation is the rate of increase of the local free-charge density. In the subsequent sections, we shall consider the effect of motion on the fields (i.e. when there is motion, the velocity is defined). However there are models (in problems of electromechanical couplings) in which the velocity $\mathbf{v}$ is not known till the fields are known.

16.2   CHARGE RELAXATION AS AN ELECTRICAL TRANSIENT

Initially we shall consider some problems dealing with the charge relaxation in stationary systems (i.e. when there is no motion, $\mathbf{v} = 0$). Also, we start with simpler systems in which the conductivity and the permittivity of each medium are uniform. Hence the changes in σ and ε occur only at the interface surfaces. It should also be appreciated that unless there is a free-charge source in the medium, there will be no steady-state volume free-charge density.

16.2.1   Charge Density in a Conducting Medium (or More Generally, Media with Uniform Properties)

Since $\mathbf{v} = 0$, the system equations are

$$\nabla \cdot \mathbf{J} + \frac{\partial \rho_{\text{fc}}}{\partial t} = 0 \tag{16.3}$$

$$\nabla \cdot \mathbf{D} = \rho_{\text{fc}} \tag{16.2}$$

$$\mathbf{D} = \varepsilon \mathbf{E} \tag{16.4}$$

$$\mathbf{J} = \sigma \mathbf{E} \tag{16.10}$$

Combining these four equations, we get the operational equation in ρ_{fc} as

$$\frac{\partial \rho_{fc}}{\partial t} + \left(\frac{\sigma}{\varepsilon}\right)\rho_{fc} = 0 \tag{16.11}$$

which can also be obtained from Eq. (16.9) or Eq. (16.7) by putting $\mathbf{v} = 0$ and substituting for $\mathbf{E}$ or ϕ in terms of the charge density ρ_{fc}. A general solution of Eq. (16.11) is

$$\rho_{fc}(x, y, z, t) = \rho_0(x, y, z, 0) \exp\left(-\frac{t}{\tau}\right) \tag{16.12}$$

where

$$\tau = \frac{\varepsilon}{\sigma} \tag{16.13}$$

Equations (16.12) and (16.13) imply that given an initial charge density ρ_0 at the instant $t = 0$, the free-charge density at each point in space decays to zero exponentially with the 'relaxation time τ'. It should be understood that Eq. (16.11) has been derived without using Eq. (16.1), and hence these conclusions do not depend on the field equations being quasi-static. However in any physical situation, the uniformly conducting medium is of finite extent, and the conservation of charge requires that those charges which are initially distributed throughout the volume *relax to the surfaces* that bound the volume. We give below the relaxation time for some typical conductors and insulators (Table 16.1).

Table 16.1 Relaxation time for conductors and insulators

Material	σ (mho/metre)	ε	τ (seconds)
Silver	6.17×10^7	ε_0	1.43×10^{-19}
Copper	5.80×10^7	ε_0	1.52×10^{-19}
Aluminium	3.72×10^7	ε_0	2.38×10^{-19}
Mercury	1.06×10^6	ε_0	8.35×10^{-18}
Sea water	4	$80\varepsilon_0$	1.77×10^{-4}
Water	4×10^{-6}	$80\varepsilon_0$	6.40×10^{-4}
CCl$_4$	4×10^{-16}	$2.24\varepsilon_0$	4.95×10^4

For the conductors, the relaxation time is extremely small, and there are insulators for which the relaxation time can be measured in minutes and hours.

16.2.1.1 Example 1

A sphere of radius R_i is made up of uniformly conducting material, and is placed concentrically in another perfectly conducting spherical shell of radius R_o. The annular space between the spheres is filled with an isotropic insulating material. A free-charge density ρ_0 is distributed uniformly throughout a spherical region of radius $R(R < R_i)$ at the centre of the conducting sphere, at the instant of time $t = 0$.

$$\therefore \quad \rho_{fc\ at\ t\ =\ 0} = \rho_0 = \frac{Q}{(4/3)\pi R^3} \tag{16.14}$$

where Q is the total charge in the central sphere of radius R.

∴   The transient charge density as given by Eq. (16.12) is

$$\rho_{fc} = \rho_0 \exp\left(-\frac{t}{\tau}\right) \qquad \text{for } r < R$$

$$= 0 \qquad \text{for } r > R \qquad (16.15)$$

where $\tau = \varepsilon/\sigma$, with ε and σ being the permittivity and the conductivity respectively of the medium.

The problem has radial symmetry, i.e. the only variation is along r. Hence, using Eq. (16.2) in the spherical coordinate system, we obtain the equation for the electric field intensity E_r as, i.e.

$$\left(\frac{1}{r^2}\right)\frac{d}{dr}\left(r^2 E_r\right) = \left(\frac{\rho_0}{\varepsilon}\right)\exp\left(-\frac{t}{\tau}\right)$$

$$\therefore \qquad E_r = \frac{Q}{4\varepsilon\pi R^2}\left(\frac{r}{R}\right)\exp\left(-\frac{t}{\tau}\right) \qquad \text{for } r < R \qquad (16.16)$$

The total charge within the radius $r = R$ is $Q\exp\left(-\dfrac{t}{\tau}\right)$, and by Gauss,

$$E_r = \left(\frac{Q}{4\varepsilon\pi r^2}\right)\exp\left(-\frac{t}{\tau}\right) \qquad \text{for } R < r < R_i \qquad (16.17)$$

Since the total charge on the sphere must be conserved, the electric field outside the conducting sphere (in the insulating medium) is

$$E_r = \frac{Q}{4\varepsilon_0\pi r^2} \qquad \text{for } R_i < r < R_o \qquad (16.18)$$

Hence from these electric field intensities, we can find the amount of free charge on the interface

$\rho_S = D_n$ (approaching from the insulating annulus) $- D_n$ (approaching from the conducting sphere)
$\underset{r \to R_i + \text{Eq. (16.18)}}{} \underset{r \to R_i - \text{Eq. (16.17)}}{}$

$$= \frac{\varepsilon_0 Q}{4\varepsilon_0\pi R_i^2} - \left(\frac{\varepsilon Q}{4\varepsilon\pi R_i^2}\right)\exp\left(-\frac{t}{\tau}\right) = \frac{Q}{4\pi R_i^2}\left[1 - \exp\left(-\frac{t}{\tau}\right)\right] \qquad (16.19)$$

The surface charge on the outer shell ($r = R_o$) is however constant. Equation (16.19) shows that the initial free-charge density relaxes to the outer surface of the conducting sphere. In the steady-state condition, there is *no* electric field within the sphere, as the field is shielded out of the sphere by the surface charge at $r = R_i$.

The current density is

$$J_r = \sigma E_r = \left(\frac{\sigma Q}{4\varepsilon\pi R^2}\right)\left[\left(\frac{r}{R}\right)\exp\left(-\frac{t}{\tau}\right)\right] \qquad \text{for } r < R$$

and

$$= \left(\frac{\sigma Q}{4\varepsilon\pi r^2}\right)\exp\left(-\frac{t}{\tau}\right) \qquad \text{for } R < r < R_i \qquad (16.20)$$

It is this current, which accounts for the conduction of free charge to the surface of the sphere.

It should be noted that there is a conduction current in the region $R < r < R_i$ even though there is no free-charge density in this part of the conducting sphere during the transient.

16.2.1.2 Example 2: Relaxation time of space charge in a partly filled tank

It is generally believed that when the conductivity of the medium is constant, the relaxation time is independent of the size and the shape of the container in which the charged medium (being liquid or fluid) is enclosed. Asano in his studies of the relaxation of petroleum products found that when an open surface of charged medium exists within a conducting container, the relaxation time is a function of the shape. He also found that the ratio of the new relaxation time to the conventional relaxation time has a maximum value of 2, which is independent of the different permittivities of the two media. We give below the simplified one-dimensional analysis of Asano's problem (as derived by him). When charge is generated or introduced in dielectric liquids like hydrocarbons, the charge creates an electric field, which can cause an ignition hazard, and hence extensive studies have been undertaken in this field. In hydrocarbons, the charge relaxation process obeys the exponential charge relaxation law when the conductivity is high, and the hyperbolic law when σ is relatively low. For the former, a constant conductivity, and for the latter a constant mobility are assumed. The hyperbolic law applies when σ for the liquid is less than 1 pS/m. For the present problem under discussion, a constant σ and an exponential charge decay will hold.

A simplified model of a tank, which partly contains a hydrocarbon (charge) liquid, is shown in Figure 16.1. The model contains two regions: a liquid phase, and a vapour phase.

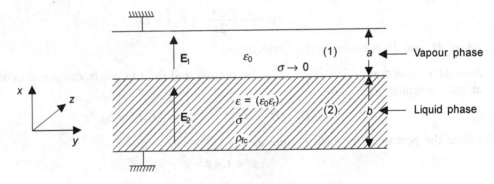

Figure 16.1 Simplified one-dimensional model of a tank containing charged liquid.

Let the charge density in the liquid be ρ_{fc}, conductivity σ, and permittivity $\varepsilon (= \varepsilon_0 \varepsilon_r)$. The free space parameters are ε_0 and $\sigma \to 0$. We assume that there is no surface charge on the interface between the liquid and the vapour.

The same three equations hold for this problem as well, i.e.

$$\nabla \times \mathbf{E} = 0 \tag{16.1}$$

$$\nabla \cdot \mathbf{D} = \rho_{fc} \tag{16.2}$$

$$\nabla \cdot \mathbf{J} = -\frac{\partial \rho_{fc}}{\partial t} \tag{16.3}$$

and the constituent relations are

$$J = \sigma E \qquad \text{and} \qquad D = \varepsilon E \tag{16.21}$$

From Eq. (16.1), it follows

$$E = - \nabla \phi \tag{16.22}$$

where ϕ is a scalar potential.

∴ For the hydrocarbon, from Eqs. (16.22) and (16.2), we get

$$\nabla^2 \phi = - \frac{\rho_{fc}}{\varepsilon} \tag{16.23}$$

and for the vapour phase

$$\nabla^2 \phi = 0 \qquad \text{i.e. Laplace's equation} \tag{16.24}$$

For the region (1), solving the one-dimensional Laplace's equation

$$E_1 = \frac{d\phi_1}{dx} = - C_1$$

and integrating the above again

$$\phi_1 = C_1 x + C_2 \tag{16.25}$$

where C_1 and C_2 are the constants of integration.

For the liquid region with the space charge,

$$E_2 = \frac{\rho_{fc} x}{\varepsilon} - D_1$$

$$\phi_2 = - \frac{\rho_{fc} x^2}{2\varepsilon} + D_1 x + D_2 \tag{16.26}$$

where D_1 and D_2 are constants of integration.

Boundary conditions. 1. Since both the bottom and the top electrodes are grounded, they are at zero potential.

$$\therefore \qquad D_2 = 0 \qquad \text{and} \qquad C_2 = -C_1(a + b)$$

Hence the potentials for each region are

$$\phi_1 = C_1(x - a - b)$$

$$\phi_2 = - \frac{\rho_{fc} x^2}{2\varepsilon} + D_1 x$$

2. On the interface $x = b$, both the potentials must be same, and as there is no surface charge on this plane, the normal component of the electric flux density must be continuous.

$$\therefore \qquad -C_1 a = - \frac{\rho_{fc} b^2}{2\varepsilon} + D_1 b \qquad \text{and} \qquad -\varepsilon_0 C_1 = \varepsilon \left(\frac{\rho_{fc} b}{\varepsilon} \right) - D_1$$

$$\therefore \qquad C_1 = \frac{- \left(\dfrac{\rho_{fc} b}{2\varepsilon} \right)}{\dfrac{a}{b} + \dfrac{\varepsilon_0}{\varepsilon}}$$

and

$$D_1 = \frac{\left(\dfrac{\rho_{fc}b}{2\varepsilon}\right)\left(\dfrac{\varepsilon_0}{\varepsilon} + \dfrac{2a}{b}\right)}{\dfrac{a}{b} + \dfrac{\varepsilon_0}{\varepsilon}}$$

Hence the potentials in each region come out to be

$$\phi_1 = \frac{\dfrac{\rho_{fc}b}{2\varepsilon}(a + b - x)}{\dfrac{a}{b} + \dfrac{\varepsilon_0}{\varepsilon}}$$

$$\phi_2 = -\left(\frac{\rho_{fc}x^2}{2\varepsilon}\right) + \frac{\left(\dfrac{\rho_{fc}bx}{2\varepsilon}\right)\left(\dfrac{\varepsilon_0}{\varepsilon} + \dfrac{2a}{b}\right)}{\dfrac{a}{b} + \dfrac{\varepsilon_0}{\varepsilon}} \tag{16.27}$$

and the corresponding **E** fields are

$$\mathbf{E}_1 = \mathbf{i}_x \left[\frac{\dfrac{\rho_{fc}b}{2\varepsilon}}{\dfrac{a}{b} + \dfrac{\varepsilon_0}{\varepsilon}} \right]$$

and

$$\mathbf{E}_2 = \mathbf{i}_x \left[\frac{\left(\dfrac{\rho_{fc}x}{\varepsilon} - \dfrac{\rho_{fc}b}{2\varepsilon}\right)\left(\dfrac{\varepsilon_0}{\varepsilon} + \dfrac{2a}{b}\right)}{\dfrac{a}{b} + \dfrac{\varepsilon_0}{\varepsilon}} \right] \tag{16.28}$$

Solution in charge decay. The enclosed control volume in the system is shown in Figure 16.1, and the surface area normal to the x-direction is taken as S. It should be noted that J_1 in the region (1)-free space is zero, because the conductivity is zero. Hence from Eq. (16.3), by integration with respect to x, we get

$$J_2S = -\frac{d}{dt}\int_0^b \rho_{fc}S dx = -\frac{d}{dt}(\rho_{fc}Sb)$$

Also

$$J_2 = -\sigma E_2 \text{ at } x = 0$$

$$\therefore \quad \sigma SE_2 = \frac{d}{dt}(\rho_{fc}Sb) \tag{16.29}$$

Combining Eq. (16.29) with (16.28) for x = 0, we get

$$\frac{\dfrac{d\rho_{fc}}{dt} + \left(\dfrac{\sigma\rho_{fc}}{2\varepsilon}\right)\left(\dfrac{\varepsilon_0}{\varepsilon} + \dfrac{2a}{b}\right)}{\dfrac{a}{b} + \dfrac{\varepsilon_0}{\varepsilon}} = 0 \tag{16.30}$$

whose solution is obtained directly as

$$\rho_{fc} = \rho_0 \exp\left(-\frac{t}{\tau_1}\right) \qquad (16.31)$$

where ρ_0 is the initial charge density, and τ_1—the new relaxation time which is given by

$$\tau_1 = \left(\frac{\varepsilon}{\sigma}\right)\left[\frac{2\left(\frac{\varepsilon_0}{\varepsilon} + \frac{a}{b}\right)}{\frac{\varepsilon_0}{\varepsilon} + \frac{2a}{b}}\right] \qquad (16.32)$$

Note that $(\varepsilon/\sigma) = \tau$, which is our conventional relaxation time. Writing $a + b = d$ and $(b/d) = h$, then

$$\frac{\tau_1}{\tau} = \frac{2\,[h + \varepsilon_r\,(1 - h)]}{h + 2\varepsilon_r\,(1 - h)} \qquad (16.33)$$

So we see that the maximum value of this ratio (τ_1/τ) is 2 and is independent of either ε_r or σ.

We can similarly solve the composite Laplacian and Poissonian field problem for the potential distribution in two or even three dimensions.

16.2.2 Media with Non-uniform Properties

In such a medium (at rest) in which the conductivity and permittivity are functions of space, a steady-state volume charge density can exist. The interface between two dissimilar media is a 'special case' of this type and the interface gradients of ε and σ are 'singularities' and hence the surface charges accumulate on the surfaces of the uniformly conducting media.

When σ and ε are functions of position in a stationary medium, the potential equation (16.9) becomes

$$\nabla \cdot (\sigma \nabla \phi) + \frac{\partial}{\partial t}\,[\nabla \cdot (\varepsilon \nabla \phi)] = 0 \qquad (16.34)$$

which cannot take the simplified form of Eq. (16.11), because σ and ε are no longer constants and they vary with the coordinate directions. We again consider a simple one-dimensional example of this type.

16.2.2.1 Example 1: A model with non-uniform properties

A material of non-uniform properties (i.e. σ and ε are functions of space coordinates) is bound by two plane parallel electrodes [Figure 16.2(a)]. An external current source drives a current through this material in the x-direction. For simplicity, we also assume σ and ε to be functions of x only. Physically such a system is created when the two electrodes with temperature difference are placed in an organic liquid. In the present one-dimensional problem, Eq. (16.34) becomes

$$\frac{\partial}{\partial x}\left[\sigma E_x + \frac{\partial}{\partial t}\,(\varepsilon E_x)\right] = 0 \qquad (16.35)$$

where $(\text{grad }\phi)_x = -E_x$. Integrating the above equation with respect to x

$$\left(\frac{\partial}{\partial t}\right)(\varepsilon E_x) + \sigma E_x = f(t) \qquad (16.36)$$

The physical interpretation of the above equation is that the sum of the displacement current and the conduction current is same all over the y–z planes. The function $f(t)$ is the current density $[i(t)/A]$ where A is the surface area of the electrodes. Hence Eq. (16.36) becomes

$$\left(\frac{\partial}{\partial t}\right)(\varepsilon E_x) + \sigma E_x = \frac{i(t)}{A} \tag{16.37}$$

Let us consider a sinusoidal time-varying driving current

$$i(t) = \text{Re}\left[\hat{I} \exp(j\omega t)\right]$$

$$\therefore \quad E_x(t) = \text{Re}\left[\hat{E}_x(x) \exp(j\omega t)\right] \tag{16.38}$$

$$\therefore \quad \hat{E}_x = \frac{\hat{I}}{A(j\omega\varepsilon + \sigma)} \tag{16.39}$$

Next we find the charge density from Eq. (16.2), which in this case becomes

$$\rho_{\text{fc}} = \nabla \cdot \mathbf{D} = \nabla \cdot (\varepsilon \mathbf{E}) = \left(\frac{\partial}{\partial x}\right)(\varepsilon E_x)$$

$$= \left(\frac{\partial}{\partial x}\right)\left[\frac{\varepsilon \hat{I} \exp(j\omega t)}{A(j\omega\varepsilon + \sigma)}\right]$$

$$\therefore \quad \hat{\rho}_{\text{fc}} = -\left(\frac{\varepsilon \hat{I}}{A}\right)\left[\frac{j\omega\left(\frac{d\varepsilon}{dx}\right) + \left(\frac{d\sigma}{dx}\right)}{(j\omega\varepsilon + \sigma)^2}\right] + \frac{\hat{I}\left(\frac{d\varepsilon}{dA}\right)}{A(j\omega\varepsilon + \sigma)} \tag{16.40}$$

For this problem, let us assume that the conductivity varies linearly with respect to x (Figure 16.2b), and ε_{r} is constant, then

$$\sigma(x) = \sigma_0 + \left(\frac{\sigma_1}{l}\right)x \tag{16.41}$$

Hence

$$\left|\hat{E}_x\right| = \frac{\left|\hat{I}\right|}{A(\omega^2\varepsilon^2 + \sigma^2)^{1/2}}$$

and

$$\left|\hat{\rho}_{\text{fc}}\right| = \frac{\varepsilon\left|\hat{I}\right|\sigma_1}{Al(\omega^2\varepsilon^2 + \sigma^2)^{1/2}} \tag{16.42}$$

E_x and ρ_{fc} distributions are shown in the Figures 16.2(c) and (d) respectively. E_x is roughly inversely proportional to x, and the charge density is inversely proportional to x^2. It should be noted that the free charge accumulation is maximum, when $\omega = 0$, i.e. the current is constant. The charge accumulation due to a non-uniform conductivity occurs in oil-immersed HVDC cables used for transmission of power.

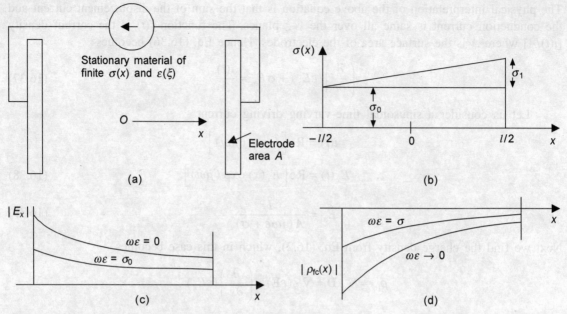

Figure 16.2   (a) A partially conducting material, bounded by plane electrodes; (b) σ distribution between the electrodes; (c) E_x distribution; and (d) ρ_{fc} distribution.

16.3   CHARGE RELAXATION WHEN THERE IS STEADY MOTION

The next aspect of charge relaxation, which we shall look at, is the effect of material motion on relaxation. Now the material properties of the media (i.e. σ and ε) are taken as constant in the bulk of the material, and change only at the interface surfaces. We again start with the general operational equation (16.9), which is

$$\nabla \cdot (\sigma \nabla \phi) + \nabla \cdot [\mathbf{v} \nabla \cdot (\varepsilon \nabla \phi)] = - \left(\frac{\partial}{\partial t} \right) [\nabla \cdot (\varepsilon \nabla \phi)] \tag{16.9}$$

To express the above equation in terms of the free-charge density, we use the equations

$$\mathbf{E} = - \nabla \phi \qquad \text{and} \qquad \nabla \cdot \mathbf{D} = \nabla \cdot (\varepsilon \mathbf{E}) = \rho_{fc}, \text{ and obtain}$$

$$\left(\frac{\sigma}{\varepsilon} \right) \rho_{fc} + \nabla \cdot (\rho_{fc} \mathbf{v}) + \left(\frac{\partial \rho_{fc}}{\partial t} \right) = 0 \tag{16.43}$$

The important case of this type is that of incompressible medium in which the material density remains constant, and the net flux of the material in a given region is zero, which means that, for the incompressible material, the divergence of the velocity must be zero (analogy to div $\mathbf{B} = 0$). Hence

$$\text{div } \mathbf{v} = 0 \tag{16.44}$$

Hence expanding the second term of Eq. (16.43)

$$\nabla \cdot (\rho_{fc} \mathbf{v}) = \mathbf{v} \cdot (\nabla \rho_{fc}) + \rho_{fc} (\nabla \cdot \mathbf{v})$$

$$= \mathbf{v} \cdot (\nabla \rho_{fc}), \text{ for incompressible medium} \tag{16.45}$$

Equation (16.43) can be rewritten as (for this case)

$$\left(\frac{\partial \rho_{fc}}{\partial t}\right) + \left(\frac{\sigma}{\varepsilon}\right)\rho_{fc} + \mathbf{v} \cdot (\nabla \rho_{fc}) = 0 \qquad (16.46)$$

This equation gives the same relaxation condition as Eq. (16.11), except that the charge relaxation now occurs with respect to the frame of the moving medium, i.e. the material motion transports the free charge as it relaxes with the time-constant (ε/σ). We shall now describe a device in which the charge is transported from a region of one potential to a region of another. The time required for a given initial distribution of charge to relax (with respect to the medium) is (ε/σ), and the time necessary for transporting the charge over a distance l with velocity $\mathbf{v}$ is (l/v). Thus the electric Reynold's number R_e:

$$R_e = \frac{\varepsilon/\sigma}{l/v} = \frac{\varepsilon v}{\sigma l} \gg 1 \qquad (16.47)$$

must be much greater than unity, if the convection is to compete with the relaxation process in deciding the location of the volume charge density.

16.3.1 Van-de-Graff Generator

This is used for generating high voltage dc power by transporting free charge against an electric field. A highly simplified model is shown in Figure 16.3. Essentially it consists of a continuous belt made of slightly conducting material, and driven by rollers at constant velocity which is

$$\mathbf{v} = \mathbf{i}_z v$$

The electrode at $z = 0$ feeds positive ions on to the surface of the belt, and the electrode at

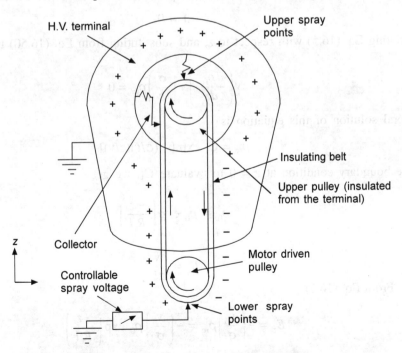

Figure 16.3 Section of a Van-de-Graff generator.

$z = l$ removes the positive charges. For our analysis, we consider these two electrodes under open-circuited condition. The belt material has constant σ and ε. The positive ions put on the belt are immobile.

The simplifying assumptions for the analysis are:

1. We consider only the portion of the belt that carries charge from

$$z = 0 \text{ to } z = l$$

2. **E** and **J** have z-component only, i.e.

$$\mathbf{E} = \mathbf{i}_z E_z \quad \text{and} \quad \mathbf{J} = \mathbf{i}_z J_z \qquad (16.48)$$

3. All variables are functions of z alone.
4. For this one-dimensional model, the effect of the applied positive ions and the induced charges in the belt can be represented by an effective free-charge density $\rho_{fc}(z)$ which also is a function of z only.
5. The boundary condition at $z = 0$ is: $\rho_{fc} = \rho_0$ $\qquad (16.49)$
6. The system is operating in steady state.

With σ constant, the constituent relation for the transport of free charges is Eq. (16.5), i.e.

$$\mathbf{J} = \sigma \mathbf{E} + \rho_{fc}\mathbf{v} \qquad (16.5)$$

Gauss' theorem [Eq. (16.2)] gives

$$\varepsilon \left(\frac{dE_z}{dz} \right) = \rho_{fc} \qquad (16.50)$$

For this problem, the open-circuit operation implies that

$$\mathbf{J} = 0 \qquad (16.51)$$

Differentiating Eq. (16.5) with respect to z, and substituting from Eq. (16.50) to eliminate E_z, we get

$$\mathrm{v} \left(\frac{d\rho_{fc}}{dz} \right) + \left(\frac{\sigma}{\varepsilon} \right) \rho_{fc} = 0 \qquad (16.52)$$

The general solution of this equation is

$$\rho_{fc} = C_1 \exp \left[- (\sigma/\varepsilon)(z/\mathrm{v}) \right] \qquad (16.53)$$

Using the boundary condition at $z = 0$ to evaluate C_1, we get

$$\rho_{fc} = \rho_0 \exp \left(\frac{-z}{R_e l} \right)$$

where

$$R_e = \frac{\varepsilon \mathrm{v}}{\sigma l} \qquad (16.54)$$

$\therefore$ From Eq. (16.5),

$$E_z = - \left(\frac{\mathrm{v}}{\sigma} \right) \rho_{fc} = - \left(\frac{\mathrm{v}}{\sigma} \right) \rho_0 \exp \left(\frac{-z}{R_e l} \right) \qquad (16.55)$$

and hence the open-circuit (o.c.) voltage is

$$V_{o.c.} = - \int_{z=0}^{z=1} E_z dz = \left(\frac{R_e^2 l^2}{\varepsilon} \right) \rho_0 \left[1 - \exp\left(-\frac{1}{R_e} \right) \right] \qquad (16.56)$$

16.4 CHARGE RELAXATION WITH MOTION AND SINUSOIDAL EXCITATION

We now consider a problem of charge relaxation, when it is associated with motion and sinusoidal excitation. This example shows the distinguishing features of relaxation and magnetic diffusion, and also an application of the phenomenon to measure the velocity of a moving medium.

A slightly conducting thin slab (of characteristic properties σ, ε) is moving to the right with a constant velocity **v** (as shown in Figure 16.4) between two plane parallel electrodes,

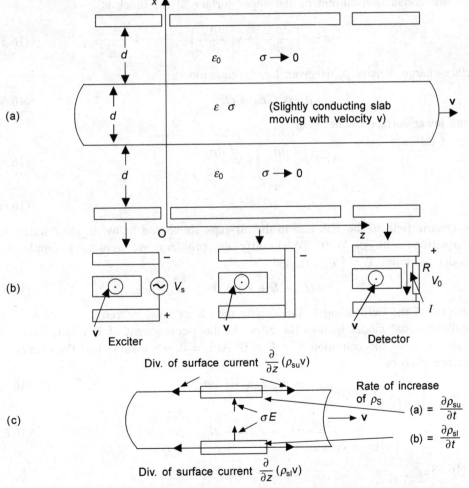

Figure 16.4 (a) A slightly conducting thin slab, moving to the right with constant velocity **v** through electric fields imposed and constrained as shown in (b); (c) conduction currents normal to the surfaces produce a surface charge accumulation as shown.

which are sub-divided into three sections with different terminations as shown in Figure 16.4(b). In the section to the left, the electrodes are excited by a sinusoidally varying potential.

Since the slab is insulated from the electrodes by the air-gaps between them, the charge would relax to the surface so as to prevent the externally imposed field from entering it. Hence as the slab leaves the exciter region of the electrodes at $z = 0$, there would be a sinusoidally varying surface-charge density ($\pm \rho_0$) on the upper and the lower surfaces of the slab respectively. As the slab passes through the region $0 < z < l$, the surface charges, which had been induced in the exciter region, tend to relax, and by the time they reach the detector region [the right section of the electrode in Figure 16.4(b)], the surface-charge densities get considerably attenuated. The charges, which remain on the surface by this time, induce image charges on the electrodes, which result a current through the resistance R, thereby generating an output signal V_0. Because of the charge relaxation, this output signal can be used as a measure of the velocity of the block.

There is no charge inside the moving slab, except on its surfaces as the normal conduction current leads to an accumulation of charges on the surface, which is convected by the motion of the slab. Hence, the conduction current on the upper surface of the block is

$$= \sigma E = \left(\frac{\partial \rho_{su}}{\partial t} \right) + v \left(\frac{\partial \rho_{su}}{\partial z} \right) \tag{16.57}$$

where the surface-charge density ρ_{su} is given by the equation

$$\rho_{su} = \varepsilon_0 E_u - \varepsilon E \tag{16.58}$$

Similarly for the lower surface of the block

$$- \sigma E = \left(\frac{\partial \rho_{sl}}{\partial t} \right) + v \left(\frac{\partial \rho_{sl}}{\partial z} \right) \tag{16.59}$$

where

$$\rho_{sl} = \varepsilon E - \varepsilon_0 E_l \tag{16.60}$$

In general, the electric field in the slab and in the air-gaps above and below it, must satisfy the electric field equations with $\rho_{fc} = 0$. To simplify the problem, we assume a simple one-dimensional model, assuming $\mathbf{E} = \mathbf{i}_x E(z, t)$, and

$$d(E_u + E + E_l) = 0 \tag{16.61}$$

because the integral of the field along a line joining the plates must be zero.

This one-dimensional model ignores the effect of the z-component of $\mathbf{E}$ which does exist and can be evaluated from the condition $\nabla \times \mathbf{E} = 0$. At $z = 0$, we assume that the exciter has induced the surface charges

$$\rho_{sl} = - \rho_{su} = \rho_0 \sin \omega t \tag{16.62}$$

$\therefore$ From Eq. (16.61),

$$E = - (E_u + E_l) = - 2E_u \tag{16.63}$$
$$\text{(from symmetry considerations } E_u = E_l)$$

and from Eq. (16.58),

$$E = - \frac{2\rho_{su}}{\varepsilon_0 + 2\varepsilon} \tag{16.64}$$

On substituting for E in Eq. (16.57),

$$\left(\frac{\partial \rho_{su}}{\partial t}\right) + v\left(\frac{\partial \rho_{su}}{\partial z}\right) + \left(\frac{2\sigma}{\varepsilon_0 + 2\varepsilon}\right)\rho_{su} = 0 \tag{16.65}$$

Similarly the corresponding equation for the lower surface can be derived ($\rho_{su} = -\rho_{sl}$ and $E_u = E_l$).

We assume the steady-state solution of the form

$$\rho_{su} = \text{Re}\left[\hat{\rho}_{su}(z)\exp(j\omega t)\right] \tag{16.66}$$

and substituting in Eq. (16.65), gives

$$\left(\frac{\partial \hat{\rho}_{su}}{\partial z}\right) + \left[\frac{2\sigma}{(\varepsilon_0 + 2\varepsilon)\,v} + \frac{j\omega}{v}\right]\rho_{su} = 0 \tag{16.67}$$

The solution to this equation is

$$\rho_{su}(z, t) = \rho_0 \exp\left(-\frac{z}{R_e l}\right)\sin\omega\left(t - \frac{z}{v}\right)$$

where

$$R_e = \frac{(\varepsilon_0 + 2\varepsilon)\,v}{2\sigma l} \tag{16.68}$$

where R_e is the electric Reynold's number, and gives a measure of the exponential damping effect, similar to that shown in Figure 15.2 of Section 15.2. Thus the relaxing charge appears as a damped wave propagating to the right with a phase velocity v and an attenuating factor whose exponent is $(-1/R_e l)$. It should be noted that the relaxation wave propagates by virtue of the material movement (as distinct from the case of magnetic diffusion where the propagating wave existed even in stationary medium), and the attenuation was determined by the combination of the material properties and the velocity of the material.

16.5 TRAVELLING WAVE CHARGE RELAXATION IN A MOVING CONDUCTOR

The physical configuration of the problem is shown in Figure 16.5. This is a slightly conducting, semi-infinite block moving to the right with a velocity v, just below a segmented electrode, which supports a travelling wave of potential given by

$$V = \text{Re}\left[\hat{V}\exp\{j(\omega t - kz)\}\right] \tag{16.69}$$

The conducting material [region (2)] has the material characteristics ε and σ which are constant and uniform, and moves to the right with constant velocity $\mathbf{v} = \mathbf{i}_z v$. For this material, there is no bulk free-charge inside. The surface charges exist on the interface plane $x = 0$ and its distribution is determined by the motion of the medium and the velocity of the travelling wave of potential.

Since there is no free charge either in region (1) or in region (2), the operational equation for the potential distribution for both the regions will be Laplacian, i.e.

$$\nabla^2\phi = \frac{\partial^2\phi}{dx^2} + \frac{\partial^2\phi}{\partial y^2} = 0 \tag{16.70}$$

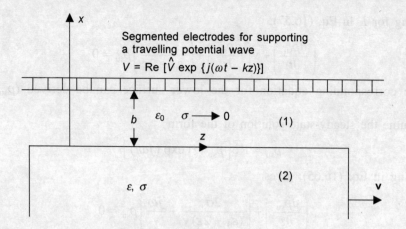

Figure 16.5 A semi-infinite block of slightly conducting material moving to the right with a constant velocity $\mathbf{v} = \mathbf{i}_z v$.

As can be seen from Figure 16.5, the problem would be two-dimensional, and hence there would be no variation in the y-direction (i.e. $\partial/\partial y \equiv 0$). To match the condition of the source potential as given by Eq. (16.69), we assume the potential to be of the form

$$\phi = \text{Re}\left[\hat{\phi} \exp\{j(\omega t - kz)\}\right] \tag{16.71}$$

in both the regions (1) and (2).

In the region (1), the potential function will take the form

$$\hat{\phi}_1 = A \sinh(kx) + B \cosh(kx) \tag{16.72}$$

where A and B are arbitrary constants to be determined by the boundary conditions.

In the region (2), the potential function will take the form

$$\hat{\phi}_2 = C \exp(+kx) \tag{16.73}$$

This assumes that k is +ve, since the potential will not go to infinity as $x \to (-\infty)$.

We need three boundary conditions to evaluate the three unknowns A, B, and C.

Boundary conditions

1. At $x = b$, $V = \text{Re}\left[\hat{V} \exp\{j(\omega t - kz)\}\right]$ (16.69)

2. At $x = 0$, $\hat{\phi}_1(0) = \hat{\phi}_2(0)$ (16.74)

3. At $x = 0$, $\rho_{S0} = \varepsilon_0 E_{1x} - \varepsilon E_{2x} = -\varepsilon_0\left(\dfrac{\partial \phi_1}{\partial x}\right) + \varepsilon\left(\dfrac{\partial \phi_2}{\partial x}\right)$ (16.75)

(conservation of the charge on the interface surface).

This condition, expressed in terms of the conduction current normal to the interface gives an increase in the surface charge (measured in a frame moving with the material) as

$$-\sigma\left(\frac{\partial \phi_2}{\partial x}\right) = \left[\left(\frac{\partial}{\partial t}\right) + \mathbf{v}\left(\frac{\partial}{\partial z}\right)\right]\left[-\varepsilon_0\left(\frac{\partial \phi_1}{\partial x}\right) + \varepsilon\left(\frac{\partial \phi_2}{\partial x}\right)\right] \tag{16.76}$$

For the assumed travelling wave solution of Eq. (16.71), this becomes

$$-\sigma\left(\frac{\partial \hat{\phi}_2}{\partial x}\right) = j(\omega - kv)\left[-\varepsilon_0\left(\frac{\partial \hat{\phi}_1}{\partial x}\right) + \varepsilon\left(\frac{\partial \hat{\phi}_2}{\partial x}\right)\right] \qquad (16.77)$$

∴ Using the boundary condition equations of (16.69), (16.74), and (16.77), we get

$$A \sinh (kb) + B \cosh (kb) = \hat{V}$$
$$B - C = 0$$
$$AjS - C\left[1 + jS\left(\frac{\varepsilon}{\varepsilon_0}\right)\right] = 0 \qquad (16.78)$$

where S = the normalized frequency measured in the moving frame of the material, normalized to the relaxation time

$$= (\omega - kv)\frac{\varepsilon_0}{\sigma} \qquad (16.79)$$

Evaluating the unknowns, we obtain

$$\phi_1 = \text{Re}\left(\frac{V}{D}\right)\left[\left(1 + jS\frac{\varepsilon}{\varepsilon_0}\right)\sinh (kx) + jS \cosh (kx)\right]\left[\exp \{j(\omega t - kz)\}\right]$$

$$\phi_2 = \text{Re}\left(\frac{\hat{V}}{D}\right)\left[jS \exp (kz) \exp\{j(\omega t - kz)\}\right] \qquad (16.80)$$

where

$$D = \left[\left\{1 + jS\left(\frac{\varepsilon}{\varepsilon_0}\right)\right\}\sinh (kb) + jS \cosh (kb)\right] \qquad (16.81)$$

For the range of values of S, there are two limiting cases:

1. $S = 0$, i.e.

$$\phi_1 = \text{Re}\, \hat{V}\left[\frac{\sinh (kx)}{\sinh (kb)}\right]\left[\exp \{j(\omega t - kz)\}\right]$$
$$\phi_2 = 0 \qquad (16.82)$$

i.e. the medium behaves as perfectly conducting, and there is no penetration of the **E**-field in the moving medium.

2. When $S \to \infty$ (i.e. very large),

$$\phi_1 = \text{Re}\, \hat{V}\left[\frac{\sinh (kx) + \left(\dfrac{\varepsilon}{\varepsilon_0}\right)\cosh (kx)}{\sinh (kb) + \left(\dfrac{\varepsilon}{\varepsilon_0}\right)\cosh (kb)}\right] \times \left[\exp \{j(\omega t - kz)\}\right]$$

$$\phi_2 = \text{Re}\, \hat{V}\left[\frac{\exp (kx) \exp \{j(\omega t - kz)\}}{\sinh (kb) + \left(\dfrac{\varepsilon}{\varepsilon_0}\right)\cosh (kb)}\right] \qquad (16.83)$$

In this case, the electric field completely penetrates the moving medium, i.e. the moving block behaves like a perfectly insulating material with no free charges at the surface, as can be seen by putting $x = 0$ in the above equations. The reason is that in this high frequency limit, one time-period of the excitation is not sufficient time for appreciable free-charge to relax to the surface. Since the magnitude of the parameter S depends directly on both the frequency ω of the imposed travelling wave excitation as well as on the velocity v of the medium, the insulating behaviour of the medium (i.e. the field penetration in the block) can be obtained by controlling either of these parameters, i.e. either increasing the frequency ω of the imposed excitation or increasing the velocity v of the moving block.

16.6   SOME COMMENTS ON THE CHARGE DECAY IN CONDUCTING MEDIA

Recently, a number of investigators have raised questions about the validity of the relaxation equation [Eqs. (16.11) and (16.12)] for the conductors. It has been argued that for good conductors, this equation gives too small a value of the relaxation time τ, which can be practically correct. It has been argued that the cause for this discrepancy is the assumption of constant conductivity ($=\sigma$) under the conditions of varying electric field. A more correct approach would be to take the 'mobility' (i.e. the magnitude of the drift velocity v per unit electric field) as constant instead, i.e.

$$\mu\,(\text{mobility}) = \frac{|\mathbf{v}|}{E}$$

(In this section μ stands for the mobility of the charges, and should not be confused with the notation for the magnetic permeability used elsewhere in this book.) The electrical conductivity is the sum of the electron and hole contributions

$$\sigma = ne\mu_e + pe\mu_e$$

where n and p are the concentrations of the electrons and holes in the medium (and e the electron charge).

We have merely stated this point here (in a textbook of this level) as a matter of interest and do not intend to pursue the subject in depth, which is really the domain of specialists.

PROBLEMS

16.1   Calculate the relaxation time for ethyl alcohol, for which $\varepsilon_r = 26$ and $\sigma = 3 \times 10^{-4}$ mho/m.

Ans.: $\tau \approx 10^{-6}$ sec.

16.2   In the problem of Section 16.2.2.1 (media with non-uniform properties), if the permittivity ε varied linearly with x, along with the conductivity, then

$$\varepsilon(x) = \varepsilon_1 + \frac{\varepsilon_2}{l}\,x, \qquad \sigma(x) = \sigma_1 + \frac{\sigma_2}{l}\,x \qquad \text{[referring to Figure 16.2(a)]}$$

Show that the free charge density is given by

$$\hat{\rho}_{fc} = -\frac{I}{a}\left[\frac{\left(\varepsilon_1 + \dfrac{\varepsilon_2}{l}\,x\right)\left(j\omega\dfrac{\varepsilon_2}{l} + \dfrac{\sigma_2}{l}\right)}{\left(j\omega\varepsilon + \sigma\right)^2} + \frac{\dfrac{\varepsilon_2}{l}}{\left(j\omega\varepsilon + \sigma\right)} \right]$$

Write down the expression for the free charge density, when the permittivity $\varepsilon(x)$ changes linearly with x, while keeping the conductivity σ constant.

17 Electromagnetic Waves

17.1 INTRODUCTION

One of the most brilliant achievements of Maxwell's theory of electromagnetism was the prediction of the existence of electromagnetic waves. This was confirmed experimentally twenty years later by the work of the German physicist 'Heinrich Hertz (1857–Jan 1894)' who made this very significant discovery in the short-span of his life of 37 years. Hertz was a very bright student who started studying engineering but changed over to physics at the University of Berlin under Hermann von Helmholtz and Gustav R. Kirchhoff, who were of the mechanistic school of thought (i.e. action at a distance) on the continent as against the field concept propounded by Maxwell in Britain. Up to mid-1880s, Hertz with his mechanistic background, found the field theory and the vector approach from the Scottish/English schools rather baffling. Yet Hertz got convinced of the reality of the electric and the magnetic wave radiation. His first experiment, with a circular loop of wire with a tiny gap between the ends detecting a spark from a discharge in a nearby induction coil, with no physical contact between the two, was the first properly understood transmission and reception of electromagnetic radiation through air.

In the present chapter, we shall start our study with the simplest type of wave, i.e. the uniform plane wave, and then develop the subject matter further. Initially we shall deal with the presence of these waves in free space, and then consider other types of media, such as conductors, dielectrics, etc. At this stage of our study, we shall not deal with the sources of the electromagnetic waves, till Chapter 19.

Our starting point would be, as in the case of the eddy currents and the magnetic diffusion, the Maxwell's equations, the only difference being that now we ignore the conduction current term of Eq. (12.11) or (12.18) from Chapter 12 (we shall make this simplifying assumption for all loss-less ideal media). Thus our operating equation would be the first limiting case of the vector Helmholtz equation, i.e. Eq. (12.38) which are

$$\nabla^2 \mathbf{H} + \beta^2 \mathbf{H} = 0 \tag{12.38a}$$

$$\nabla^2 \mathbf{E} + \beta^2 \mathbf{E} = 0 \tag{12.38b}$$

where $\beta^2 = \omega^2 \mu_0 \varepsilon_0 = \omega^2/c^2$, $c = 1/\sqrt{\mu_0 \varepsilon_0}$, in free space. Sometimes in place of β we use the notation k, which is also called the wave number of the wave.

17.2 UNIFORM PLANE ELECTROMAGNETIC WAVE IN FREE SPACE

In fact, we have already met with and discussed the nature and the behaviour of these waves earlier in Chapter 12, Section 12.6. For that analysis, we had simplified the associated mathematics very significantly by rotating the coordinate system such that the **E** vector coincided with the x-axis. This adjustment maintained the complete generality of the problem and simplified the analysis considerably. However such simplification is not always possible. There are configurations and considerations when it is not possible to fiddle with the coordinate system to simplify the problem. So now, we keep our analysis general and make no simplifying arrangements at the start of our problem (as we had done in Section 12.6). As before, we start with the Maxwell's equations, neglecting the conduction current **J**; i.e.

$$\nabla \times \mathbf{E} = -\frac{\partial \mathbf{B}}{\partial t}, \quad \nabla \cdot \mathbf{B} = 0 \tag{17.1}$$

$$\nabla \times \mathbf{H} = -\frac{\partial \mathbf{D}}{\partial t}, \quad \nabla \cdot \mathbf{D} = 0 \qquad \text{(there is no charge in the medium)} \tag{17.2}$$

and the constituent relations, relevant to our present problem

$$\mathbf{B} = \mu_0 \mu_r \mathbf{H} = \mu \mathbf{H} \qquad \text{and} \qquad \mathbf{D} = \varepsilon_0 \varepsilon_r \mathbf{E} = \varepsilon \mathbf{E} \tag{17.3}$$

As we have seen in Section 12.3, these equations reduce to

$$\nabla^2 \mathbf{H} = \mu \varepsilon \left(\frac{\partial^2 \mathbf{H}}{\partial t^2} \right) \tag{17.4a}$$

$$\nabla^2 \mathbf{E} = \mu \varepsilon \left(\frac{\partial^2 \mathbf{E}}{\partial t^2} \right) \tag{17.4b}$$

which are wave equations.

We now define the uniform plane electromagnetic waves (in words):

*These are waves in which the field vectors **E** and **H** have constant values of magnitude and phase on planes perpendicular to the direction of propagation.*

Let us assume the direction of propagation to be the $+z$-axis of our coordinate system. Then, by definition, **E** and **H** will have constant values on all planes perpendicular to the z-axis.

$$\therefore \qquad \frac{\partial \mathbf{E}}{\partial x} = \frac{\partial \mathbf{E}}{\partial y} = \frac{\partial \mathbf{H}}{\partial x} = \frac{\partial \mathbf{H}}{\partial y} = 0 \tag{17.5a}$$

Note that, so far, we have imposed no constraints on the vectors **E** and **H**. However it will come out later that these vectors **E** and **H** can have no components in the z-direction, i.e.

$$E_z = 0, \quad H_z = 0 \tag{17.5b}$$

(At this stage we impose no such condition.)

$\therefore$ The wave equations derived from the Maxwell's equations reduce to

$$\nabla^2 \mathbf{H} \equiv \frac{\partial^2 \mathbf{H}}{\partial z^2} = \mu\varepsilon \left(\frac{\partial^2 \mathbf{H}}{\partial t^2} \right) \tag{17.6}$$

which implies

$$\frac{\partial^2 H_x}{\partial z^2} = \mu\varepsilon \left(\frac{\partial^2 H_x}{\partial t^2} \right), \quad \frac{\partial^2 H_y}{\partial z^2} = \mu\varepsilon \left(\frac{\partial^2 H_y}{\partial t^2} \right), \quad \text{and} \quad \frac{\partial^2 H_z}{\partial z^2} = \mu\varepsilon \left(\frac{\partial^2 H_z}{\partial t^2} \right) \tag{17.7}$$

and

$$\nabla^2 \mathbf{E} \equiv \frac{\partial^2 \mathbf{E}}{\partial z^2} = \mu\varepsilon \left(\frac{\partial^2 \mathbf{E}}{\partial t^2} \right) \tag{17.8}$$

which implies

$$\frac{\partial^2 E_x}{\partial z^2} = \mu\varepsilon \left(\frac{\partial^2 E_x}{\partial t^2} \right), \quad \frac{\partial^2 E_y}{\partial z^2} = \mu\varepsilon \left(\frac{\partial^2 E_y}{\partial t^2} \right), \quad \text{and} \quad \frac{\partial^2 E_z}{\partial z^2} = \mu\varepsilon \left(\frac{\partial^2 E_z}{\partial t^2} \right) \tag{17.9}$$

i.e. six similar equations which will reduce to four similar equations.

To start with, we solve for $H_{x:}$. The expression for the solution is of the form

$$H_{x:} = f_1(z - ut) + f_2(z + ut) \tag{17.10}$$

where u is independent of t.

Proof. Let

$$(z - ut) = m, \quad (z + ut) = n \tag{17.11}$$

then

$$\frac{\partial m}{\partial z} = 1, \quad \frac{\partial n}{\partial z} = 1, \quad \frac{\partial m}{\partial t} = -u, \quad \frac{\partial n}{\partial t} = +u \tag{17.12}$$

$$\therefore \qquad \frac{\partial H_x}{\partial z} = \left(\frac{\partial f_1}{\partial m} \right)\left(\frac{\partial m}{\partial z} \right) + \left(\frac{\partial f_2}{\partial n} \right)\left(\frac{\partial n}{\partial z} \right) = \left(\frac{\partial f_1}{\partial m} \right) + \left(\frac{\partial f_2}{\partial n} \right) \tag{17.13}$$

and

$$\frac{\partial^2 H_x}{\partial z^2} = \left(\frac{\partial}{\partial z} \right)\left(\frac{\partial f_1}{\partial m} + \frac{\partial f_2}{\partial n} \right) = \left(\frac{\partial^2 f_1}{\partial m^2} \right) + \left(\frac{\partial^2 f_2}{\partial n^2} \right) \tag{17.14}$$

and

$$\frac{\partial H_x}{\partial t} = \left(\frac{\partial f_1}{\partial m} \right)\left(\frac{\partial m}{\partial t} \right) + \left(\frac{\partial f_2}{\partial n} \right)\left(\frac{\partial n}{\partial t} \right) = -u\left(\frac{\partial f_1}{\partial m} \right) + u\left(\frac{\partial f_2}{\partial n} \right) \tag{17.15}$$

and hence

$$\frac{\partial^2 H_x}{\partial t^2} = \left(\frac{\partial}{\partial m} \right)\left[-u\left(\frac{\partial f_1}{\partial m} \right) \right]\left(\frac{\partial m}{\partial t} \right) + \left(\frac{\partial}{\partial n} \right)\left[u\left(\frac{\partial f_2}{\partial n} \right) \right]\left(\frac{\partial n}{\partial t} \right)$$

$$= u^2 \left(\frac{\partial^2 f_1}{\partial m^2} \right) + u^2 \left(\frac{\partial^2 f_2}{\partial n^2} \right) = u^2 \left[\left(\frac{\partial^2 f_1}{\partial m^2} \right) + \left(\frac{\partial^2 f_2}{\partial n^2} \right) \right] \tag{17.16}$$

$\therefore$ From Eqs. (17.14) and (17.16), we obtain

$$\frac{\partial^2 H_x}{\partial z^2} = \left(\frac{1}{u^2}\right)\left(\frac{\partial^2 H_x}{\partial t^2}\right) \tag{17.17}$$

which is same as Eq. (17.7) for H_x when

$$u = \frac{1}{\sqrt{\mu \varepsilon}} \tag{17.18}$$

Thus each term, i.e.

$$f_1(z - ut) \quad \text{or} \quad f_2(z + ut) \tag{17.19}$$

is a solution of the **H** and **E** equation.

The sum of the two terms is a general solution.

Let us consider the first part of the solution, i.e.

$$H_{x:} = f_1(z - ut) \tag{17.20}$$

which is the equation of a wave travelling in the +z-direction. The diagram (Figure 17.1) shows $H_{x:}$ at $t = 0$ and $t = 1$, i.e. after 1 second, it will have the same distribution as it had at $t = 0$, i.e. the same solution in x- and y-coordinates, but it will be shifted by a distance u along the z-axis in the positive direction.

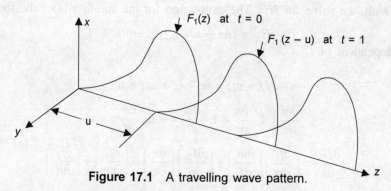

Figure 17.1 A travelling wave pattern.

Thus the wave $H_{x:} = f_1(z - ut)$ moves a distance u along the z-axis in one second.

$\therefore$ Its velocity $= u = \dfrac{1}{\sqrt{\mu_0 \mu_r \varepsilon_0 \varepsilon_r}} =$ velocity of light [in free space $(= c)$].

Similarly it can be proved that $H_{x:} = f_2(z + ut)$ is a wave moving with velocity u in the $(-z)$-direction. In general, f_2 is not same as f_1, and hence the two waves need not necessarily have the same shape. In some cases, only one of these waves may be present, i.e. an isolated transmitting aerial. In other cases, the outgoing wave may be reflected back, thus producing two waves travelling in opposite directions at a point.

The most common type of wave is the 'sinusoidal wave', and examples of this type are: light waves, radio waves, etc. By solving the wave equation of the other components of **E** and **H**, we obtain relations of the same form. The **E** and **H** waves cannot be independent of one another because of the curl equations of Maxwell, i.e.

$$\nabla \times \mathbf{E} = -\mu_0 \mu_r \left(\frac{\partial \mathbf{H}}{\partial t}\right) \quad \text{and} \quad \nabla \times \mathbf{H} = \varepsilon_0 \varepsilon_r \left(\frac{\partial \mathbf{D}}{\partial t}\right)$$

Hence, to find the relationship between the components of **E** and **H**, we rewrite the equations for the scalar components of the field vectors from the above two equations; rewriting in the form:

$$\frac{\partial E_z}{\partial y} - \frac{\partial E_y}{\partial z} = -\mu\left(\frac{\partial H_x}{\partial t}\right) \tag{17.21a}$$

$$\frac{\partial E_x}{\partial z} - \frac{\partial E_z}{\partial x} = -\mu\left(\frac{\partial H_y}{\partial t}\right) \tag{17.21b}$$

$$\frac{\partial E_y}{\partial x} - \frac{\partial E_x}{\partial y} = -\mu\left(\frac{\partial H_z}{\partial t}\right) \tag{17.21c}$$

$$\frac{\partial H_z}{\partial y} - \frac{\partial H_y}{\partial z} = \varepsilon\left(\frac{\partial E_x}{\partial t}\right) \tag{17.22a}$$

$$\frac{\partial H_x}{\partial z} - \frac{\partial H_z}{\partial x} = \varepsilon\left(\frac{\partial E_y}{\partial t}\right) \tag{17.22b}$$

$$\frac{\partial H_y}{\partial x} - \frac{\partial H_x}{\partial y} = \varepsilon\left(\frac{\partial E_z}{\partial t}\right) \tag{17.22c}$$

But for plane waves, we have defined $\partial \mathbf{E}/\partial x = 0 = \partial \mathbf{E}/\partial y$, i.e.

$$\frac{\partial E_z}{\partial x} = \frac{\partial E_z}{\partial y} = \frac{\partial E_y}{\partial x} = \frac{\partial E_y}{\partial y} = \frac{\partial E_x}{\partial x} = \frac{\partial E_x}{\partial y} = 0 \tag{17.23}$$

and similarly for **H**, i.e.

$$\frac{\partial H_z}{\partial x} = \frac{\partial H_z}{\partial y} = \frac{\partial H_y}{\partial x} = \frac{\partial H_y}{\partial y} = \frac{\partial H_x}{\partial x} = \frac{\partial H_x}{\partial y} = 0 \tag{17.24}$$

Substituting from Eqs. (17.23) and (17.24) in Eqs. (17.21) and (17.22), we obtain

$$H_z = 0 \quad \text{and} \quad E_z = 0 \tag{17.25}$$

and

$$\frac{\partial E_y}{\partial z} = \mu\left(\frac{\partial H_x}{\partial t}\right) \tag{17.26a}$$

$$\frac{\partial E_x}{\partial z} = -\mu\left(\frac{\partial H_y}{\partial t}\right) \tag{17.26b}$$

$$\frac{\partial H_y}{\partial z} = -\varepsilon\left(\frac{\partial E_x}{\partial t}\right) \tag{17.27a}$$

$$\frac{\partial H_x}{\partial z} = \varepsilon\left(\frac{\partial E_y}{\partial t}\right) \tag{17.27b}$$

But from Eq. (17.20), we have $H_{x:} = f_1(z - ut)$.

$$\therefore \quad \frac{\partial H_x}{\partial z} = f_1'(z - ut), \text{ where } f_1' \text{ is the derivative of } f_1 \text{ with respect to } (z - ut).$$

But

$$\frac{\partial H_x}{\partial z} = \varepsilon \left(\frac{\partial E_y}{\partial t} \right) \quad \text{and} \quad \therefore \frac{\partial E_y}{\partial t} = \left(\frac{1}{\varepsilon} \right) f_1'(z - ut)$$

$\therefore$ Integrating with respect to time,

$$E_y = -\left(\frac{1}{u\varepsilon} \right) f_1 (z - ut) = -\left(\frac{1}{u\varepsilon} \right) H_x.$$

But $u = 1/\sqrt{\mu\varepsilon}$

$\therefore$
$$E_y = - \sqrt{\frac{\mu}{\varepsilon}} \, H_x., \text{ and similarly } E_x = \sqrt{\frac{\mu}{\varepsilon}} \, H_y \qquad (17.28)$$

$$\therefore \quad \frac{|\mathbf{E}|}{|\mathbf{H}|} = \sqrt{\frac{\mu}{\varepsilon}} \qquad (17.29)$$

where $\mathbf{E}$ and $\mathbf{H}$ are perpendicular to each other, and also perpendicular to the direction of propagation. The rotation from the electric field vector $\mathbf{E}$ to the magnetizing intensity vector $\mathbf{H}$ is right-handed about the direction of propagation. The ratio of $|\mathbf{E}| / |\mathbf{H}| \left(= \sqrt{\mu/\varepsilon} \right)$ at any point in space is known as the 'characteristic or wave impedance of the material'. In free space,

$$|\mathbf{E}| = \sqrt{\frac{\mu_0}{\varepsilon_0}} \, |\mathbf{H}| = Z_0 \, |\mathbf{H}| \qquad (17.30)$$

where Z_0 = characteristic impedance of free space. Its units: The unit of $\mathbf{E}$ is volts/metre, of $\mathbf{H}$ is amp-turn/metre, and hence the unit of Z is volts/amp or ohms (Ω).

In free space, the velocity

$$u_0 = (\mu_0 \varepsilon_0)^{-\frac{1}{2}} = c = 2.998 \times 10^8 \text{ metres/sec} \qquad (17.31)$$

i.e. the velocity of light.

The most common forms of electrical waves vary sinusoidally with time and position. If the frequency is $= f$ Hz, and the wavelength $= \lambda$, then the frequency of repetition of the wave pattern is

$$f = \frac{u}{\lambda} \quad \text{or} \quad f\lambda = u \qquad (17.32)$$

The angular frequency ω is

$$\omega = 2\pi f = \frac{2\pi u}{\lambda} \qquad (17.33)$$

$$\therefore \quad \frac{\omega}{u} = \frac{2\pi}{\lambda} = \beta \text{ (or sometimes } k) \qquad (17.34)$$

where β is the wave number of the wave.

So we can now write the general expressions for both the electric and the associated magnetic wave, i.e.

$$E_x = E_{Fx} \sin \left[\left(\frac{2\pi}{\lambda} \right)(ut - z) \right] + E_{Bx} \sin \left[\left(\frac{2\pi}{\lambda} \right)(ut + z) \right]$$

$$= E_{Fx} \sin\left[\omega\left(t - \frac{z}{u}\right)\right] + E_{Bx} \sin\left[\omega\left(t + \frac{z}{u}\right)\right]$$

$$= E_{Fx} \sin(\omega t - \beta z) + E_{Bx} \sin(\omega t + \beta z) \tag{17.35}$$

Similarly,

$$H_x = H_{Fx} \sin(\omega t - \beta z) + H_{Bx} \sin(\omega t + \beta z) \tag{17.36}$$

where

E_{Fx} = amplitude of the x-component of the forward travelling **E** wave

E_{Bx} = amplitude of the x-component of the backward travelling **E** wave

Similarly for the **H** wave.

Usually the exponential equation and the complex j notation are used, i.e.

$$E_x = E_{Fx} \exp[j(\omega t - \beta z)] + E_{Bx} \exp[j(\omega t + \beta z)] \tag{17.37a}$$

and

$$H_x = H_{Fx} \exp[j(\omega t - \beta z)] + H_{Bx} \exp[j(\omega t + \beta z)] \tag{17.37b}$$

It should be noted that the forward and the backward travelling waves involve a sign change in their corresponding characteristic equations, i.e.

$$E_{Fx} = \sqrt{\frac{\mu}{\varepsilon}} \, H_{Fy}, \quad E_{Fy} = -\sqrt{\frac{\mu}{\varepsilon}} \, H_{Fx:} \tag{17.38a}$$

and

$$E_{Bx} = -\sqrt{\frac{\mu}{\varepsilon}} \, H_{By}, \quad E_{By} = \sqrt{\frac{\mu}{\varepsilon}} \, H_{Bx:} \tag{17.38b}$$

$\therefore$ The relations of Eqs. (17.28) and (17.29) also hold for both the forward-going and the backward-going waves, i.e.

$$\frac{E_{Fx}}{H_{Fy}} = -\frac{E_{Fx}}{H_{Fx}} = \sqrt{\frac{\mu}{\varepsilon}} = Z \tag{17.39a}$$

$$-\frac{E_{Bx}}{H_{By}} = \frac{E_{By}}{H_{Bx}} = \sqrt{\frac{\mu}{\varepsilon}} = Z \tag{17.39b}$$

i.e. **E** and **H** are perpendicular to one another in each travelling wave, and the ratio of E to H is same in both the waves.

The vector ($\mathbf{E} \times \mathbf{H}$), i.e. the Poynting vector for the wave follows the direction of propagation of the wave in each case.

So next, we consider the energy relations for the electromagnetic wave.

$\therefore$ Stored energy in the electric field/unit volume = W_e

$$= \frac{\varepsilon |\mathbf{E}|^2}{2} = \left(\frac{\varepsilon}{2}\right)\left(E_x^2 + E_y^2\right) \tag{17.40}$$

and, the stored energy in the magnetic field/unit volume = W_m

$$= \frac{\mu |\mathbf{H}|^2}{2} = \left(\frac{\mu}{2}\right)\left(H_x^2 + H_y^2\right) \tag{17.41}$$

But, Eq. (17.40) = Eq. (17.41), i.e.

$$\left(\frac{\varepsilon}{2}\right)\left(E_x^2 + E_y^2\right) = \left(\frac{\mu}{2}\right)\left(H_x^2 + H_y^2\right) \tag{17.42}$$

∴ The energy density at each point, at each instant, is equally divided between the electric and the magnetic energy.

Poynting vector for the forward wave = $E_{Fx}H_{Fy} - E_{Fy}H_{Fx}$

$$= \left(\frac{1}{Z}\right)\left(E_{Fx}^2 + E_{Fy}^2\right) = Z\left(H_{Fx}^2 + H_{Fy}^2\right) \tag{17.43}$$

Similarly for the backward travelling wave,

the corresponding Poynting vector = $E_{Bx}H_{By} - E_{By}H_{Bx}$

$$= \left(\frac{1}{Z}\right)\left(E_{Bx}^2 + E_{By}^2\right) = Z\left(H_{Bx}^2 + H_{By}^2\right) \tag{17.44}$$

When a forward travelling wave and a backward travelling wave are of equal amplitude and of same phase, the combination produces a pattern which is stationary in space and does not travel with time; i.e. from Eqs. (17.35), if $E_{Bx} = E_{Fx}$, then we have

$$E_x = E_{Fx}[\sin(\omega t - \beta z) + \sin(\omega t + \beta z)]$$
$$= 2E_{Fx}[\sin(\beta z)\cos(\omega t)] \tag{17.45}$$

This is a sinusoidal wave fixed in space, with its amplitude fluctuating at the frequency $f(=\omega/2\pi)$.

For $\beta z = (2\pi/\lambda)z$, $\sin(\beta z) = \sin[(2\pi/\lambda)z]$. This will be zero, when $z =$ a multiple of $(\lambda/2)$.

∴ $E_x = 0$ at these points for all instants of time.

These are the *NODES* in the electric field (Figure 17.2).

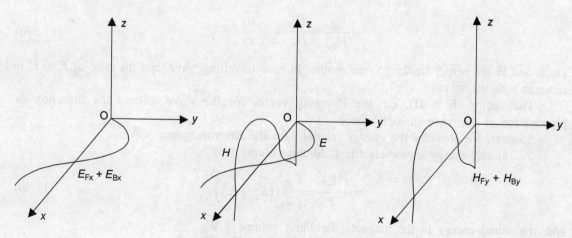

Figure 17.2 Standing wave patterns.

The associated magnetic field is H_y or B_y, and hence the corresponding standing magnetic field (wave) will be

$$H_y = -2H_{Fy}\,[\cos(\beta z)\sin(\omega t)] \qquad (17.46)$$

Its nodes are half-way through the nodes of the **E** field. So we see that the standing waves are produced by the mutual interference of two waves of the same periodicity.

17.2.1 Some General Comments on Uniform Plane Waves

Maxwell's equations do not impose any limits on the frequency of the electromagnetic waves. Uptill now the spectrum that has been studied experimentally, ranges from the long radio waves (at frequencies of about 10^4 Hz and wavelengths about 3×10^4 metres) to the very high energy gamma rays (of frequencies 10^{24} Hz and higher, and of wavelengths of the order of 3×10^{-16} metres and shorter) noticed in cosmic radiation. The known spectrum thus covers a range of greater than 20 orders of magnitude. Radio, light, heat waves, X-rays, and gamma rays are all electromagnetic, though their sources, detectors as well as their modes of interaction with matter, vary widely as the frequency changes. A fundamental identity of all these types of waves is demonstrated by the fact that in free space, they are all transverse waves with a common velocity of propagation c (i.e. the velocity of light).

We have also seen from our analysis in Section 12.2 that (for example) a plane electromagnetic wave propagating in the positive z-direction, **E** is independent of x and y [Eq. (17.5)]

$$\therefore \qquad \nabla \cdot \mathbf{E} = \frac{\partial E_z}{\partial z} = 0 \qquad (17.47)$$

i.e. the z-component of **E** cannot be a function of z, and this was found to be equal to zero [i.e. Eq. (17.5a)]; and the same argument applies to the **H** field. (Note that at present, our interest is in the uniform plane 'wave' and *not* in the 'uniform field'.)

Thus a plane electromagnetic wave propagating in free space is therefore 'transverse', since it has no longitudinal components. A uniform plane wave is also called a 'plane-polarized wave'. So now we define the term 'plane of polarization of a wave'.

The plane of polarization is the plane containing the direction of propagation and the **E** vector (though originally it used to be the **H** vector). A plane polarized wave is also called 'linearly polarized'. Since the **E** vector is the reference vector, 'vertical polarization' would mean that the **E** vector is in the vertical direction, and the 'horizontal polarization' means that the **E** vector is in the horizontal direction (Figure 17.3). Also, without any loss of generality, we can assume a wave to be plane polarized with its **E** vector along the direction of the x-axis. This is

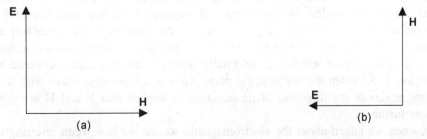

Figure 17.3 (a) Vertically polarized and (b) horizontally polarized wave representation.

because any plane-polarized wave can be considered to be the sum of two waves that are plane-polarized in perpendicular directions, and in phase. This is shown in Figure 17.4.

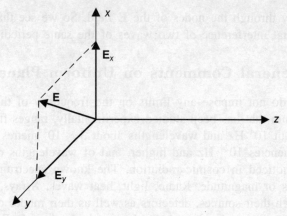

Figure 17.4   Resolution of **E** into two orthogonal components.

We can also add two plane-polarized waves (orthogonal space wise) that differ in phase, i.e.

$$E_x = E_1 \cos \omega \left(t - \frac{z}{u} \right) \quad \text{and} \quad E_y = E_2 \cos \left[\omega \left(t - \frac{z}{u} \right) + \psi \right] \quad (17.48)$$

For these two waves at $z = 0$,

$$E_x = E_1 \cos \omega t \quad \text{and} \quad E_y = E_2 \cos (\omega t + \psi) \quad (17.49)$$

The equations of (17.49) are the parametric equations of an ellipse. For this combination, the maxima of E_x and E_y do not occur at the same time, and their sum **E** describes an ellipse about the z-axis. Such a resultant wave is called an 'elliptically polarized wave'.

If E_x and E_y have equal amplitudes, but are 90° out of phase, i.e. $E_1 = E_2$, and $\psi = \pi/2$, then:

$$E_x^2 + E_y^2 = E_1^2 \quad (17.50)$$

i.e. the ellipse has degenerated into a circle, and the wave is said to be circularly polarized.

The polarization is said to be right-handed or left-handed depending on whether the vectors **E** and **H** rotate clockwise or counterclockwise for an observer looking at the source.

In discussing the propagation of waves, we use the term wave-front, which we shall explain formally. When a wave is progressing, let us consider a surface S, separating region 1 (in Figure 17.5) which has been affected by the disturbance, from the region 2 which has *not* been affected. In this, we neglect any superimposed magnetic field, say, like the earth's magnetic field. When we say that the velocity of propagation of the wave is c, we mean that the position of the surface S, after a further time δt has shifted to a position S' which lies a distance $c\delta t$ along the normal to S in the region which was originally region 2 and this region covered by $c\delta t$ now lies in the region 1. So when we say that the plane wave is a transverse wave with the vectors **E** and **H** at right angles to the direction of propagation, it implies that **E** and **H** are coplanar with the wave-front surface S.

So far, when we talked about the electromagnetic waves, we have been referring to **E** and **H** waves, which are related by the equation

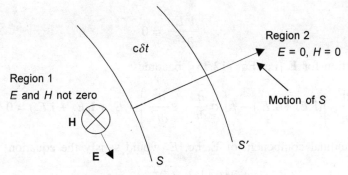

Figure 17.5 Wave-front progressing.

$$|\mathbf{E}| = Z_0 |\mathbf{H}|$$

where $Z_0 = 377 \ \Omega = \sqrt{\mu_0/\varepsilon_0}$, and is the characteristic impedance of free space. However, if instead of referring to the **H** as the magnetic wave, we were to use the **B**, then the relationship between **E** and **B** would be $\mathbf{B} = \mu_0\mathbf{H}$ in free space,

$$|\mathbf{E}| = \left(\frac{Z_0}{\mu_0}\right)|\mathbf{H}| = c|\mathbf{B}| \tag{17.51}$$

17.3 THE E AND H VECTORS IN LINEAR, ISOTROPIC, HOMOGENEOUS AND STATIONARY MEDIA (LIH MEDIA)

We start by defining these terms:

A medium is homogeneous if its properties do not vary from point to point. A medium is isotropic if its properties are same in all directions from any given point. A medium is linear and isotropic if

$$\mathbf{D} = \varepsilon\mathbf{E}, \quad \mathbf{H} = \frac{\mathbf{B}}{\mu}, \quad \mathbf{J} = \sigma\mathbf{E} \tag{17.52}$$

where ε, μ, and σ are constants independent of **E** and **H**, and independent of direction.

The wave equations for such media follow from Eqs. (12.32) and (12.35), which give us

$$\nabla^2\mathbf{E} - \mu\sigma\left(\frac{\partial\mathbf{E}}{\partial t}\right) - \mu\varepsilon\left(\frac{\partial^2\mathbf{E}}{\partial t^2}\right) = 0 \tag{12.35}$$

and

$$\nabla^2\mathbf{H} - \mu\sigma\left(\frac{\partial\mathbf{H}}{\partial t}\right) - \mu\varepsilon\left(\frac{\partial^2\mathbf{H}}{\partial t^2}\right) = 0 \tag{12.32}$$

assuming charge-free region.

We also assume that the plane wave is propagating in positive direction of the z-axis. Hence $(\partial/\partial x) = 0$ and $(\partial/\partial y) = 0$. Then the equation for the divergence of **D** becomes:

$$\nabla \cdot \mathbf{D} = \nabla \cdot (\varepsilon\mathbf{E}) = \varepsilon\left(\frac{\partial E_z}{\partial z}\right) = 0 \ \text{(no free charge)} \tag{17.53}$$

$$\therefore \quad \frac{\partial^2 E_z}{\partial z^2} = 0 \tag{17.54}$$

Then the wave equation for **E** [i.e. Eq. (12.35)] becomes:

$$\left(\frac{\partial^2}{\partial z^2}\right)(\mathbf{i}_x E_x + \mathbf{i}_y E_y) - \mu\left(\sigma \frac{\partial}{\partial t} + \varepsilon \frac{\partial^2}{\partial t^2}\right)(\mathbf{i}_x E_x + \mathbf{i}_y E_y + \mathbf{i}_z E_z) = 0 \tag{12.35}$$

$\therefore$ The longitudinal component of **E**, i.e. E_z would satisfy the equation

$$\varepsilon\left(\frac{\partial^2 E_z}{\partial t^2}\right) + \sigma\left(\frac{\partial E_z}{\partial t}\right) = 0 \tag{17.55}$$

So, if E_z exists, it will be of the form:

$$E_z = a + b \, \exp\left(\frac{-\sigma t}{\varepsilon}\right) \tag{17.56}$$

a and b being the constants of integration [a form which is consistent with the requirements of Eq. (17.53)]. Thus E_z would decrease exponentially with time, and there is no E_z wave. If $\sigma = 0$, then E_z would be of the form $a + bt$, and again there is no E_z wave. Hence, for waves, we can say: $E_z = 0$.

Note: We would come to the same conclusion even if the charge density ρ_C was not zero.

Thus, for plane electromagnetic waves, the **E** vector is transverse in LIH media. We can similarly prove that the **H** vector is also a transverse wave.

Hence, the plane electromagnetic waves are transverse in any LIH and stationary medium. We shall now have a look at their relative orientation. Without any loss of generality, we can assume a plane-polarized wave with the **E** vector in the x–z plane, i.e. parallel to the x-axis, and sinusoidally varying with time. Hence

$$\mathbf{E} = \mathbf{i}_x E_{Ox} \exp\left[j(\omega t - kz)\right] \tag{17.57}$$

where k is in general complex. Then from the Maxwell's equation

$$\nabla \times \mathbf{E} = -\left(\frac{\partial \mathbf{B}}{\partial t}\right)$$

we get

$$\mathbf{i}_x 0 + \mathbf{i}_y(-jkE_{Ox}) + \mathbf{i}_z 0 = -j\omega\mu \, (\mathbf{i}_x H_x + \mathbf{i}_y H_y)$$

$$\therefore \quad\quad H_x = 0 \quad\quad \text{and} \quad\quad \mathbf{H} = \mathbf{i}_y H_y = \mathbf{i}_y\left(\frac{k}{\omega\mu}\right)E_{Ox} \exp\left[j(\omega t - kz)\right] \tag{17.58}$$

$$\therefore \quad\quad \left|\frac{\mathbf{E}}{\mathbf{H}}\right| = \frac{\omega\mu}{k} \tag{17.59}$$

Hence the **E** and **H** vectors in a plane-polarized wave in an LIH medium are (1) orthogonal (i.e. mutually perpendicular), (2) so oriented that their vector product (**E** × **H**) points in the direction of propagation, and (3) not necessarily in phase because the wave number k can be complex, and hence the waves can get attenuated as they propagate.

17.4   PROPAGATION OF PLANE ELECTROMAGNETIC WAVES IN PERFECT LOSS-LESS NON-CONDUCTORS (INSULATORS OR DIELECTRICS)

In loss-less dielectrics, $\sigma = 0$, and as a rule, $\rho_C = 0$. Hence the wave equations (12.35) and (12.32) reduce to

$$\nabla^2 \mathbf{E} - \mu\varepsilon \left(\frac{\partial^2 \mathbf{E}}{\partial t^2} \right) = 0 \qquad (17.60a)$$

and

$$\nabla^2 \mathbf{H} - \mu\varepsilon \left(\frac{\partial^2 \mathbf{H}}{\partial t^2} \right) = 0 \qquad (17.60b)$$

E and **H** vectors are then of the same form as in Section 17.3, i.e.

$$\mathbf{E} = \mathbf{i}_x E_{Ox} \exp\left[j(\omega t - \beta z) \right] \qquad (17.61)$$

Since $\sigma = 0$, we shall see that the wave number β will not be complex. From Eq. (17.61), the **H** wave comes out to be (as in Section 17.3):

$$\mathbf{H} = \mathbf{i}_y \left(\frac{\beta}{\omega\mu} \right) E_{Ox} \exp\left[j(\omega t - \beta z) \right] \qquad (17.62)$$

Substituting for **E** and **H** from Eqs. (17.61) and (17.62) in Eq. (17.60), we find

$$-\beta^2 + \omega^2 \mu\varepsilon = 0 \qquad (17.63)$$

$\therefore$ The wave number, $\qquad \beta = \omega \sqrt{\mu\varepsilon} = \dfrac{\omega}{u} \qquad (17.64)$

is real, and hence there is no attenuation of either of the two waves. The phase velocity

$$u = \frac{\omega}{\beta} = \frac{1}{\sqrt{\mu\varepsilon}} = \frac{c}{\sqrt{\mu_r \varepsilon_r}} \qquad (17.65)$$

$\therefore$ The phase velocity of the waves in the non-conductors is less than that in free space, and the 'index of refraction', n is

$$n = \frac{c}{u} = \sqrt{\mu_r \varepsilon_r} \qquad (17.66)$$

In a non-magnetic medium, $\mu_r = 1$, and

$$n = \sqrt{\varepsilon_r} \qquad (17.67)$$

Note that, in general, n and ε_r are both functions of frequency.

In the non-conductors, the **E** and **H** vectors are in phase, and the electric and the magnetic energy densities are equal, i.e.

$$\frac{1}{2} \varepsilon E^2 = \frac{1}{2} \mu H^2$$

$\therefore$ The total instantaneous energy density $= \varepsilon E^2 = \mu H^2$

The average total energy density $= \varepsilon E_{rms}^2 = \mu H_{rms}^2$

The average value of the Poynting vector:

$$\overline{\mathbf{S}} = \mathbf{i}_z \left(\frac{1}{2}\right) E_{Ox} H_{Ox} = \mathbf{i}_z \left(\frac{1}{2}\right) \sqrt{\frac{\varepsilon}{\mu}} \, E_{Ox}^2$$

$$= \mathbf{i}_z \sqrt{\frac{\varepsilon}{\mu}} \, E_{\text{rms}}^2 = \mathbf{i}_z (u\varepsilon) E_{\text{rms}}^2 \text{ watts/metre}^2 \qquad (17.68)$$

The average value of the Poynting vector is thus equal to the phase velocity u multiplied by the average energy density.

17.5 PROPAGATION OF PLANE ELECTROMAGNETIC WAVES IN CONDUCTING MEDIA

For a conducting medium $\sigma \neq 0$, the wave equations (12.35) and (12.32) for a wave travelling along the z-axis, with $\rho_C = 0$, have to be solved, i.e.

$$\nabla^2 \mathbf{E} - \mu\sigma \left(\frac{\partial \mathbf{E}}{\partial t}\right) - \mu\varepsilon \left(\frac{\partial^2 \mathbf{E}}{\partial t^2}\right) = 0 \qquad (12.35)$$

$$\nabla^2 \mathbf{H} - \mu\sigma \left(\frac{\partial \mathbf{H}}{\partial t}\right) - \mu\varepsilon \left(\frac{\partial^2 \mathbf{H}}{\partial t^2}\right) = 0 \qquad (12.32)$$

The solutions of **E** and **H** vectors with sinusoidal time variations come out to be:

$$\mathbf{E} = \mathbf{i}_x E_{Ox} \exp\left[j(\omega t - kz)\right] \qquad (17.69)$$

$$\mathbf{H} = \mathbf{i}_y \left(\frac{k}{\omega\mu}\right) E_{Ox} \exp\left[j(\omega t - kz)\right] = \mathbf{i}_y H_{Oy} \exp\left[j(\omega t - kz)\right] \qquad (17.70)$$

By substituting, we get

$$-k^2 + \omega^2 \mu\varepsilon - j\omega\mu\sigma = 0$$

or

$$k^2 = \omega^2 \mu\varepsilon - j\omega\mu\sigma = \omega^2 \mu\varepsilon \left[1 - j\left(\frac{\sigma}{\omega\varepsilon}\right)\right]$$

$$= \omega^2 \mu_0 \mu_r \varepsilon_0 \varepsilon_r \left[1 - j\left(\frac{\sigma}{\omega\varepsilon}\right)\right] = \left(\frac{\omega^2 \mu_r \varepsilon_r}{c^2}\right)\left[1 - j\left(\frac{\sigma}{\omega\varepsilon}\right)\right]$$

$$= \left(\frac{4\pi^2 \mu_r \varepsilon_r}{\lambda_0^2}\right)\left[1 - j\left(\frac{\sigma}{\omega\varepsilon}\right)\right], \qquad \frac{\omega}{c} = \frac{2\pi}{\lambda_0}$$

$$\qquad (17.71)$$

where λ_0 is the wavelength in free space.

As k^2 is complex, we write

$$k = k_r - jk_i \qquad (17.72)$$

$$\therefore \qquad k_r = \left(\frac{2\pi}{\lambda_0}\right) \sqrt{\frac{\mu_r \varepsilon_r}{2}} \left[\left(1 + \frac{\sigma^2}{\omega^2 \varepsilon^2}\right)^{1/2} + 1\right]^{1/2}$$

and

$$k_i = \left(\frac{2\pi}{\lambda_0}\right)\sqrt{\frac{\mu_r \varepsilon_r}{2}}\left[\left(1 + \frac{\sigma^2}{\omega^2 \varepsilon^2}\right)^{1/2} - 1\right]^{1/2} \tag{17.73}$$

The real part of the wave number k, i.e. k_r is $(2\pi/\lambda)$, where λ is the wavelength in the medium. The imaginary part k_i is the reciprocal of the distance δ over which the amplitude is attenuated by a factor of e. The quantity $\delta = 1/k_i$ is called the 'attenuation distance'.

The phase velocity is

$$u = \frac{\omega}{k_r} \tag{17.74}$$

corresponding to an index of refraction

$$n = \frac{c}{u} = \left(\frac{c}{\omega}\right)k_r = \left(\frac{\lambda_0}{2\pi}\right)k_r = \frac{\lambda_0}{\lambda} \tag{17.75}$$

and following Eq. (17.59):

$$\left|\frac{\mathbf{E}}{\mathbf{H}}\right| = \frac{\omega\mu}{k}$$

$$= \sqrt{\frac{\mu}{\varepsilon}}\left[\left(1 + \frac{\sigma^2}{\omega^2 \varepsilon^2}\right)\right]^{-1/4} \exp\left[j \tan^{-1}\left(\frac{k_i}{k_r}\right)\right] \tag{17.76}$$

the quantity $[\tan^{-1}(k_i/k_r)]$ denotes the phase of $\mathbf{E}$ with respect to $\mathbf{H}$.

The expressions for $\mathbf{E}$ and $\mathbf{H}$ vectors are

$$\mathbf{E} = \mathbf{i}_x E_{Ox} \exp\left[j(\omega t - k_r z) - k_i z\right]$$

and

$$\mathbf{H} = \mathbf{i}_y H_{Oy} \exp\left[j(\omega t - k_r z - \tan^{-1}\left(\frac{k_i}{k_r}\right) - k_i z\right] \tag{17.77}$$

where

$$\frac{E_{Ox}}{H_{Oy}} = \sqrt{\frac{\mu}{\varepsilon}}\left(1 + \frac{\sigma^2}{\omega^2 \varepsilon^2}\right)^{-1/4} \tag{17.78}$$

The ratio of the electric energy to the magnetic energy is

$$\left|\frac{(1/2)\,\varepsilon E^2}{(1/2)\,\mu H^2}\right| = \left(1 + \frac{\sigma^2}{\omega^2 \varepsilon^2}\right)^{-1/2} \tag{17.79}$$

17.6 PROPAGATION OF PLANE ELECTROMAGNETIC WAVES IN GOOD CONDUCTORS

In Section 17.5, we studied the propagation of electromagnetic waves in conductors. So now to define what we mean by 'good' conductors, we start at the values of k_r and k_i for conducting media as obtained in Eq. (17.73). In good conductors, the ratio $\omega\varepsilon/\sigma$ [as we have already mentioned in Chapter 12, Section 12.5, Eqs. (12.37) and (12.39)] is much smaller than unity, i.e.

$$\frac{\omega\varepsilon}{\sigma} \leq \frac{1}{50} \text{ (say)} \tag{17.80}$$

which means that the conduction current density ($\mathbf{J} = \sigma\mathbf{E}$) must be at least 50 times greater than the displacement current density ($\partial\mathbf{D}/\partial t$). So we define 'good conductors' as those for which the above condition is satisfied. Hence copper is a good conductor for frequencies up to about 2×10^{16} Hz or to the ultraviolet.

For good conductors, Eq. (17.71) simplifies to

$$k^2 = -j\omega\mu\sigma \tag{17.81}$$

and

$$\therefore \quad k = \sqrt{-j\omega\mu\sigma} = \left(\sqrt{\frac{\omega\mu\sigma}{2}}\right)(1-j) \tag{17.82}$$

Hence, now

$$k_r = k_i = \sqrt{\frac{\omega\mu\sigma}{2}}$$

$$\therefore \qquad \delta = d\sqrt{2} = \sqrt{\frac{2}{\omega\mu\sigma}} = \frac{\lambda}{2\pi} \tag{17.83}$$

And, from Eq. (17.59), for the plane-polarized waves

$$\left|\frac{\mathbf{E}}{\mathbf{H}}\right| = \frac{\omega\mu}{k} = \sqrt{\frac{\omega\mu}{\sigma}} \exp\left(\frac{j\pi}{4}\right) \tag{17.84}$$

$\therefore$ In good conductors, the $\mathbf{E}$ vector leads the $\mathbf{H}$ vector by $\pi/4$, whereas for the non-conductors (i.e. dielectrics) we found that $\mathbf{E}$ and $\mathbf{H}$ are in phase. The reason for this difference is due to the fact that for good conductors, the $\mathbf{H}$ vector is from the conduction current, and for loss-less dielectrics, the $\mathbf{H}$ vector is produced by the displacement currents. Hence we can write the expressions for $\mathbf{E}$ and $\mathbf{H}$ for good conductors, similar to Eqs. (17.69) and (17.70), i.e.

$$\mathbf{E} = \mathbf{i}_x E_{Ox} \exp\left[j\left(\omega t - \frac{z}{d\sqrt{2}}\right) - \frac{z}{d\sqrt{2}}\right] \tag{17.85a}$$

$$\mathbf{H} = \mathbf{i}_y \left(\frac{\sigma}{\omega\mu}\right)^{1/2} E_{Ox} \exp\left[j\left(\omega t - \frac{z}{d\sqrt{2}} - \frac{\pi}{4}\right) - \frac{z}{d\sqrt{2}}\right] \tag{17.85b}$$

or, if we write in terms of cosine functions:

$$\mathbf{E} = \mathbf{i}_x E_{Ox} \exp\left(-\frac{z}{d\sqrt{2}}\right) \cos\left(\omega t - \frac{z}{d\sqrt{2}}\right) \tag{17.86a}$$

$$\mathbf{H} = \mathbf{i}_y \left(\frac{\sigma}{\omega\mu}\right)^{1/2} E_{Ox} \exp\left(-\frac{z}{d\sqrt{2}}\right) \cos\left(\omega t - \frac{z}{d\sqrt{2}} - \frac{\pi}{4}\right)$$

$$= \mathbf{i}_y H_{Oy} \exp\left(-\frac{z}{d\sqrt{2}}\right) \cos\left(\omega t - \frac{z}{d\sqrt{2}} - \frac{\pi}{4}\right) \tag{17.86b}$$

These results are similar to those, which we have obtained for good conductors in Chapter 15, Section 15.2. The distributions for **E** and **H** would be same as discussed there. The quantity δ derived here is the 'skin depth $(d\sqrt{2})$' of the above-mentioned section.

The amplitude of the wave is attenuated by a factor of $(1/e) = 0.368$ in one radian length $(\lambda/2\pi)$, and by a factor of $(1/e)^{2\pi} \simeq 2 \times 10^{-3}$ in one wavelength λ, whereas the Poynting vector $(\mathbf{E} \times \mathbf{H})$ is attenuated by $(1/e)^2 = 0.135$ in $(\lambda/2\pi)$, and by $(1/e)^{4\pi} \simeq 4 \times 10^{-6}$ in one wavelength λ. The attenuation is so rapid that the wave is barely noticeable. Table 17.1 shows the skin-depth for various conductors at different frequencies. It should be noted that the attenuation in iron is much larger compared with that in silver, even though iron is a poor conductor compared with silver because of the fact that iron's permeability is much higher.

Table 17.1   Skin-depth for conductors (mm)

Conductor	σ (mho/m)	μ_r	Skin-depth $[(d\sqrt{2})$ mm]			
			60 Hz	500 Hz	10^4 Hz	10^6 Hz
Silver	6.15×10^7	1.00	8.48	2.94	0.66	0.066
Copper	5.8×10^7	1.00	8.63	2.99	0.68	0.068
Aluminium	3.54×10^7	1.00	10.1	3.81	0.85	0.085
Iron	1.0×10^7	1000	0.65	0.22	0.05	0.005

The phase velocity

$$u = \frac{\omega}{k_r} = \frac{\omega\lambda}{2\pi} = \sqrt{\frac{2\omega}{\mu\sigma}} \qquad (17.87)$$

is proportional to the square root of the frequency.

The ratio of the electric to the magnetic energy density is

$$\frac{(1/2)\,\varepsilon E^2}{(1/2)\,\mu H^2} = \frac{\omega\varepsilon}{\sigma} \le \frac{1}{50} \qquad (17.88)$$

and so most of the energy is in the magnetic form. This is a consequence of the medium being 'good' conductor which causes E/J to be small. Hence the electric field intensity is weak, but the current density, and hence **H** is relatively large.

17.7   REFLECTION AND REFRACTION OF PLANE ELECTROMAGNETIC WAVES

So far we have studied the propagation of the electromagnetic waves in different types of infinite continuous media. We shall now study the effects of discontinuity in the medium of propagation. We shall investigate again the behaviour of these waves in different combinations of different types of media, i.e. dielectrics, conductors (including good conductors) and combinations of these. We remind ourselves that the dielectrics are non-conductors, and they may be either magnetic or non-magnetic; we shall restrict ourselves to non-magnetic dielectrics.

We assume an ideally thin, infinitely plane interface between the two linear, isotropic and homogeneous (LIH) media. An incident wave along $\mathbf{n}_i$ would, in general, give rise to a reflected wave along $\mathbf{n}_r$, and a transmitted wave along $\mathbf{n}_t$. These three waves, combined together, satisfy the continuity conditions for the tangential components of **E** and **H**, and for the normal components of **D** and **B** at the interface (Figure 17.6). During the initial stages of our study, we shall exclude the total reflection from the dielectric, and we assume the media to extend to infinity on both the sides of the interface.

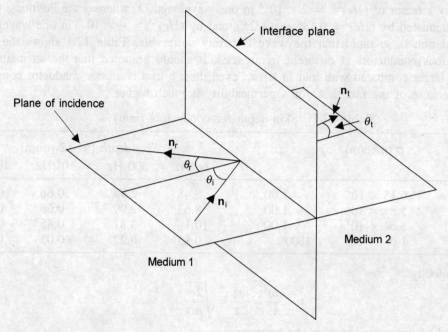

Figure 17.6 An electromagnetic wave in medium 1, incident on the interface between media 1 and 2, giving rise to both the reflected wave in the medium 1 and the transmitted wave in the medium 2.

For the present study we shall classify our analysis not by the different types of media discontinuities but by the way by which the incident wave hits the interface surface of discontinuity, i.e. (1) the incident wave meeting the interface normally; and (2) the incident wave meeting the interface obliquely, in which case, the interference pattern produced in the first medium, by the combination of the incident and the reflected waves would be stationary in one direction and travelling in an orthogonal direction. The properties of such patterns are of great practical importance in design and study of waveguides.

So before we start our study of reflection and refraction of waves, we shall remind ourselves of the facts that when a wave meets a discontinuity in the media of propagation, then, in general, it (the incident wave) produces a transmitted wave in the second medium and a reflected wave which travels back in the first medium, the exact directions of propagation being decided upon by the interface continuity conditions. We shall now consider waves incident normally on different types of interface surfaces, starting first with a perfectly conducting surface. However, before we start discussing each case separately, we shall state, in general terms, some fundamental points about the laws of electromagnetic reflection and refraction, and some basic points regarding the techniques of solving such problems.

17.8 THE LAWS OF REFLECTION AND SNELL'S LAW OF REFRACTION

Referring to Figure 17.6, we consider the electromagnetic wave incident on the interface, to be both plane and plane-polarized, so that its electric field intensity is of the form

$$\mathbf{E}_{1i} = \mathbf{E}_{0i} \exp\left[j\omega_i(t - \mathbf{n}_i \cdot \mathbf{r}/u_1)\right] \qquad (17.89)$$

where u_1 is the phase velocity of the wave in the medium 1. The time $t = 0$, and the origin $r = 0$ can be chosen arbitrarily. We, however, choose the origin at a convenient point on the interface plane. The above equation defines a plane wave for all values of t and $\mathbf{r}$, but we shall use it only for medium 1, and when we consider normal incidence, then $\mathbf{n}_i \cdot \mathbf{r} = z$ (+ve z-direction). The reflected and the refracted waves from the plane interface are also plane and plane-polarized (obeying the same laws at all points on the interface), and are of the form

$$\mathbf{E}_r = \mathbf{E}_{0r} \exp\left[j\omega_r(t - \mathbf{n}_r \cdot \mathbf{r}/u_1)\right] \qquad (17.90a)$$

and

$$\mathbf{E}_t = \mathbf{E}_{0t} \exp\left[j\omega_t(t - \mathbf{n}_t \cdot \mathbf{r}/u_2)\right] \qquad (17.90b)$$

where u_2 is the phase velocity of the wave in the medium 2. It should be noted that so far no assumptions have been made about the amplitudes, phases, frequencies, and the directions of the reflected and the refracted waves. The amplitudes $\mathbf{E}_{0r}$, $\mathbf{E}_{0t}$ can be complex if required.

The characteristics of the reflected and the transmitted waves are obtained from the interface continuity conditions that the tangential components of $\mathbf{E}$ and $\mathbf{H}$ must be continuous across the interface, i.e. the sum of the tangential components of $\mathbf{E}_i$ and $\mathbf{E}_r$ must equal that of $\mathbf{E}_t$ on the interface ($z = 0$). Similar condition holds for $\mathbf{H}$. These conditions must hold for all instants of time and at all points on the interface ($z = 0$),

$$\therefore \quad \omega_i = \omega_r = \omega_t \qquad (17.91)$$

i.e. all the three waves must be of same frequency.

Also, since these conditions hold at all the points on the interface,

$$\therefore \quad \frac{\mathbf{n}_i \cdot \mathbf{r}_i}{u_1} = \frac{\mathbf{n}_r \cdot \mathbf{r}_i}{u_1} = \frac{\mathbf{n}_t \cdot \mathbf{r}_i}{u_2} \qquad (17.92)$$

where $\mathbf{r}_i$ is any point on the interface.

From the first two terms of the above equation

$$(\mathbf{n}_i - \mathbf{n}_r) \cdot \mathbf{r}_i = 0 \qquad (17.93)$$

Since $\mathbf{r}_i$ lies on the interface, the vector $(\mathbf{n}_i - \mathbf{n}_r)$ must be normal to the interface plane $z = 0$, i.e. referring to the Figure 17.6,

$$\theta_i = \theta_r \qquad (17.94)$$

which means that the angle of reflection equals the angle of incidence. Since $(\mathbf{n}_i - \mathbf{n}_r)$ is parallel to $\mathbf{n}$ (the normal to the interface), the three vectors $\mathbf{n}_i$, $\mathbf{n}_r$ and $\mathbf{n}$ are coplanar. These are the laws of reflection of the waves.

The plane containing these three vectors is called the 'plane of incidence'.

Going back to Eq. (17.92), we get

$$\left(\frac{\mathbf{n}_i}{u_1} - \frac{\mathbf{n}_t}{u_2}\right) \cdot \mathbf{r}_i = 0 \qquad (17.95)$$

∴ The vector in the brackets must be normal to the interface plane $z = 0$, and hence $\mathbf{n}_i$, $\mathbf{n}_t$ and $\mathbf{n}$ are coplanar, and hence all the four normal vectors $\mathbf{n}_i$, $\mathbf{n}_t$, $\mathbf{n}_r$ and $\mathbf{n}$ must lie in the plane of incidence. Furthermore, the tangential components of $(\mathbf{n}_i/u_1)$ and $(\mathbf{n}_t/u_2)$ must be equal, i.e.

$$\frac{\sin \theta_i}{u_1} = \frac{\sin \theta_t}{u_2} \qquad (17.96)$$

or since the wave number $\beta = \omega/u$, the above equality can be expressed as

$$\beta_1(\sin \theta_i) = \beta_2(\sin \theta_t)$$

or

$$\frac{\sin \theta_t}{\sin \theta_i} = \frac{\beta_1}{\beta_2} = \frac{n_1}{n_2} = \frac{\sqrt{\mu_{r1}\varepsilon_{r1}}}{\sqrt{\mu_{r2}\varepsilon_{r2}}} \qquad (17.97)$$

where n is the index of refraction. This is the 'Snell's law of refraction'. Thus the quantity '$\beta \sin \theta$' is conserved across the interface. The above laws are general, and apply to any two media. They hold true for total reflection as well.

17.9 NORMAL INCIDENCE OF PLANE WAVES AT A PERFECTLY CONDUCTING BOUNDARY

We consider a plane-polarized, plane wave, incident normally on a perfectly conducting sheet. The direction of propagation is along the z-axis. The single frequency, uniform wave hits the plane, perfect conductor at $z = 0$. Now, there must be a reflected wave in addition to the incident wave, the reason being that a single travelling wave cannot satisfy the boundary condition on the perfect conducting surface on which the **E** field must be zero at all instants of time. (Also no energy can pass through the perfect conductor.) And hence all the energy from the incident wave must be returned by the reflected wave. Hence the incident and the reflected waves would be of equal amplitude, and together they form a standing wave pattern, whose properties we shall study now.

In our standard mathematical notations, the incident waves of **E** and **H** representing sinusoidal plane waves, moving towards $z \to +\infty$ are given by

$$E_{x+} = E_+ = \hat{E}_+ \cos \omega\left(t - \frac{z}{c}\right), \qquad B_{y+} = B_+ = \hat{B}_+ \cos \omega\left(t - \frac{z}{c}\right)$$

where

$$\hat{B}_+ = \frac{\hat{E}_+}{c} \qquad (17.98)$$

Expressed as phasors, these are

$$\{E_{x+}\} = \hat{E}_+ \exp\left(\frac{-j\omega z}{c}\right) \quad \text{and} \quad \{B_{y+}\} = \hat{B}_+ \exp\left(\frac{-j\omega z}{c}\right)$$

As before, we write β (= the wave number) for (ω/c), and omit { } for the phasors on the understanding that all quantities are phasors. Thus

$$E_{x+} = E_+ = \hat{E}_+ \exp(-j\beta z), \quad B_{y+} = B_+ = \hat{B}_+ \exp(-j\beta z), \quad \left(\hat{B}_+ = \frac{\hat{E}_+}{c}\right) \qquad (17.99)$$

This wave approaches the perfectly conducting boundary occupying the plane $z = 0$ from the negative side (Figure 17.7). **E** and **B** are both tangential to the interface. At the surface of the perfect conductor, the electric force is zero at all time, and hence there must be a reflected wave E_- such that $E_+ + E_- = 0$ at $z = 0$.

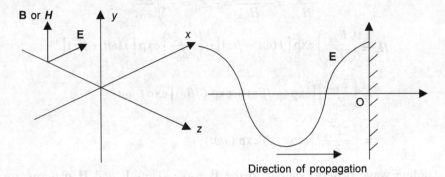

Figure 17.7 Incident E wave meeting $z = 0$ perfectly conducting surface, normally.

$$\therefore \qquad E_- = - \hat{E}_+ \exp(j\beta z) \qquad (17.100a)$$

and the associated magnetic vector B_- will have the same direction as B_+ (to give the propagation towards $z \to -\infty$) so that

$$B_- = \hat{B}_+ \exp(j\beta z) \qquad (17.100b)$$

The total field is therefore

$$E_+ + E_- = \hat{E}_+ [\exp(-j\beta z) - \exp(j\beta z)] = -2j\hat{E}_+ \sin \beta z \qquad (17.101a)$$

$$B_+ + B_- = \hat{B}_+ [\exp(-j\beta z) + \exp(j\beta z)] = 2j\hat{B}_+ \cos \beta z \qquad (17.101b)$$

i.e. the travelling wave pattern has thus been replaced by a stationary pattern called a *standing wave*. It is such that $z = 0$ is always a zero or a *node* in the E-pattern, and a maximum or an *anti-node* in the B-pattern. Note that $E_+ + E_-$ and $B_+ + B_-$ are in space-quadrature; also that the power flow in the z-direction is zero (Figure 17.8).

If we need the **H** wave, this can be obtained either from the **B** wave or the **E** wave using the characteristic impedance of the medium, i.e.

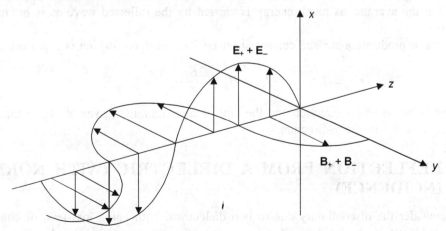

Figure 17.8 Standing wave patterns for **E** and **B**.

$$\frac{E_{x+}}{H_{y+}} = -\frac{E_{y+}}{H_{x+}} = Z_0 = \sqrt{\frac{\mu_0}{\varepsilon_0}}$$

and

$$\frac{E_{x-}}{H_{y-}} = -\frac{E_{y-}}{H_{x-}} = -Z_0 = -\sqrt{\frac{\mu_0}{\varepsilon_0}}$$

$\therefore$

$$H_y = \left(\frac{E_{x+}}{Z_0}\right) \exp\left[j(\omega t - \beta z)\right] - \left(\frac{E_{x-}}{Z_0}\right) \exp\left[j(\omega t + \beta z)\right]$$

$$= \left(\frac{E_{x+}}{Z_0}\right) \left[\exp(-j\beta z) + \exp(j\beta z)\right] \exp(j\omega t)$$

$$= \left(\frac{2E_{x+}}{Z_0}\right) (\cos \beta z) \exp(j\omega t) \tag{17.102}$$

This is a standing wave pattern, similar to the **B** wave. Thus **E** and **H** patterns are mutually perpendicular in space (i.e. in space quadrature), and related in magnitude by Z_0; and they are in time-quadrature.

For the standing wave pattern of the **E** vector, **E** = 0 on the conductor surface ($z = 0$) at all t, and also for the values of $\beta z = -n\pi$, where n is an integer.

$\therefore$ Successive nodes (or zeroes) are located at

$$z = -\frac{n\pi}{\beta} = -\frac{n\lambda}{2} \tag{17.103}$$

where λ is the wavelength of the pattern.

H has maxima at the conductor surface and at all points where **E** = 0, i.e. $z = -n\lambda/2$.

Zeroes of **H** and maxima of **E** are at points where

$$\beta z = \frac{-(2n+1)\pi}{2} \quad \text{or} \quad z = \frac{-(2n+1)\pi}{2\beta} = \frac{-(2n+1)\lambda}{4} \tag{17.104}$$

$\therefore$ At an instant of time, occurring twice in each cycle, all the energy is in the magnetic field, and then 90° later all the energy is in the electric field.

The average value of the Poynting vector (**E** $\times$ **H**) is zero at each cross-sectional plane.

$\therefore$ On the average, as much energy is carried by the reflected wave as is brought by the incident wave.

The wave produces a surface current sheet on the interface—which is a perfect conductor.

$$J_{Sx} = H_y = \frac{2E_{x+}}{Z_0} \tag{17.105}$$

The current is in the +ve x-direction and the unit of its magnitude [given above in Eq. (17.105)] is amps/metre width in the y-direction.

17.10   REFLECTION FROM A DIELECTRIC (WITH NORMAL INCIDENCE)

We next consider the discontinuity due to two dielectrics, both being loss-less, of characteristic properties $\mu_1(= \mu_0\mu_{r1})$, $\varepsilon_1(= \varepsilon_0\varepsilon_{r1})$ and $\mu_2(= \mu_0\mu_{r2})$, $\varepsilon_2(= \varepsilon_0\varepsilon_{r2})$ respectively. A wave is incident on the interface $z = 0$ normally from the region 1, the direction of propagation being the $+z$-direction (Figure 17.9). The resultant pattern would be:

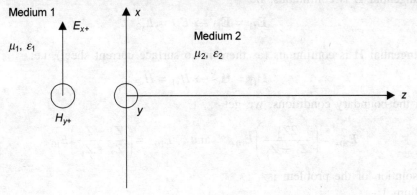

Figure 17.9 A plane wave incident on a dielectric interface.

in the medium 1: incident and reflected waves;

and

in the medium 2: transmitted wave only.

In the medium 1, the incident waves are

$$\mathbf{E}_{1+}(z) = \mathbf{i}_x E_{10+} \exp [\, j\,(\omega t - \beta_1 z)] \tag{17.106a}$$

$$\mathbf{H}_{1+}(z) = \mathbf{i}_y H_{10+} \exp [\, j\,(\omega t - \beta_1 z)]$$

$$= \mathbf{i}_y \left(\frac{E_{10+}}{Z_1} \right) \exp [\, j\,(\omega t - \beta_1 z)] \tag{17.106b}$$

where $\beta_1 = \omega \sqrt{\mu_1 \varepsilon_1}$, $Z_1 = \sqrt{\mu_1/\varepsilon_1}$, and both the waves are travelling in the $+z$-direction.

The reflected waves, travelling in the $-z$-direction, in the medium 1 are

$$\mathbf{E}_{1-}(z) = \mathbf{i}_x E_{10-} \exp [\, j\,(\omega t + \beta_1 z)] \tag{17.107a}$$

$$\mathbf{H}_{1-}(z) = \mathbf{i}_y H_{10-} \exp [\, j\,(\omega t + \beta_1 z)]$$

$$= \mathbf{i}_y \left(\frac{E_{10-}}{Z_1} \right) \exp [\, j\,(\omega t + \beta_1 z)] \tag{17.107b}$$

Also the transmitted waves would travel in the $+z$-direction, in the medium 2:

$$\mathbf{E}_{2+}(z) = \mathbf{i}_x E_{20+} \exp [\, j\,(\omega t - \beta_2 z)] \tag{17.108a}$$

$$\mathbf{H}_{2+}(z) = \mathbf{i}_y H_{20+} \exp [\, j\,(\omega t - \beta_2 z)]$$

$$= \mathbf{i}_y \left(\frac{E_{20+}}{Z_2} \right) \exp [\, j\,(\omega t - \beta_2 z)] \tag{17.108b}$$

where

$$\beta_2 = \omega \sqrt{\mu_2 \varepsilon_2}, \quad Z_2 = \sqrt{\frac{\mu_2}{\varepsilon_2}}$$

The unknowns in these equations are E_{10-} and E_{20+}, and the known specified quantity is E_{10+}.

The boundary conditions on the interface are:

On the plane $z = 0$,

(1) tangential $\mathbf{E}$ is continuous, i.e.

$$\mathbf{E}_{t1} = \mathbf{E}_{t2} \rightarrow E_{x1} = E_{x2}$$

and

(2) tangential $\mathbf{H}$ is continuous (as there is no surface current sheet), i.e.

$$\mathbf{H}_{t1} = \mathbf{H}_{t2} \rightarrow H_{y1} = H_{y2}$$

From the boundary conditions, we get

$$E_{20+} = \left(\frac{2Z_2}{Z_2 + Z_1}\right) E_{10+} \quad \text{and} \quad E_{10-} = \left(\frac{Z_2 - Z_1}{Z_2 + Z_1}\right) E_{10+} \tag{17.109}$$

The solution of the problem is:

In the medium 1:

$$\mathbf{E}_1 = \mathbf{i}_x E_{10+} \left[\exp\left(-j\beta_1 z\right) + \left(\frac{Z_2 - Z_1}{Z_2 + Z_1}\right) \exp\left(j\beta_1 z\right) \right] \exp\left(j\omega t\right) \tag{17.110a}$$

$$\mathbf{H}_1 = \mathbf{i}_x \left(\frac{E_{10+}}{Z_1}\right) \left[\exp\left(-j\beta_1 z\right) - \left(\frac{Z_2 - Z_1}{Z_2 + Z_1}\right) \exp\left(j\beta_1 z\right) \right] \exp\left(j\omega t\right) \tag{17.110b}$$

$$\mathbf{E}_2 = \mathbf{i}_x E_{10+} \left[\left(\frac{2Z_2}{Z_2 + Z_1}\right) \exp\left(-j\beta_2 z\right) \right] \exp\left(j\omega t\right) \tag{17.110c}$$

$$\mathbf{H}_2 = \mathbf{i}_x E_{10+} \left[\left(\frac{2}{Z_2 + Z_1}\right) \exp\left(-j\beta_2 z\right) \right] \exp\left(j\omega t\right) \tag{17.110d}$$

It should be noted that, in general, any discontinuity at a boundary will cause a reflected wave. In the present problem, the fraction of the incident wave, that is reflected, is

$$\frac{\mathbf{E}_{1-}}{\mathbf{E}_{1+}} = \frac{Z_2 - Z_1}{Z_2 + Z_1}$$

$$= \rho_E \text{ (the reflection coefficient)} \tag{17.111}$$

The above equation indicates that at the interface between two infinite dielectrics, the reflections can be eliminated only if $Z_2 = Z_1$. The fraction of the incident wave that is transmitted into the medium 2 is

$$\frac{\mathbf{E}_{2+}}{\mathbf{E}_{1+}} = \frac{2Z_2}{Z_2 + Z_1}$$

$$= \tau_E \text{ (the transmission coefficient)} = 1 + \rho_E \tag{17.112}$$

Next we have a look at the energy associated with each wave.

∴ The Poynting vector associated with the incident radiation is

$$\mathbf{S}_{1+av} = \mathbf{i}_z \left|\mathbf{E}_{1+}\right| \left|\mathbf{H}_{1+}\right| \cos\theta = \mathbf{i}_z \frac{\left|E_{1+}\right|^2}{Z_1} = \mathbf{i}_z \frac{\left|E_{10+}\right|^2}{Z_1} \tag{17.113}$$

θ being the time-phase angle between **E** and **H** vectors of the incident waves. For the present case, E_x and H_y are in time-phase, and hence $\theta = 0$.

The Poynting vector associated with the reflected radiation is

$$\mathbf{S}_{1-av} = -\mathbf{i}_z \left[\frac{|E_{10+}|^2}{Z_1} \right] \left(\frac{Z_2 - Z_1}{Z_2 + Z_1} \right)^2 \qquad (17.114)$$

and $\theta = 180°$ for this wave travelling in the $-z$-direction.

∴   The total $\mathbf{S}_{av}$ in the medium $1 = \mathbf{S}_{1+av} + \mathbf{S}_{1-av}$

$$= \mathbf{i}_z \left[\frac{|E_{10+}|^2}{Z_1} \right] \left[1 - \left(\frac{Z_2 - Z_1}{Z_2 + Z_1} \right)^2 \right]$$

$$= \mathbf{i}_z \left[\frac{|E_{10+}|^2}{Z_1} \right] \left[\frac{4 Z_1 Z_2}{(Z_2 + Z_1)^2} \right]$$

$$= \mathbf{i}_z |E_{10+}|^2 \left[\frac{4 Z_2}{(Z_2 + Z_1)^2} \right] \qquad (17.115)$$

In the medium 2:

The average value of the Poynting vector for the transmitted wave:

$$\mathbf{S}_{2+av} = \mathbf{i}_z \frac{|E_{2+}|^2}{Z_2} = \mathbf{i}_z \frac{|E_{20+}|^2}{Z_2}$$

$$= \mathbf{i}_z \left[\frac{|E_{10+}|^2}{Z_1} \right] \left[\frac{4 Z_1 Z_2}{(Z_2 + Z_1)^2} \right]$$

$$= \mathbf{i}_z |E_{10+}|^2 \left[\frac{4 Z_2}{(Z_2 + Z_1)^2} \right] \qquad (17.116)$$

∴   There is no energy dissipation in the dielectrics at the interface.

17.11   THREE DIELECTRICS (NORMAL INCIDENCE)

The same method as discussed in Section 17.10 holds for any number of dielectrics. We consider three media as shown in Figure 17.10. A uniform plane wave: $\mathbf{E}_i = \mathbf{i}_x E_{1+} \exp [j (\omega t - \beta_1 z)]$ is incident from $z = -\infty$ on the first interface between the media 1 and 2. There would be transmitted and reflected waves at each interface for both **E** and **H** vectors, which would be mutually perpendicular, so that the resulting pattern would be given by the equations as stated below:

$$\mathbf{E}_{x1} = \mathbf{i}_x [E_{1+} \exp (-j\beta_1 z) + E_{1-} \exp (j\beta_1 z)] \exp (j\omega t) \qquad (17.117a)$$

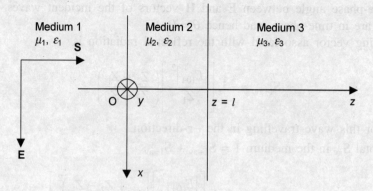

Figure 17.10 Plane wave in three dielectrics.

$$\mathbf{H}_{y1} = \mathbf{i}_y \left[\left(\frac{E_{1+}}{Z_1} \right) \exp\left(-j\beta_1 z \right) - \left(\frac{E_{1-}}{Z_1} \right) \exp\left(-j\beta_1 z \right) \right] \exp\left(j\omega t \right) \qquad (17.117b)$$

$$\mathbf{E}_{x2} = \mathbf{i}_x \left[E_{2+} \exp\left(-j\beta_2 z \right) + E_{2-} \exp\left(j\beta_2 z \right) \right] \exp\left(j\omega t \right) \qquad (17.117c)$$

$$\mathbf{H}_{y2} = \mathbf{i}_y \left[\left(\frac{E_{2+}}{Z_2} \right) \exp\left(-j\beta_2 z \right) - \left(\frac{E_{2-}}{Z_2} \right) \exp\left(-j\beta_2 z \right) \right] \exp\left(j\omega t \right) \qquad (17.117d)$$

$$\mathbf{E}_{x3} = \mathbf{i}_x E_{3+} \exp\left(-j\beta_3 z \right) \exp\left(j\omega t \right) \qquad (17.117e)$$

$$\mathbf{H}_{y3} = \mathbf{i}_y \left(\frac{E_{3+}}{Z_3} \right) \exp\left(-j\beta_3 z \right) \exp\left(j\omega t \right) \qquad (17.117f)$$

The unknowns are E_{1-}, E_{2+}, E_{2-}, and E_{3+}.

The boundary conditions at the two interfaces give:

(1) On $z = 0$, $\mathbf{E}_{x1} = \mathbf{E}_{x2}$ and $\mathbf{H}_{y1} = \mathbf{H}_{y2}$, from which we get

$$E_{1+} + E_{1-} = E_{2+} + E_{2-} \qquad \text{and} \qquad E_{1+} - E_{1-} = \left(\frac{Z_1}{Z_2} \right)(E_{2+} - E_{2-})$$

where

$$Z_1 = \sqrt{\frac{\mu_1}{\varepsilon_1}} \qquad \text{and} \qquad Z_2 = \sqrt{\frac{\mu_2}{\varepsilon_2}}$$

(2) On $z = l$, $\mathbf{E}_{x2} = \mathbf{E}_{x3}$ and $\mathbf{H}_{y2} = \mathbf{H}_{y3}$, from which we get

$$E_{2+} \exp\left(-j\beta_2 l \right) + E_{2-} \exp\left(+j\beta_2 l \right) = E_{3+} \exp\left(-j\beta_3 l \right)$$

and

$$E_{2+} \exp\left(-j\beta_2 l \right) - E_{2-} \exp\left(+j\beta_2 l \right) = \left(\frac{Z_2}{Z_3} \right) E_{3+} \exp\left(-j\beta_3 l \right)$$

where

$$\beta_2 = \omega\sqrt{\mu_2 \varepsilon_2} = \frac{\omega}{u_2} = \frac{2\pi}{\lambda_2}$$

$$\beta_3 = \omega\sqrt{\mu_3 \varepsilon_3} = \frac{\omega}{u_3} = \frac{2\pi}{\lambda_3}$$

From these equations, the four unknowns come out to be:

$$E_{1-} = \left(\frac{E_{1+}}{K}\right)\left[(Z_2 - Z_1) + (Z_2 + Z_1)\left(\frac{Z_3 - Z_2}{Z_3 + Z_2}\right)\exp\left(-j2\beta_2 l\right)\right] \quad (17.118a)$$

$$E_{2+} = \frac{2E_{1+}Z_2}{K} \quad (17.118b)$$

$$E_{2-} = \left(\frac{2E_{1+}Z_2}{K}\right)\left(\frac{Z_3 - Z_2}{Z_3 + Z_2}\right)\exp\left(-j2\beta_2 l\right) \quad (17.118c)$$

$$E_{3+} = \left[\frac{4E_{1+}Z_2 Z_3}{K(Z_3 + Z_2)}\right]\exp\left[-j(\beta_2 - \beta_3)l\right] \quad (17.118d)$$

where

$$K = \left[(Z_2 + Z_1) + (Z_2 - Z_1)\left(\frac{Z_3 - Z_2}{Z_3 + Z_2}\right)\exp\left(-j2\beta_2 l\right)\right] \quad (17.118e)$$

Let us consider a special case of a slab of dielectric in a homogeneous medium of infinite extent, like a sheet of glass or polystyrene in free space (or air), then $\varepsilon_1 = \varepsilon_3$ and $Z_3 = Z_1$, and therefore, from Eqs. (17.118),

$$\frac{E_{1-}}{E_{1+}} = \frac{\left(Z_2^2 - Z_1^2\right)\left[1 - \exp\left(-j2\beta_2 l\right)\right]}{\left(Z_2 - Z_1\right)^2 - \left(Z_2 + Z_1\right)^2 \exp\left(-j2\beta_2 l\right)} \quad (17.119)$$

i.e. the reflections will be eliminated, if $Z_2 = Z_1$, or

$$\exp\left(-j2\beta_2 l\right) = 1 \qquad \text{or} \qquad 2\beta_2 l = 2n\pi$$

Since $\beta_2 = \omega/u_2 = (2\pi f)/(f\lambda_2)$, the required thickness of the slab = l, must be:

$$l = \frac{n\pi}{\beta_2} = \frac{n\lambda_2}{2}$$

where λ_2 is the wavelength in the medium 2, and n is an integer, i.e. all the reflections are eliminated when the thickness of the dielectric plate is one-half the wavelength or its multiple.

Going back to the general case of three dielectrics again, from the first equation of (17.118), the required condition for no reflections gets complicated by the presence of the phase angle term $\exp\left(-j2\beta_2 l\right)$ in part of the numerator. So in this case a double constraint is required, i.e.

$\exp\left(-j2\beta_2 l\right) = \pm 1$, which implies that:

$$2\beta_2 l = 2n\pi \qquad \text{or} \qquad 2\beta_2 l = (2n + 1)\pi$$

so that $l = (2n + 1)\lambda_2/4$ (in the latter case) $\quad (17.120)$

i.e. l has to be a quarter wavelength [or $(3/4)\lambda_2$, $(5/4)\lambda_2$, ...) and the modified ratio then becomes

$$\frac{E_{1-}}{E_{1+}} = \frac{K_1}{K_2} = (Z_2^2 - Z_1 Z_3)(Z_2^2 + Z_1 Z_3) \quad (17.121)$$

where

$$K_1 = (Z_2 - Z_1) - (Z_2 + Z_1)\left(\frac{Z_3 - Z_2}{Z_3 + Z_2}\right)$$

$$K_2 = (Z_2 + Z_1) - (Z_2 - Z_1)\left(\frac{Z_3 - Z_2}{Z_3 + Z_2}\right)$$

so that for the condition of no reflection,

$$Z_2 = \sqrt{Z_1 Z_3} \qquad\qquad (17.122)$$

Thus, for no reflections, the required conditions are:

(1) the thickness l of the second medium must be a quarter wavelength as measured in that medium.

(2) the characteristic impedance of the second medium must be equal to the geometric mean of the characteristic impedances of the other two media.

It should be noted that when the reflections are eliminated, the whole energy is transmitted, since we are considering loss-less media. A practical application of this technique is in the reduction of radar reflections. But the limitation of this method is that it eliminates, though completely, one frequency only. Another application of this technique is in optics, where the camera lenses are coated with one-quarter wavelength thick coatings to eliminate certain colour lights.

17.12 THREE REGION PROBLEM WITH A THIN CONDUCTING LAYER (WITH NORMAL INCIDENCE)

This configuration will be shown to be another way of eliminating reflections, but here we shall not transmit all the energy as in the previous arrangement, and instead absorb it. We consider the general problem as follows.

A plane-polarized and plane electromagnetic wave is incident normally on a perfectly conducting surface. A thin conducting sheet is placed at a distance l from this surface and parallel to it (Figure 17.11). This sheet is so thin that it can be assumed to be a plane, and its surface resistivity is ρ_S Ω/metre^2. The surface of the perfect conductor lies on the plane $z = l$ as shown in the coordinate system of the figure.

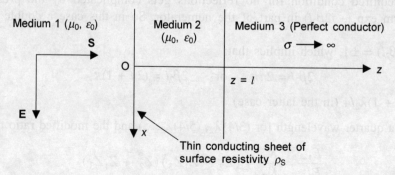

Figure 17.11 A plane wave normally incident on a thin conducting sheet, placed in front of a perfectly conducting plane.

The incident wave is $= \mathbf{E}_{i+} = \mathbf{i}_x E_{1+} \exp [j(\omega t - \beta z)]$
where $\beta = \omega/u = 2\pi/\lambda$, λ = wavelength, and $f = \omega/(2\pi)$ = frequency of repetition = u/λ = c/λ, since it is free space in this problem.

Across the conducting sheet (of finite surface resistivity), the wave will be partly reflected and partly transmitted.

$\therefore$ In both the regions 1 and 2, there will be both the reflected and the transmitted waves. But there will be no transmission through the perfectly conducting surface $z = l$ (of the region 3). The electric and the magnetic waves in the two regions would be:

$$\mathbf{E}_{1x} = \mathbf{i}_x \, [E_{1+} \exp(-j\beta z) + E_{1-} \exp(+j\beta z)] \exp(j\omega t) \qquad (17.123a)$$

$$\mathbf{E}_{2x} = \mathbf{i}_x \, [E_{2+} \exp(-j\beta z) + E_{2-} \exp(+j\beta z)] \exp(j\omega t) \qquad (17.123b)$$

$$\mathbf{H}_{1y} = \mathbf{i}_y \, [H_{1+} \exp(-j\beta z) + H_{1-} \exp(+j\beta z)] \exp(j\omega t) \qquad (17.123c)$$

$$\mathbf{H}_{2y} = \mathbf{i}_y \, [H_{2+} \exp(-j\beta z) + H_{2-} \exp(+j\beta z)] \exp(j\omega t) \qquad (17.123d)$$

The relationships between **E** and **H** are given by:

$$\left(\frac{E_{1+}}{H_{1+}}\right) = -\left(\frac{E_{1-}}{H_{1-}}\right) = \left(\frac{E_{2+}}{H_{2+}}\right) = -\left(\frac{E_{2-}}{H_{2-}}\right) = Z_0 = \sqrt{\mu_0/\varepsilon_0}$$

$$(\because \quad Z_1 = Z_2 = Z_0)$$

Hence,

$$\mathbf{H}_{1y} = \mathbf{i}_y \left[\left(\frac{E_{1+}}{Z_0}\right) \exp(-j\beta z) - \left(\frac{E_{1-}}{Z_0}\right) \exp(+j\beta z)\right] \exp(j\omega t) \qquad (17.124a)$$

$$\mathbf{H}_{2y} = \mathbf{i}_y \left[\left(\frac{E_{2+}}{Z_0}\right) \exp(-j\beta z) - \left(\frac{E_{2-}}{Z_0}\right) \exp(+j\beta z)\right] \exp(j\omega t) \qquad (17.124b)$$

The unknowns at this stage are: E_{1-}, E_{2+}, E_{2-}. To evaluate these, the requisite boundary conditions are:

(1) On the perfectly conducting surface $z = l$, $E_{2x} = 0$
(2) On the conducting sheet $z = 0$

(a) $E_{1x} = E_{2x}$ and (b) $\oint_C \mathbf{H} \cdot d\mathbf{l}$ = enclosed current (Figure 17.12), or $\nabla \times \mathbf{H} = \mathbf{J}$;

$$\therefore \quad (H_{1y} - H_{2y})\Delta w = \left(\frac{I_S}{w}\right)\Delta w$$

where (I_S/w) is the current in the conductor [in the x-direction perpendicular to the plane of the paper (Figure 17.12)] per unit width.

$$\therefore \quad (H_{1y} - H_{2y}) = \frac{E_{1x}}{\rho_S}$$

The three relevant equations obtained are:

$$E_{2x} = 0 = E_{2+} \exp(-j\beta l) + E_{2-} \exp(+j\beta l) \qquad (17.125a)$$

$$E_{1+} + E_{1-} = E_{2+} + E_{2-} \qquad (17.125b)$$

$$\left(\frac{E_{1+}}{Z_0} - \frac{E_{1-}}{Z_0}\right) - \left(\frac{E_{2+}}{Z_0} - \frac{E_{2-}}{Z_0}\right) = \frac{E_{1+} + E_{1-}}{\rho_S} \qquad (17.125c)$$

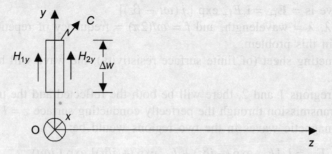

Figure 17.12 A closed contour C in the plane $z = 0$ (view of the y-z plane). Induced currents are in the x-direction into the plane of the paper.

From Eqs. (17.125a and b), we get

$$E_{2+} = \frac{E_{1+} + E_{1-}}{1 - \exp(-j2\beta l)}$$

and

$$E_{2-} = -\left[\frac{E_{1+} + E_{1-}}{1 - \exp(-j2\beta l)}\right] \exp(-j2\beta l)$$

Substituting these values for E_{2+} and E_{2-} in Eq. (17.125c),

$$E_{1+} - E_{1-} - \frac{E_{1+} + E_{1-}}{1 - \exp(-j2\beta l)} - \left[\frac{E_{1+} + E_{1-}}{1 - \exp(-j2\beta l)}\right] \exp(-j2\beta l) = \left(\frac{Z_0}{\rho_S}\right)(E_{1+} + E_{1-})$$

Solving this equation for E_{1-},

$$E_{1-} = \frac{E_{1+}\left[\exp(-j2\beta l)(Z_0 - 2\rho_S) - Z_a\right]}{2\rho_S + Z_0\left[1 - \exp(-j2\beta l)\right]}$$

To eliminate reflections, $E_{1-} = 0$, i.e. $[\exp(-j2\beta l)(Z_0 - 2\rho_S) - Z_0)] = 0$.

This is possible, only if $\exp(-j2\beta l)$ is real [i.e. $= \cos(2\beta l) - j \sin(2\beta l)$].

∴ $\sin(2\beta l) = 0$, i.e. $(2\beta l) = \pm\pi$; or $l = \pi/(2\beta) = (\pi/2)\{\lambda/(2\pi)\} = \lambda/4$.

∴ l must be $= \lambda/4$, or more generally $= (2n + 1)\lambda/4$, and $(Z_0 - 2\rho_S) - Z_0 = 0$, or $\rho_S = Z_0$. Thus all the incident power is absorbed by the conducting sheet only if the sheet has a surface resistivity equal to Z_0, and is placed one-quarter wavelength from a perfectly conducting plane.

17.13   OBLIQUE INCIDENCE OF PLANE WAVES

So far we have considered a number of problems where the plane wave meets the interface of discontinuity normally, in which case the transmitted wave does not change its direction of propagation. We have seen in Section 17.8 that when the incident wave meets the interface of discontinuity, then the transmitted wave in the medium 2 changes its direction, i.e. the angle that the direction of propagation of the transmitted wave makes with the normal to the interface is different from the angle made by the direction of propagation of the incident wave with the same normal to the interface; thus, referring to Figure 17.6, $\theta_i \neq \theta_t$.

When the incident wave is normal to the interface, the mathematical representation of the orientation of the **E** and **H** vectors can always be simplified by a suitable choice of the coordinate system. But this is not so for the oblique incidence of the waves. For this purpose, we have to carefully define the plane of incidence (which we have already done before, but for convenience and clarity, we recapitulate here).

The plane of incidence is defined by a normal to the surface on which the wave impinges and a ray following the direction of propagation.

Following the notation of the direction vectors of the incident, the transmitted and the reflected waves as n_i, n_t, n_r and n (= normal to the interface), these were all proved to be coplanar, and the plane containing these vectors is being defined as the plane of incidence. We also remember that the **E** and **H** vectors in a plane electromagnetic wave are perpendicular to the direction of propagation and to each other. The **E** vector of the incident wave can then be oriented in any direction perpendicular to the vector n_i. It is a normal practice to consider two orientations of the **E** vector, i.e. either **E** is parallel to the plane of incidence or **E** is normal to the plane of incidence. In fact any incident wave can be resolved into these two components. So we shall discuss the behaviour of the waves with these two orientations separately in different sections. However now the direction of propagation is no longer along a coordinate axis direction, and hence the equations for the three waves (i.e. the incident, the reflected and the transmitted) will now be somewhat more complicated, and the expressions for the exponents longer. Hence, if we choose an arbitrary point (x, z) on the direction of propagation of the wave, the equations for the waves can be written as (with respect to Figure 17.13, and following the results of Section 17.8)

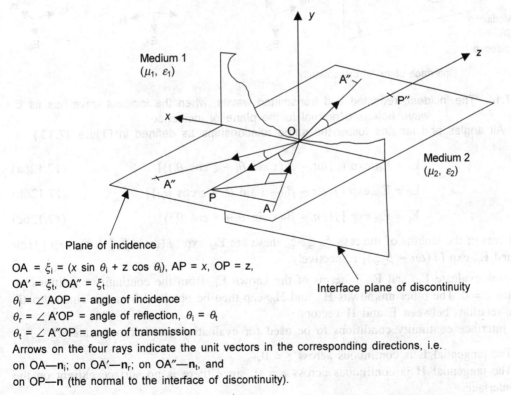

OA $= \xi_i = (x \sin \theta_i + z \cos \theta_i)$, AP $= x$, OP $= z$,

OA$'$ $= \xi_r$, OA$''$ $= \xi_t$

$\theta_i = \angle$ AOP = angle of incidence

$\theta_r = \angle$ A$'$OP = angle of reflection, $\theta_i = \theta_t$

$\theta_t = \angle$ A$''$OP = angle of transmission

Arrows on the four rays indicate the unit vectors in the corresponding directions, i.e.

on OA—n_i; on OA$'$—n_r; on OA$''$—n_t, and

on OP—n (the normal to the interface of discontinuity).

Figure 17.13 Coordinate system used for reflection and refraction of waves.

$$\mathbf{E}_i = \mathbf{E}_{0i} \exp\left[j\{\omega t - \beta_1(x \sin \theta_i + z \cos \theta_i)\}\right] \tag{17.126a}$$

$$\mathbf{E}_r = \mathbf{E}_{0r} \exp\left[j\{\omega t - \beta_1(-x \sin \theta_r + z \cos \theta_r)\}\right] \tag{17.126b}$$

$$\mathbf{E}_t = \mathbf{E}_{0t} \exp\left[j\{\omega t - \beta_2(x \sin \theta_t + z \cos \theta_t)\}\right] \tag{17.126c}$$

17.13.1 Oblique Incidence: Incident Wave Polarized with Its E Vector Normal to the Plane of Incidence

The **E** and **H** vectors of the incident wave are oriented as shown in Figure 17.14. Both the media are assumed to be isotropic and loss-less; and hence the **E** vectors of the reflected as well as the transmitted waves would also be normal to the plane of incidence as shown in the figure. The three waves can be written as

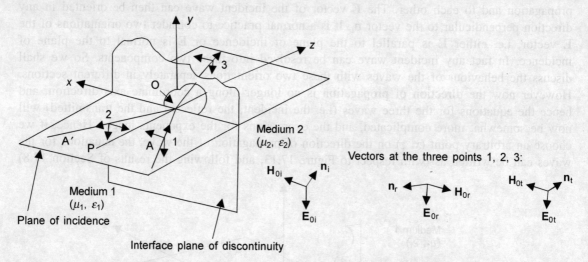

Figure 17.14 The incident, reflected and transmitted waves, when the incident wave has its **E** wave polarized normal to the plane of incidence.
(*Note:* All angles and lengths follow the same relationships as defined in Figure 17.13.)

$$\mathbf{E}_i = \mathbf{E}_{0i} \exp\left[j\{\omega t - \beta_1(x \sin \theta_i + z \cos \theta_i)\}\right] \tag{17.126a}$$

$$\mathbf{E}_r = \mathbf{E}_{0r} \exp\left[j\{\omega t - \beta_1(-x \sin \theta_r + z \cos \theta_r)\}\right] \tag{17.126b}$$

$$\mathbf{E}_t = \mathbf{E}_{0t} \exp\left[j\{\omega t - \beta_2(x \sin \theta_t + z \cos \theta_t)\}\right] \tag{17.126c}$$

where in terms of the lengths of the rays ξ_i, ξ_r, ξ_t, these are $\mathbf{E}_{0i} \exp\left[j(\omega t - \beta_1 \xi_i)\right]$, $\mathbf{E}_{0r} \exp\left[j(\omega t - \beta_1 \xi_r)\right]$, and $\mathbf{E}_{0t} \exp\left[j(\omega t - \beta_2 \xi_t)\right]$ respectively.

We now evaluate $\mathbf{E}_{0r}$ and $\mathbf{E}_{0t}$ in terms of the known $\mathbf{E}_{0i}$ from the continuity conditions on the interface $z = 0$. The other unknowns $\mathbf{H}_{0r}$ and $\mathbf{H}_{0t}$ can then be obtained from the characteristic impedance relations between **E** and **H** vectors.

The interface continuity conditions to be used for evaluating the unknowns are:

1. The tangential **E** is continuous across $z = 0$.
2. The tangential **H** is continuous across $z = 0$, since there is no surface current on the interface.

$\therefore$ These conditions have to be met for all x and at all t.

$$\therefore \quad E_{0i} + E_{0r} = E_{0t} \tag{17.127}$$

(since **E** vector is parallel to the interface plane, as can be seen from Figure 17.7)

and

$$H_{0i} \cos \theta_i + H_{0r} \cos \theta_r = H_{0t} \cos \theta_t \tag{17.128}$$

Now,

$$\frac{E_{0i}}{H_{0i}} = Z_1 = \sqrt{\frac{\mu_1}{\varepsilon_1}} = \frac{\mu_1}{\sqrt{\mu_1 \varepsilon_1}} = \frac{\omega \mu_1}{\omega \sqrt{\mu_1 \varepsilon_1}}$$

$$= \frac{\omega \mu_1}{\beta_1}$$

Similarly,

$$\frac{E_{0r}}{H_{0r}} = \frac{\omega \mu_1}{\beta_1} \quad \text{and} \quad \frac{E_{0t}}{H_{0t}} = \frac{\omega \mu_2}{\beta_2} \tag{17.129}$$

So Eq. (17.128) becomes

$$\left(\frac{\beta_1}{\mu_1} \right)(E_{0i} - E_{0r}) \cos \theta_i = \left(\frac{\beta_2}{\mu_2} \right) E_{0t} \cos \theta_t \tag{17.130}$$

Now,

$$\beta_1 = \omega \sqrt{\mu_1 \varepsilon_1} = \omega \sqrt{\mu_0 \mu_{r1} \varepsilon_0 \varepsilon_{r1}} = \omega \sqrt{\mu_0 \varepsilon_0} \sqrt{\mu_{r1} \varepsilon_{r1}} = \left(\frac{\omega}{c} \right) n_1$$

and similarly $\beta_2 = \left(\dfrac{\omega}{c} \right) n_2$, and hence Eq. (17.130) becomes

$$\left(\frac{n_1}{\mu_1} \right)(E_{0i} - E_{0r}) \cos \theta_i = \left(\frac{n_2}{\mu_2} \right) E_{0t} \cos \theta_t \tag{17.131}$$

Hence, combining Eqs. (17.131) and (17.127), we get

$$\left(\frac{E_{0r}}{E_{0i}} \right)_N = \frac{\left(\dfrac{n_1}{\mu_1} \right) \cos \theta_i - \left(\dfrac{n_2}{\mu_2} \right) \cos \theta_t}{\left(\dfrac{n_1}{\mu_1} \right) \cos \theta_i + \left(\dfrac{n_2}{\mu_2} \right) \cos \theta_t} \tag{17.132a}$$

$$\left(\frac{E_{0t}}{E_{0i}} \right)_N = \frac{2 \left(\dfrac{n_1}{\mu_1} \right) \cos \theta_i}{\left(\dfrac{n_1}{\mu_1} \right) \cos \theta_i + \left(\dfrac{n_2}{\mu_2} \right) \cos \theta_t} \tag{17.132b}$$

where the subscript N indicates that E_{0i} is normal to the plane of incidence. These equations [(17.132a and b)] are two of the 'Fresnel's equations'. The other two will be deduced in the next section. The Fresnel's equations state the ratios of the amplitudes of the incident, reflected and the transmitted waves. They apply to any two media, and we shall find that they are valid even for total reflection.

17.13.2   Oblique Incidence: Incident Wave Polarized with Its E Vector Parallel to the Plane of Incidence

In this case the **E** vectors of all the three waves would lie in the plane of incidence as shown in Figure 17.15, and the **H** vectors would be normal to this plane and parallel to the interface plane of discontinuity between the dielectrics. We have again to use the similar interface continuity conditions, i.e. the continuity of tangential **E** and tangential **H** on the plane $z = 0$.

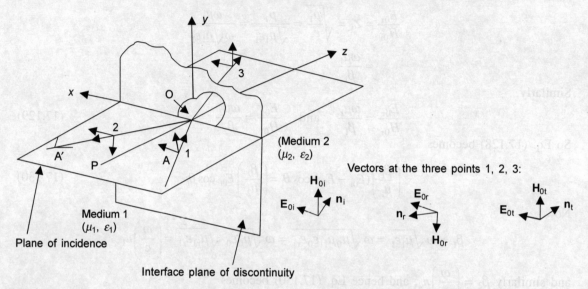

Figure 17.15   The incident, reflected, and transmitted waves, when the incident wave has its **E** wave polarized in the plane of incidence.
(*Note:* All the angles and the lengths follow the same relationships as in Figures 17.13 and 17.14. All subsequent similar figures in this chapter follow the same conventions as in these three diagrams, unless otherwise specifically stated.)

Applying the continuity conditions:

$$H_{0i} - H_{0r} = H_{0t} \quad \text{or} \quad \left(\frac{\beta_1}{\omega \mu_1} \right)(E_{0i} - E_{0r}) = \left(\frac{\beta_2}{\omega \mu_2} \right) E_{0t} \tag{17.133}$$

and

$$(E_{0i} + E_{0r}) \cos \theta_i = E_{0t} \cos \theta_t \tag{17.134}$$

Solving these two equations, as in the previous section, with the used substitutions for β in terms of the indices of refraction,

$$\left(\frac{E_{0r}}{E_{0i}} \right)_P = \frac{- \left(\dfrac{n_2}{\mu_2} \right) \cos \theta_i + \left(\dfrac{n_1}{\mu_1} \right) \cos \theta_t}{\left(\dfrac{n_2}{\mu_2} \right) \cos \theta_i + \left(\dfrac{n_1}{\mu_1} \right) \cos \theta_t} \tag{17.135a}$$

$$\left(\frac{E_{0t}}{E_{0i}} \right)_P = \frac{2 \left(\dfrac{n_1}{\mu_1} \right) \cos \theta_i}{\left(\dfrac{n_2}{\mu_2} \right) \cos \theta_i + \left(\dfrac{n_1}{\mu_1} \right) \cos \theta_t} \tag{17.135b}$$

where the subscript P stands for E_{0i} being parallel to the plane of incidence. The four equations (17.132) and (17.135) are known as the 'Fresnel's equations'. When $\theta_i = \theta_t = 0$, we get the normal incidence of the incident wave, and the plane of incidence becomes indeterminate, and the pairs of equations (17.132) and (17.135) become identical; i.e.

$$\frac{E_{0r}}{E_{0i}} = \frac{\left(\dfrac{n_1}{\mu_1}\right) - \left(\dfrac{n_2}{\mu_2}\right)}{\left(\dfrac{n_1}{\mu_1}\right) + \left(\dfrac{n_2}{\mu_2}\right)} \tag{17.136a}$$

$$\frac{E_{0t}}{E_{0i}} = \frac{2\left(\dfrac{n_1}{\mu_1}\right)}{\left(\dfrac{n_1}{\mu_1}\right) + \left(\dfrac{n_2}{\mu_2}\right)} \tag{17.136b}$$

17.14 REFLECTION AND REFRACTION AT THE INTERFACE BETWEEN TWO NON-MAGNETIC DIELECTRICS (LOSS-LESS)

When we have an interface between two non-magnetic dielectrics, then $\mu_{r1} = \mu_{r2} = 1$, and then the equation for the Snell's law of refraction [Eq. (17.97)] becomes

$$\frac{\sin \theta_t}{\sin \theta_i} = \frac{n_1}{n_2} = \sqrt{\frac{\varepsilon_{r1}}{\varepsilon_{r2}}} \tag{17.137}$$

It should be noted that the index of refraction [Eq. (17.66)] would always be a number equal to or greater than unity. Also, the larger angle is in the medium with the lower index of refraction.

Considering a wave polarized with its **E** vector normal to the plane of incidence, the Fresnel's equations are:

$$\left(\frac{E_{0r}}{E_{0i}}\right)_N = \frac{\left(\dfrac{n_1}{n_2}\right)\cos \theta_i - \cos \theta_t}{\left(\dfrac{n_1}{n_2}\right)\cos \theta_i + \cos \theta_t} \tag{17.138a}$$

$$\left(\frac{E_{0t}}{E_{0i}}\right)_N = \frac{2\left(\dfrac{n_1}{n_2}\right)\cos \theta_i}{\left(\dfrac{n_1}{n_2}\right)\cos \theta_i + \cos \theta_t} \tag{17.138b}$$

It is seen that $(E_{0t}/E_{0i})_N$ is always real and positive. This means that at the interface, the transmitted wave is always in phase with the incident wave. On the other hand $(E_{0r}/E_{0i})_N$ can be either positive or negative depending on the value of (n_1/n_2). If, for example, $(n_1/n_2) > 1$, then $\theta_t > \theta_i$, and $\cos \theta_i > \cos \theta_t$. On the other hand, if $(n_1/n_2) < 1$, then $\theta_t < \theta_i$, and $\cos \theta_i < \cos \theta_t$. Hence the reflected wave is either in phase with the incident wave at the interface of discontinuity if $n_1 > n_2$, or is 180° out of phase if $n_1 < n_2$. Both these types of reflections are shown in Figure 17.16.

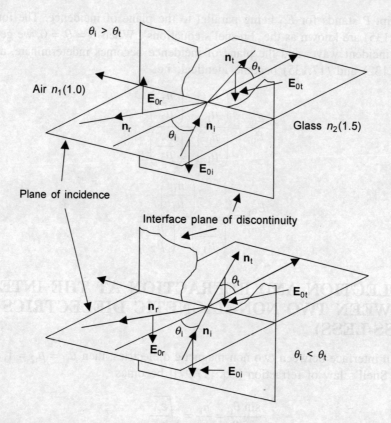

Figure 17.16 The relative phases, at the interface, of **E** in the transmitted and the reflected waves for $n_2 > n_1$ and $n_2 < n_1$ with E_{1oi} normal to the plane of incidence.

Next we consider the incident wave polarized with its **E** vector parallel to the plane of incidence. In this case, the Fresnel's equations become

$$\left(\frac{E_{0r}}{E_{0i}}\right)_P = \frac{-\cos\theta_i + \left(\dfrac{n_1}{n_2}\right)\cos\theta_t}{\cos\theta_i + \left(\dfrac{n_1}{n_2}\right)\cos\theta_t} \tag{17.139a}$$

$$\left(\frac{E_{0t}}{E_{0i}}\right)_P = \frac{2\left(\dfrac{n_1}{n_2}\right)\cos\theta_i}{\cos\theta_i + \left(\dfrac{n_1}{n_2}\right)\cos\theta_t} \tag{17.139b}$$

The second ratio (called the transmission coefficient) is again positive, which means that the incident $\mathbf{E}_i$ wave and the transmitted $\mathbf{E}_t$ wave are in phase (similar to the previous case, when **E** was normal to the plane of incidence).

But the reflection ratio (for $\mathbf{E}_{0r}$) can be either positive or negative, i.e. $\mathbf{E}_r$ and $\mathbf{E}_i$ can be either in phase or 180° out of phase (Figure 17.17).

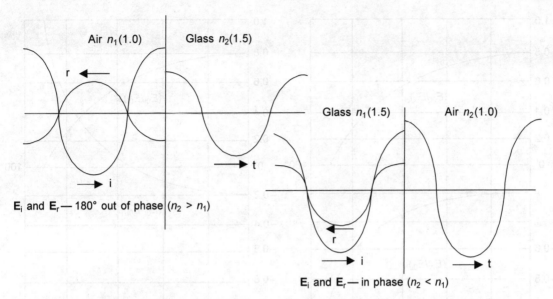

Figure 17.17 Graphs of E_i, E_r, E_t at normal incidence of the air-glass interface.

The $\mathbf{E}_{0r}$ will be in-phase with $\mathbf{E}_{0i}$ at the interface, if

$$\left(\frac{n_1}{n_2}\right)\cos\theta_t - \cos\theta_i > 0 \tag{17.140}$$

But

$$\frac{n_1}{n_2} = \frac{\sin\theta_t}{\sin\theta_i} \quad \text{(Snell's law)}$$

$\therefore$ if

$$\sin\theta_t\cos\theta_t - \sin\theta_i\cos\theta_i > 0$$

or

$$\sin 2\theta_t - \sin 2\theta_i > 0$$

or if

$$\sin(\theta_t - \theta_i)\cos(\theta_t + \theta_i) > 0 \tag{17.141}$$

this inequality is satisfied,

either if

$$\theta_t > \theta_i \quad \text{and} \quad (\theta_t + \theta_i) < \pi/2$$

or if

$$\theta_t < \theta_i \quad \text{and} \quad (\theta_t + \theta_i) > \pi/2 \tag{17.142}$$

Thus the phase of the reflected wave does not depend only on the ratio of the refractive indices, i.e. (n_1/n_2); it also depends on both θ_t and θ_i. The ratio (E_{0r}/E_{0i}) can be either positive or negative, both for $n_2 > n_1$ and for $n_2 < n_1$, as seen in Eq. (17.142).

These ratios have been plotted, i.e. the reflected and the transmitted ratios for both the orientations (**E** vector normal to the plane of incidence, and then parallel to the plane of incidence) in Figure 17.18.

17.15 BREWSTER ANGLE AND TOTAL REFLECTION

From the discussion of Section 17.14, it is seen that in the polarization of the **E** vector parallel to the plane of incidence, there is an angle of incidence, called the 'Brewster angle', for which there is no reflected wave. This is seen from Eq. (17.141), when

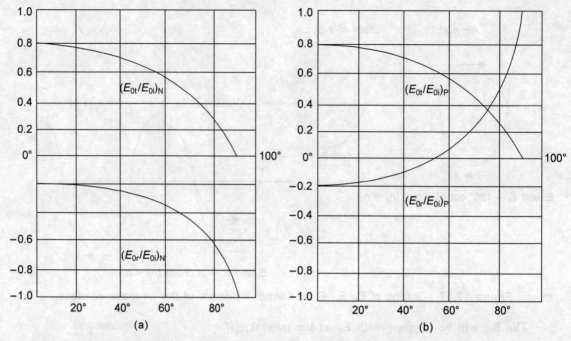

Figure 17.18 The ratios (E_{0t}/E_{0i}) and (E_{0r}/E_{0i}) as functions of the angle of incidence θ_i for $n_1/n_2 = 1.0/1.5$, for (a) **E** vector normal to the plane of incidence; and for (b) **E** vector parallel to the plane of incidence.

$$\sin (\theta_t - \theta_i) \cos (\theta_t + \theta_i) = 0$$

this gives the condition, which happens (i.e. no reflected wave) either when $\theta_i = \theta_t = 0$ or when $\theta_t + \theta_i = \pi/2$.

The first condition is wrong because this has been derived from the inequality (n_1/n_2) $\cos \theta_i - \cos \theta_t > 0$ being multiplied by $\sin \theta_i$ which is zero when $\theta_i = 0$.

∴ The condition for zero reflection is

$$\theta_i + \theta_t = \frac{\pi}{2} \tag{17.143}$$

This means that the conditions of continuity are satisfied by only two waves (for this situation), i.e. the incident wave and the transmitted wave as there is *no* reflected wave. This also implies that for this incident angle $(= \theta_{iB})$, there would be a reflected wave only if the incident wave is polarized with its **E** vector normal to the plane of incidence. For this purpose, this angle of incidence (which is usually called the Brewster's angle) is also called the 'Polarizing angle', since an unpolarized wave incident on an interface at this angle is reflected as a polarized wave with its **E** vector normal to the plane of incidence. This angle is diagrammatically shown in Figure 17.19.

We shall now derive the expression for the Brewster's angle in terms of the media parameters. We start from the expression for the reflection ratio for the case of polarization with the **E** vector parallel to the plane of incidence, i.e. Eq. (17.139), which is

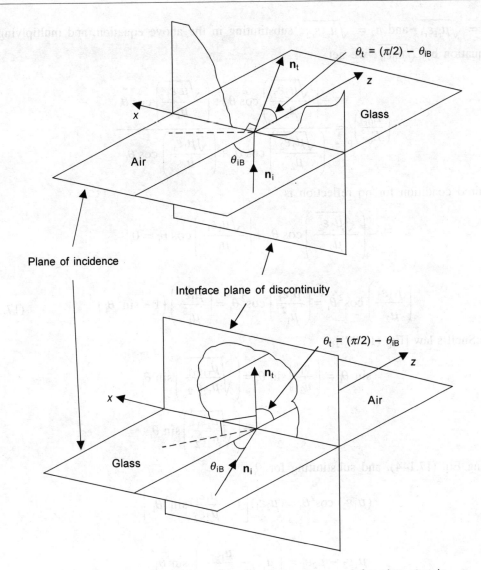

Figure 17.19 Brewster angle for air to glass and for glass to air.

$$\left(\frac{E_{0r}}{E_{0i}}\right)_P = \frac{-\cos\theta_i + \left(\dfrac{n_1}{n_2}\right)\cos\theta_t}{\cos\theta_i + \left(\dfrac{n_1}{n_2}\right)\cos\theta_t} \tag{17.139a}$$

and considering the more general expression of Section 17.13.2 (which imposes no constraint on the permeability of the media), i.e. Eq. (17.135) which states:

$$\left(\frac{E_{0r}}{E_{0i}}\right)_P = \frac{-\left(\dfrac{n_2}{\mu_2}\right)\cos\theta_i + \left(\dfrac{n_1}{\mu_1}\right)\cos\theta_t}{\left(\dfrac{n_2}{\mu_2}\right)\cos\theta_i + \left(\dfrac{n_1}{\mu_1}\right)\cos\theta_t} \tag{17.135a}$$

Since $n_1 = \sqrt{\mu_{r1}\varepsilon_{r1}}$ and $n_2 = \sqrt{\mu_{r2}\varepsilon_{r2}}$, substituting in the above equation, and multiplying the above equation by $\sqrt{\mu_0\varepsilon_0}$, we get

$$\left(\frac{E_{0r}}{E_{0i}}\right)_P = \frac{-\left(\dfrac{\sqrt{\mu_2\varepsilon_2}}{\mu_2}\right)\cos\theta_i + \left(\dfrac{\sqrt{\mu_1\varepsilon_1}}{\mu_1}\right)\cos\theta_t}{\left(\dfrac{\sqrt{\mu_2\varepsilon_2}}{\mu_2}\right)\cos\theta_i + \left(\dfrac{\sqrt{\mu_1\varepsilon_1}}{\mu_1}\right)\cos\theta_t}$$

The required condition for no reflection is

$$-\left(\frac{\sqrt{\mu_2\varepsilon_2}}{\mu_2}\right)\cos\theta_i + \left(\frac{\sqrt{\mu_1\varepsilon_1}}{\mu_1}\right)\cos\theta_t = 0$$

or

$$\left(\frac{\mu_2\varepsilon_2}{\mu_2^2}\right)\cos^2\theta_i = \left(\frac{\mu_1\varepsilon_1}{\mu_1^2}\right)\cos^2\theta_t = \left(\frac{\mu_1\varepsilon_1}{\mu_1^2}\right)\left(1 - \sin^2\theta_t\right) \tag{17.144}$$

From the Snell's law [Eq. (17.97)],

$$\sin\theta_t = \left(\frac{n_1}{n_2}\right)\sin\theta_i = \left(\sqrt{\frac{\mu_{r1}\varepsilon_{r1}}{\mu_{r2}\varepsilon_{r2}}}\right)\sin\theta_i$$

$$= \left(\sqrt{\frac{\mu_1\varepsilon_1}{\mu_2\varepsilon_2}}\right)\sin\theta_i$$

Simplifying Eq. (17.144), and substituting for θ_t,

$$(\mu_1\varepsilon_2)\cos^2\theta_i = (\mu_2\varepsilon_1)\left[1 - \frac{\mu_1\varepsilon_1}{\mu_2\varepsilon_2}\sin^2\theta_i\right]$$

or

$$\mu_1\varepsilon_2 - \mu_2\varepsilon_1 = \left(\mu_1\varepsilon_2 - \frac{\mu_1\varepsilon_1^2}{\varepsilon_2}\right)\sin^2\theta_i$$

$$\therefore\quad \sin^2\theta_i = \varepsilon_2\left[\frac{\mu_1\varepsilon_2 - \mu_2\varepsilon_1}{\mu_1(\varepsilon_2^2 - \varepsilon_1^2)}\right] \tag{17.145a}$$

and

$$\cos^2\theta_i = \varepsilon_1\left[\frac{\mu_2\varepsilon_2 - \mu_1\varepsilon_1}{\mu_1(\varepsilon_2^2 - \varepsilon_1^2)}\right] \tag{17.145b}$$

$$\therefore\quad \theta_i = \tan^{-1}\left[\frac{\varepsilon_2(\mu_1\varepsilon_2 - \mu_2\varepsilon_1)}{\varepsilon_1(\mu_2\varepsilon_2 - \mu_1\varepsilon_1)}\right]^{1/2} = \theta_{iB} \tag{17.145c}$$

This θ_{iB} is the Brewster's angle. For loss-less, non-magnetic dielectrics, $\mu_1 = \mu_2 = \mu_0$, this angle becomes

$$\theta_{iB} = \tan^{-1}\left(\sqrt{\frac{\varepsilon_2}{\varepsilon_1}}\right) = \tan^{-1}\left(\frac{n_2}{n_1}\right) \tag{17.146}$$

We shall now derive the Brewster's angle from the impedance considerations. This is the condition of 'perfect matching'. For this derivation, we refer to the equations of the Section 17.13.2 and Figure 17.15 of the same section. From that figure, the components of characteristic impedances from the incident and the transmitted waves are obtained as

$$Z_{iz} = \frac{E_{ix}}{H_{iy}} = \frac{E_{0i}\cos\theta_i}{H_{0i}} = Z_{0i}\cos\theta_i \tag{17.147a}$$

$$Z_{tz} = \frac{E_{tx}}{H_{ty}} = \frac{E_{0t}\cos\theta_t}{H_{0t}} = Z_{0t}\cos\theta_t \tag{17.147b}$$

For perfect matching,

$$Z_{iz} = Z_{tz} \tag{17.148}$$

or

$$Z_{0i}\cos\theta_i = Z_{0t}\cos\theta_t \tag{17.149}$$

We have

$$Z_{0i} = \sqrt{\frac{\mu_1}{\varepsilon_1}} \qquad \text{and} \qquad Z_{0t} = \sqrt{\frac{\mu_2}{\varepsilon_2}}$$

∴ From Eq. (17.149), we obtain

$$\left(\sqrt{\frac{\mu_1}{\varepsilon_1}}\right)\left(\sqrt{1-\sin^2\theta_i}\right) = \left(\sqrt{\frac{\mu_2}{\varepsilon_2}}\right)\left(\sqrt{1-\sin^2\theta_t}\right)$$

From the Snell's law [Eq. (17.97)],

$$\sin\theta_t = \left(\frac{n_1}{n_2}\right)\sin\theta_i = \left(\sqrt{\frac{\mu_{r1}\varepsilon_{r1}}{\mu_{r2}\varepsilon_{r2}}}\right)\sin\theta_i$$

$$= \left(\sqrt{\frac{\mu_1\varepsilon_1}{\mu_2\varepsilon_2}}\right)\sin\theta_i$$

∴ Substituting in the above, and squaring and cross-multiplying

$$(\mu_1\varepsilon_2)(1-\sin^2\theta_i) = \mu_2\varepsilon_1\left[1-\left(\frac{\mu_1\varepsilon_1}{\mu_2\varepsilon_2}\right)\sin^2\theta_i\right]$$

$$\therefore \quad \sin^2\theta_i = \frac{\varepsilon_2(\mu_1\varepsilon_2 - \mu_2\varepsilon_1)}{\mu_1(\varepsilon_2^2 - \varepsilon_1^2)}$$

which is the same as Eq. (17.145a).

Next we write the reflection coefficient ratio of Eq. (17.135) in terms of the characteristic impedances, i.e.

$$\left(\frac{E_{0r}}{E_{0i}}\right)_P = \frac{-\left(\dfrac{n_2}{\mu_2}\right)\cos\theta_i + \left(\dfrac{n_1}{\mu_1}\right)\cos\theta_t}{\left(\dfrac{n_2}{\mu_2}\right)\cos\theta_i + \left(\dfrac{n_1}{\mu_1}\right)\cos\theta_t} \qquad (17.135a)$$

$$= \frac{-\left(\sqrt{\dfrac{\varepsilon_2}{\mu_2}}\right)\cos\theta_i + \left(\sqrt{\dfrac{\varepsilon_1}{\mu_1}}\right)\cos\theta_t}{\left(\sqrt{\dfrac{\varepsilon_2}{\mu_2}}\right)\cos\theta_i + \left(\sqrt{\dfrac{\varepsilon_1}{\mu_1}}\right)\cos\theta_t}$$

$$\therefore \qquad \left(\frac{E_{0r}}{E_{0i}}\right)_P = \frac{Z_{02}\cos\theta_t - Z_{01}\cos\theta_i}{Z_{02}\cos\theta_t + Z_{01}\cos\theta_i} \qquad (17.150)$$

This is a more useful form to derive the condition for perfect matching from impedance considerations.

The Brewster's angle corresponding to the parallel magnetic field (i.e. parallel to the plane of incidence), can also be similarly obtained, this being useful in radio wave reflections.

Before we go on to discuss the next topic of total reflection, we shall define the energy flow across the present interface. The average energy flow (or flux) per unit area in the incident wave is given by the average value of the Poynting vector as shown in Eq. (17.68). Hence,

$$\overline{\mathbf{S}}_{i\,av} = \frac{1}{2}\left(\sqrt{\frac{\varepsilon_1}{\mu_1}}\right) E_{0i}^2 \mathbf{n}_i \qquad (17.151a)$$

$$\overline{\mathbf{S}}_{r\,av} = \frac{1}{2}\left(\sqrt{\frac{\varepsilon_1}{\mu_1}}\right) E_{0r}^2 \mathbf{n}_r \qquad (17.151b)$$

$$\overline{\mathbf{S}}_{t\,av} = \frac{1}{2}\left(\sqrt{\frac{\varepsilon_2}{\mu_2}}\right) E_{0t}^2 \mathbf{n}_t \qquad (17.151c)$$

where $\mathbf{n}_i$, $\mathbf{n}_r$, and $\mathbf{n}_t$ are the unit vectors in the directions of incidence, reflection, and transmission respectively.

The *coefficients of energy reflection R* and *energy transmission T* are defined as the ratios of the average energy fluxes per unit time and per unit area at the interface, i.e.

$$R = \left|\frac{\overline{\mathbf{S}}_{r\,av}\cdot\mathbf{n}}{\overline{\mathbf{S}}_{i\,av}\cdot\mathbf{n}}\right| = \frac{E_{0r}^2}{E_{0i}^2} \qquad (17.152a)$$

$$T = \left|\frac{\overline{\mathbf{S}}_{t\,av}\cdot\mathbf{n}}{\overline{\mathbf{S}}_{i\,av}\cdot\mathbf{n}}\right| = \left(\sqrt{\frac{\varepsilon_{r2}\mu_{r1}}{\varepsilon_{r1}\mu_{r2}}}\right)\frac{E_{0r}^2}{E_{0i}^2} \qquad (17.152b)$$

where $\mathbf{n}$ is the unit vector normal to the interface.

If we consider the interface between two loss-less, non-magnetic dielectrics, then from the Fresnel's equations, we have

$$R_N = \left[\frac{\left(\dfrac{n_1}{n_2} \right) \cos \theta_i - \cos \theta_t}{\left(\dfrac{n_1}{n_2} \right) \cos \theta_i + \cos \theta_t} \right]^2 \qquad (17.153a)$$

$$T_N = \frac{4 \left(\dfrac{n_1}{n_2} \right) \cos \theta_i \cos \theta_t}{\left\{ \left(\dfrac{n_1}{n_2} \right) \cos \theta_i + \cos \theta_t \right\}^2} \qquad (17.153b)$$

$$R_P = \left[\frac{- \cos \theta_i + \left(\dfrac{n_1}{n_2} \right) \cos \theta_t}{\cos \theta_i + \left(\dfrac{n_1}{n_2} \right) \cos \theta_t} \right]^2 \qquad (17.153c)$$

$$T_P = \frac{4 \left(\dfrac{n_1}{n_2} \right) \cos \theta_i \cos \theta_t}{\left\{ \cos \theta_i + \left(\dfrac{n_1}{n_2} \right) \cos \theta_t \right\}^2} \qquad (17.153d)$$

As we are considering loss-less dielectrics, in both the cases, $R + T = 1$, as all the energy would be conserved.

At the Brewster's angle θ_{iB} [defined by Eq. (17.146)],

$$R_P = 0 \qquad \text{and} \qquad T_P = 1$$

17.15.1 Total Reflection

According to the Snell's law,

$$\frac{\sin \theta_t}{\sin \theta_i} = \sqrt{\frac{\mu_1 \varepsilon_1}{\mu_2 \varepsilon_2}} = \frac{n_1}{n_2} \qquad (17.154)$$

If $(\mu_1 \varepsilon_1) > (\mu_2 \varepsilon_2)$, then $\sin \theta_t$ can be > 1, for a real value of $\sin \theta_i$ (which is apparently a mathematically absurd result). The critical angle of incidence for which $\sin \theta_t = 1$, and $\theta_t = \pi/2$, is

$$\sin \theta_{ic} = \frac{n_2}{n_1} \qquad (17.155)$$

Experimentally it has been observed that when $\theta_i \geq \theta_{ic}$, the wave starting in the medium 1 and incident on the interface, is totally reflected back in the medium 1 (Figure 17.20). This phenomenon is called the 'total reflection', and does not depend on the orientation of the **E** vector of the incident wave. For the light, propagating in glass with an index of refraction of 1.6, the critical angle of incidence is 38.7°. It should be noted that the Snell's law, the laws of reflection and refraction, and the Fresnel's equations are all applicable to the total reflection (by disregarding the fact that $\sin \theta_t > 1$ for the time being, and writing as) i.e.

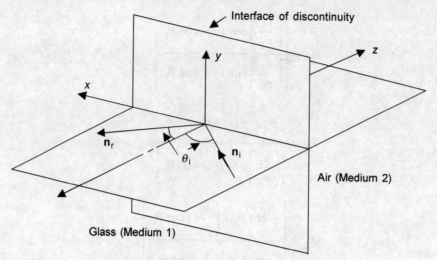

Figure 17.20   Total reflection.

$$\cos \theta_t = -\left(1 - \sin^2 \theta_t\right)^{1/2} = -\left[1 - \left(\frac{n_1}{n_2}\right)^2 \sin^2 \theta_i\right]^{1/2}$$

$$= -j\left(\frac{n_1}{n_2}\right)\left[\sin^2 \theta_i - \left(\frac{n_2}{n_1}\right)^2\right]^{1/2} \tag{17.156}$$

where $n_1 > n_2$.

Let us consider the incident wave

$$\mathbf{E}_{0i} \exp\left[j\{\omega t - \beta_1(x \sin \theta_i + z \cos \theta_i)\}\right]$$

And the transmitted wave

$$\mathbf{E}_{0t} \exp\left[j\{\omega t - \beta_2(x \sin \theta_t + z \cos \theta_t)\}\right]$$

So now the question is: what does it mean if $\sin \theta_t > 1$?

Let $\beta \sin \theta_t = \gamma$, then $\beta \cos \theta_t = \beta\sqrt{1 - \sin^2 \theta_t} = \pm j\alpha$

∴   The transmitted wave becomes

$$\mathbf{E}_{0t} \exp\left[j(\omega t - \gamma_2 x) \exp(\pm \alpha z)\right]$$

which means that the wave is travelling only in the x-direction (i.e. along the interface of the discontinuity), i.e. a surface wave, decreasing [or increasing for $\exp(+\alpha z)$] exponentially in the z-direction—normal to the plane $z = 0$. To understand this expression, we consider, in a more rigorous manner the expressions for the reflected and the transmitted waves when the $\mathbf{E}$ vector is normal to the plane of incidence, i.e.

$$\mathbf{E}_i = \mathbf{i}_y E_{0i} \exp\left[j\{\omega t - \beta_1(x \sin \theta_i + z \cos \theta_i)\}\right]$$

$$\mathbf{E}_r = \mathbf{i}_y E_{0r} \exp\left[j\{\omega t - \beta_1(-x \sin \theta_r + z \cos \theta_r)\}\right]$$

$$\mathbf{E}_t = \mathbf{i}_y E_{0t} \exp\left[j\{\omega t - \beta_2(x \sin \theta_t + z \cos \theta_t)\}\right]$$

From the Fresnel's equations (17.132),

$$\left(\frac{E_{0r}}{E_{0i}}\right)_N = \frac{\left(\dfrac{n_1}{\mu_1}\right)\cos\theta_i - \left(\dfrac{n_2}{\mu_2}\right)\cos\theta_t}{\left(\dfrac{n_1}{\mu_1}\right)\cos\theta_i + \left(\dfrac{n_2}{\mu_2}\right)\cos\theta_t} \qquad (17.132a)$$

$$\left(\frac{E_{0t}}{E_{0i}}\right)_N = \frac{2\left(\dfrac{n_1}{\mu_1}\right)\cos\theta_i}{\left(\dfrac{n_1}{\mu_1}\right)\cos\theta_i + \left(\dfrac{n_2}{\mu_2}\right)\cos\theta_t} \qquad (17.132b)$$

For non-magnetic, loss-less dielectrics,

$$\mu_1 = \mu_2 = \mu_0 \qquad \text{and} \qquad \cos\theta_t = -j\left(\frac{n_1}{n_2}\right)\left[\sin^2\theta_i - \left(\frac{n_2}{n_1}\right)^2\right]^{1/2}$$

Substituting in Eqs. (17.132) and simplifying,

$$\left(\frac{E_{0r}}{E_{0i}}\right)_N = \frac{\cos\theta_i + j\sqrt{\sin^2\theta_i - \left(\dfrac{n_2}{n_1}\right)^2}}{\cos\theta_i - j\sqrt{\sin^2\theta_i - \left(\dfrac{n_2}{n_1}\right)^2}}$$

$$\left(\frac{E_{0t}}{E_{0i}}\right)_N = \frac{2\cos\theta_i}{\cos\theta_i - j\sqrt{\sin^2\theta_i - \left(\dfrac{n_2}{n_1}\right)^2}}$$

Rationalizing, we get

$$\left(\frac{E_{0r}}{E_{0i}}\right)_N = \frac{\left[\cos\theta_i + j\sqrt{\sin^2\theta_i - \left(\dfrac{n_2}{n_1}\right)^2}\right]^2}{1 - \left(\dfrac{n_2}{n_1}\right)^2}$$

$$\left(\frac{E_{0t}}{E_{0i}}\right)_N = \frac{2\cos\theta_i\left[\cos\theta_i + j\sqrt{\sin^2\theta_i - \left(\dfrac{n_2}{n_1}\right)^2}\right]}{1 - \left(\dfrac{n_2}{n_1}\right)^2}$$

On further simplifying, these expressions finally reduce to:

$$\left(\frac{E_{0r}}{E_{0i}}\right)_N = \exp\left[j\,2\tan^{-1}\left\{\frac{\sqrt{\sin^2\theta_i - \left(\frac{n_2}{n_1}\right)^2}}{\cos\theta_i}\right\}\right] = \exp\left(j\alpha\right) \tag{17.157a}$$

and

$$\left(\frac{E_{0t}}{E_{0i}}\right)_N = \frac{2\cos\theta_i}{1 - \left(\frac{n_2}{n_1}\right)^2}\exp\left[j\tan^{-1}\left\{\frac{\sqrt{\sin^2\theta_i - \left(\frac{n_2}{n_1}\right)^2}}{\cos\theta_i}\right\}\right] \tag{17.157b}$$

It should be noted that the amplitude of the reflected wave is equal to the amplitude of the incident wave, so that the coefficient of reflection R is equal to unity. The energy is totally reflected, and the net flux of energy through the interface is zero.

From the above equations, it is also seen that the transmitted wave E_{0t} is not zero, though the net flux of the energy across the interface is zero. The medium 2 can be equated to a pure inductance, the average power to which is zero (the power flow being oscillatory, oscillating one way and then the other), but there is still a current (reactive type) through the inductance.

The transmitted wave is

$$\mathbf{E}_t = \mathbf{i}_y E_{0t}\exp\left[j\left\{\omega t - \left(\frac{n_1}{n_2}\right)\beta_2 x\sin\theta_i\right\} + \left(\frac{n_1}{n_2}\right)\beta_2\left\{\sqrt{\sin^2\theta_i - \left(\frac{n_2}{n_1}\right)^2}\right\}z\right] \tag{17.158}$$

which travels unattenuated parallel to the interface. Its wavelength in the x-direction (parallel to the interface) is

$$\lambda_x = \frac{\lambda_0}{n_1\sin\theta_i} = \frac{\lambda_1}{\sin\theta_i} \tag{17.159}$$

where λ_x is the distance along the x-axis between two neighbouring equiphase points in the incident wave.

This result that the wave travels unattenuated parallel to the interface is quite remarkable. The question as to whether the transmitted wave extends to the other side of the interface cannot be answered on the basis of the present discussion, which is based on the assumption that the incident wave extends to infinity. In reality, what happens is that the incident ray, instead of being reflected abruptly at the interface, penetrates into the medium 2, where it is bent back into the medium 1. The transmitted wave is damped exponentially in the direction normal to the interface (the z-direction), in such a way that its amplitude reduces by a factor e over a distance, which is

$$\delta_z = \frac{\lambda_2}{2\pi\left[\left(\frac{n_1}{n_2}\right)^2\sin^2\theta_i - 1\right]^{1/2}} \tag{17.160}$$

It should be noted that the critical angle θ_c [$= \sin^{-1}(n_2/n_1)$] is somewhat larger than the Brewster angle θ_{iB} [$= \tan^{-1}(n_2/n_1)$]. For the glass-air interface, where the refractive index of the glass is 1.6, $\theta_c = 38.7°$ and $\theta_{iB} = 32°$.

17.15.2 Reflection and Refraction, and Fresnel's Equations in Total Reflection

It is impossible to satisfy the continuity conditions of the tangential **E** and **H** at the interface of discontinuity, with only the incident and the reflected waves. So we are forced to conclude that there would be some sort of transmitted wave, of a rather special nature, since it is not observable under ordinary conditions. It must, of course, satisfy the general wave equation for the non-magnetic dielectrics, i.e.

$$\frac{\partial^2 E_t}{\partial x^2} + \frac{\partial^2 E_t}{\partial z^2} = \mu_0 \varepsilon_2 \left(\frac{\partial^2 E_t}{\partial t^2} \right) \tag{17.161}$$

(In our coordinate system, for the configurations we have been considering, there is no variation in the y-direction, i.e. $\partial/\partial y = 0$). The incident wave has been defined as

$$\mathbf{E}_i = \mathbf{E}_{0i} \exp\left[j\{\omega t - \beta_1 (x \sin \theta_i + z \cos \theta_i)\}\right] \tag{17.162}$$

The reflected wave can be written as

$$\mathbf{E}_r = \mathbf{E}_{0r} \exp\left[j(\omega t - \beta_{1x} x + \beta_{1z} z)\right] \tag{17.163}$$

where $\mathbf{E}_{0r}$, β_{1x}, β_{1z} are unknown constants. The reflected wave would have the same angular frequency ω as the incident wave. Let the transmitted wave be written as

$$\mathbf{E}_t = (\mathbf{i}_x E_{0tx} + \mathbf{i}_y E_{0ty} + \mathbf{i}_z E_{0tz}) \exp\left[j(\omega t - \beta_{2x} x + \beta_{2z} z)\right] \tag{17.164}$$

where E_{0tx}, E_{0ty}, E_{0tz}, β_{2x}, β_{2z} are also unknown constants. Again there is no variation along the y-direction. The **H** vectors are represented similarly in which the letter E is replaced by H, and the origin of the coordinate system is chosen on the interface plane $z = 0$, as shown in Figure 17.6.

First, we evaluate the wave numbers. On the interface $z = 0$, the exponents must be equal for $\mathbf{E}_i$ and $\mathbf{E}_r$.

$$\therefore \quad \beta_{1x} = \beta_1 \sin \theta_i = \left(\frac{2\pi n_1}{\lambda_0} \right) \sin \theta_i \tag{17.165}$$

To evaluate β_{1z}, substituting in the wave equation in the medium 1,

$$\beta_{1x}^2 + \beta_{1z}^2 = \mu_0 \varepsilon_1 \omega^2 = \left(\frac{2\pi n_1}{\lambda_0} \right)^2 \tag{17.166}$$

$$\therefore \quad \beta_{1z}^2 = \left(\frac{2\pi n_1}{\lambda_0} \right)^2 (1 - \sin^2 \theta_i)$$

$$\therefore \quad \beta_{1z} = \left(\frac{2\pi n_1}{\lambda_0} \right) \cos \theta_i = \beta_1 \cos \theta_i \tag{17.167}$$

$$\therefore \quad \mathbf{E}_r = \mathbf{E}_{0r} \exp\left[j\{\omega t - \beta_1 (x \sin \theta_i - z \cos \theta_i)\}\right] \tag{17.168a}$$

which is a plane wave reflected from the interface at an angle equal to the angle of incidence.

FOR THE TRANSMITTED WAVE

Again equating the exponents of the incident and the transmitted waves on the interface $z = 0$, we have

$$\beta_{2x} = \beta_1 \sin \theta_i = \left(\frac{2\pi n_1}{\lambda_0}\right) \sin \theta_i \qquad (17.168b)$$

To evaluate β_{2z}, using the wave equation (17.161) for $\mathbf{E}_t$

$$\beta_{2x}^2 + \beta_{2z}^2 = \omega^2 \mu_0 \varepsilon_2$$

$$\therefore \qquad \beta_{2z} = \pm \left[\left(\frac{2\pi n_2}{\lambda_0}\right)^2 - \left(\frac{2\pi n_1}{\lambda_0}\right)^2 \sin^2\theta_i\right]^{1/2}$$

$$= \pm j\left(\frac{2\pi n_2}{\lambda_0}\right)\left[\left(\frac{n_1}{n_2}\right)^2 \sin^2\theta_i - 1\right]^{1/2} \qquad (17.169)$$

$\therefore$ The transmitted wave is

$$\mathbf{E}_t = \mathbf{E}_{0t} \exp\left[j\left\{\omega t - \left(\frac{2\pi n_1}{\lambda_0}\right) x \sin \theta_i\right\} - \left(\frac{2\pi n_2}{\lambda_0}\right)\left\{\left(\frac{n_1}{n_2}\right)^2 \sin^2\theta_i - 1\right\}^{1/2} z\right] \quad (17.170)$$

The sign before the z-term of the exponent is $-$ve, because $\mathbf{E}$ cannot become infinite as $z \to \infty$.

Note that

$$\beta_{2z} = j\left(\frac{2\pi n_2}{\lambda_0}\right)\left[\left(\frac{n_1}{n_2}\right)^2 \sin^2\theta_i - 1\right]^{1/2}$$

$$\therefore \qquad \cos \theta_t = -\left[1 - \left(\frac{n_1}{n_2}\right)^2 \sin^2 \theta_i\right]^{1/2} = -\left(1 - \sin^2\theta_t\right)^{1/2} \qquad (17.171)$$

Next we evaluate the amplitudes of $\mathbf{E}$ and $\mathbf{H}$ in the reflected and the transmitted waves. We take the incident $\mathbf{E}$ wave normal to the plane of incidence. Hence the reflected and the transmitted $\mathbf{E}$ waves will also be normal to the plane of incidence, i.e.

$$\mathbf{E}_i = \mathbf{i}_y E_{0i} \exp\left[j(\omega t - \beta_1 \mathbf{n}_i \cdot \mathbf{r})\right] \qquad (17.172a)$$

$$\mathbf{E}_r = \mathbf{i}_y E_{0r} \exp\left[j(\omega t - \beta_1 \mathbf{n}_r \cdot \mathbf{r})\right] \qquad (17.172b)$$

$$\mathbf{E}_t = \mathbf{i}_y E_{0t} \exp\left[j(\omega t - \beta_{2x} x - \beta_{2z} z)\right] \qquad (17.172c)$$

writing the exponents in a more compact form, $\mathbf{n}_i$ and $\mathbf{n}_r$ being the unit vectors along the ray of incidence and the ray of reflection respectively; and β_{2x} and β_{2z} are now known quantities.

For the $\mathbf{H}$ vector, $\mathbf{H}$ is now in the plane of incidence in the incident and the reflected waves, and will have both x- and z-components, i.e.

$$\mathbf{H}_i = H_{0i}(\mathbf{i}_x \cos \theta_i + \mathbf{i}_z \sin \theta_i) \exp\left[j(\omega t - \beta_1 \mathbf{n}_i \cdot \mathbf{r})\right] \qquad (17.173a)$$

$$\mathbf{H_r} = H_{0r}(-\mathbf{i}_x \cos\theta_i + \mathbf{i}_z \sin\theta_i)\exp\left[j(\omega t - \beta_1\mathbf{n_r}\cdot\mathbf{r})\right] \tag{17.173b}$$

For the transmitted wave, the amplitude expression is kept more general,

$$\mathbf{H_t} = (\mathbf{i}_x H_{0tx} + \mathbf{i}_y H_{0ty} + \mathbf{i}_z H_{0tz})\exp\left[j(\omega t - \beta_{2x}x - \beta_{2z}z)\right] \tag{17.174}$$

Applying the boundary condition of continuous tangential $\mathbf{E}$ on the interface $z = 0$, we get

$$E_{0i} + E_{0r} = E_{0t} \tag{17.175}$$

The continuity of the tangential $\mathbf{H}$ on $z = 0$ requires

$$H_{0ty} = 0 \qquad \text{and} \qquad (H_{0i} - H_{0r})\cos\theta_i = H_{0tx}, \text{ which is}$$

$$\sqrt{\frac{\varepsilon_0}{\mu_0}}\, n_1(E_{0i} - E_{0r})\cos\theta_i = H_{0tx} \tag{17.176}$$

Continuity of normal $\mathbf{B}$ (or of $\mathbf{H}$, since the media are non-magnetic) at the interface $z = 0$, gives

$$\sqrt{\frac{\varepsilon_0}{\mu_0}}\, n_1(E_{0i} + E_{0r})\sin\theta_i = H_{0tz} \tag{17.177}$$

So we have three equations, i.e. (17.175) to (17.177) to evaluate four unknowns E_{0r}, E_{0t}, H_{0tx}, H_{0tz}. Hence we choose one of the Maxwell's equations and apply it to the transmitted wave, i.e.

$$\nabla \cdot \mathbf{B_t} = \mu_0\nabla \cdot \mathbf{H_t} = 0$$

$$\therefore \qquad \beta_{2x}H_{0tx} + \beta_{2z}H_{0tz} = 0 \tag{17.178}$$

$\therefore$ Solving these equations, we get

$$\left(\frac{H_{0tx}}{E_{0i}}\right)_N = -\left(\sqrt{\frac{\varepsilon_0}{\mu_0}}\right)\frac{j\left[2n_1\cos\theta_i\sqrt{\sin^2\theta_i - \left(\dfrac{n_2}{n_1}\right)^2}\right]}{\cos\theta_i - j\sqrt{\sin^2\theta_i - \left(\dfrac{n_2}{n_1}\right)^2}} \tag{17.179a}$$

$$\left(\frac{H_{0tz}}{E_{0i}}\right)_N = \frac{-\left(\sqrt{\dfrac{\varepsilon_0}{\mu_0}}\right)(n_1\sin 2\theta_i)}{\cos\theta_i - j\sqrt{\sin^2\theta_i - \left(\dfrac{n_2}{n_1}\right)^2}} \tag{17.179b}$$

Thus for the transmitted wave, H_{0tx} is imaginary and H_{0tz} is real, and hence the two components are 90° out of phase; thus this wave rotates in the plane of incidence.

If the Poynting vector was evaluated, it will be seen that the z-component of $\bar{\mathbf{S}}_{av}$ is zero. Thus the behaviour of the wave patterns during the phenomenon of total reflection explains how an optical fibre is capable of *guiding a wave*, while offering *low* radiative losses.

17.16 REFLECTION AND REFRACTION AT THE SURFACE OF A GOOD CONDUCTOR

We have seen that the wave number of a good conductor (in Section 17.6) is

$$k_2 = \frac{2\pi n_2}{\lambda_0} = \sqrt{\frac{\omega \mu_2 \sigma_2}{2}} \, (1 - j)$$

$$= \frac{1}{d\sqrt{2}} (1 - j) = \frac{1}{\delta} (1 - j) \qquad (17.180)$$

where δ (or $d\sqrt{2}$) is the skin-depth. Since the index of refraction n_2 is complex and very large, the application of the Snell's law

$$\frac{\sin \theta_t}{\sin \theta_i} = \frac{n_1}{n_2}$$

leads to a very small value of $\sin \theta_t$. Thus,

$$\sin \theta_t = \frac{n_1}{n_2} \sin \theta_i \quad \text{and} \quad \cos \theta_t = \sqrt{1 - \left(\frac{n_1}{n_2}\right)^2 \sin^2 \theta_i}$$

Though $\cos \theta_t$ is complex, but because $n_2 \gg n_1$, the imaginary part is negligible, and

$$\cos \theta_t \simeq 1 \rightarrow \theta_t \simeq 0 \rightarrow \sin \theta_t \simeq 0 \qquad (17.181)$$

Thus we can justifiably say that the wave penetrates the conductor normally, whatever the angle of incidence might be. Hence the concept of the skin-depth applies to an electromagnetic wave incident at any angle to the surface of a good conductor. For all values of θ_i, the transmitted wave is a plane wave propagating along the normal to the surface, with enormous damping which is the characteristic of these waves in good conductors.

When the incident wave has its **E** vector normal to the plane of incidence, the Fresnel's equations are

$$\left(\frac{E_{0r}}{E_{0i}}\right)_N = \frac{n_1 \mu_{r2} \cos \theta_i - \left(\dfrac{\lambda_0}{2\pi\delta}\right)(1 - j)}{n_1 \mu_{r2} \cos \theta_i + \left(\dfrac{\lambda_0}{2\pi\delta}\right)(1 - j)} \simeq -1 \qquad (17.182a)$$

$$\left(\frac{E_{0t}}{E_{0i}}\right)_N = \frac{2 n_1 \mu_{r2} \cos \theta_i}{n_1 \mu_{r2} \cos \theta_i + \left(\dfrac{\lambda_0}{2\pi\delta}\right)(1 - j)} \ll 1 \qquad (17.182b)$$

The first ratio of Eq. (17.182) implied that $\mathbf{E}_r$ of the reflected wave is in the opposite direction to that of $\mathbf{E}_{0i}$. The transmitted wave is a weak wave with a high degree of attenuation. For the reflected wave, there is a slight loss of intensity, whereas in the case of total reflection there was no loss of intensity and the reflection coefficient in that case was equal to unity.

When the E wave is parallel to the plane of incidence, the behaviour pattern is similar to that of the previous case, i.e.

$$\left(\frac{E_{0r}}{E_{0i}}\right)_P \simeq -1 \quad \text{and} \quad \left(\frac{E_{0t}}{E_{0i}}\right)_P \ll 1 \qquad (17.183)$$

The wave components are shown diagrammatically in Figure 17.21.

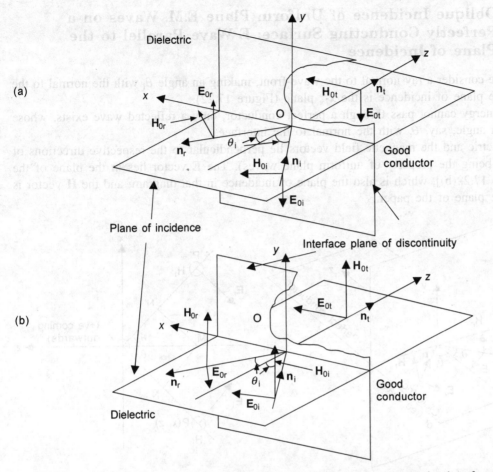

Figure 17.21 The incident, reflected and transmitted waves across the interface between a dielectric and a good conductor: (a) The incident wave with the **E** vector normal to the plane of incidence; (b) the incident wave with its **E** vector parallel to the plane of incidence. The coefficient of reflection is approximately unity in both the cases. The tangential **E** of the incident and the reflected waves nearly cancel each other on the interface.

17.17 OBLIQUE INCIDENCE OF UNIFORM PLANE WAVES ON A PERFECTLY CONDUCTING SURFACE

We shall close this chapter by considering this limiting boundary condition problem, which will serve as an introduction to the study of wave guiding in the next chapter. As in a number of previous problems, in this problem also, we shall study two cases, i.e.

1. Incident **E** wave polarized in the plane of incidence.
2. Incident **E** wave polarized normal to the plane of incidence.

Note: In the next section, we shall establish the geometrical basis of the exponents of the expressions for the obliquely travelling waves (i.e. waves not travelling along the coordinate directions). In fact, this part of the analysis explains the physical basis of the mathematical expressions used from Sections 17.13 onwards.

17.17.1 Oblique Incidence of Uniform Plane E.M. Waves on a Perfectly Conducting Surface: E Wave Parallel to the Plane of Incidence

As before, we consider a ray normal to the wave-front, making an angle θ_i with the normal to the interface. The plane of incidence is the x-z plane (Figure 17.22).

Since energy cannot pass through a perfect conductor, only a reflected wave exists, whose ray makes an angle, say, θ_r with the normal to the interface.

The electric and the magnetic field vectors lie perpendicular to the respective directions of propagation (being the property of uniform plane waves). The **E** vector lies in the plane of the paper [Figure 17.22(b)], which is also the plane of incidence in that diagram; and the **H** vector is normal to the plane of the paper.

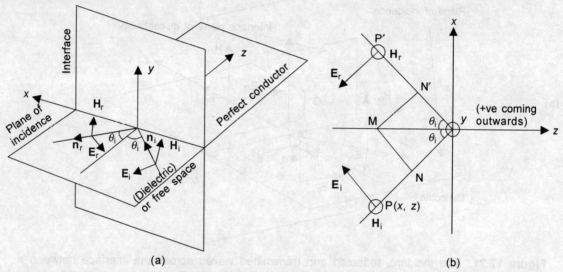

(a)   (b)

Figure 17.22 The incident and the reflected waves, for oblique incidence (with the **E** vector in the plane of incidence) on the perfectly conducting interface ($\sigma \to \infty$): (a) Isometric view; (b) view along the plane of incidence (z-x plane).

Let us say that a wave is now approaching in a direction PO making an angle θ_i with the normal to the interface. $\mathbf{E}_i$ lies in the plane z-x, and will be at right angles to PO as shown. $\mathbf{B}_i$ will be parallel to Oy. Let the point P on the ray of the wave be the point $(-x, 0, -z)$, then (as shown in the figure), PM is parallel to the x-axis and MN perpendicular to PO.

$$\therefore \qquad \text{PO} = \text{PN} + \text{NO} = z \cos \theta_i + x \sin \theta_i \ (= l) \qquad (17.184)$$

Hence the factor $\exp(-j\beta z)$ (for the normally incident waves) is replaced by $\exp[-j\beta(z \cos \theta_i + x \sin \theta_i)]$, since z in the case of the normally incident wave and $(z \cos \theta_i + x \sin \theta_i)$, in this case, measures the distance along the line of wave propagation; and

$$\mathbf{E}_i = \mathbf{E}_{0i+} \exp j[\omega t - \beta(z \cos \theta_i + x \sin \theta_i)] \qquad (17.185)$$

with which is associated the **H** wave

$$\mathbf{H}_i = \mathbf{H}_{0i+} \exp j[\omega t - \beta(z \cos \theta_i + x \sin \theta_i)] \qquad (17.186)$$

in the direction shown in Figure 17.15 and Figure 17.22(b).

These waves, i.e. represented by Eqs. (17.185) and (17.186), could be described as a train of waves of amplitude

$$\mathbf{E}_{0i+} \exp(-j\beta x \sin \theta_i), \qquad \mathbf{H}_{0i+} \exp(-j\beta x \sin \theta_i)$$

moving towards the interface $z = 0$, with a velocity c sec θ_i. By comparing with the case of normal incidence (Section 17.9), these waves give rise to the reflected waves along OP', where

$$OP' = l' = (z \cos \theta_r - x \sin \theta_r) \tag{17.187}$$

$\therefore$ The reflected waves are

$$\mathbf{E}_r = \mathbf{E}_{0r} \exp(+j\beta l') = \mathbf{E}_{0r-} \exp j[\omega t + \beta(-x \sin \theta_r + z \cos \theta_r)] \tag{17.188a}$$

$$\mathbf{H}_r = \mathbf{H}_{0r} \exp(+j\beta l') = \mathbf{H}_{0r-} \exp j[\omega t + \beta(-x \sin \theta_r + z \cos \theta_r)] \tag{17.188b}$$

$\therefore$ The resultant wave pattern due to the combination of the incident and the reflected wave is

$$E_x = [E_{0i+} \cos \theta_i \exp\{-j\beta(x \sin \theta_i + z \cos \theta_i)\}$$
$$-E_{0r-} \cos \theta_r \exp\{j\beta(-x \sin \theta_r + z \cos \theta_r)\}] \exp(j\omega t) \tag{17.189a}$$

$$E_z = [-E_{0i+} \sin \theta_i \exp\{-j\beta(x \sin \theta_i + z \cos \theta_i)\}$$
$$-E_{0r-} \sin \theta_r \exp\{j\beta(-x \sin \theta_r + z \cos \theta_r)\}] \exp(j\omega t) \tag{17.189b}$$

It should be noted that since $\mathbf{E}$ lies in the plane of incidence, it has two components, i.e. x- and z-, whilst $\mathbf{H}$ will be along the y-axis. Hence,

$$H_y = [H_{0i+} \exp\{-j\beta(x \sin \theta_i + z \cos \theta_i)\}$$
$$+ H_{0r-} \exp\{j\beta(-x \sin \theta_r + z \cos \theta_r)\}] \exp(j\omega t) \tag{17.190}$$

Now we apply the boundary conditions on the interface of the perfect conductor (i.e. $z = 0$ plane):

No tangential $\mathbf{E}$ on $z = 0$, i.e. $E_x = 0$, for all x

$$\therefore \quad (E_x)_{z=0} = 0 = E_{0i+} \cos \theta_i \exp(-j\beta x \sin \theta_i) - E_{0r-} \cos \theta_r \exp(-j\beta x \sin \theta_r)$$

$\therefore \quad \theta_r = \theta_i \rightarrow$ angle of reflection = angle of incidence, and $E_{0i+} = E_{0r-}$, i.e. the amplitudes of the incident and the reflected waves are the same. Also, the characteristic impedance relationship gives

$$\frac{E_{0i+}}{H_{0i+}} = Z_0 = \frac{E_{0r-}}{H_{0r-}} \qquad \text{(for free space)}$$

$\therefore$ Substituting in Eqs. (17.189) and (17.190), we get

$$\mathbf{E}_x = \mathbf{i}_x[-2jE_{0i+} \cos \theta_i \sin(\beta z \cos \theta_i) \exp j(\omega t - \beta x \sin \theta_i)] \tag{17.191a}$$

$$\mathbf{E}_z = \mathbf{i}_z[-2E_{0i+} \sin \theta_i \cos(\beta z \cos \theta_i) \exp j(\omega t - \beta x \sin \theta_i)] \tag{17.191b}$$

$$\mathbf{H}_y = \mathbf{i}_y\left[2\left(\frac{E_{0i+}}{Z_0}\right) \cos(\beta z \cos \theta_i) \exp j(\omega t - \beta x \sin \theta_i)\right] \tag{17.191c}$$

These equations represent travelling waves with respect to the x-direction, but standing waves with respect to z-direction.

On the perfectly conducting plane $z = 0$, $\mathbf{E}_x = 0$ at all instants of time; and also in parallel planes at distances (nd) in front of the perfect conductor surface $z = 0$, where

$$z = d = \frac{\pi}{\beta \cos \theta_i} = \frac{\lambda}{2 \cos \theta_i} = \frac{1}{2f \sqrt{\mu_0 \varepsilon_0} \cos \theta_i} \tag{17.192}$$

$$\left\{ \because \quad \beta = \frac{2\pi}{\lambda} \quad \text{and} \quad \beta z \cos \theta_i = \pi \Rightarrow z = \frac{\pi}{\beta \cos \theta_i} \right\}$$

The alternating amplitude of $\mathbf{E}_x$ is maximum in the planes which are odd multiples of $(d/2)$ in front of the conducting interface $z = 0$.

H_y and E_z are maximum, when $\mathbf{E}_x = 0$, i.e. $z = 0$, and (nd), n being integers.

H_y and E_z are zero, when $\mathbf{E}_x = $ maximum, i.e. $z = $ odd multiple of $(d/2)$.

Also H_y and E_z are $90°$ ($= \pi/2$) out of phase with $\mathbf{E}_x$.

It should also be noted that the distance between the successive maxima and the zero, measured normal to the interface plane becomes greater as the incidence becomes more oblique, i.e. as θ_i increases.

17.17.2 Oblique Incidence of Uniform Plane E.M. Waves on a Perfectly Conducting Surface: E Vector Normal to the Plane of Incidence

As before in the previous section, we consider again a wave approaching in a direction PO which makes an angle θ_i with the normal to the interface of discontinuity. The **E** vector is now parallel to Oy (the origin of the coordinate system being on the interface plane as shown in Figure 17.23); and hence in Figure 17.23(b) it is normal to the plane of the paper, but **B** or **H** will lie in the plane of incidence (Ozx), and will be at right angles to PO, as shown. Let P be the point $(- x, 0, - z)$, then PM is parallel to the x-axis and MN is perpendicular to PO, and hence:

$$\text{PO} = \text{PN} + \text{NO} = z \cos \theta_i + x \sin \theta_i \ (= 1) \tag{17.193}$$

Hence, comparing with the normal incidence problem, the factor $\exp (- j\beta z)$ is now replaced by $\exp [- j\beta (z \cos \theta_i + x \sin \theta_i)]$, since z in the previous case (Section 17.9) and $(z \cos \theta_i + x \sin \theta_i)$ in the present case measure distances along the line of propagation; and

$$\begin{aligned} \mathbf{E}_i &= \mathbf{E}_{0i} \exp [- j\beta (z \cos \theta_i + x \sin \theta_i)] \\ &= \mathbf{E}_{0i+} \exp j [\omega t - \beta (z \cos \theta_i + x \sin \theta_i)] \end{aligned} \tag{17.194}$$

with which is associated the **H** wave;

$$\begin{aligned} \mathbf{H}_i &= \mathbf{H}_{0i} \exp [- j\beta (z \cos \theta_i + x \sin \theta_i)] \\ &= \mathbf{H}_{0i+} \exp j [\omega t - \beta (z \cos \theta_i + x \sin \theta_i)] \end{aligned} \tag{17.195}$$

in the directions shown in Figure 17.23.

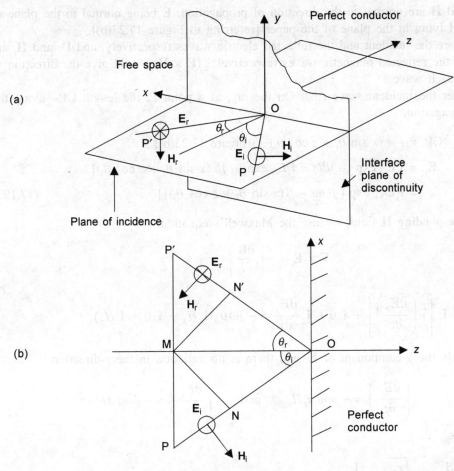

Figure 17.23 The incident and the reflected waves, for oblique incidence, with **E** vector normal to the plane of incidence, on a perfectly conducting interface ($\sigma \to \infty$): (a) Isometric view; and (b) view along the plane of incidence.

The previous two equations, i.e. (17.194) and (17.195) could also be described as a train of waves of amplitude $\mathbf{E}_{0i} \exp(-j\beta x \sin \theta_i)$ and $\mathbf{H}_{0i} \exp(-j\beta x \sin \theta_i)$ moving towards the boundary interface $z = 0$ with a velocity (c sec θ_i). By the Section 17.9, these give rise to reflected waves in which the signs of $\mathbf{E}_{0i}$ (but not $\mathbf{H}_{0i}$) and of z are changed, i.e.

$$\mathbf{E}_r = -\mathbf{E}_{0i} \exp[j\beta(z \cos \theta_i - x \sin \theta_i)] \tag{17.196a}$$

$$\mathbf{H}_r = -\mathbf{H}_{0i} \exp[j\beta(z \cos \theta_i - x \sin \theta_i)] \tag{17.196b}$$

We have written down the expressions for the reflected waves, based on physical arguments. However, alternatively, the same results can be obtained by using formal mathematics based on the Maxwell's equations, which we indicate below.

The ray OP, in Figure 17.23, is normal to the wave-front, and makes an angle θ_i with the normal to the interface of the conducting region, i.e. the plane $z = 0$. Since there is no energy penetration through a perfect conductor, only the reflected wave exists, which, say, makes an angle θ_r with the normal to the interface plane.

Both **E** and **H** are normal to the direction of propagation, **E** being normal to the plane of the paper, and **H** lying in the plane of the paper [referring to Figure 17.23(b)].

$\mathbf{E_i}$ and $\mathbf{E_r}$ are the incident and the reflected electric waves respectively, and $\mathbf{H_i}$ and $\mathbf{H_r}$ are the incident and the reflected magnetic waves respectively. $(\mathbf{E} \times \mathbf{H})$ would give the direction of propagation for each wave.

We consider the incident wave first. On the ray, at a point P, the length OP—along the direction of propagation,

$$OP = l = (x \sin \theta_i + z \cos \theta_i) \quad [(\text{Figure } 17.23(b)]$$

$$\mathbf{E_i} = \mathbf{i}_y E_{0i} \exp(-j\beta l) = \mathbf{i}_y E_{0i} \exp[-j\beta(x \sin \theta_i + z \cos \theta_i)]$$

$$= \mathbf{i}_y E_{0i+} \exp[j\{\omega t - \beta(x \sin \theta_i + z \cos \theta_i)\}] \quad (17.197)$$

To find the corresponding **H** field, we use the Maxwell's equation,

$$\nabla \times \mathbf{E} = -\left(\frac{\partial \mathbf{B}}{\partial t}\right)$$

or

$$\mathbf{i}_x\left[-\left(\frac{\partial \mathbf{E}_y}{\partial z}\right)\right] + \mathbf{i}_y 0 + \mathbf{i}_z \frac{\partial \mathbf{E}_y}{\partial x} = -j\omega\mu_0(\mathbf{i}_x H_x + \mathbf{i}_y 0 + \mathbf{i}_z H_z)$$

since there is only the y-component of **E**, and there is no variation in the y-direction.

$$\therefore \qquad -\left(\frac{\partial E_y}{\partial z}\right) = -j\omega\mu_0 \mathbf{i}_x H_x \quad \text{and} \quad \left(\frac{\partial E_y}{\partial x}\right) = -j\omega\mu_0 H_z$$

Now $\beta = \omega\sqrt{\mu_0\varepsilon_0}$

$$\therefore \qquad \frac{\beta}{\omega\mu_0} = \sqrt{\frac{\varepsilon_0}{\mu_0}} = \frac{1}{Z_0}$$

$$\therefore \qquad H_{ix} = \left(\frac{1}{j\omega\mu_0}\right)\left(\frac{\partial E_y}{\partial z}\right)$$

$$= -\left[\left(\frac{j\beta\cos\theta_i}{j\omega\mu_0}\right)\right]E_{0i}\exp[-j\beta(x\sin\theta_i + z\cos\theta_i)]$$

$$= -\left(\frac{E_{0i}}{Z_0}\right)\cos\theta_i \exp[-j\beta(x\sin\theta_i + z\cos\theta_i)] \quad (17.198)$$

$$H_{iz} = -\left(\frac{1}{j\omega\mu_0}\right)\left(\frac{\partial E_y}{\partial x}\right)$$

$$= \left(\frac{j\beta\sin\theta_i}{j\omega\mu_0}\right)E_{0i}\exp[-j\beta(x\sin\theta_i + z\cos\theta_i)]$$

$$= \left(\frac{E_{0i}}{Z_0}\right)\sin\theta_i \exp[-j\beta(x\sin\theta_i + z\cos\theta_i)] \quad (17.199)$$

Next, we derive the expressions for the reflected wave,

$$\mathbf{E}_r = \mathbf{i}_y E_{0r} \exp(-j\beta l'), \qquad \text{where } l' = OP' = (-x \sin\theta_r + z \cos\theta_r),$$

where the −ve sign is due to θ_r being measured in the sense opposite to that of θ_i.

$$\therefore \qquad\qquad \mathbf{E}_r = \mathbf{i}_y E_{0r} \exp[j\beta(-x \sin\theta_r + z \cos\theta_r)] \qquad\qquad (17.200)$$

and the corresponding **H** vector:

$$H_{rx} = \left(\frac{1}{j\omega\mu_0}\right)\left(\frac{\partial E_y}{\partial z}\right)$$

$$= \left(\frac{j\beta \cos\theta_r}{j\omega\mu_0}\right) E_{0r} \exp[j\beta(-x \sin\theta_r + z \cos\theta_r)]$$

$$= \left(\frac{E_{0r}}{Z_0}\right) \cos\theta_r \exp[j\beta(-x \sin\theta_r + z \cos\theta_r)] \qquad\qquad (17.201)$$

$$H_{rz} = -\left(\frac{1}{j\omega\mu_0}\right)\left(\frac{\partial E_y}{\partial x}\right)$$

$$= -\left(\frac{-j\beta \sin\theta_r}{j\omega\mu_0}\right) E_{0r} \exp[j\beta(-x \sin\theta_r + z \cos\theta_r)]$$

$$= \left(\frac{E_{0r}}{Z_0}\right) \sin\theta_r \exp[j\beta(-x \sin\theta_r + z \cos\theta_r)] \qquad\qquad (17.202)$$

∴   Combining the incident and the reflected waves, the resultant is obtained as

$$E_y = E_{0i} \exp[-j\beta(x \sin\theta_i + z \cos\theta_i)] + E_{0r} \exp[j\beta(-x \sin\theta_r + z \cos\theta_r)] \qquad (17.203a)$$

$$H_x = -\left(\frac{E_{0i}}{Z_0}\right) \exp[-j\beta(x \sin\theta_i + z \cos\theta_i)] \cos\theta_i$$

$$+ \left(\frac{E_{0r}}{Z_0}\right) \exp[j\beta(-x \sin\theta_r + z \cos\theta_r)] \cos\theta_r \qquad\qquad (17.203b)$$

$$H_z = \left(\frac{E_{0i}}{Z_0}\right) \exp[-j\beta(x \sin\theta_i + z \cos\theta_i)] \sin\theta_i$$

$$+ \left(\frac{E_{0r}}{Z_0}\right) \exp[j\beta(-x \sin\theta_r + z \cos\theta_r)] \sin\theta_r \qquad\qquad (17.203c)$$

Now we apply the boundary condition on the reflecting plane $z = 0$ which is that there is no tangential **E** on the perfectly conducting surface, i.e.

for $z = 0$, $E_y = 0$

$$= E_{0i} \exp[-j\beta(x \sin\theta_i)] + E_{0r} \exp[-j\beta(x \sin\theta_r)], \text{ for all } x \text{ (and } t)$$

$$\therefore \qquad \theta_i = \theta_r \qquad \text{and} \qquad E_{0r} = -E_{0i}$$

∴   The resultant field components are

$$E_y = - j2E_{0i} \sin (\beta z \cos \theta_i) \exp (- j\beta x \sin \theta_i)$$

$$= - j2E_{0i+} \sin (\beta z \cos \theta_i) \exp j(\omega t - \beta x \sin \theta_i) \qquad (17.204a)$$

$$H_x = - 2\left(\frac{E_{0i}}{Z_0}\right) \cos \theta_i \cos (\beta z \cos \theta_i) \exp (- j\beta x \sin \theta_i)$$

$$= - 2\left(\frac{E_{0i+}}{Z_0}\right) \cos \theta_i \cos (\beta z \cos \theta_i) \exp j(\omega t - \beta x \sin \theta_i) \qquad (17.204b)$$

$$H_z = - 2j\left(\frac{E_{0i}}{Z_0}\right) \sin \theta_i \sin (\beta z \cos \theta_i) \exp (- j\beta x \sin \theta_i)$$

$$= - 2j\left(\frac{E_{0i+}}{Z_0}\right) \sin \theta_i \sin (\beta z \cos \theta_i) \exp j(\omega t - \beta x \sin \theta_i) \qquad (17.204c)$$

$\therefore$ These are travelling waves in the x-direction, but standing patterns in the z-direction.

On the plane $z = 0$ (i.e. the interface between the perfect conductor and the free space), $E_y = 0$, $H_z = 0$, i.e. no tangential **E** field and no normal **H** field; and only the tangential **H** (i.e. H_x) field exists.

$\therefore$ There will be circulating currents (i.e. eddy currents) in the y-direction, i.e. J_y, on this plane.

$\therefore$ On the plane $z = 0$, there will be zeroes of E_y and H_z; and maxima of H_x. These values will be repeated at intervals of $z = d$, such that $\sin (\beta d \cos \theta_i) = 0 = \sin \pi$ or $\sin n\pi$, where $n = $ all integers.

$$\therefore \quad d_n = \frac{n\pi}{\beta \cos \theta_i} = \frac{n}{2f\sqrt{(\mu_0 \varepsilon_0)} \cos \theta_i}, \quad \beta = 2\pi f \sqrt{\mu_0 \varepsilon_0}$$

$$\therefore \quad d_1 = \frac{\pi}{\beta \cos \theta_i} \qquad (17.205)$$

Also, E_y and H_z will have maxima, and H_x be zero at odd multiples of $(d_1/2)$ in front of the interface $z = 0$.

Hence $d_1 = $ distance between successive zeroes and successive maxima; and $(d_1/2) = $ distance between successive zero and maximum.

Also, since $d_1 = \pi/(\beta \cos \theta_i)$, d_1 depends on θ_i—the angle of incidence of the wave on the reflecting surface. As θ_i increases to $(\pi/2)$, $\cos \theta_i \to 0$, and hence d_1 increases. A pattern of **E** wave crests (maxima) and zeroes is shown in Figure 17.24.

The standing wave pattern in the z-direction has been produced by the interaction between the incident wave and the reflected wave. Physically what has happened is when a positive crest of the incident **E** wave meets the reflecting surface ($z = 0$), it changes to a negative crest, and vice versa. The **H** and the **E** waves behave like water waves approaching a wall; and where the crests of the incident and the reflected waves coincide, at those points there is doubling of amplitudes. On the boundary (i.e. $z = 0$), whilst the resulting E_y is zero, the H_x has doubled because for H_x the positive crest is reflected as positive crest, and on the other hand H_z behaves like E_y wave. Thus, there are planes like $A_1 A_1'$, AA' (referring to Figure 17.24) which are in the same condition as the reflecting surface $z = 0$, i.e. on all these planes E_y and H_z are both zeroes and H_x maximum. The wave pattern is stationary in the z-direction, but gliding or travelling along the x-direction. Thus, *we have now 'guided' the wave along the x-direction.*

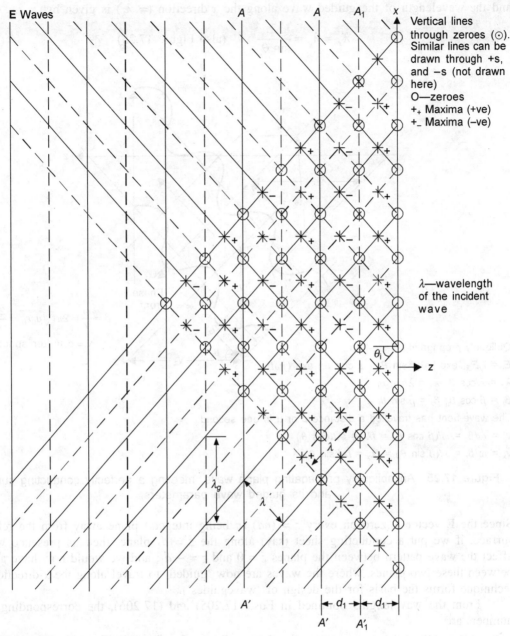

Figure 17.24 Resultant **E** wave pattern, when the incident **E** wave, normal to the plane of incidence, meets a perfectly conducting surface obliquely.

If λ is the wavelength of the incident wave (in the direction of its propagation), where $\lambda = 2\pi/\beta$, then the wavelength of the standing wave pattern in the z-direction ($= \lambda_z$) is given by

$$\lambda_z = 2d_1 = \frac{2\pi}{\beta \cos \theta_i} = \frac{\lambda}{\cos \theta_i} \tag{17.206}$$

and the wavelength of the guided wave along the x-direction ($= \lambda_x$) is given by

$$\lambda_x = \lambda_g = \frac{\lambda}{\sin\theta_i} \qquad \text{(also Figure 17.25)} \qquad (17.207)$$

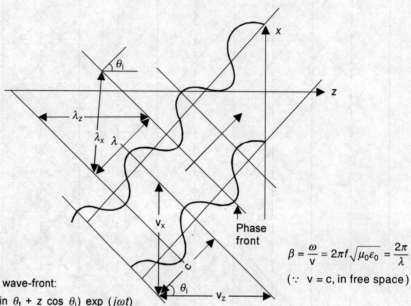

Obliquely propagating wave-front:

$E_i = \mathbf{i}_y E_{0i+} \exp[j\beta(x \sin\theta_t + z \cos\theta_i) \exp(j\omega t)$

$\lambda_z = \lambda/\cos\theta_i; \ \lambda_x = \lambda/\sin\theta_i$

$\beta_z = \beta \cos\theta_i; \ \beta_x = \beta \sin\theta_i$

The wave-front has travelled a distance c or u in one second.

$v_z = \omega/\beta_z = \omega/(\beta \cos\theta_i) = f\lambda_z = f\lambda/(\cos\theta_i)$

$v_x = \omega/\beta_x = \omega/(\beta \sin\theta_i) = f\lambda_x = f\lambda/(\sin\theta_i)$

$$\beta = \frac{\omega}{v} = 2\pi f \sqrt{\mu_0 \varepsilon_0} = \frac{2\pi}{\lambda}$$

$(\because \ v = c, \text{ in free space})$

Figure 17.25 An obliquely propagating plane wave, meeting a perfectly conducting surface, and its guided wave parameters.

Since the **E** vector is zero on every $z = (nd)$ (n being integers) plane away from the reflecting surface, if we put a conducting sheet (say) along the $z = d_1$ plane, then its presence will not affect the wave pattern between the planes $z = 0$ and $z = -d_1$; and we would now have a region between these two planes, where the waves are now 'guided' to travel along the x-direction (this technique forms the basis for the design of 'waveguides').

From the wavelengths obtained in Eqs. (17.205) and (17.206), the corresponding wave-numbers are

$$\beta_z = \text{the wave-number for the standing wave pattern} = \beta \cos\theta_i \qquad (17.208a)$$

$$\beta_x = \text{the wave-number for the guided wave pattern} \quad = \beta \sin\theta_i \qquad (17.208b)$$

$$\therefore \qquad \beta_z^2 + \beta_x^2 = \beta^2 \qquad (17.209a)$$

and

$$\frac{1}{\lambda_z^2} + \frac{1}{\lambda_x^2} = \frac{1}{\lambda^2} \qquad (17.209b)$$

Generalizing the position of the second conducting sheet (i.e. instead of keeping it along the plane $z = -d_1$), it can be placed on any of the zero-field planes without altering the wave pattern between the planes $z = 0$ and $z = (md_1)$ where m is an integer. Such an operation is called an 'm-mode operation', whereas $m = 1$ is called 'mode 1 operation', for which,

$$2d_1 = \frac{2\pi}{\beta \cos \theta_i} = \frac{\lambda}{\cos \theta_i}$$

$\therefore \quad \cos \theta_1 = \dfrac{\lambda}{2d_1}$, and, in general, for mode m operation,

$$\cos \theta_m = \frac{m\lambda}{2d_1} \tag{17.210}$$

and, for this mode, the wavelength of the guided wave is

$$(\lambda_g =) \lambda_{gm} = \frac{\lambda}{\sin \theta_m} = \frac{\lambda}{\left[1 - \left(\dfrac{m\lambda}{2d_1}\right)^2\right]^{1/2}} \tag{17.211}$$

$\therefore$ The velocity of the guided wave (along the x-direction) is

$$v_g = f\lambda_g = \frac{f\lambda}{\left[1 - \left(\dfrac{m\lambda}{2d_1}\right)^2\right]^{1/2}} = v_x \tag{17.212}$$

where

$f\lambda$ = the velocity of the incident wave

= c, in free space

= v, in general, in any medium

The phase coefficient of the guided wave is

$$\beta_x = \beta_g = \frac{2\pi}{\lambda_x} = \frac{2\pi}{\lambda_g} = \left(\frac{2\pi}{\lambda}\right)\left[1 - \left(\frac{m\lambda}{2d_1}\right)^2\right]^{1/2}$$

$$= \beta \sin \theta_m \tag{17.213}$$

So, for the wave to propagate in this direction, β_x (or β_g) must be real, i.e. $E_{gx} \exp [j (\omega t - \beta_x x)]$.

$\therefore$ As λ is increased (or f is decreased), a point is reached at which β_x is zero, i.e. $\beta_x = \beta_g = 0$. If λ is increased still further, β_g becomes an imaginary quantity, and then there is no wave motion between the conducting plates; i.e. the frequency ($= f_c$) at which β_g is zero, is called the 'cut-off frequency' of the system. This gives

$$\beta_g = 0 \quad \text{or} \quad 1 - \left(\frac{m\lambda_c}{2d_1}\right)^2 = 0$$

$$\therefore \qquad \lambda_c = \frac{2d_1}{m} \tag{17.214}$$

$$\therefore \qquad f_c = \frac{v}{\lambda_c} = \frac{vm}{2d_1} \tag{17.215}$$

Given the order of the mode, m, the spacing d_1 and the velocity (to be general, in a dielectric) v, the cut-off frequency can be found.

$\therefore$ The phase velocity of the guided wave expressed in terms of the cut-off frequency is given as

$$v_g = \frac{v}{\left[1 - \left(\frac{m\lambda}{2d_1}\right)^2\right]^{1/2}} = \frac{v}{\left[1 - \left(\frac{m}{2d_1}\right)^2 \left(\frac{v}{f}\right)^2\right]^{1/2}}$$

$$= \frac{v}{\left[1 - \left(\frac{f_c}{f}\right)^2\right]^{1/2}} = v_x \qquad (17.216)$$

$$\therefore \qquad \lambda_x \text{ or } \lambda_g = \frac{v_x}{f} = \frac{\lambda}{\left[1 - \left(\frac{f_c}{f}\right)^2\right]^{1/2}} \qquad (17.217)$$

when $m = 1$, there is the longest wavelength and the lowest frequency. This is usable for a given guide frequency and is the mode most commonly used in rectangular waveguides, which are made by introducing two more parallel conducting plates at right angles to the direction of the **E** vector, and parallel to the z-axis. This is the basic structure of the rectangular waveguides (which we shall study in some further details in Chapter 18).

If f is $\gg f_c$, then $v_g \simeq v$, and the wave-fronts in the guides are almost normal to the sides.

Also, note that the phase velocity of the guided wave $v_g > v$ [Eq. (17.26)] which in free space is the velocity of light ($v = c$). Thus though the 'wave-front' can travel at speeds greater than the velocity of light, any information can only pass down the guide at the speed with which any individual wave-front progresses in the x-direction, i.e. $v \sin \theta_i$, which is $< v$. To understand this point, it should be noted that the energy propagates in a direction normal to the wave-front with the velocity c or v (to be more general). For the guided wave travelling in the x-direction, the information or the energy will travel at a speed

$$v \cos\left(\frac{\pi}{2} - \theta_i\right) = v \sin \theta_i$$

This is the 'group velocity' of the wave, i.e.

$$v_{gr} = \left[1 - \left(\frac{f_c}{f}\right)^2\right]^{1/2} \qquad (17.218)$$

this is due to the zigzag motion of the wave-front.

We shall now evaluate the Poynting vector for the resultant guided wave, i.e. from Eqs. (17.204), E_y with H_z gives a Poynting vector in the x-direction

$$\bar{S}_{x\,av} = \left(\frac{1}{2}\right) \text{Re}\left[\{-j2E_{0i+} \sin(\beta z \cos \theta_i) \exp(-j\beta x \sin \theta_i)\} \right.$$

$$\left. \times \left\{-2j\left(\frac{E_{0i+}}{Z_0}\right) \sin \theta_i \sin(\beta z \cos \theta_i) \exp(-j\beta x \sin \theta_i)\right\}\right]$$

$$= 2\left(\frac{E_{0i+}^2}{Z_0}\right)\sin\,\theta_i\,\sin^2\,(\beta z\,\cos\,\theta_i) \qquad (17.219)$$

From the same equations, E_y with H_x would give a Poynting vector in the z-direction,

$$\overline{S}_{x\,av} = \left(\frac{1}{2}\right)\text{Re}\left[-j2E_{0i+}\,\sin\,(\beta z\,\cos\,\theta_i)\,\exp\,(-j\beta x\,\sin\,\theta_i)\right]$$

$$\times\left[-2\left(\frac{E_{0i+}}{Z_0}\right)\cos\,\theta_i\,\cos\,(\beta z\,\cos\,\theta_i)\,\exp\,(-j\beta x\,\sin\,\theta_i)\right]$$

$$= 0,\ \text{on averaging} \qquad (17.220)$$

Thus it is seen that the energy flow is entirely parallel to the interface plane $z = 0$, along the x-axis.

In the system we have studied, it is seen that the **E** wave is at right angles to the direction of propagation (i.e. transverse to the direction of propagation) whereas the **H** wave has both the transverse and the longitudinal components. Hence this type of wave is called the TE wave (Transverse Electric); or some authors refer to it as the **H** wave. There are other modes of operation, such as TM (Transverse Magnetic) in which the magnetic field has only the transverse component whilst the **E** wave has both the transverse and the longitudinal components. There is also the TEM wave in which both the electric and the magnetic fields are transverse to the direction of propagation. Also, when the parallel conducting plates are positioned for mode 1 operation (i.e. in two successive zero planes), the pattern obtained is denoted as TE 1 mode. Higher modes are also possible. All these aspects are the subject matter of our study in Chapter 18.

17.18 PLANE WAVES ON CYLINDRICAL CONDUCTORS

So far we have seen that the plane waves can be propagated in free space and infinite dielectric media with plane faces. However plane waves can also be propagated along the z-direction (say, this direction being the direction of the axis) along a set of conductors, so long as all the sections of the conductor set normal to the z-axis are identical, i.e. the conductors are circular cylindrical, for example. Initially we assume the conductors to be perfect ($\sigma \to \infty$ or $\rho \to 0$) and the medium to be loss-less. It follows from our study of skin effect and eddy currents in Chapter 15 that on perfect conductors the currents flow in 'infinitely thin surface layers' with no fields inside and there would be no energy dissipation. This problem can be posed in a number of ways.

In this case, the vector potential **A** as well as the Hertz vector $\mathbf{Z}_e$ would have only the z-component, i.e. parallel to the direction of the currents. The solution of the propagation equation for the Hertz vector would yield both a scalar and a vector potential (Section 13.9). By a suitable choice of the constraint equation, the scalar potential can be eliminated (i.e. Eq. 13.117), in which case the vector potential becomes normal to z-direction.

It is also possible to obtain the same result more directly by solving the scalar wave propagation equation, which is

$$\left(\frac{\partial^2 W}{\partial x^2} + \frac{\partial^2 W}{\partial y^2}\right) + \left(\frac{\partial^2 W}{\partial z^2} - \mu\varepsilon\frac{\partial^2 W}{\partial t^2}\right) \qquad (17.221)$$

(for the loss-less dielectric medium)

It should be noted that even though the equation is written in Cartesian coordinate system, the cylindrical coordinate values can be obtained easily since $x = r \cos \phi$ and $y = r \sin \phi$. The solution to the above equation can be obtained by dividing the equation into two bracketted parts and setting each bracket to zero, i.e.

$$\frac{\partial^2 W}{\partial x^2} + \frac{\partial^2 W}{\partial y^2} = 0 \qquad (17.222a)$$

and

$$\frac{\partial^2 W}{\partial z^2} - \mu\varepsilon \frac{\partial^2 W}{\partial t^2} = 0 \qquad (17.222b)$$

The first equation is a two-dimensional Laplace's equation in x and y and the second equation is a one-dimensional wave equation in z and t.

The solution to the two-dimensional Laplace's equation can be written in terms of conjugate functions of complex variables. So if V_1 and V_2 [where $V_1 = V_1(x, y)$ and $V_2 = V_2(x, y)$] are the solutions of Eq. (17.222a), then W_1 and W_2 are the complex potential functions so that

$$W_1 = U_1 + jV_1 = F_1(x + jy) \quad \text{and} \quad W_2 = U_2 + jV_2 = F_2(x + jy) \qquad (17.223)$$

where $j = \sqrt{-1}$.

Differentiating W_i with respect to x and y gives

$$\frac{\partial W_i}{\partial x} = \frac{\partial U_i}{\partial x} + j\frac{\partial V_i}{\partial x} = F_i'(x + jy) = \left\{ F_i'(z)\frac{\partial z}{\partial x} = F_i'(z) \right\}$$

and

$$\frac{\partial W_i}{\partial y} = \frac{\partial U_i}{\partial y} + j\frac{\partial V_i}{\partial y} = jF_i'(x + jy) = \left\{ F_i'(z)\frac{\partial z}{\partial y} = jF_i'(z) \right\} \qquad (17.224)$$

In the above two equations, $z = x + jy$ and this z is not to be confused with the space variable z of Eqs. (17.221) and (17.222b).

From these two equations, equating the real and imaginary parts separately, we get

$$\frac{\partial V_i}{\partial x} = -\frac{\partial U_i}{\partial y} \quad \text{and} \quad \frac{\partial V_i}{\partial y} = \frac{\partial U_i}{\partial x} \qquad (17.225)$$

i.e. the two sets (or families) of curves $U(x, y) = $ constant and $V(x, y) = $ constant intersect each other orthogonally. So one set may be chosen to be equipotential (so that this will be the potential function), and the other set would represent the lines of force (known as the stream function). From these the electric field intensity and the electric flux can be obtained as

$$\frac{dW_i}{dz} = \frac{dU_i + jdV_i}{dx + jdy} = \frac{\dfrac{\partial U_i}{\partial x}dx + \dfrac{\partial U_i}{\partial y}dy + j\left(\dfrac{\partial V_i}{\partial x}dx + \dfrac{\partial V_i}{\partial y}dy\right)}{dx + jdy}$$

$$= \frac{\dfrac{\partial V}{\partial y}(dx + jdy) + j\dfrac{\partial V}{\partial x}(dx + jdy)}{dx + jdy}$$

$$= \frac{\partial V}{\partial y} + j\frac{\partial V}{\partial x} = \frac{\partial U}{\partial x} - j\frac{\partial U}{\partial y} \tag{17.226}$$

by substituting from Eqs. (17.225).

Irrespective of whether U_i or V_i is the potential function, the magnitude of the electric field at a point would be given by $\left|\dfrac{\partial W}{\partial z}\right|$.

Let

  dn be an element of length in the direction of maximum increase of potential, and

  ds be the element of length obtained by rotating dn counterclockwise through $\pi/2$ radians,

then

$$\left|\frac{dW}{dz}\right| = \frac{\partial U_i}{\partial n} = \frac{\partial V_i}{\partial s} \quad \text{or} \quad \left|\frac{dW}{dz}\right| = \frac{\partial V_i}{\partial n} = -\frac{\partial U_i}{\partial s} \tag{17.227}$$

depending on whether U or V is the potential function.

If V is the potential function, then the flux through any section of an equipotential surface is given by

$$\text{Flux} = -\varepsilon \int_{U_1}^{U_2} \frac{\partial V}{\partial n}\, ds = \varepsilon \int_{U_1}^{U_2} \frac{\partial U}{\partial s}\, ds = \varepsilon(U_2 - U_1) \tag{17.228}$$

Hence the capacitance per unit length is given by

$$C = \frac{|Q|}{|V_2 - V_1|} = \frac{\varepsilon|U|}{|V_2 - V_1|} \tag{17.229}$$

The solutions to the one-dimensional wave Eq. (17.222b) can be written as

$$f_1\left(z - t/\sqrt{\mu\varepsilon}\right) \quad \text{and} \quad f_2\left(z + t/\sqrt{\mu\varepsilon}\right) \tag{17.230}$$

Hence the solution to the scalar wave propagation Eq. (17.221) can be expressed as

$$W = V_1(x, y)\, f_1\left(z - t/\sqrt{\mu\varepsilon}\right) + V_2(x, y)\, f_2\left(z + t/\sqrt{\mu\varepsilon}\right) \tag{17.231}$$

$$\text{(z being the space variable here)}$$

where V_1 and V_2 are the solutions of the two-dimensional Laplace's Eq. (17.222a) and W_1 and W_2 are the complex potential functions related to V_1 and V_2 by Eqs. (17.223).

At this stage, we define a new two-dimensional vector operator ∇_2 which is

$$\nabla_2 = \mathbf{i}_x \frac{\partial}{\partial x} + \mathbf{i}_y \frac{\partial}{\partial y} \tag{17.232}$$

so that

$$\nabla_2 V = \mathbf{i}_x \frac{\partial V}{\partial x} + \mathbf{i}_y \frac{\partial V}{\partial y} \tag{17.233}$$

then

$$-\mathbf{i}_z \times \nabla_2 V = \nabla_2 U \qquad \text{and} \qquad \mathbf{i}_z \times \nabla_2 U = \nabla_2 V \left.\right\}$$

and

$$\nabla \times \left[\nabla_2 U \{ f(z) \} \right] = \mathbf{i}_z \times \nabla_2 \left[U \{ f'(z) \} \right] \qquad (17.234)$$

from Eq. (17.225).

From Eqs. (13.77) and (13.78), the vector potential for a transverse electric field can be written as

$$\mathbf{A} = \nabla \times (\mathbf{i}_z W)$$

$$= -\mathbf{i}_z \times \nabla_2 \, V_1(x, y) \, f_1\!\left(z - t/\sqrt{\mu\varepsilon}\right) - \mathbf{i}_z \times \nabla_2 V_2(x, y) \, f_2\!\left(z + t/\sqrt{\mu\varepsilon}\right)$$

$$= \nabla_2 U_1(x, y) \, f_1\!\left(z - t/\sqrt{\mu\varepsilon}\right) + \nabla_2 U_2(x, y) \, f_2\!\left(z + t/\sqrt{\mu\varepsilon}\right) \qquad (17.235)$$

Obviously the first term above represents waves travelling in the +ve z-direction and the second term is for the waves travelling in the −ve z-direction.

From the vector potential, the magnetic and the electric fields would be derived as:

$$\mathbf{B} = \nabla \times \mathbf{A} = \nabla_2 V(x, y) f'\!\left(z \mp t/\sqrt{\mu\varepsilon}\right) \qquad (17.236)$$

$$\mathbf{E} = -\frac{\partial \mathbf{A}}{\partial t} = \pm \frac{1}{\sqrt{\mu\varepsilon}} \, \nabla_2 U(x, y) f'\!\left(z \mp t/\sqrt{\mu\varepsilon}\right) \qquad (17.237)$$

The +ve wave takes the upper sign in the above two equations. Combining Eqs. (17.234), (17.236) and (17.237), we get

$$\sqrt{\mu\varepsilon} \; \mathbf{E} = \mp \, \mathbf{i}_z \times \mathbf{B} \qquad (17.238)$$

In a particular system, let it be assumed that the current goes out on one set of conducting cylinders and returns on another set. Equation (17.237) shows that all the members of one set would have the same potential at one value of z (the space variable) and hence for any other value of z. The relation between the total current and the charge (per unit length) in either set [of members, n in number (say)] can be found by using Gauss' theorem, as

$$Q = \sum_{i=1}^{n} \oint \varepsilon E_n \, ds_i = \sqrt{\mu\varepsilon} \sum_{i=1}^{n} \oint H_i ds_i = \sqrt{\mu\varepsilon} \; I \qquad (17.239)$$

If L is the self-inductance per unit length, C the capacitance per unit length and S is the area outside the conductors in a plane of constant z, then

$$\frac{LI^2}{2} = \iint_S \frac{B^2}{2\mu} dS = \iint_S \frac{\varepsilon E^2}{2} dS = \frac{Q^2}{2C} = \frac{\mu\varepsilon}{2C} I^2 \qquad (17.240)$$

Hence L and C are related as

$$LC = \mu\varepsilon = \frac{1}{v^2} \qquad (17.241)$$

Thus, LC is the reciprocal of the square of the electromagnetic wave velocity in the medium outside the conductors.

So far we have started from the vector potential and evaluated **E** and **B**. We now consider the inverse problem which is that **E** and **B** are specified either at a point in space as a function of time or as a function of space variable z at a given instant of time.

First we consider the case where **E** and **B** are specified in the plane $z = 0$ as functions of time. Then **A** for any z can be written down from Eq. (17.235). Thus,

$$\mathbf{A} = \frac{1}{2} \nabla_2 \, U(x, y) \left[f\left(t - z\sqrt{\mu\varepsilon}\right) + f\left(t + z\sqrt{\mu\varepsilon}\right) - g\left(t - z\sqrt{\mu\varepsilon}\right) - g\left(t + z\sqrt{\mu\varepsilon}\right) \right] \quad (17.242)$$

If U and V are given by Eqs. (17.223), then the fields at $z = 0$ can be obtained from **A** as:

$$\left. \begin{aligned} \mathbf{E}_{z=0} &= -\left(\frac{\partial \mathbf{A}}{\partial t}\right)_{z=0} = -\nabla_2 U(x, y)\, f'(t) \\[2mm] \mathbf{B}_{z=0} &= (\nabla \times \mathbf{A})_{z=0} = -\sqrt{\mu\varepsilon}\, \nabla_2\, V(x, y)\, g'(t) \end{aligned} \right\} \quad (17.243)$$

On the other hand, when **E** and **B** are given as functions of z at $t = 0$, **A** can again be written from Eq. (17.235) as:

$$\mathbf{A} = \frac{1}{2} \nabla_2 U\,(x, y) \left[f\left(z\sqrt{\mu\varepsilon} + t\right) - f\left(z\sqrt{\mu\varepsilon} - t\right) - g\left(z\sqrt{\mu\varepsilon} + t\right) - g\left(z\sqrt{\mu\varepsilon} - t\right) \right] \quad (17.244)$$

As before, if U and V are given by Eq. (17.223), then from **A** at $t = 0$, the fields can be expressed as

$$\mathbf{E}_{t=0} = -\nabla_2 U(x, y)\, f'\left(z\sqrt{\mu\varepsilon}\right), \quad \mathbf{B}_{t=0} = -\sqrt{\mu\varepsilon}\, \nabla_2 V(x, y)\, g'\left(z\sqrt{\mu\varepsilon}\right) \quad (17.245)$$

17.18.1 Propagation in a Medium of Finite Conductivity (Intrinsic Impedance)

So far the dielectric medium of propagation was assumed to be loss-less. Now we consider a medium of finite conductivity $(= \sigma)$ or finite resistivity $\left(= \rho = \dfrac{1}{\sigma}\right)$. In such a medium, the scalar wave propagation Eq. (17.221) modifies to

$$\left(\frac{\partial^2 W}{\partial x^2} + \frac{\partial^2 W}{\partial y^2}\right) + \left(\frac{\partial^2 W}{\partial z^2} - \mu\sigma \frac{\partial W}{\partial t} - \mu\varepsilon \frac{\partial^2 W}{\partial t^2}\right) = 0 \quad (17.246)$$

In this equation, when the second bracket is equated to zero, the solution is no longer a simple one-dimensional wave propagation due to the presence of the term $\mu\sigma \dfrac{\partial W}{\partial t}$. Writing its solution as

$$W = ZT, \quad \text{where } Z = Z(z), \quad T = T(t) \quad (17.247)$$

the equation becomes

$$\frac{Z''}{Z} = \mu\sigma \frac{T'}{T} + \mu\varepsilon \frac{T''}{T} = K \leftarrow \text{separation constant} \quad (17.248)$$

The solution is exponential in form and it can take either of the two forms, i.e.

(i) If the separation constant is real, the solution will be harmonic is space and will be a 'transient' state solution;

(ii) If the separation constant is imaginary, the solution will have harmonics in time and it will be a 'steady-state' behaviour solution.

We now consider the steady-state solutions in which the time-variation is given by $\exp(j\omega t)$.

The function $f\left(z - t/\sqrt{\mu\varepsilon}\right)$ of Eq. (17.230) is now replaced by $\exp\left(\pm z\,\Gamma + j\omega t\right)$ where

$$\Gamma^2 = j\omega\mu\,(\sigma + j\omega\varepsilon) = (\alpha + j\beta)^2 \tag{17.249}$$

17.18.2 Solution of Propagation Equation in Cylindrical Coordinates

In Section 17.18, we solved for the special type of cylindrical waves moving in the z-direction obtained by setting the terms of the two parts of the scalar wave equation (17.221) to separately equal to zero, i.e.

$$\left(\frac{\partial^2 W}{\partial x^2} + \frac{\partial^2 W}{\partial y^2}\right) + \left(\frac{\partial^2 W}{\partial z^2} - \mu\varepsilon\frac{\partial^2 W}{\partial t^2}\right) = 0 \tag{17.221}$$

The above equation was reduced to two equations by equating each bracket (shown above) to zero separately, i.e.

$$\frac{\partial^2 W}{\partial x^2} + \frac{\partial^2 W}{\partial y^2} = 0 \quad \text{and} \quad \left(\frac{\partial^2 W}{\partial z^2} - \mu\varepsilon\frac{\partial^2 W}{\partial t^2}\right) = 0 \tag{17.222}$$

But this is not the only way to solve Eq. (17.221). On the other hand, the first equation of (17.222) can be equated to $\pm\beta_{mn}^2$, the second equation to $\mp\beta_{mn}^2$ and the time variation can be assumed to be of the sinusoidal variation type, i.e. $\exp(j\omega t)$ so that the second equation would then become

$$\frac{\partial^2 W}{\partial z^2} + \omega^2\mu\varepsilon W = \mp\beta_{mn}^2 \tag{17.259}$$

We can write $\omega^2\mu\varepsilon = \beta^2$ and scalar function W can be considered as $W = UZ$, where $U = U(x, y)$ and $Z = Z(z)$.

Then Eqs. (17.222) reduce to the form

$$\nabla_2^2 U \pm \beta_{mn}^2 U = 0 \quad \text{and} \quad \frac{d^2 Z}{dz^2} + (\beta^2 \mp \beta_{mn}^2)\,Z = 0 \tag{17.260}$$

where

$$\nabla_2^2 \equiv \frac{\partial^2}{\partial x^2} + \frac{\partial^2}{\partial y^2}$$

If now instead of Cartesian coordinate system, a cylindrical coordinate system (r, ϕ, z) is used and the substitution

$$k_{mn}^2 = \beta^2 - \beta_{mn}^2 \quad \text{and} \quad k'^2_{mn} = \beta^2 + \beta_{mn}^2 \tag{17.261}$$

then the solution for W will be of the forms:

$$W = \{A\,e^{jk_{mn}z} + B\,e^{-jk_{mn}z}\}\{CJ_m(\beta_{mn}r) + DY_m(\beta_{mn}r)\}\cos(m\phi + \delta_m) \qquad (17.262)$$

$$W = \{Ae^{jk'_{mn}z} + Be^{-jk'_{mn}z}\}\{CI_m(\beta_{mn}r) + DK_m(\beta_{mn}r)\}\cos(m\phi + \delta_m) \qquad (17.263)$$

When C, D, k_{mn}, k'_{mn} are all real, both these equations represent waves propagating only in the z-direction. If $\beta_{mn}^2 > \beta^2$ so that k_{mn} is imaginary, Eq. (17.262) represents a wave exponentially damped in the z-direction. If C is real and D is complex, then Eq. (17.262) has a radial propagation component. If z is absent (i.e. no z variation) and $k_{mn} = 0$ and $k'_{mn} = 0$, then Eqs. (17.262) and (17.263) represent cylindrical wavefronts.

Defining transverse electric and transverse magnetic waves as those whose electric and magnetic fields, respectively, are normal to the direction of propagation (which is z-direction in the present case), then

$$\mathbf{A} = \frac{\mathbf{i}_r}{r}\frac{\partial W_{te}}{\partial \phi} - \mathbf{i}_\phi\,\phi\,\frac{\partial W_{te}}{\partial r} - \left[\mathbf{i}_r\,\frac{\partial^2 W_{tm}}{\partial r\,\partial z} + \mathbf{i}_\phi\,\phi\,\frac{\partial^2 W_{tm}}{r\partial\phi\partial z} + \mathbf{i}_z\left(\beta^2 W_{tm} + \frac{\partial^2 W_{tm}}{\partial z^2}\right)\right] \qquad (17.264)$$

$$\mathbf{B} = \mathbf{i}_r\,\frac{\partial^2 W_{te}}{\partial r\partial z} + \mathbf{i}_\phi\,\phi\,\frac{\partial^2 W_{te}}{r\partial\phi\partial z} + \mathbf{i}_z\left(\beta^2 W_{te} + \frac{\partial^2 W_{te}}{\partial z^2}\right) + \mathbf{i}_r\,\frac{\beta^2}{r}\frac{\partial W_{tm}}{\partial\phi} + \mathbf{i}_\phi\,\phi\,\beta^2\frac{\partial W_{tm}}{\partial r} \qquad (17.265)$$

where
$$\left.\begin{array}{l} \alpha = \sqrt{\left[\left(\dfrac{\omega\mu}{2}\right)\left\{\sqrt{(\omega^2\varepsilon^2 + \sigma^2)} - \omega\varepsilon\right\}\right]} \\[4mm] \beta = \sqrt{\left[\left(\dfrac{\omega\mu}{2}\right)\left\{\sqrt{(\omega^2\varepsilon^2 + \sigma^2)} + \omega\varepsilon\right\}\right]} \end{array}\right\} \qquad (17.250)$$

Here Γ = the propagation constant

α = the attenuation constant

β = the phase constant or wave number.

The expression for $\mathbf{A}$ now becomes

$$\begin{aligned} \mathbf{A} &= \nabla \times \mathbf{i}_z W \\ &= \pm\,\mathbf{i}_z \times \nabla_2 V(x, y)\exp(\mp\Gamma z + j\omega t) \\ &= \mp\,\nabla_2 U(x, y)\exp(\mp\Gamma z + j\omega t) \end{aligned} \qquad (17.251)$$

Hence the $\mathbf{B}$ and the $\mathbf{E}$ fields will be:

$$\begin{aligned} \mathbf{B} &= \nabla \times \mathbf{A} \\ &= \text{real part} \mp \Gamma\nabla_2 V(x, y)\exp(\mp\Gamma z + j\omega t) \\ &= \mp\,\nabla_2 V(x, y)\{\exp(\mp\alpha z)\}\{\alpha\cos(\omega t \mp \beta z) - \beta\sin(\omega t \mp \beta z)\} \end{aligned} \qquad (17.252)$$

$$\begin{aligned} \mathbf{E} &= -\frac{\partial \mathbf{A}}{\partial t} \\ &= \text{real part} - j\omega\nabla_2 U(x, y)\exp(\mp\Gamma z + j\omega t) \end{aligned}$$

$$= \omega \nabla_2 U(x, y) \{\exp(\mp \alpha z)\} \{\sin(\omega t \mp \beta z)\} \qquad (17.253)$$

and

$$\Gamma E = \mp j\omega(i_z \times B) \qquad (17.254)$$

or

$$\Gamma i_z \times E = \pm j\omega B$$

From the above Eqs. (17.251), (17.252) and (17.253), it is obvious that these fields are not plane waves, but are attenuated (or damped) waves and their amplitudes are exponentially attenuated by the factor $e^{-\alpha z}$ as the waves progress in the z-direction.

If now, we define

R = the resistance per unit length between the conductors, and

C = the capacitance per unit length,

then

$$CR = \rho\varepsilon = \frac{\varepsilon}{\sigma} \qquad (17.255)$$

(Ref: Problem 4.31 in *Electromagnetism: Problems with Solutions*, 2nd Edition, 2008)

The shunt admittance Y and the series impedance Z_L are given by

$$Y = \frac{1}{R} + j\omega C = \frac{\sigma + j\omega\varepsilon}{\varepsilon} \frac{\mu\varepsilon}{L} = \frac{\Gamma^2}{j\omega L}, \qquad \text{where } Z_L = j\omega L \qquad (17.256)$$

Hence the characteristic impedance of the line will be

$$Z_c = \sqrt{\frac{Z_L}{Y}} = \frac{j\omega L}{\Gamma} = \frac{V}{I} = \frac{LE}{B} = \frac{j\omega\mu\varepsilon}{\Gamma C} \qquad (17.257)$$

When the conductors consist of two infinite parallel planes 1 metre apart, then since an infinite tubular section of $1\,\text{m}^2$ running in the z-direction has C per unit length as equal to ε, the characteristic impedance will be

$$Z_c = \sqrt{\left(\frac{j\omega\mu}{s + j\omega\varepsilon}\right)} = \frac{j\omega\mu}{\alpha + j\beta} \qquad (17.258)$$

PROBLEMS

17.1 For a uniform plane wave in air the magnetic field is given by

$$H = i_z\, 2 \exp\left[j\{\omega t - \pi z/(20)\}\right]$$

Calculate (i) the wavelength, (ii) the frequency, and (iii) the value of E at $1/(15)$ μsec, $z = 5$ m.

Ans.: 40 m, 7.5 MHz, $i_x(- 533)$ V/m

17.2 A 5 GHz plane wave is propagating in a large block of polystyrene ($\varepsilon_r = 2.5$), the amplitude of the electric field being 10 mV/m. Find

(i) the velocity of propagation,

(ii) the wavelength, and

(iii) the amplitude of the magnetic field intensity.

Ans.: 1.896×10^8 m/sec, 3.79 cm, 41.9 μA/m

17.3 The amplitude of the electric field component of a sinusoidal plane wave in free space is 20 V/m. Calculate the power per square metre carried by the wave.

Ans.: 0.53 W/m^2

17.4 A plane, linearly-polarized wave $\mathbf{E}_i$, $\mathbf{H}_i$, in free space, as described by the equations

$$\mathbf{E}_i = \mathbf{i}_x E_0 \exp\left[j(\omega t - \beta z)\right], \qquad \mathbf{H}_i = \mathbf{i}_y H_0 \exp\left[j(\omega t - \beta z)\right]$$

is incident on the plane surface ($z = 0$) of a semi-infinite block of loss-less dielectric of permittivity ε_r, and gives rise to a transmitted wave $\mathbf{E}_t$, $\mathbf{H}_t$, and a reflected wave $\mathbf{E}_r$, $\mathbf{H}_r$. This surface is coated with a thin layer of resistive material, of resistivity ρ_S, such that the thickness of this layer can be neglected. Show that the ratio of the amplitude of the reflected wave to that of the incident wave will be

$$= \frac{1 - Z_0 \left(\dfrac{1}{\rho_S} + \dfrac{1}{Z_r} \right)}{1 + Z_0 \left(\dfrac{1}{\rho_S} + \dfrac{1}{Z_r} \right)}$$

where $Z_0 = \sqrt{\dfrac{\mu_0}{\varepsilon_0}}$, $\qquad Z_r = \sqrt{\dfrac{\mu_0}{\varepsilon_r}}$.

What will be this ratio, if this layer of resistive material is removed from the incident surface?

17.5 A slab of solid dielectric material is coated on one side with a perfectly conducting sheet. A uniform, plane, sinusoidal wave is directed towards the uncoated side at normal incidence. Show that, if the frequency is such that the thickness of the slab is half a wavelength, the wave reflected from the dielectric surface will be equal in amplitude to the incident wave and opposite in phase. Calculate this frequency for a loss-less dielectric of permittivity 2.5 and thickness 5 cm.

Ans.: (i) Necessary condition is $k\beta d = \pi$, where $d = \left(\dfrac{1}{2}\right)$ wavelength, and velocity in

the dielectric medium (2) $= c/k$, $k = \sqrt{2.5}$

(ii) For $d = 5$ cm, $f = 1900$ MHz.

17.6 A plane wave of angular frequency ω in free space (μ_0, ε_0) is incident normally on a half-space of a very good conductor (μ_0, ε_0, σ). Show that the ratio of the reflected to the incident time-averaged Poynting vector is approximately

$$R_S = 1 - 2\beta\delta$$

where $\beta = \omega\sqrt{\mu_0\varepsilon_0}$ and $\delta = \sqrt{\dfrac{2}{\omega\mu\sigma}}$.

17.7 A time-harmonic, plane wave is incident normally on a planar resistive sheet which is the plane interface $z = 0$ separating the half-space $z < 0$ (medium 1) from another half-space $z > 0$ (medium 2). Let the media 1 and 2 be characterized by the constitute parameters μ_1, ε_1 and μ_2, ε_2 respectively. A thin planar layer of resistive material is sandwiched between the half-space. The thickness of the layer is assumed to be very small compared with a wavelength so that it can be approximated by a sheet of zero thickness, and can be assumed to occupy the $z = 0$ plane. The surface current density $\mathbf{J_S}$ on the resistor sheet and the $\mathbf{E}$ field tangential to it are related as follows:

$$\mathbf{J_S} = \sigma_S \mathbf{E_t} = \frac{\mathbf{E_t}}{\rho_S}$$

where

σ_S = surface conductivity = $1/\rho_S$

ρ_S = surface resistivity.

Show that the ratios of the reflected $\mathbf{E}$ wave and the transmitted $\mathbf{E}$ wave to the incident wave are

$$\rho_E = \frac{E^r_{xo}}{E^i_{xo}} = \frac{Z_{2r} - Z_1}{Z_{2r} + Z_1},$$

and

$$\tau_E = \frac{E^t_{xo}}{E^i_{xo}} = \frac{2Z_{2r}}{Z_{2r} + Z_1},$$

where

$$\frac{1}{Z_{2r}} = \frac{1}{\rho_S} + \frac{1}{Z_2}$$

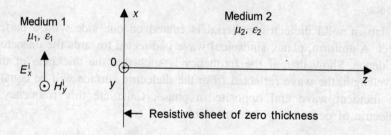

Medium 1
$\mu_1,\ \varepsilon_1$

Medium 2
$\mu_2,\ \varepsilon_2$

E^i_x

$\odot\ H^i_y$

← Resistive sheet of zero thickness

Z_1, Z_2 = characteristic impedances of the media 1 and 2 respectively and the suffix o represents the amplitude of the corresponding wave. Hence show that the power dissipated in the resistive sheet per unit square area is

$$= \frac{\left|E^i_{xo}\right|^2}{2}\frac{\tau_E^2}{\rho_S}$$

The subscripts i and t have been made into superscripts here to eliminate confusion by overcrowding of suffices.

18 Waveguides

18.1 INTRODUCTION

In Chapter 17, we considered the propagation of electromagnetic waves, without referring to their sources or their destinations, and one of our conclusions was that they (the waves) are capable of transporting energy. In fact, the electromagnetic waves are used to transport energy from one place to another. An example of such application is the antenna of a television (or broadcasting) station, radiating the energy carrying information signals to all possible receivers in the vicinity. Naturally, a large portion of the energy of such waves is lost. Another and an important application is in the transmission of electromagnetic energy from a source to a single receiver. In such cases, it is desirable to minimize the transmission losses to the particular receiver. Since the electromagnetic waves propagating through free space are not the most suitable type for this purpose, it is necessary to design and devise some system to guide the energy of the wave along a desired route. All such systems can logically be called 'guides' of the electromagnetic waves, and the waves propagating along these guides are called the 'guided electromagnetic waves'. In Section 17.17.2, we were introduced to the basic concepts underlying the techniques of 'guiding' the electromagnetic waves.

Of the many such practical examples of 'guiding energy transfer', we shall quote only a few, starting with the first one which is also applicable at low (i.e. power frequency of 50 or 60 Hz) frequency. At these low frequencies, the electrical energy, which is the output of either a thermal or hydroelectric power station, is guided to various receivers by means of power transmission lines. Theoretically speaking, the power stations could radiate all that energy, and allow the consumers to hunt for as much of it, as per their requirement, from air. But such a method would be extremely uneconomical and possibly practically impossible.

At the higher end of the frequency spectrum, when a private message has to be sent from one person in one city to another person in another city (may even be in a different country), it would be very uneconomical and not the most efficient way of using a very powerful transmitter, creating electromagnetic waves all over the interlinked countries between the two cities. Instead the electromagnetic waves are propagated along the telephone lines, or optical fibres, and radio links with suitable signal amplifiers for regenerating the strength of the signals, thus compensating for the losses taking place during the transmission.

Another example is that of the transmission of extremely high (electromagnetic) pulses from a radar transmitter to its antenna. These energy pulses are sent through suitably designed conducting metal tubes (e.g. of rectangular or circular cross-sections), so that by guiding the waves to suitable paths, the energy losses are kept to a minimum. Such devices (i.e. these tubular pieces) are referred to as 'waveguides'. There are many varieties of waveguides for electromagnetic waves.

Though the types of electromagnetic waves propagating along the transmission lines and through the waveguides have some significant differences, they have some important features of similarity and there are underlying conceptual similarities in both.

In the transmission lines, the electromagnetic waves have both the **E** and the **H** vectors transverse to the direction of propagation, and are generally referred to as TEM (= Transverse Electromagnetic) waves. It should be noted that the coaxial cable problem discussed in Chapter 14, Section 14.4.2, was of the TEM wave type. However, in the transmission lines, **E** and **H** are not constants in a transverse plane, and hence the TEM waves along the transmission lines are *not* uniform. The most common types of transmission lines are the two-wire line, the coaxial cable, and the stripline.

The waveguides can be either metal tubes of rectangular or circular cross-section, or dielectric rods of different cross-sections. The electromagnetic waves propagating through them are not of the TEM type. Also, only the waves having a wavelength smaller than a certain critical wavelength, can propagate through the wave guides, the critical wavelength being a function of the transverse dimensions of the guides. The waveguides are used at very high frequencies.

18.2 TRANSMISSION LINES

The transmission lines, most often met with in practice, are made up of two (very nearly) parallel, cylindrical conductors. Since the conductor shapes can never be perfect, an exact rigorous analysis would be rather difficult. Hence, instead of treating the lines as a boundary value problem, the theory of travelling waves in lines (and also in cables) can be developed from the circuit standpoint. The lines are represented as a complicated combination of resistors, capacitors, and inductors. So, instead of the electric and the magnetic field intensities at all points where the fields of the lines exist, we consider the unknown voltage between the two lines and the current through them.

18.2.1 Transmission Lines with Negligible Losses (Loss-less Lines)

We consider the cable as a pair of conductors, in which each length δz has the inductance $L\delta z$, and between the conductors in each length δz is the capacitance $C\delta z$ (Figure 18.1). So, at a point A on the line (where its voltage is V),

The charge in the capacitor is $= CV\delta z$

And the current in the capacitor = the rate of increase of the charge

$$= C\left(\frac{\partial V}{\partial t}\right)\delta z$$

∴ Equating the inflowing and the outflowing currents at the point A (referring to Figure 18.1), we have

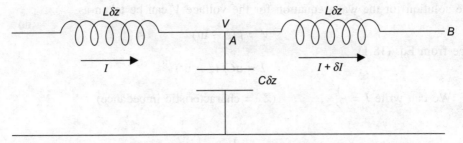

Figure 18.1 Circuit element representation of the transmission line.

$$I = C \left(\frac{\partial V}{\partial t} \right) \delta z + (I + \delta I)$$

or

$$\delta I + C \left(\frac{\partial V}{\partial t} \right) \delta z = 0$$

or, in the limit

$$\left(\frac{\partial I}{\partial z} \right) + C \left(\frac{\partial V}{\partial t} \right) = 0 \tag{18.1}$$

Next, considering the potentials along the line,

Potential at the point A − Potential at the point B = $L\delta z \left(\frac{\partial}{\partial t} \right)(I + \delta I) = -\delta V$

or

$$L\delta z \left(\frac{\partial I}{\partial t} \right) = -\delta V, \text{ neglecting higher order terms.}$$

In the limit,

$$\left(\frac{\partial V}{\partial z} \right) + L \left(\frac{\partial I}{\partial t} \right) = 0 \tag{18.2}$$

Eliminating I between Eqs. (18.1) and (18.2), we get

$$\left(\frac{\partial^2 V}{\partial z^2} \right) = \left(\frac{1}{u^2} \right) \left(\frac{\partial^2 V}{\partial t^2} \right), \text{ where } u^2 = \frac{1}{LC} \tag{18.3}$$

which is the usual one-dimensional wave equation.

It should be noted that L and C are related by the second equation of (18.3) and as the velocity of the wave u depends on the permittivity of the dielectric medium, the inductance and the capacitance are not so independent as the mode of deriving them would appear to be. From the earlier chapters, we have obtained that for the unit length of two parallel wires, their (L and C) expressions are

$$L = \left(\frac{\mu_0}{2\pi} \right) \ln \left(\frac{b}{a} \right) \quad \text{and} \quad C = \frac{-2\pi\varepsilon_0\varepsilon_r}{\ln \left(\frac{b}{a} \right)}$$

neglecting the internal flux for the inductance.

The solution for the wave equation for the voltage V can be taken as

$$V = f(z - ut)$$

and hence from Eq. (18.1),

$$I = uCf(z - ut)$$

∴   We can write $I = \dfrac{V}{Z_c}$,   (Z_c = characteristic impedance)

where

$$Z_c = \frac{1}{uC} = \sqrt{\frac{L}{C}} \tag{18.4}$$

The value of the surge impedance Z for the air-cored cable is about 500 Ω and 30 Ω for a coaxial cable with solid insulation.

We shall now consider the behaviour of a line under two sets of different conditions:

1. *Transient shock condition.*   This condition is obtained when a switch in the line is closed suddenly. Sudden switching and lightening are the two main sources, which cause the transient behaviour of the circuits. This is equivalent to the application of a unit step function to the line. This function is a wave which suddenly rises from $V = 0$ to $V = 1$ at the time $t = 0$, and then remains constant at that value thereafter (Figure 18.2). Any other types of shocks can be

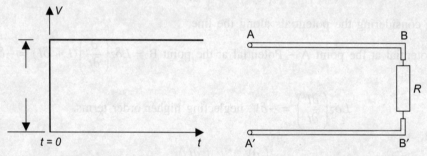

Figure 18.2   A unit-step function of voltage applied to the end AA′ of a transmission line whose other end BB′ has been terminated by a resistance R.

built up by a successive superimposition of the unit steps. Let a voltage step of the type mentioned be applied to the terminals AA′ of a cable, whose other end BB′ is terminated by a resistance R as shown in Figure 18.2.

(1) The first effect of this step function is that a voltage wave of magnitude V and a current (V/Z_c) travel along the cable from A to B with a velocity u [Figure 18.3(a)].

(2) On reaching B, a reflected wave of voltage V' and a current (V'/Z_c) starts travelling from B to A. The magnitude of V' is determined by R such that (voltage/current) at BB′ = R. At this stage:

Potential drop across   BB′ = $V + V'$, and

the current flowing out at   B = $\dfrac{V}{Z_c} - \dfrac{V'}{Z_c}$

∴ $\dfrac{V + V'}{\dfrac{V - V'}{Z_c}} = R$

and hence

$$V' = \left(\frac{R - Z_c}{R + Z_c}\right)V \qquad \text{[(Figure 18.3(b)]}} \qquad (18.5)$$

There are three limiting cases of this stage, i.e.

(a) O.C. (open circuit) termination $R \to \infty$;   ∴ $V' = V$ and $I' = I$
(b) S.C. (short circuit) termination $R = 0$;   ∴ $V' = -V$ and $I' = I$
(c) Matched termination, $R = Z_c$;   ∴ $V' = 0$ and $I' = 0$, i.e. no reflected wave.

(3) The reflected wave on reaching AA′, meets the generator impedance, which produces the unit function p.d.: this is ideally a zero impedance, but in fact negligibly small impedance. Hence this returning wave meets an S.C. condition at AA′. Thus for the next stage, a wave $-V'$ travels from A to B, as shown in Figure 18.3(c).

(4) On reaching B, it is reflected back according to (2), and the reflected wave is

$$= -\left(\frac{R - Z_c}{R + Z_c}\right)V' - \left(\frac{R - Z_c}{R + Z_c}\right)^2 V$$

as shown in Figure 18.3(d).

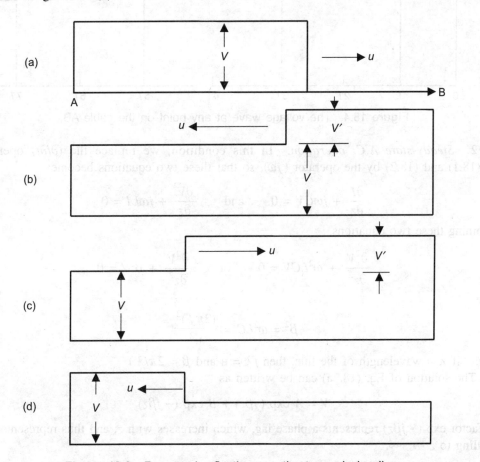

Figure 18.3 Repeated reflections on the transmission line.

With the passage of time, the cycle repeats the process. The voltage waveform at any point in the cable is thus obtained, starting from $t = 0$, and adding up the voltages associated with the waves that have arrived at that point, up to the instant of time under consideration. If T is the period of time required by the waves to traverse the length AB of the cable, then starting from $t = 0$ to $t = T$, there will be no voltage at these points on AB (Figure 18.4), i.e.

$V_i = 0$ from $t = 0$ to $t = T$

$V_i = V(1 + \alpha)$, where $\alpha = [(R - Z_c)/(R + Z_c)]$, from $t = T$ to $t = 3T$

$V_i = V(1 - \alpha^2)$,   from $t = 3T$ to $t = 5T$

$V_i = V(1 + \alpha^3)$,   from $t = 5T$ to $t = 7T$

$V_i = V(1 - \alpha^4)$,   from $t = 7T$ to $t = 9T$

and so on. This is all shown in Figure 18.4.

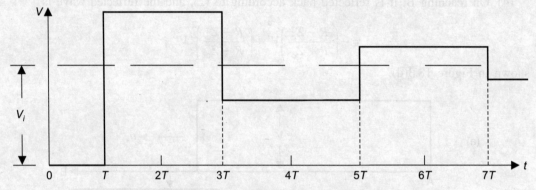

Figure 18.4 The voltage wave at any point on the cable AB.

2. *Steady-state A.C. operation.* In this condition, we replace the $(\partial/\partial t)$ operator in Eqs. (18.1) and (18.2) by the operator $(j\omega)$, so that these two equations become:

$$\frac{\partial I}{\partial z} + j\omega CV = 0 \quad \text{and} \quad \frac{\partial V}{\partial z} + j\omega LI = 0 \tag{18.6}$$

Combining these two equations,

$$\frac{\partial^2 V}{\partial z^2} + \omega^2 LCV = 0 \quad \text{or} \quad \frac{\partial^2 V}{\partial z^2} + \beta^2 V = 0 \tag{18.7a}$$

where

$$\beta^2 = \omega^2 LC = \frac{(2\pi f)^2}{u^2} \tag{18.7b}$$

(*Note:* if λ = wavelength of the line, then $f\lambda$ = u and $\beta = 2\pi/\lambda$.)

The solution of Eq. (18.7a) can be written as

$$V = A \exp (j\beta z) + B \exp (-j\beta z) \tag{18.8}$$

The factor $\exp (-j\beta z)$ represents a phase lag, which increases with z; and thus represents a wave travelling to $z \to +\infty$.

Similarly, exp $(j\beta z)$ represents a wave travelling to $z \to -\infty$.

Since the modulus of exp $(\pm j\beta z)$ is unity, it means that the amplitudes of these waves remain unchanged as they travel.

However the more convenient form of the solution of Eqs. (18.7) is

$$V = A' \cos (\beta z) + B' \sin (\beta z) \tag{18.9}$$

$\therefore$ From the second equation of (18.6),

$$I = - \left(\frac{1}{j\omega L} \right) \beta \, [- A' \sin (\beta z) + B' \cos (\beta z)]$$

$$= \left(\frac{j}{Z_c} \right) [- A' \sin (\beta z) + B' \cos (\beta z)] \tag{18.10}$$

For convenience, we rearrange the coordinate system, and place the origin at the receiving end, i.e. B is $z = 0$ and A is $z = -l$, where l = the length of the section AB of the cable. Further, we use the suffices S and R respectively to denote the quantities at the sending end $(z = -l)$ and the receiving end $(z = 0)$, i.e.

at the sending end $(z = -l)$, the quantities are V_S, I_S; and

at the receiving end $(z = 0)$, the quantities are V_R, I_R.

Evaluating the unknowns A' and B' from the conditions at $z = 0$, from Eqs. (18.9) and (18.10),

$$V_R = A' + 0 \quad \text{and} \quad I_R = \left(\frac{j}{Z_c} \right) (- 0 + B')$$

$\therefore$ $$A' = V_R \quad \text{and} \quad B' = \frac{Z_c I_R}{j} = - jZ_c I_R$$

$\therefore$ $$V = V_R \cos (\beta z) - jZ_c I_R \sin (\beta z) \tag{18.11a}$$

and

$$I = I_R \cos (\beta z) - j \left(\frac{V_R}{Z_c} \right) \sin (\beta z) \tag{18.11b}$$

And, at the sending end $(z = -l)$,

$$V_S = V_R \cos (\beta l) + jZ_c I_R \sin (\beta l) \tag{18.12a}$$

$$I_S = I_R \cos (\beta l) + j \left(\frac{V_R}{Z_c} \right) \sin (\beta l) \tag{18.12b}$$

We consider the case, when the receiving end is open-circuited. Then, $I_R = 0$.

$\therefore$ $$V = V_R \cos (\beta z) \quad \text{and} \quad I = - j \left(\frac{V_R}{Z_c} \right) \sin (\beta z)$$

This above shows the standing wave patterns for both V and I, and both of them oscillate in unison. The wave shapes are shown in Figure 18.5. The conditions at the sending end depend on the length of the line, and the wavelength of the wave. One case of interest is when $l = \lambda/4$, i.e. quarter wave line,

$$\beta l = \left(\frac{2\pi}{\lambda} \right) \left(\frac{\lambda}{4} \right) = \frac{\pi}{2}$$

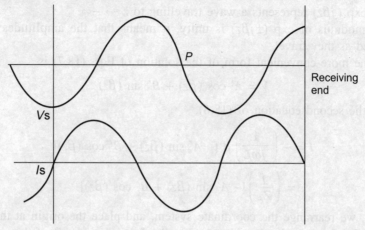

Figure 18.5 Standing wave patterns for V and I for an O.C. transmission line.

∴ From Eqs. (18.12),

$$V_S = jZ_cI_R, \qquad I_S = j\left(\frac{V_R}{Z_c}\right)$$

If we write $\qquad V_S = Z_SI_S \qquad$ and $\qquad V_R = Z_RI_R, \qquad$ then, we get

$$Z_S = \frac{Z_c^2}{Z_R} \tag{18.13}$$

∴ If the receiving end is short-circuited, i.e. $Z_R = 0$, then $Z_S \to \infty$; i.e. the sending end appears to be open-circuited, and vice versa. Thus the quarter wavelength line can be used as an 'impedance transformer' to alter the apparent value of the impedance across a pair of terminals.

When a line is used for communication with high frequency currents, the standing waves of the type shown above are highly undesirable. This is because a detector (say, at a point P) will receive no signals. Such a state can be avoided, if the line is terminated with matched load, i.e. a pure resistance of magnitude equal to Z_c.

∴ $V_R = Z_cI_R$, and Eqs. (18.11) become

$$V = V_R[\cos(\beta z) - j\sin(\beta z)] = V_R \exp(-\beta z) \tag{18.14a}$$

$$I = I_R[\cos(\beta z) - j\sin(\beta z)] = I_R \exp(-\beta z) \tag{18.14b}$$

which are travelling waves [as $\exp(j\omega t)$ is implicit in these expressions] moving to $z \to +\infty$, and thus the reflected waves are eliminated.

Again, expressing the voltage and the current equations of (18.11) in terms of impedances, we have

$$V = I_R[Z_L \cos(\beta z) - jZ_c \sin(\beta z)] \tag{18.15a}$$

$$I = \left(\frac{I_R}{Z_c}\right)[Z_c \cos(\beta z) - jZ_L \sin(\beta z)] \tag{18.15b}$$

where the terminating resistance R has now been replaced by a more general load impedance Z_L, so that $Z_R = Z_L$.

Hence the impedance of the line (terminated by Z_L), at a distance z from the sending end, is

$$Z(z) = \frac{V(z)}{I(z)} = Z_c \left[\frac{Z_L - jZ_c \tan (\beta z)}{Z_c - jZ_L \tan (\beta z)} \right] \qquad (18.16)$$

When the line is open-circuited, $Z_L \to \infty$; and

$$\therefore \quad Z(z) = \frac{jZ_c}{\tan (\beta z)} \qquad (18.17)$$

and when the line is short-circuited, $Z_L = 0$; and

$$Z(z) = -jZ_c \tan (\beta z) \qquad (18.18)$$

We notice that, in both the cases (i.e. O.C. and S.C.) the impedance of the line is purely imaginary, and hence they may replace any capacitor or inductor coil.

The reflection coefficient Γ is now given by

$$\Gamma = \frac{Z_L - Z_c}{Z_L + Z_c} \qquad \text{(the voltage reflection coefficient)*} \qquad (18.19)$$

We can rewrite the voltage equation of (18.15) in terms of the reflection coefficient as

$$V(z) = \left(\frac{1}{2} \right) I_R [(Z_L - Z_c) \exp (\beta z) + (Z_L + Z_c) \exp (-\beta z)]$$

$$= \left(\frac{1}{2} \right) I_R [(Z_L + Z_c) \exp (\beta z)\{(\Gamma + \exp (-2\beta z)\}] \qquad (18.20)$$

Since $\left| \exp (-2\beta z) \right| = 1$, the ratio of the maximum to the minimum amplitude of the voltage along the line is

$$\frac{V_{max}}{V_{min}} = s = \frac{1 + |\Gamma|}{1 - |\Gamma|} \qquad (18.21)$$

This ratio is known as the 'voltage standing wave ratio', which is abbreviated to VSWR. The above equation shows the range of s to be $1 \leq s \leq \infty$.

18.2.2   Lossy Transmission Lines

As before in the previous Section 18.2.1, we consider the transmission line cable as a pair of conductors of circular cross-section, which is characterized by the following parameters per unit length: resistance R (taking both the conductors into account), inductance L, capacitance C, and conductance G. The circuit representation of a section of this line is shown in Figure 18.6.

Considering the voltage and the current relations along the line, as shown in Figure 18.6 [similar to Eqs. (18.1) and (18.2) of the last section]:

$$V(z, t) - R\delta z I(z, t) - L\delta z \left(\frac{\partial}{\partial t} \right) I(z, t) = V(z, t) + \delta V(z, t)$$

and

$$I(z, t) - G\delta z [V(z, t) + \delta V(z, t)] - C\delta z \left(\frac{\partial}{\partial t} \right) [V(z, t) + \delta V(z, t)] = I(z, t) + \delta I(z, t)$$

---

*As distinct from the coefficients of energy reflection R_P and R_N of Chapter 17, p. 145.

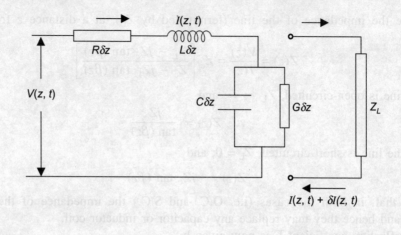

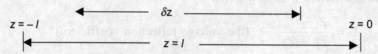

Figure 18.6 Circuit representation of a section of a lossy transmission line.

Simplifying and ignoring $(\delta z)^2$ and higher degree terms,

$$\left(\frac{\partial}{\partial z}\right)V(z,\ t) + RI(z,\ t) + L\left(\frac{\partial}{\partial t}\right)I(z,\ t) = 0 \qquad (18.22a)$$

$$\left(\frac{\partial}{\partial z}\right)I(z,\ t) + GV(z,\ t) + C\left(\frac{\partial}{\partial t}\right)V(z,\ t) = 0 \qquad (18.22b)$$

The most important case for practical problems is when $V(z,\ t)$ and $I(z,\ t)$ vary sinusoidally with time. So we can write:

$$I(z,\ t) = \text{Re}[I(z)\ \exp\ (j\omega t)] \qquad \text{and} \qquad V(z,\ t) = \text{Re}[V(z)\ \exp\ (j\omega t)] \qquad (18.23)$$

where $I(z)$ and $V(z)$ are complex amplitudes of the current and the voltage along the line. Hence Eqs. (18.22) become:

$$\left(\frac{d}{dz}\right)V(z) + (R + j\omega L)I(z) = 0 \qquad (18.24a)$$

$$\left(\frac{d}{dz}\right)I(z) + (G + j\omega C)V(z) = 0 \qquad (18.24b)$$

Differentiating the first equation with respect to z and combining with the second; and doing the vice versa, we get

$$\left(\frac{d^2}{dz^2}\right)V(z) + (R + j\omega L)(G + j\omega C)V(z) = 0 \qquad (18.25a)$$

$$\left(\frac{d^2}{dz^2}\right)I(z) + (R + j\omega L)(G + j\omega C)I(z) = 0 \qquad (18.25b)$$

both of which are complex one-dimensional wave equations.

Let
$$(R + j\omega L)(G + j\omega C) = \gamma^2 = (\alpha + j\beta)^2 \tag{18.26}$$

which gives

$$\alpha = \left(\frac{1}{\sqrt{2}}\right)\left[\sqrt{(R + j\omega L)(G + j\omega C)} + \left(RG - \omega^2 LC\right)\right]^{1/2} \tag{18.27a}$$

$$\beta = \left(\frac{1}{\sqrt{2}}\right)\left[\sqrt{(R + j\omega L)(G + j\omega C)} - \left(RG - \omega^2 LC\right)\right]^{1/2} \tag{18.27b}$$

where

γ is the complex propagation constant

α is the attenuation constant

β is the phase constant.

Equations (18.25) then become

$$\left(\frac{d^2}{dz^2}\right)V(z) + \gamma^2 V(z) = 0 \tag{18.28a}$$

$$\left(\frac{d^2}{dz^2}\right)I(z) + \gamma^2 I(z) = 0 \tag{18.28b}$$

The solution of both these equations is the same, i.e.

$$V(z) = V_1 \exp(-\gamma z) + V_2 \exp(\gamma z) \tag{18.29a}$$

$$I(z) = I_1 \exp(-\gamma z) + I_2 \exp(\gamma z) \tag{18.29b}$$

where V_1, V_2, I_1, and I_2 are unknown constants to be determined, but they are not all independent. These solutions appear as the sum of two waves, one travelling in the +ve z-direction and the other one in the −ve z-direction. Substituting from the above equations in Eqs. (18.24), we get

$$-\gamma V_1 \exp(-\gamma z) + \gamma V_2 \exp(\gamma z) + (R + j\omega L)[I_1 \exp(-\gamma z) + I_2 \exp(\gamma z)] = 0$$

This equation can be satisfied only if the coefficients of $\exp(-\gamma z)$ and $\exp(\gamma z)$ cancel out separately for all z, i.e.

$$\frac{V_1}{I_1} = \frac{R + j\omega L}{\gamma} = \sqrt{\frac{R + j\omega L}{G + j\omega C}} = Z_c \tag{18.30a}$$

$$\frac{V_2}{I_2} = -\frac{R + j\omega L}{\gamma} = -\sqrt{\frac{R + j\omega L}{G + j\omega C}} = -Z_c \tag{18.30b}$$

where Z_c is the characteristic impedance of the line.

If now we consider the transmission line to be terminated at the receiving end by a load impedance Z_L (= Z_R) which is located at $z = 0$ [i.e. the origin of the coordinate system being located at the receiving end where the load impedance is connected, and the −ve z-direction is towards the sending end, where the voltage source is connected (Figure 18.6), the length of this section of this line under consideration being l], then at $z = 0$,

$$Z_L \ (= Z_R) = \left[\frac{V(z)}{I(z)} \right]_{z=0} = \frac{V_1 + V_2}{I_1 + I_2}$$

$$= Z_c \left(\frac{I_1 - I_2}{I_1 + I_2} \right)$$

From this equation, the reflection coefficient $(= \Gamma_R)$ is obtained as

$$\Gamma_R = \frac{V_2}{V_1} = \frac{Z_R - Z_c}{Z_R + Z_c} \qquad (18.31a)$$

and

$$\frac{I_2}{I_1} = \frac{Z_c - Z_R}{Z_c + Z_R} \qquad (18.31b)$$

Expressing the solutions of Eqs. (18.29) in hyperbolic function form, we have

$$V = A_1 \cosh(\gamma z) + B_1 \sinh(\gamma z) \qquad (18.32a)$$

$$I = A_2 \cosh(\gamma z) + B_2 \sinh(\gamma z) \qquad (18.32b)$$

where the unknowns A_1, B_1, A_2, B_2 are determined by the use of the boundary conditions at the receiving end $(z = 0)$ and at the sending end $(z = -l)$, as shown in Figure 18.7.

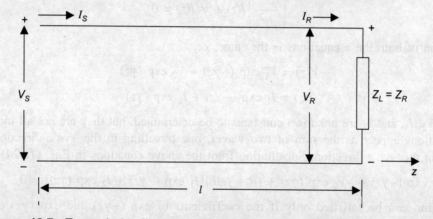

Figure 18.7 Transmission line terminated with a load impedance $(Z_L = Z_R)$ at the receiving end.

The boundary conditions are:

(a) at $z = 0$, $V = V_R$, $I = I_R$; and

(b) at $z = -l$, $V = V_S$, $I = I_S$ (18.33)

Substituting these equations in (18.32), and also using Eqs. (18.24), we get

$$V_S = V_R \cosh(\gamma l) + Z_c I_R \sinh(\gamma l) \qquad (18.34a)$$

$$I_S = I_R \cosh(\gamma l) + \left(\frac{V_R}{Z_c} \right) \sinh(\gamma l) \qquad (18.34b)$$

These are general transmission line equations correlating the voltages and the currents at the two ends of the line. Hence the general expression for the input impedance of the line is

$$Z_{in} = \frac{V_S}{I_S}$$

$$= \frac{V_R \cosh(\gamma l) + Z_c I_R \sinh(\gamma l)}{I_R \cosh(\gamma l) + \left(\dfrac{V_R}{Z_c}\right) \sinh(\gamma l)} \tag{18.35}$$

From the general expression for the input impedance, we now look at certain special cases of interest, as in the previous section, i.e.

(1) a line, short-circuited at the receiving end, i.e. $Z_R = 0$

∴ $V_R = 0$, and the input impedance $= Z_{sc} = Z_c \tanh(\gamma l)$ $\tag{18.36}$

(2) for an open-circuited line, $Z_R \to \infty$, $I_R = 0$

∴   the input impedance $= Z_{oc} = Z_c \coth(\gamma l)$ $\tag{18.37}$

(3) the product of these two gives us: $Z_{sc} Z_{oc} = Z_c^2$ $\tag{18.38}$

The low-loss or loss-less (idealized) line characteristics can also be obtained from the equations of this section, by considering the limit, when: $R \ll \omega L$ and $G \ll \omega C$.

Then, $Z = R + j\omega L = j\omega L$ and $Y = G + j\omega C = j\omega C$, and

$$Z_c = \sqrt{\frac{R + j\omega L}{G + j\omega C}} = \sqrt{\frac{L}{C}} \tag{18.39}$$

$$\gamma = \sqrt{(R + j\omega L)(G + j\omega C)} \simeq j\omega \sqrt{LC} = \alpha + j\beta$$

∴ $\alpha = 0$ and $\beta = \omega \sqrt{LC}$ $\tag{18.40}$

For low-loss lines, the approximation for β is very good, but at times the approximation of zero for α may not be good enough, even though α is very small compared with β. A better approximation is obtained by rearranging the terms in γ, and using the binomial expansion as shown below:

$$\gamma = j\omega \sqrt{LC} \sqrt{\left(1 + \frac{R}{j\omega L}\right)\left(1 + \frac{G}{j\omega C}\right)}$$

$$= j\omega \sqrt{LC} \left(1 + \frac{R}{j2\omega L}\right) + \left(\frac{G}{j2\omega C}\right)$$

$$\simeq j\omega \sqrt{LC} \left(1 + \frac{R}{j2\omega L} + \frac{G}{j2\omega C}\right)$$

$$\simeq \frac{R}{2\sqrt{\dfrac{L}{C}}} + \frac{G\sqrt{\dfrac{L}{C}}}{2} + j\omega \sqrt{LC} \tag{18.41}$$

so that

$$\alpha \simeq \left(\frac{1}{2}\right)\left(\frac{R}{Z_c} + GZ_c\right) \quad \text{and} \quad \beta \simeq \omega \sqrt{LC} \tag{18.42}$$

This value of α needs to be used only for calculating the line losses. For the calculations of the voltage and the current distributions, the attenuation of most of the *low-loss ultra high frequency transmission lines* is so small that $\alpha = 0$ gives satisfactory results. For many purposes, the low-loss lines may be treated as loss-less, i.e. $R = G = \alpha = 0$. Hence the equations of the general transmission lines reduce to the form given below for the low-loss high frequency lines:

$$V_S = V_R \cos(\beta l) + jI_R Z_c \sin(\beta l) \tag{18.43a}$$

$$I_S = I_R \cos(\beta l) + j\left(\frac{V_R}{Z_c}\right)\sin(\beta l) \tag{18.43b}$$

where $Z_c = \sqrt{\dfrac{L}{C}}$ is a pure resistance.

The input impedance of such a line is

$$Z_S = \frac{V_S}{I_S}$$

$$= Z_c \left[\frac{Z_R \cos(\beta l) + jZ_c \sin(\beta l)}{Z_c \cos(\beta l) + jZ_R \sin(\beta l)}\right] \tag{18.44}$$

18.2.3   Other Types of Transmission Lines

The coaxial cable has already been analyzed in detail in Chapter 14 (Sections 14.3.2, 14.4.1–14.4.2), and so we shall not repeat it here, even though it is a device to produce guided electromagnetic waves. However it is recommended that the students of the subject would find it beneficial to reread these above-mentioned sections, at this stage, following the knowledge gained so far, for further clarity of understanding.

The other commonly used transmission line is the 'stripline' which consists of two parallel strips of finite ε, μ, σ such that each strip's width b is much greater than its thickness a (i.e. $b \gg a$). We shall not discuss this device in detail here.

Next we shall discuss some basic types of waveguides.

18.3   WAVEGUIDES

18.3.1   Introduction

So far, in this chapter, we have described some different types of transmission lines which have been defined as guiding systems having two parallel conductors (but there may be more conductors in a system as in three-phase power lines which have three or four parallel conductors). The currents in the two conductors at any cross-section are of equal magnitude, but opposite in direction, and hence the electric and the magnetic field vectors are in planes, which are transverse to the direction of the lines, and hence are also transverse to the direction of energy propagation. The waves propagating along the transmission lines are thus transverse electromagnetic waves (TEM).

Waveguides are guiding systems, which generally have the form of highly conducting tubes or dielectric rods of different cross-sections, i.e. rectangular, circular, etc., and the electromagnetic energy is transported through such systems. There are many types of waveguides. In this short introduction, we shall start with the type known as the rectangular waveguide, which has the form of a tube of rectangular cross-section.

Also, for the ease of analysis, we consider here an idealized system with perfectly conducting walls, and two-dimensional in nature, though in reality the waveguides are never perfectly straight nor infinitely long. However, in spite of all these limitations, the picture we derive on the basis of this idealized model, closely resembles the real situation.

The rectangular waveguides are metallic guides (as are the two-wire transmission lines), and these are used efficiently over frequencies ranging from few tens of kHz to few tens of GHz. As the frequencies go further towards optical spectrum, the metallic waveguides become inefficient because of excessive losses in them and then the dielectric waveguides are used in the form of optical fibres. Since these are cylindrical in structure, their behaviours are analysed by solving the operating equations in the cylindrical polar coordinate system. So the cylindrical waveguides are dielectric waveguides which are more useful in the sub-millimetre and optical wavelength range (i.e. in terms of frequency this will be in units of THz). However, there are two types of dielectric waveguides i.e. cylindrical waveguides (e.g. optical fibres) and slab waveguides which are of rectangular geometry and are used in thin films and integrated optical devices.

The waveguides and many derived structures are the basic building blocks of any microwave system. The engineering problems related to such structures are varied, and in our introductory discussion, we shall deal with only important basic concepts. An important concept which will be developed is the 'modal propagation' of waves in these guided structures.

18.3.1.1 *Parallel plane waveguide*

In Section 17.17.2, it was shown that when a uniform plane E.M. wave, with its E vector normal to the plane of incidence, hits a perfectly conducting plane obliquely, it produces a reflected wave which interacts with the incident wave to produce a wave pattern such that this wave pattern is stationary or standing in the direction normal to the reflecting surface (i.e. in this case in the z-direction as shown in Figures 17.23 and 17.24 of Section 17.17.2) and sliding parallel to the reflecting surface, i.e. in the x-direction.

The interference pattern (say, of **E** field) has zero value on the reflecting surface ($z = 0$ plane). There are successive parallel planes of zero E alternated by +ve and –ve crests of the **E**-wave as shown in Figure 17.24. It was further stated that if another conducting plane was introduced in this pattern along the plane of zero **E** [(say), the first plane of zeros from the $z = 0$], then in the gap between these two parallel conducting planes (of width $z = d$), there is an E-wave pattern which is stationary in the z-direction, and gliding parallel to the x-direction. So starting from a wave which hits the $z = 0$ surface at any oblique angle θ,. a wave has been produced which travels in the x-direction, i.e. the wave has been guided along the x-direction. This is how the parallel plane waveguide has been developed. The mathematics of such a guided wave has been derived and discussed in Section 17.17.2 and so it will not be repeated here. Summarizing the results, the resultant electric and the magnetic field components are:

$$\left. \begin{aligned} \mathbf{E} &= -\mathbf{i}_y\, j2\, E_{0i+} \sin(\beta z \cos\theta_i)\exp[\,j(\omega t - \beta x \sin\theta_i)] \\[6pt] \mathbf{H} &= -\mathbf{i}_x\, j2\!\left(\frac{E_{0i+}}{Z_0}\right)\cos\theta_i\, \cos(\beta z \cos\theta_i)\exp[\,j(\omega t - \beta x \sin\theta_i)] \\[6pt] &\quad -\mathbf{i}_z\, 2\!\left(\frac{E_{0i+}}{Z_0}\right)\sin\theta_i\, \sin(\beta z \cos\theta_i)\exp[\,j(\omega t - \beta x \sin\theta_i)] \end{aligned} \right\} \qquad (17.204)$$

These are travelling waves in the x-direction but standing (or stationary) patterns in the z-direction.

The electric field E_y which is parallel to the conducting boundary $z = 0$ (i.e. xy-coordinate plane), becomes zero on that plane, as well as parallel planes located at $z = d$ such that

$$\sin(\beta d \cos\theta_i) = 0 = \sin\pi \ \text{ or } \ \sin n\pi$$

$$\therefore \qquad d = \frac{n\pi}{\beta\cos\theta_i}, \quad \beta = 2\pi f\sqrt{\mu_0\varepsilon_0}$$

$$\therefore \qquad d = \frac{\pi}{\beta\cos\theta_i}$$

If λ is the wavelength of the incident wave (in the direction of its propagation), then $\lambda = 2\pi/\beta$ and hence

$$\left. \begin{aligned} d &= \frac{\pi}{\beta\cos\theta_i} = \frac{\lambda}{2\cos\theta_i} \\[10pt] \text{and more generally} \qquad & \\[6pt] x = d &= \frac{n\pi}{\beta\cos\theta_i} = \frac{n\lambda}{2\cos\theta_i} \qquad n = 0,1,2,\dots \end{aligned} \right\} \qquad (17.205)$$

This means that the fields remain unaffected, if another conducting plane is interposed at any x given by Eq. (17.205). Hence we find that for a given angle of incidence θ_i, the height of the second conducting boundary, in order to maintain this described field pattern in the intermediate gap, will be a discrete multiple of $\lambda/(2\cos\theta_i)$. Or rewriting this equation by reversal,

$$\cos\theta_i = \frac{n\lambda}{2d} = \frac{n\pi}{\beta d} \qquad (A)$$

So now we can say that when there are two parallel conducting boundaries separated by a distance d, the fields between them will be due to superposition of waves incident at angles θ_i given by the above equation. Since n is an integer, there will be discrete values of θ_i. It should be noted that when there is a single boundary, the field generated by the reflection of the incident wave would have survived at any angle of incidence, i.e. θ_i could change in a continuous manner. But when there are parallel boundaries, the boundary conditions on the two boundaries can be satisfied only by certain discrete values of θ_i and so the field pattern in the gap would survive only for these specific values of θ_i. So there have been some drastic changes in the process which are stated below:

(i) There has been a change from the continuous domain of θ to the discrete domain.

(ii) For a given boundary separation d and a specified frequency f, there are only a finite number of angles θ, as $\cos\theta \le 1$.

(iii) When $d_n < \lambda/2$, then from Eq. (A) $\cos\theta$ becomes greater than 1 which is not possible. This means that no waves can be launched between the two conducting planes, if the gap between them is $< \lambda/2$, i.e. less than the half wavelength.

(iv) As d increases or λ decreases, the number of angles (i.e. θ) at which waves can be launched also increases.

In the field expressions [i.e. Eqs. (17.204)], $\cos\theta_i$ can be replaced by λ and dn from Eqs. (17.205), i.e.

$$\cos\theta_i = \frac{n\lambda}{2d} = \frac{n\pi}{\beta d}$$

and

$$\beta z \cos\theta_i = \frac{2\pi z}{\lambda}\frac{n\lambda}{2d} = \frac{n\pi z}{d}$$

and

$$\sin\theta_i = \sqrt{\left[1 - \left(\frac{n\lambda}{2d}\right)^2\right]} = \frac{\beta_x}{\beta}$$

and the wave number (the phase constant) for the guided wave pattern $= \beta_x = \beta\sin\theta_i$.

∴ The field existing between the two conducting boundaries can be written as

$$\mathbf{E} = -\mathbf{i}_y\, j2\, E_{0i+}\sin\left(\frac{n\pi z}{d}\right)\exp[\,j(\omega t - \beta_x x)]$$

$$\mathbf{H} = -\mathbf{i}_x\, 2\left(\frac{E_{0i+}}{Z_0}\right)\left(\frac{n\pi}{\beta d}\right)\cos\left(\frac{n\pi z}{d}\right)\exp[\,j(\omega t - \beta_x x)]$$

$$-\mathbf{i}_z\, j\, 2\left(\frac{E_{0i+}}{Z_0}\right)\left(\frac{\beta_x}{\beta}\right)\sin\left(\frac{n\pi z}{d}\right)\exp[\,j(\omega t - \beta_x x)]$$

(17.204a)

It should be noted that for a given value of n, the variation of the field in the z-direction is fixed and independent of the frequency. For example, for $n = 1$, the field pattern is half sine wave; and for $n = 2$, the field pattern is one complete cycle (both the bounding planes $z = 0$ and $z = d$, and so on.).

Thus the field pattern is unique for a given n, and that there is no gradual change from one pattern to another.

These unique field patterns are called the 'modal field patterns', and the propagation of these waves in the form of these discrete patterns is called 'modal propagation.'

Since the time-varying electric field cannot exist alone, it will be associated with orthogonal magnetic field. For $n = 0$, the E field will be zero, and so both H_x and H_z will also vanish.

The field components in this problem are such that the E field is transverse to the direction of propagation, and so it is called 'Transverse Electric' or TE mode. (m is put as a suffix to indicate the order of the mode and so n used earlier would be replaced by m.)

A similar 'Transverse Magnetic' or TM mode pattern would be obtained if the incident wave had the **E**-wave parallel to the plane of incidence which has been described in Section 17.17.1.

The corresponding field expressions for the TM mode would be

$$
\left.
\begin{aligned}
\mathbf{E} &= -\mathbf{i}_x \, j2E_{0i+}\left(\frac{m\pi}{\beta d}\right)\sin\left(\frac{m\pi z}{d}\right)\exp[\,j(\omega t - \beta_x x)] \\[2mm]
&\quad -\mathbf{i}_z \, 2E_{0i+}\left(\frac{\beta_x}{\beta}\right)\cos\left(\frac{m\pi z}{d}\right)\exp[\,j(\omega t - \beta_x x)] \\[2mm]
\mathbf{H} &= \mathbf{i}_y \, 2\left(\frac{E_{0i+}}{Z_0}\right)\cos\left(\frac{m\pi z}{d}\right)\exp[\,j(\omega t - \beta_x x)]
\end{aligned}
\right\}
\qquad (17.191')
$$

by similar algebraic manipulations as for the TE mode expressions.

Note: The suffix m for either TE mode or TM mode (or TEM) denotes the order of the mode, i.e. the number of half-cycles of the wave pattern in the gap width d.

18.3.1.2 Cut-off frequency

The modal propagation constant or the wave number in the direction of propagation (i.e. x-direction) is

$$
\beta_x = \beta \sin\theta_i = \beta\sqrt{\left[1 - \left(\frac{m\lambda_1}{2d}\right)^2\right]}
$$

$$
= \sqrt{\left[\beta^2 - \left(\frac{m\pi}{d}\right)^2\right]}
$$

From the field expressions (17.204a), it follows directly that if the resulting pattern is to be travelling in the x-direction [i.e. $\exp\{j(\omega t - \beta_x x)\}$] then β_x must be real. If β_x is not real, i.e. becomes imaginary, then $j\beta_x x$ becomes real and then the function does not represent a travelling wave. It then becomes an attenuated standing alternating pattern.

Hence the condition for wave propagation is

$$
\beta_x = \text{Real} \Rightarrow \beta \geq \frac{m\pi}{d}
$$

Since

$$
\beta = \frac{2\pi}{\lambda} = \frac{2\pi f}{u}
$$

where u is the velocity of the uniform plane wave in the medium under consideration, and we get

$$
f \geq \frac{mu}{2d}
$$

or

$$
\lambda \leq \frac{2d}{m}
$$

So for a given waveguide height d, the frequency f must be higher than a certain threshold value, for the wave to propagate for a particular mode. This threshold value of the frequency is called the cut-off frequency for that mode, i.e.

$$f_c \text{ (or } f_{cm}) = \frac{m\text{u}}{2d_1}$$

and the corresponding cut-off wavelength $\lambda_c \text{ (or } \lambda_{cm}) = \dfrac{2d}{m}$.

18.3.2   Rectangular Waveguides

The present analysis is essentially a continuation of the matter discussed in Section 17.17.2 (and should be read as such, since the present discussion is a direct follow up of that section), where we analyzed in detail the wave pattern produced by the oblique incidence of a plane wave, with its **E** vector normal to the plane of incidence, on a perfectly conducting surface. We found that parallel to the reflecting interface plane $z = 0$, there are planes like AA' (referring to Figure 17.24) on which $E_i + E_r = 0$ for all x and y at all t. This means that the wave pattern can still exist, if one of these parallel planes is replaced by a second conducting wall (similar to the $z = 0$ plane). If the nearest of such planes to $z = 0$ is taken, i.e. A_1A_1' (Figure 17.24), then its distance d_1 from the reflecting surface is related with the free space wavelength (denoted by λ_0), i.e.

$$d_1 = \frac{\lambda_0}{2 \cos \theta_i} = \frac{\lambda_0}{2} \sec \theta_i \qquad (18.45)$$

The above equation refers to Eq. (17.206) of Section 17.17.2 where λ the wavelength of the incident wave has now been expressed as λ_0, as the wave is in free space, and hence,

$$\lambda_0 = \frac{1}{\left(\sqrt{\mu_0 \varepsilon_0}\right) f} = \frac{c}{f}$$

Or, conversely, we can argue that, given two perfectly conducting planes d_1 distance apart, a wave pattern can be set up at an angular frequency ω, such that:

$$\omega = 2\pi f = \frac{2\pi c}{\lambda_0} = \frac{\pi c}{d_1 \cos \theta_i} \qquad (18.46)$$

The field $E_i + E_r$ does not vary with y, and hence can terminate on the $\pm$ charges on the planes at $y = 0$ and $y = b$. Thus a 'rectangular waveguide' is produced.

The field patterns are as shown in Figures 18.8(a) and (b). These are shown in two orthogonal planes, i.e. y-z plane and x-y plane. The separate fields E_i, E_r, H_i, H_r and $\angle\theta_i$, which were used for generating this final pattern, are really parts of the building scaffolding, and are now omitted.

From Figure 18.8(b), it will be seen that the field alternates longitudinally (in the x-direction—the direction of propagation of the guided wave—as distinct from the direction of propagation of the incident wave). It will also be noted that the **E** field (the resultant field) is transverse and **H** has both the transverse and the longitudinal components. The field travels with a velocity v_x given by

$$v_x = c \operatorname{cosec} \theta_i \qquad (18.47)$$

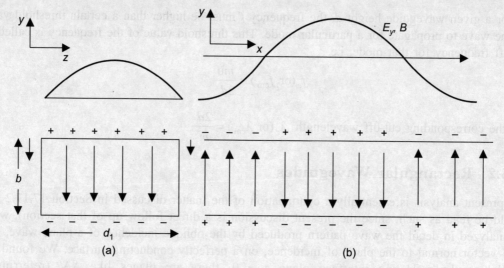

Figure 18.8 Field pattern in a rectangular waveguide (refer to Figure 17.24, for correspondence with the incident wave direction).

and the wavelength of the longitudinal waves is

$$\lambda_x = \lambda_0 \operatorname{cosec} \theta_i \tag{18.48}$$

(It should be noted that v_x is greater than c, and so v_x will exceed the velocity of light in an air-filled waveguide). It should be carefully noted that the velocity with which the signals are transmitted is the so called 'group velocity' v_{gr}, which is given by

$$v_{gr} = c \sin \theta_i \tag{18.49}$$

This is most simply explained by thinking of the transmission as by a sequence of reflected waves on two parallel planes $z = 0$ and $z = d_1$, as shown in Figure 18.9.

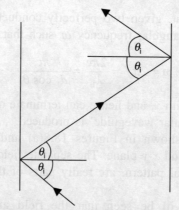

Figure 18.9 Group velocity v_{gr}.

To obtain the cut-off frequency, using Eqs. (18.45) and (18.48), we get

$$\left(\frac{\lambda_0}{2a}\right)^2 + \left(\frac{\lambda_0}{\lambda_x}\right)^2 = 1$$

or

$$\left(\frac{1}{\lambda_x}\right)^2 + \left(\frac{1}{2a}\right)^2 = \left(\frac{1}{\lambda_0}\right)^2 = \left(\frac{\omega}{2\pi c}\right)^2 \qquad (18.50)$$

(We have replaced d_1 by a for simplicity of notation.)

$\therefore$ For λ_x to be real, $\dfrac{\omega}{\pi c}$ must be $> \dfrac{1}{a}$,

i.e. ω must be $> \dfrac{\pi c}{a}$.

$\therefore$ The limiting value of the cut-off frequency is given by

$$\omega_c = \frac{\pi c}{a} \qquad (18.51)$$

which from Eqs. (18.46) and (18.49) corresponds to $\theta_i = 0$ and $v_{gr} = 0$.

Below this frequency there can be no propagation. This quantity relates the width of the waveguide to the proposed frequency.

If now we look at the lines of **E** and **H** in a plane containing the direction of propagation (as shown in Figure 18.10), then the lines of **E** ($= E_y$) in the x-y plane are lines transverse to the direction of propagation, and the lines of **H** are closed loops in the z-x plane ($y = $ constant).

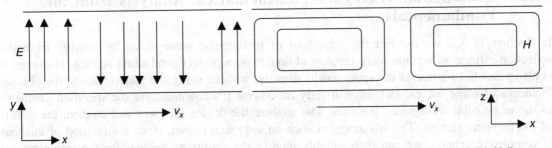

Figure 18.10   **E** and **H** lines along the direction of propagation: (a) **E** lines and (b) **H** lines.

The pattern, which we have discussed above, is only one of the many possible *modes of operation*, known as the TE$_{10}$ mode where TE stands for the 'Transverse Electric', because the **E** field is entirely across the guide (i.e. totally normal to the direction of propagation). The suffix 10 is given because the standing wave of **E** has one-half cycle in the x-direction and none in the y-direction.

In general, there is a possibility of m, n, half-cycles in these two directions, leading to TE$_{mn}$ mode. If we had chosen the second plane AA' (of Figure 17.24), then we should have obtained TE$_{20}$ mode, with two half-cycles of **E** in the standing waves.

In addition, there is a whole series of modes in which the magnetic field is transverse; the TM$_{11}$ being the lowest. The TM$_{11}$ modes are as shown below in Figure 18.11.

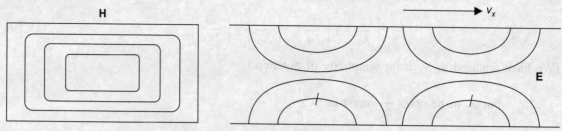

Figure 18.11 TM$_{11}$ mode in a rectangular waveguide.

These broad types of waves can exist in all transmission systems. In a coaxial cable, for example the mode usually considered is TEM mode, but it can be shown that this cannot occur in a single-conductor waveguide (which is simply-connected). This is because a transverse magnetic field must have the basic form shown above (possibly with several vortices); $\oint \mathbf{H} \cdot d\mathbf{l}$ has a finite value round any closed line, showing that the current must be enclosed. This requires:

either (a) one or more central conductors (i.e. multiply-connected);

or (b) a displacement current, which necessitates a longitudinal electric field.

Thus TEM waves can only occur if there are conductors in the waveguides.

18.3.3 Rectangular Waveguide: Mathematical Analysis from the Fundamentals

In Section 18.3.2, we derived the behaviour of rectangular waveguides by starting from the reflection patterns of a plane wave incident obliquely on a perfect conducting surface. However, it is also possible to arrive at the same results directly, without using the pattern due to the oblique incidence of plane waves, and solve directly the Maxwell's equations for the specified geometry of the rectangular waveguide. We shall now analyze the device this way and confirm the results of the previous section. The advantage of such an approach is that, since the method of analysis is completely general, we can then suitably modify the results to account for the imperfections and changes in a practical device.

We start with the rectangular tube as shown in Figure 18.12, with its coordinate system shown in the figure, and the direction of propagation in the guide being +z-direction. The guide is

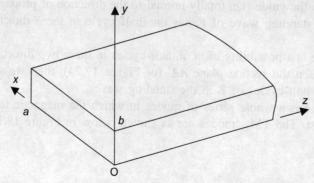

Figure 18.12 A rectangular waveguide, with cross-section $a * b$, and the coordinate system as shown.

assumed to be infinitely long, and its walls are (initially) made of perfect conductor, and the dielectric inside is loss-less; it has the characteristic properties: ε, and μ, with σ being zero.

It has been seen earlier that using complex notation for the sinusoidally time-varying excitations, a wave travelling in the $+z$-direction is denoted by $\exp(-j\beta z)$. When there is attenuation, $j\beta$ has to be replaced by γ, such that $\gamma = \alpha + j\beta$. So to maintain the generality, we indicate the propagation in the $+z$-direction by $\exp(-\gamma z)$. Hence the complex field vectors are of the form:

$$\mathbf{E} = \mathbf{E}(x, y) \exp(-\gamma z) \qquad \text{and} \qquad \mathbf{H} = \mathbf{H}(x, y) \exp(-\gamma z) \tag{18.52}$$

From the Maxwell's equations,

$$\nabla \times \mathbf{H} = \frac{\partial \mathbf{D}}{\partial t} \qquad \text{and} \qquad \nabla \times \mathbf{E} = -\frac{\partial \mathbf{B}}{\partial t}, \text{ we get}$$

$$\mathbf{i}_x\left(\frac{\partial H_z}{\partial y} - \frac{\partial H_y}{\partial z}\right) + \mathbf{i}_y\left(\frac{\partial H_x}{\partial z} - \frac{\partial H_z}{\partial x}\right) + \mathbf{i}_z\left(\frac{\partial H_y}{\partial x} - \frac{\partial H_x}{\partial y}\right)$$

$$= j\omega\varepsilon\left(\mathbf{i}_x E_x + \mathbf{i}_y E_y + \mathbf{i}_z E_z\right)$$

or

$$\mathbf{i}_x\left(\frac{\partial E_z}{\partial y} - \frac{\partial E_y}{\partial z}\right) + \mathbf{i}_y\left(\frac{\partial E_x}{\partial z} - \frac{\partial E_z}{\partial x}\right) + \mathbf{i}_z\left(\frac{\partial E_y}{\partial x} - \frac{\partial E_x}{\partial y}\right)$$

$$= -j\omega\mu\left(\mathbf{i}_x H_x + \mathbf{i}_y H_y + \mathbf{i}_z H_z\right)$$

using $\mathbf{B} = \mu\mathbf{H}$, $\mathbf{D} = \varepsilon\mathbf{E}$, and $\dfrac{\partial}{\partial t} = j\omega$.

Combining these equations with Eqs. (18.52), and equating the vector components, we get the following scalar equations:

$$\frac{\partial H_z}{\partial y} + \gamma H_y = j\omega\varepsilon E_x \tag{18.53a}$$

$$\frac{\partial H_z}{\partial x} + \gamma H_x = -j\omega\varepsilon E_y \tag{18.53b}$$

$$\frac{\partial H_y}{\partial x} - \frac{\partial H_x}{\partial y} = j\omega\varepsilon E_z \tag{18.53c}$$

$$\frac{\partial E_z}{\partial y} + \gamma E_y = -j\omega\mu H_x \tag{18.53d}$$

$$\frac{\partial E_z}{\partial x} + \gamma E_x = j\omega\mu H_y \tag{18.53e}$$

$$\frac{\partial E_y}{\partial x} - \frac{\partial E_x}{\partial y} = -j\omega\mu H_z \tag{18.53f}$$

From Eqs. (18.53), by combining (a) and (e) we get E_x and H_y, and by combining (b) and (d) we get H_x and E_y as given below:

$$H_x = -\left(\frac{\gamma}{k^2}\right)\left(\frac{\partial H_z}{\partial x}\right) + \left(\frac{\omega\varepsilon}{k^2}\right)\left(\frac{\partial E_z}{\partial y}\right) \tag{18.54a}$$

$$H_y = -\left(\frac{\gamma}{k^2}\right)\left(\frac{\partial H_z}{\partial y}\right) - \left(\frac{\omega\varepsilon}{k^2}\right)\left(\frac{\partial E_z}{\partial x}\right) \tag{18.54b}$$

$$E_x = -\left(\frac{\gamma}{k^2}\right)\left(\frac{\partial E_z}{\partial x}\right) - \left(\frac{\omega\mu}{k^2}\right)\left(\frac{\partial H_z}{\partial y}\right) \tag{18.54c}$$

$$E_y = -\left(\frac{\gamma}{k^2}\right)\left(\frac{\partial E_z}{\partial y}\right) + \left(\frac{\omega\mu}{k^2}\right)\left(\frac{\partial H_z}{\partial x}\right) \tag{18.54d}$$

where $k^2 = \gamma^2 + \omega^2\mu\varepsilon$.

The wave equations for E_z and H_z are obtained from the equations of (18.53) along with the Maxwell's divergence equations in charge-free region, i.e.

$$\nabla \cdot \mathbf{D} = 0 \quad \text{and} \quad \nabla \cdot \mathbf{B} = 0 \tag{18.55}$$

We differentiate (18.53a) with respect to y, (18.53b) with respect to x, and then add them and substitute from (18.53f) and (18.55) to get

$$\frac{\partial^2 H_z}{\partial x^2} + \frac{\partial^2 H_z}{\partial y^2} + \gamma^2 H_z = -\omega^2\mu\varepsilon H_z \tag{18.56}$$

and similarly differentiate (18.53d) with respect to y, (18.53e) with respect to x, then add them and substitute from (18.53e) and (18.55) to obtain:

$$\frac{\partial^2 E_z}{\partial x^2} + \frac{\partial^2 E_z}{\partial y^2} + \gamma^2 E_z = -\omega^2\mu\varepsilon E_z \tag{18.57}$$

Equations (18.54), (18.56) and (18.57) give us the relationship between the field components within the rectangular guide. It should be noticed that if both E_z and H_z are zero simultaneously, then all the fields within the guide will also vanish. Hence for such a waveguide structure (in which there is no inner conductor in the space of the guide—mathematically this region is 'singly-connected' whereas a region with conductor inside is 'multiply-connected'), there must exist either an E_z or an H_z component, i.e. *a* component directed in the direction of propagation. Thus two possible field configurations can exist in this waveguide, i.e. (1) the transverse electric (TE mode) waves for which $E_z = 0$, and (2) the transverse magnetic waves (TM mode) for which $H_z = 0$.

For the guide shown in Figure 18.12, the resultant boundary conditions are (we have assumed the enclosing boundaries to be perfect conductors, at this stage)

(1)   at $y = 0$ and $y = b$, $E_x = E_z = 0$; and

(2)   at $x = 0$ and $x = a$, $E_y = E_z = 0$.

Physically the conditions state that there can be no tangential electric field on any of the boundary surfaces.

18.3.3.1 *Transverse electric waves in rectangular waveguides*

In this type of waveguide, if $E_z = 0$, the electric field intensity vector is in the transverse plane, and such waves are referred to as transverse electric or TE waves.

When $E_z = 0$, Eqs. (18.53) simplify to:

$$\gamma E_y = -j\omega\mu H_x \qquad (18.58d)$$

$$\gamma E_x = j\omega\mu H_y \qquad (18.58e)$$

$$\frac{\partial E_y}{\partial x} - \frac{\partial E_x}{\partial y} = -j\omega\mu H_z \qquad (18.58f)$$

$$\frac{\partial H_z}{\partial y} + \gamma H_y = j\omega\varepsilon E_x \qquad (18.58a)$$

$$\frac{\partial H_z}{\partial x} + \gamma H_x = -j\omega\varepsilon E_y \qquad (18.58b)$$

$$\frac{\partial H_y}{\partial x} - \frac{\partial H_x}{\partial y} = 0 \qquad (18.58c)$$

We now express all the field components in terms of H_z, i.e. we combine Eqs. (18.58b) and (18.58d), and get

$$\frac{\partial H_z}{\partial x} + \gamma H_x = -j\omega\varepsilon\left[-j\left(\frac{\omega\mu}{\gamma}\right)H_x\right]$$

from which

$$H_x = -\left(\frac{\gamma}{k^2}\right)\left(\frac{\partial H_z}{\partial x}\right) \qquad (18.59)$$

Similarly from (18.58a) and (18.58e), we get

$$H_y = -\left(\frac{\gamma}{k^2}\right)\left(\frac{\partial H_z}{\partial y}\right) \qquad (18.60)$$

Combining these two equations with (18.58e) and (18.58d), we get

$$E_x = -\left(\frac{\omega\mu}{k^2}\right)\left(\frac{\partial H_z}{\partial y}\right) \qquad (18.61)$$

$$E_y = \left(\frac{\omega\mu}{k^2}\right)\left(\frac{\partial H_z}{\partial x}\right) \qquad (18.62)$$

and the equation for H_z is

$$\frac{\partial^2 H_z}{\partial x^2} + \frac{\partial^2 H_z}{\partial y^2} + k^2 H_z = 0 \qquad (18.63)$$

We solve this equation by using the method of separation of variables, i.e.

$$H_z = H_z(x, y) = XY = X(x)Y(y) \qquad (18.64)$$

Equation (18.63) becomes

$$\left(\frac{1}{X}\right)\left(\frac{\partial^2 X}{\partial x^2}\right) + \left(\frac{1}{Y}\right)\left(\frac{\partial^2 Y}{\partial y^2}\right) + k^2 = 0 \qquad (18.65)$$

Since the first term is a function of x only, and the second term is a function of y only, the above equation can be satisfied only if each term is a constant, such that

$$\frac{\partial^2 X}{\partial x^2} = -k_x^2 X, \qquad \frac{\partial^2 Y}{\partial y^2} = -k_y^2 Y \tag{18.66}$$

where

$$k_x^2 + k_y^2 = k^2 = \gamma^2 + \omega^2 \mu \varepsilon \tag{18.67}$$

The solutions of Eqs. (18.66) are of the form

$$X = A_x \sin(k_x x) + B_x \cos(k_x x)$$

and

$$Y = A_y \sin(k_y y) + B_y \cos(k_y y)$$

so that

$$H_z = \sum_{k_x}\sum_{k_y} [A_x \sin(k_x x) + B_x \cos(k_x x)][A_y \sin(k_y y) + B_y \cos(k_y y)] \tag{18.68}$$

The unknown constants A_x, B_x, A_y, B_y, and k_x, k_y have to be determined by using the boundary conditions stated in the previous section.

The first set of boundary conditions state that

$$\text{at } y = 0, \text{ and } y = b, \; E_x = 0 \text{ and } E_z = 0$$

From Eqs. (18.61) and (18.68), we get

$$\sum_{k_x}\sum_{k_y} [A_x \sin(k_x x) + B_x \cos(k_x x)][A_y \cos(k_y y) - B_y \sin(k_y y)]k_y = 0$$

for $y = 0$ and $y = b$, for all values of x.

$$\therefore \quad A_y = 0 \quad \text{and} \quad k_y = \frac{n\pi}{b}, \text{ where } n = 0, 1, 2, 3, \ldots .$$

The second set of boundary conditions states that at $z = 0$ and at $x = b$, $E_y = 0$ and $E_z = 0$.
$\therefore$ From Eqs. (18.62) and (18.68),

$$\sum_{k_x}\sum_{k_y} [A_x \cos(k_x x) - B_x \sin(k_x x)]k_x [A_y \sin(k_y y) + B_y \cos(k_y y)] = 0$$

for $x = 0$ and $x = a$ for all values of y.

$$\therefore \quad A_x = 0 \text{ and } k_x = \frac{m\pi}{a}, \text{ where } m = 0, 1, 2, 3, \ldots .$$

$$H_z = H_z(x, y) = H_0 \cos\left(\frac{m\pi x}{a}\right)\cos\left(\frac{n\pi y}{b}\right) \tag{18.69}$$

where $m, n = 0, 1, 2, 3, \ldots$, and H_0 stands for the product $(B_x B_y)$ of the constants from Eq. (18.68), and is determined by the intensity of the wave propagating through the guide. It should be noted that these boundary conditions cannot be satisfied if $H_z = 0$ all over the region inside the guide, and, if $H_z = 0$, then the equations define a wave for which **E** and **H** are constant in the transverse planes. So we have here proved mathematically that a rectangular waveguide cannot support a TEM wave.

All other components of TE type of waves, which can be supported by the waveguide, can now be calculated by using the equations from (18.59) to (18.62). An infinite number of modes corresponding to different values of m and n can propagate through the waveguide. The general (*mn*) wave (or TE$_{mn}$ mode, where the physical significance of *m* and *n* has been explained in Section 18.3.2) is supported by the waveguide, and the particular types are TE$_{10}$, TE$_{01}$, TE$_{11}$, TE$_{12}$, TE$_{45}$, etc. It should also be noted that the mode TE$_{00}$ cannot exist, because then $H_z = H_0 =$ constant, so that then all the field components become zero.

From Eq. (18.67), we have

$$k^2 = k_x^2 + k_y^2 = \left(\frac{m\pi}{a}\right)^2 + \left(\frac{n\pi}{b}\right)^2 = \gamma^2 + \omega^2 \mu\varepsilon$$

$$\therefore \qquad \gamma = \left[\left(\frac{m\pi}{a}\right)^2 + \left(\frac{n\pi}{b}\right)^2 - \omega^2\mu\varepsilon\right]^{1/2} \tag{18.70}$$

In the transmission line theory, which we studied in the earlier part of this chapter, γ the propagation constant was found to be a complex number, i.e. $\gamma = \alpha + j\beta$, where α is the attenuation constant (or factor) (i.e. attenuation per unit length), and β is the phase-shift constant (i.e. phase-shift per unit length). If γ is real, then $\beta = 0$, i.e. there is no phase-shift along the tube, which means that for real γ [i.e. at low frequencies, since $\omega^2\mu\varepsilon$ is $< (m\pi/a)^2 + (n\pi/b)^2$] there is no wave motion along the guide. However as the frequency is increased, there is a critical value of ω ($= \omega_c$) at which the expression under the square-root sign is zero, and for higher values of ω, γ will be imaginary, i.e.

$$\gamma = j\beta = j\left[\omega^2\mu\varepsilon - \left\{\left(\frac{m\pi}{a}\right)^2 + \left(\frac{n\pi}{b}\right)^2\right\}\right]^{1/2}, \quad \text{when } \omega > \omega_c \tag{18.71}$$

where

$$\omega_c = \left(\frac{1}{\mu\varepsilon}\right)^{1/2}\left[\left(\frac{m\pi}{a}\right)^2 + \left(\frac{n\pi}{b}\right)^2\right]^{1/2} = 2\pi f_c \tag{18.72}$$

This critical value of the frequency is called the cut-off frequency [see Eq. (18.51)].

The corresponding cut-off wavelength

$$\lambda_c = \frac{u}{f_c}\left(= \frac{c}{f_c}\right) = \frac{2\pi}{\left[\left(\frac{m\pi}{a}\right)^2 + \left(\frac{n\pi}{b}\right)^2\right]^{1/2}} \tag{18.73}$$

The velocity of wave propagation

$$v = \frac{\omega}{\beta} = \frac{\omega}{\left[\omega^2\mu\varepsilon - \left\{\left(\frac{m\pi}{a}\right)^2 + \left(\frac{n\pi}{b}\right)^2\right\}\right]^{1/2}} \tag{18.74}$$

which indicates that the velocity of propagation of the wave in the guide is greater than the phase velocity in free space. As the frequency is increased above the cut-off frequency, the phase velocity decreases from an infinitely large value and approaches the velocity of light in free space c, as the frequency is kept on increasing indefinitely.

The cut-off frequencies of different modes are different. The mode TE$_{10}$ for which $m = 1$, $n = 0$, has the lowest cut-off frequency, i.e.

$$(f_c)_{TE10} = \frac{1}{2a\sqrt{\mu\varepsilon}} = \frac{c}{2a}, \text{ for } a \gg b \qquad (18.75)$$

which matches with the value obtained in Eq. (18.51).

The next lowest cut-off frequency is for TE_{01} mode, for which

$$(f_c)_{TE01} = \frac{c}{2b} \qquad (18.76)$$

∴   In the range $(c/2a) < f < (c/2b)$, only TE_{10} mode can propagate through the guide. The field equations for the TE_{mn} mode are:

$$E_x = j\left(\frac{\omega\mu}{k^2}\right) H_0 \frac{n\pi}{b} \cos\left(\frac{m\pi x}{a}\right) \sin\left(\frac{n\pi y}{b}\right) \qquad (18.77a)$$

$$E_y = -j\left(\frac{\omega\mu}{k^2}\right) H_0 \frac{m\pi}{a} \sin\left(\frac{m\pi x}{a}\right) \cos\left(\frac{n\pi y}{b}\right) \qquad (18.77b)$$

$$H_x = j\left(\frac{\beta}{k^2}\right) H_0 \frac{m\pi}{a} \sin\left(\frac{m\pi x}{a}\right) \cos\left(\frac{n\pi y}{b}\right) \qquad (18.77c)$$

$$H_y = j\left(\frac{\beta}{k^2}\right) H_0 \frac{n\pi}{b} \cos\left(\frac{m\pi x}{a}\right) \sin\left(\frac{n\pi y}{b}\right) \qquad (18.77d)$$

$$H_z = H_0 \cos\left(\frac{m\pi x}{a}\right) \cos\left(\frac{n\pi y}{b}\right) \qquad (18.77e)$$

In the above expressions, γ has been replaced by $j\beta$, which is valid for the frequencies above the cut-off frequency f_c.

Implicit in the above expressions are the terms $[\exp(-j\beta z) \exp(j\omega t)]$, and the real part of the total expression has to be considered. Also, by convention, the x-coordinate is assumed to coincide with the larger transverse dimension, and hence the TE_{10} mode has the lowest cut-off frequency (lower than the TE_{01} mode), and this is called the 'dominant mode'.

18.3.3.2   *Energy transmission in the TE₁₀ mode of rectangular waveguides*

The field components in the TE_{10} mode are obtained by substituting $m = 1$, $n = 0$, in Eqs. (18.77), which give:

$$E_x = 0 \qquad (18.78a)$$

$$E_y = -j\left(\frac{\omega\mu a}{\pi}\right) H_0 \sin\left(\frac{\pi x}{a}\right) \exp(-j\beta z) \qquad (18.78b)$$

$$H_x = j\left(\frac{\beta a}{\pi}\right) H_0 \sin\left(\frac{\pi x}{a}\right) \exp(-j\beta z) \qquad (18.78c)$$

$$H_y = 0 \qquad (18.78d)$$

$$H_z = H_0 \cos\left(\frac{\pi x}{a}\right) \exp\left(-j\beta z\right) \tag{18.78e}$$

All these expressions have exp $(j\omega t)$ implicit in them.

$$\beta = \sqrt{\omega^2 \mu\varepsilon - \left(\frac{\pi}{a}\right)^2} = \omega\sqrt{\mu\varepsilon}\sqrt{1 - \frac{\left(\frac{\pi}{a}\right)^2}{\omega^2 \mu\varepsilon}}$$

$$= \omega\sqrt{\mu\varepsilon}\sqrt{1 - \left(\frac{c}{2af}\right)^2} = \omega\sqrt{\mu\varepsilon}\sqrt{1 - \left(\frac{f_c}{f}\right)^2} \tag{18.79}$$

where $\omega = 2\pi f$; $c = \sqrt{\mu\varepsilon}$ and $f_c = \dfrac{c}{2a} = \dfrac{1}{2a\sqrt{\mu\varepsilon}}$ both in free space.

The wavelength of the wave propagating along the z-direction of the guide is ($= \lambda_z$):

$$\lambda_z = \frac{2\pi}{\beta} = \frac{2\pi c}{2\pi f\sqrt{1 - \left(\frac{f_c}{f}\right)^2}} = \frac{c}{f\sqrt{1 - \left(\frac{f_c}{f}\right)^2}}$$

$$= \frac{\lambda}{\sqrt{1 - \frac{f_c^2}{f^2}}} \tag{18.80}$$

λ, being the wavelength of the plane wave of the same frequency.

Hence the velocity of propagation of the wave along the waveguide (in the z-direction) is:

$$v_p = f\lambda_z = \frac{c}{\sqrt{1 - \frac{f_c^2}{f^2}}} \tag{18.81}$$

This velocity of propagation as described before is greater than the velocity of light in vacuum. It is only a 'geometrical velocity', and the energy propagation is at a lower velocity which is the group velocity. The average power transmission through the guide is obtained by integrating the complex Poynting vector, over a cross-section of the guide. The complex Poynting vector is in the direction of propagation, i.e. in the z-direction.

$$\mathbf{S}_{av} = \left(\frac{1}{2}\right)\mathbf{E}_{transverse} \times \mathbf{H}^*_{transverse} = -\left(\frac{1}{2}\right)E_y H_x^* \mathbf{i}_z$$

$$\therefore \quad |\mathbf{S}_{av}| = \int_0^a \int_0^b \operatorname{Re}\left[\left(\frac{1}{2}\right)E_y H_x^*\right] dx\,dy$$

$$= \frac{\omega\mu\beta a^2 H_0^2}{2\pi^2}\int_0^a \int_0^b \sin^2\left(\frac{\pi x}{a}\right) dx\,dy$$

$$= \frac{\omega\mu\beta a^3 b H_0^2}{4\pi^2} \tag{18.82}$$

Typical dimensions of a guide to transmit a TE_{10} mode with a free space wavelength of 10 cm would be $a = 7.5$ cm and $b = 2.5$ cm.

18.3.3.3 Transverse magnetic wave in rectangular waveguides

If now in the rectangular waveguide $H_z = 0$, then the magnetic field is in the transverse plane, and such waves are called the transverse magnetic or TM waves.

When $H_z = 0$, Eqs. (18.53) become:

$$\gamma H_y = j\omega\varepsilon E_x \tag{18.83a}$$

$$\gamma H_x = -j\omega\varepsilon E_y \tag{18.83b}$$

$$\frac{\partial H_y}{\partial x} - \frac{\partial H_x}{\partial y} = j\omega\varepsilon E_z \tag{18.83c}$$

$$\frac{\partial E_z}{\partial y} + \gamma E_y = -j\omega\mu H_x \tag{18.83d}$$

$$\frac{\partial E_z}{\partial x} + \gamma E_x = j\omega\mu H_y \tag{18.83e}$$

$$\frac{\partial E_y}{\partial x} - \frac{\partial E_x}{\partial y} = 0 \tag{18.83f}$$

This time we express the field components in terms of E_z.

Combining Eqs. (18.83d) and (18.83b),

$$\frac{\partial E_z}{\partial y} + \gamma\left(\frac{-\gamma}{j\omega\varepsilon}\right)H_x = -j\omega\mu H_x$$

$$\therefore \quad H_x = \left(\frac{j\omega\varepsilon}{k^2}\right)\left(\frac{\partial E_z}{\partial y}\right) \tag{18.84}$$

Similarly from Eqs. (18.83e) and (18.83a),

$$H_y = -\left(\frac{j\omega\varepsilon}{k^2}\right)\left(\frac{\partial E_z}{\partial x}\right) \tag{18.85}$$

Combining these two equations with (18.83a) and (18.83b),

$$E_x = -\left(\frac{\gamma}{k^2}\right)\left(\frac{\partial E_z}{\partial x}\right) \tag{18.86}$$

$$E_y = -\left(\frac{\gamma}{k^2}\right)\left(\frac{\partial E_z}{\partial y}\right) \tag{18.87}$$

and the equation for E_z is

$$\frac{\partial^2 E_z}{\partial x^2} + \frac{\partial^2 E_z}{\partial y^2} + k^2 E_z = 0 \tag{18.88}$$

The method of solving this equation is same as that of Eq. (18.63). Using the same method of separation of variables, the solution can be written as

$$E_z = \sum_{k_x}\sum_{k_y}[C_x \sin(k_x x) + D_x \cos(k_x x)][C_y \sin(k_y y) + D_y \cos(k_y y)] \tag{18.89}$$

Applying the boundary conditions:

(1)   On $y = 0$ and $y = b$, $E_x = 0$, $E_z = 0$.

From Eq. (18.89):

$$(E_z)_{y = 0} = \Sigma\Sigma \: [C_x \sin (k_x x) + D_x \cos (k_x x)]D_y = 0 \text{ for all } x.$$

$\therefore$ $D_y = 0$; and from $y = b$ plane, $\sin (k_y b) = \sin n\pi$

$\therefore$ $k_y = \left(\dfrac{n\pi}{b} \right)$, where $n = 1, 2, 3, \dots$.

(2)   On $x = 0$ and $x = a$, $E_z = 0$.

This condition gives: $D_x = 0$; and $\sin (k_x a) = \sin m\pi$, $m = 1, 2, 3, \dots$. Note that in this case $m = 0$ and $n = 0$ are not admissible values.

$\therefore$ The final expression for E_z is

$$E_z = E_0 \sin \left(\frac{m\pi x}{a} \right) \sin \left(\frac{n\pi y}{b} \right) \tag{18.90}$$

where m and $n = 1, 2, 3, \dots$; $E_0 = C_x C_y$ [from Eq. (18.89)]

Note that as in the previous case,

$$k^2 = k_x^2 + k_y^2 = \left(\frac{m\pi}{a} \right)^2 + \left(\frac{n\pi}{b} \right)^2 = \gamma^2 + \omega^2 \mu\varepsilon$$

or

$$\gamma = \left[\left(\frac{m\pi}{a} \right)^2 + \left(\frac{n\pi}{b} \right)^2 - \omega^2 \mu\varepsilon \right]^{1/2}$$

$$= \alpha + j\beta \tag{18.91}$$

where α and β have the same meanings ascribed to them in Section 18.3.3.1. Since, if γ was real, β the phase-shift constant would be zero and there would be no wave in the guide. There would be, as before, a critical value of ω ($= \omega_c$) for which γ is zero, and above which γ would be imaginary, i.e. $= j\beta$ and there would be wave propagation in the guide. This value of ω would give the cut-off frequency, whose expression is same as for the TE mode, i.e.

$$\omega_c = \left(\frac{1}{\sqrt{\mu\varepsilon}} \right) \sqrt{ \left(\frac{m\pi}{a} \right)^2 + \left(\frac{n\pi}{b} \right)^2 } = 2\pi f_c \tag{18.92}$$

m and n being $1, 2, 3, \dots$.

$\therefore$ $$f_c = \left(\frac{1}{2\pi\sqrt{\mu\varepsilon}} \right) \sqrt{ \left(\frac{m\pi}{a} \right)^2 + \left(\frac{n\pi}{b} \right)^2 } \tag{18.93}$$

and the corresponding cut-off wavelength is

$$\lambda_c = \frac{2\pi}{\sqrt{ \left(\dfrac{m\pi}{a} \right)^2 + \left(\dfrac{n\pi}{b} \right)^2 }} \tag{18.94}$$

The wave number β for propagation in the TM mode is

$$\beta = \left[\omega^2 \mu\varepsilon - \left\{ \left(\frac{m\pi}{a} \right)^2 + \left(\frac{n\pi}{b} \right)^2 \right\} \right]^{1/2} \tag{18.95}$$

The velocity of wave propagation will be:

$$v = \frac{\omega}{\beta} = \frac{\omega}{\left[\omega^2 \mu\varepsilon - \left\{ \left(\frac{m\pi}{a} \right)^2 + \left(\frac{n\pi}{b} \right)^2 \right\} \right]^{1/2}} \tag{18.96}$$

This is again greater than the phase velocity in free space; and its behaviour pattern is similar to that in the TE mode. The wavelength in the guide is

$$\lambda = \frac{v}{f} = \frac{2\pi}{\left[\omega^2 \mu\varepsilon - \left\{ \left(\frac{m\pi}{a} \right)^2 + \left(\frac{n\pi}{b} \right)^2 \right\} \right]^{1/2}} \tag{18.97}$$

which is also greater than the free space wavelength. The lowest value for the TM mode is $m = n = 1$, i.e. TM_{11}. The expressions for the field vectors of the TM_{mn} mode are as given below:

$$E_x = - j \left(\frac{\beta}{k^2} \right) E_0 \frac{m\pi}{a} \cos \left(\frac{m\pi x}{a} \right) \sin \left(\frac{n\pi y}{b} \right) \tag{18.98a}$$

$$E_y = - j \left(\frac{\beta}{k^2} \right) E_0 \frac{n\pi}{b} \sin \left(\frac{m\pi x}{a} \right) \cos \left(\frac{n\pi y}{b} \right) \tag{18.98b}$$

$$E_z = E_0 \sin \left(\frac{m\pi x}{a} \right) \sin \left(\frac{n\pi y}{b} \right) \tag{18.98c}$$

$$H_x = j \left(\frac{\omega\varepsilon}{k^2} \right) E_0 \frac{n\pi}{b} \sin \left(\frac{m\pi x}{a} \right) \cos \left(\frac{n\pi y}{b} \right) \tag{18.98d}$$

$$H_y = - j \left(\frac{\omega\varepsilon}{k^2} \right) E_0 \frac{m\pi}{a} \cos \left(\frac{m\pi x}{a} \right) \sin \left(\frac{n\pi y}{b} \right) \tag{18.98e}$$

In these expressions, γ again has been replaced by $j\beta$ which is valid for the frequencies above the cut-off frequency. And also the terms $[\exp(-j\beta z) \exp(j\omega t)]$ are implicit in these expressions.

18.3.4   Phase Velocity and Group Velocity

During our discussion of wave propagation of guided waves between parallel planes and in waveguides, we have mentioned two types of velocities. The first one is the 'phase velocity' ($= v_{ph}$) which is the velocity of propagation of equiphase surfaces along the guide. (It should be noted that the phase velocity is identical with the velocity of propagation of the wave-fronts in the rigorous sense only when we are dealing with non-dispersive waves). The geometrical significance of the phase velocity is shown on the ω–k plot of Figure 18.13(a), i.e.

$$v_{ph} = \frac{\omega}{k}$$

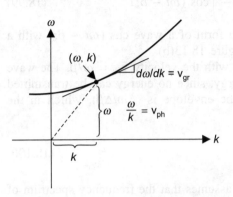

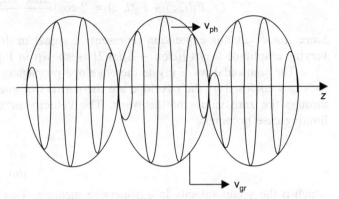

Figure 18.13(a) The slope of the line joining the point (w, k) and the origin is the phase velocity. The tangent of the w-k curve at this same point is the group velocity.

Figure 18.13(b) Sum of two sinusoidal waves of different frequencies.

For evanescent waves, the phase velocity approaches infinity as $k \to 0$, and it is certainly unreasonable to assume that a pulse will propagate with this velocity.

The second type of velocity we have come across is the group velocity (= v_{gr}) which in these particular cases, could be taken as the velocity of energy propagation in the direction of the axis of the guide. In general, the group velocity of the waves with frequencies in the neighbourhood of ω is defined as, $v_{gr} = (d\omega/dk)$, or as the slope shown in Figure 18.13(a).

Its physical significance is then the velocity of propagation of a group of waves with essentially the same wave-number and frequency.

For waveguide propagation, the phase velocity v_{ph} is always greater than $v_0 \left[= \sqrt{(\mu\varepsilon)^{-1/2}} \right]$, whereas the group velocity is always less than v_0.

It should be clearly understood that by itself, a purely sinusoidal wave cannot transmit any information other than its own presence. If a signal has to be transmitted, then the wave must be suitably modified. Whatever the method, the result is a 'package of frequencies' which is close to the fundamental frequency (i.e. the frequency of the wave without a signal). The velocity of the package carrying the information is the main interest.

We shall try to explain this by considering the simplest possible package made up of only two waves of angular frequencies ω_1 and ω_2 which are close to the fundamental frequency ω. Since the frequencies are different, their phase constants, (say) β_1 and β_2 respectively, would also be different. So we add the two waves, in the forms of:

$$F_1(t, z) = \cos(\omega_1 t - \beta_1 z) \quad \text{and} \quad F_2(t, z) = \cos(\omega_2 t - \beta_2 z)$$

By standard trigonometrical relation, which gives the sum as

$$F_1(t, z) + F_2(t, z) = 2 \cos\left[\frac{(\omega_1 + \omega_2)t}{2} - \frac{(\beta_1 + \beta_2)z}{2}\right] \cos\left[\frac{(\omega_2 - \omega_1)t}{2} - \frac{(\beta_2 - \beta_1)z}{2}\right]$$

Let ω_1 and ω_2 be very near the fundamental frequency ω ($\omega_2 > \omega > \omega_1$), so that:

$$(\omega_2 + \omega_1)/2 = \omega, \quad (\beta_2 + \beta_1)/2 = \beta, \quad (\omega_2 - \omega_1) = \Delta\omega, \quad \text{and} \quad (\beta_2 - \beta_1) = \Delta\beta.$$

The above sum of these two waves then can be expressed as

$$F_1(t, z) + F_2(t, z) = 2 \cos\left(\frac{\Delta\omega t - \Delta\beta z}{2}\right) \cos(\omega t - \beta z) \tag{18.99}$$

Since $\Delta\omega \ll \omega$, this expression represents a signal in the form of a wave $\cos(\omega t - \beta z)$ with a varying amplitude $2 \cos[(\Delta\omega t - \Delta\beta z)/2]$ as shown in Figure 18.13(b).

The sinusoidal wave inside the envelope propagates with the velocity $v_{ph} = \omega/\beta$. The wave packages enclosed by the envelope are the carriers of energy, since no energy can be transmitted through the zero values of the wave. The velocity of the envelope is $(\Delta\omega/\Delta\beta)$, which in the limiting case becomes:

$$v_{gr} = \frac{d\omega}{d\beta} = \frac{1}{\dfrac{d\beta}{d\omega}} \tag{18.100}$$

which is the group velocity in a dispersive medium. This assumes that the frequency spectrum of the signal is quite narrow. The group velocity is therefore interpreted as the velocity at which the group of waves, defined by the envelope, propagates in the z-direction. Note that, because the phase and the group velocities are different, the waves will appear to move with respect to the envelope.

If we consider the rectangular waveguide in TE$_{10}$ mode, the phase constant was obtained as:

$$\beta = \omega \left[\sqrt{\mu\varepsilon} \sqrt{1 - \left(\frac{f_c}{f}\right)^2} \right] \qquad \text{[Eq. (18.79)]}$$

Using Eq. (18.100), the signal velocity in the guide is

$$v_{gr} = \frac{1}{\sqrt{\mu\varepsilon}} \sqrt{1 - \left(\frac{f_c}{f}\right)^2} = c \left[\sqrt{1 - \left(\frac{f_c}{f}\right)^2} \right] \tag{18.101}$$

and, in this case only:

$$v_{gr} v_{ph} = c^2 \tag{18.102}$$

18.3.5 Rectangular Waveguide: Attenuation due to Lossy Dielectric, and Imperfectly Conducting Walls

We shall briefly recapitulate the wave behaviour in imperfect conductors and lossy dielectrics.

Maxwell's equations become:

$$\nabla \times \mathbf{E} = -\omega\mu\mathbf{H} \tag{18.103a}$$

$$\nabla \times \mathbf{H} = (\sigma + j\omega\varepsilon)\mathbf{E} = j\omega\varepsilon\left(1 + \frac{\sigma}{j\omega\varepsilon}\right)\mathbf{E} \tag{18.103b}$$

$\therefore$ We have to replace ε by $[\varepsilon\{1 - j\sigma/(\omega\varepsilon)\}]$ in all the formulae for propagation, impedance, etc.; e.g.

$$\gamma (= j\beta) = j\omega \sqrt{(\mu\varepsilon)\left(1 + \frac{j\sigma}{\omega\varepsilon}\right)}, \quad \text{which is complex} \tag{18.104}$$

$$= \alpha + j\beta$$

$$Z_0 = \left[\frac{\mu}{\varepsilon\left(1 - \frac{j\sigma}{\omega\varepsilon}\right)}\right]^{1/2} \leftarrow \text{characteristic impedance of the medium} \qquad (18.105)$$

$$\frac{\sin \theta_r}{\sin \theta_i} = \left[\frac{\mu_1\varepsilon_1}{\mu_2\varepsilon_2\left(1 - \frac{j\sigma}{\omega\varepsilon_2}\right)}\right]^{1/2} \qquad (18.106)$$

The critical quantity in this expression is $\sigma/\omega\varepsilon_2$.

For a good conductor, $\sigma/\omega\varepsilon_2 \gg 1$,

$$\frac{\sin \theta_r}{\sin \theta_i} = \left[\frac{\mu_1\varepsilon_1}{\frac{\mu_2\sigma}{j\omega}}\right]^{1/2} = \left(\frac{j\omega\varepsilon_1}{\sigma}\right)^{1/2} \qquad (18.107)$$

which is very small.

$\therefore$ $\sin \theta_r$ is very small for any value of θ_i, i.e. the propagation takes place almost normally into the conducting medium. Also, since the above expression is complex, the wave gets exponentially damped as it propagates.

18.3.5.1 *Attenuation due to lossy dielectric*

We consider the TE_{10} mode in the rectangular waveguide. For the loss-less dielectric, the propagation constant γ is

$$\gamma = j\beta = jk\left[\sqrt{1 - \left(\frac{f_c}{f}\right)^2}\right] = j\omega\left(\sqrt{\mu\varepsilon}\right)\left[\sqrt{1 - \left(\frac{f_c}{f}\right)^2}\right] \qquad (18.108)$$

where $k^2 = \omega^2(\mu\varepsilon)$.

For the lossy dielectric, we have replaced

$$\varepsilon \text{ by } \varepsilon\left(1 - \frac{j\sigma}{\omega\varepsilon}\right) \qquad (18.109)$$

$\therefore$ k gets modified as shown below, i.e.

$$k = \omega\left(\sqrt{\mu\varepsilon}\right)\sqrt{1 + \frac{\sigma}{j\omega\varepsilon}} = \omega\left(\sqrt{\mu\varepsilon}\right)\left(1 + \frac{\sigma}{j2\omega\varepsilon}\right) \qquad (18.110)$$

$\therefore$ The propagation constant is now complex, i.e.

$$\gamma = \alpha + j\beta = j\omega\left(\sqrt{\mu\varepsilon}\right)\left(1 + \frac{\sigma}{j2\omega\varepsilon}\right)\sqrt{1 - \left(\frac{f_c}{f}\right)^2} \qquad (18.111)$$

$\therefore$ The attenuation constant

$$\alpha = \omega\left(\sqrt{\mu\varepsilon}\right)\frac{\sigma}{2\omega\varepsilon}\sqrt{1 - \left(\frac{f_c}{f}\right)^2}$$

$$= \left(\sqrt{\frac{\mu}{\varepsilon}} \right) \left(\frac{\sigma}{2} \right) \sqrt{1 - \left(\frac{f_c}{f} \right)^2} \qquad \text{Nepers/metre} \qquad (18.112)$$

and the phase-shift constant

$$\beta = \omega \left(\sqrt{\mu \varepsilon} \right) \sqrt{1 - \left(\frac{f_c}{f} \right)^2} \qquad (18.113)$$

18.3.5.2 *Attenuation due to imperfectly conducting walls*

Let us initially consider transmission lines with sending waves (V_S, I_S):

$$V = V_S \exp(-\alpha z), \qquad I = I_S \exp(-\alpha z) \qquad (18.114)$$

$$\therefore \quad \text{Transmitted power} = VI \cos \phi = V_S I_S \cos \phi \exp(-2\alpha z) = W \qquad (18.115)$$

$$\therefore \quad \frac{dW}{dz} = -2\alpha W \qquad (18.116)$$

$$\therefore \quad \alpha = \frac{\text{Power loss per unit length}}{2 \times \text{Power sent from the sending point}} \qquad (18.117)$$

$$\text{Power dissipated} = \left(\frac{1}{2} \right) \text{Re} \left(\mathbf{E}_t \times \mathbf{H}_t^* \right) = \left(\frac{1}{2} \right) \text{Re} \left(\mathbf{H}_t Z_{in} \times \mathbf{H}_t^* \right)$$

$$= \left(\frac{1}{2} \right) \text{Re} \left(\left| \mathbf{H}_t \right|^2 Z_{in} \right)$$

$$= \left| \mathbf{H}_t \right|^2 \left(\frac{1}{2} \right) \text{Re} \sqrt{\frac{j\omega\mu}{\sigma}}$$

(see below for this step)

$$= \left| \mathbf{H}_t \right|^2 \left(\frac{1}{2} \right) \sqrt{\frac{\omega\mu}{\sigma}} = \left(\frac{1}{2} \right) \left| \mathbf{J} \right|^2 R_S \qquad (18.118)$$

Note: To calculate the input impedance due to (say) the bottom wall (of the waveguide),

$$Z_{in} = \frac{E_t}{H_t} = \left[\frac{\mu}{\varepsilon \left(1 - \dfrac{j\sigma}{\omega\varepsilon} \right)} \right]^{1/2} = \sqrt{\frac{j\omega\mu}{\sigma}} \qquad (18.119)$$

The tangential E_t exists on the wall because now there is an ohmic loss in the wall as it is now an imperfect conductor.

Also, when there is a surface current, $H_{t1} - H_{t2} = J_S$.

For a perfect conductor, $H_{t2} = 0$, and hence $H_{t1} = J_S$ $\qquad (18.120)$

Referring to Figure 18.12, we consider first the top and the bottom walls, which are planes $y = 0$ and $y = b$. We write the field vectors [from Eqs. (18.78)] as:

$$E_y = A_0 \sin\left(\frac{\pi x}{a}\right) \exp(-\gamma z) \tag{18.121a}$$

$$H_x = -\left(\frac{\gamma}{\omega\mu}\right) A_0 \sin\left(\frac{\pi x}{a}\right) \exp(-\gamma z) \tag{18.121b}$$

$$H_z = -\left(\frac{\pi}{j\omega\mu a}\right) A_0 \cos\left(\frac{\pi x}{a}\right) \exp(-\gamma z) \tag{18.121c}$$

$\therefore$ On the top and the bottom walls, $y = 0$ and $y = b$,

$$J_z = -\left(\frac{\gamma}{\omega\mu}\right) A_0 \sin\left(\frac{\pi x}{a}\right) \exp(-\gamma z) \tag{18.122a}$$

$$J_x = -\left(\frac{\pi}{j\omega\mu a}\right) A_0 \cos\left(\frac{\pi x}{a}\right) \exp(-\gamma z) \tag{18.122b}$$

$\therefore$ The total power loss in the top + bottom plates per unit length in the z-direction is

$$= \int_0^a |J|^2 R_S dx \cdot 2 = \int_0^a \left(|J_z|^2 + |J_x|^2\right) R_S dx \cdot 2$$

$$= \left[\left(\frac{\beta^2}{\omega^2\mu^2}\right) A_0^2 \left(\frac{a}{2}\right) + \left(\frac{\pi^2}{\omega^2\mu^2 a^2}\right) A_0^2 \left(\frac{a}{2}\right)\right] R_S \cdot 2 \tag{18.123}$$

Next, we consider the side walls $x = 0$ and $x = a$; on these side walls, since $H_y = 0$, only J_y will be produced by H_z, i.e.

$$J_y = -\left(\frac{\pi}{j\omega\mu a}\right) A_0 \cos\left(\frac{\pi x}{a}\right) \exp(-\gamma z) \tag{18.124}$$

$\therefore$ The power loss in the two side plates per unit length

$$= \left(\frac{\pi^2}{\omega^2\mu^2 a^2}\right) A_0^2 \, a R_S \tag{18.125}$$

The transmitted power through the guide

$$= \int_0^a \int_0^b \left(\frac{1}{2}\right) \mathrm{Re}\left(\mathbf{E}_y \times \mathbf{H}_x^*\right) dx dy$$

$$= \int_0^a \left(\frac{j\gamma}{\omega\mu}\right) A_0^2 \sin^2\left(\frac{\pi x}{a}\right) dx \tag{18.126}$$

$$= \left(\frac{j\gamma}{\omega\mu}\right) A_0^2 \, b \left(\frac{a}{2}\right)$$

Note: $\exp(-2\gamma z)$ has been assumed in all these expressions, and R_S the resistance of the walls per unit length.

18.3.5.3 *Parallel plane waveguide (as a limiting case of the rectangular waveguide)*

Initially, the parallel plane waveguide was derived from the reflection of uniform plane waves hitting a perfectly conducting plane surface obliquely and studying the interference pattern obtained therefrom. The rectangular waveguide was first derived from the parallel plane waveguide by adding two parallel conducting surfaces orthogonally. The rectangular waveguide was also analysed by using general mathematical approach, from fundamental considerations. Now, we shall treat the parallel plane waveguide as a limiting case of the rectangular waveguide.

A rectangular waveguide with its edges parallel to the coordinate axes is shown in Figure 18.13(c) (as was shown in Figure 18.12 as well). For the rectangular waveguide, with its dimensions as shown in Figure 18.13(c), we have

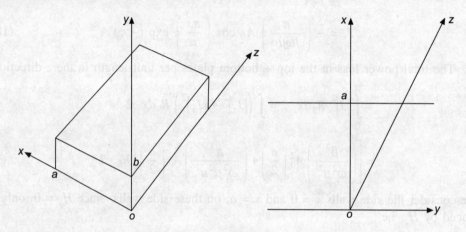

Figure 18.13(c)   Rectangular waveguide ($a \times b$) and its limit as $b \to \infty$ giving the plane parallel waveguide.

$$\gamma = \left[\left(\frac{m\pi}{a} \right)^2 + \left(\frac{n\pi}{b} \right)^2 - \omega^2 \mu\varepsilon \right]^{1/2} \tag{18.70}$$

When $\omega > \omega_c$,

$$\gamma = j\beta = j \left[\omega^2 \mu\varepsilon - \left\{ \left(\frac{m\pi}{a} \right)^2 + \left(\frac{n\pi}{b} \right)^2 \right\} \right]^{1/2} \tag{18.71}$$

where

$$\omega_c = \left(\frac{1}{\mu\varepsilon} \right)^{1/2} \left[\left(\frac{m\pi}{a} \right)^2 + \left(\frac{n\pi}{b} \right)^2 \right]^{1/2} = 2\pi f_c$$

To get the limit $b \to \infty$, then

$$j\beta = j \left[\omega^2 \mu\varepsilon - \left(\frac{m\pi}{a} \right)^2 \right]^{1/2} \quad \text{and} \quad k^2 = \left(\frac{m\pi}{a} \right)^2$$

and the field equations for the TE mode become [(from Eqs. (18.77)]

$$E_x = 0$$

$$E_y = -\frac{j\omega\mu}{m\pi/a} H_0 \sin\left(\frac{m\pi x}{a}\right) \exp[j(\omega t - \beta z)]$$

$$H_x = \frac{j\beta}{m\pi/a} H_0 \sin\left(\frac{m\pi x}{a}\right) \exp[j(\omega t - \beta z)]$$

$$H_y = 0$$ $$(18.77')$$

$$H_z = H_0 \cos\left(\frac{m\pi x}{a}\right) \exp[j(\omega t - \beta z)]$$

These are same as Eqs. (17.204a) of Section 18.3.1.1.

Note: In the above equation, the direction of propagation is z, whereas in Section 18.3.1.1 the direction of wave propagation is x.

Next we consider the TM mode for the rectangular waveguide. As before, we take the limit as $b \to \infty$, but in this case all the five expressions [i.e. Eq. (18.98)] become identically equal to zero. So the question that arises is 'can the fields of the TM mode be derived thus or that the TM mode does not exist. The answer to this apparent confusion lies in the fact that H_0 is an arbitrary mathematical constant and it can be infinite. The expressions appeared to become zeroes as $b \to \infty$ was because of the implicit assumption that E_0 in finite. So we define a new constant E_0' such that

$$E_0' = E_0 \sin\frac{n\pi y}{b}$$

which is finite when $b \to \infty$.

Then the field expressions of Eqs. (18.98) become:

$$E_z = E_0' \sin\left(\frac{m\pi a}{a}\right) \exp[j(\omega t - \beta z)]$$

$$E_x = -\frac{j\beta}{m\pi/a} E_0' \cos\left(\frac{m\pi x}{a}\right) \exp[j(\omega t - \beta z)]$$

$$E_y = 0$$ $$(19.98')$$

$$H_x = 0$$

$$H_y = -\frac{j\omega\mu}{m\pi/a} E_0' \cos\left(\frac{m\pi x}{a}\right) \exp[j(\omega t - \beta z)]$$

As before these are same as Eqs. (17.191') of Section 18.3.1.1. Again it should be noted that the direction of propagation has changed from x to z which causes a change in one of the field components. The relationship between E_{0i+} and H_0 and E_{0i} and E_0' can be written down by comparing the two sets of equations.

18.3.6   Cylindrical Waveguide

We start with the solution of Maxwell's equations in cylindrical coordinates (Figure 18.14).
We consider the Maxwell's equation

$$\oint \mathbf{E} \cdot d\mathbf{l} = -\left(\frac{d\Phi}{dt}\right)$$

and apply it to the elemental contour ABCDA of the circular guide as shown in Figure 18.14(b).

$$E_r dr + \left[E_\theta + \left(\frac{\partial E_\theta}{\partial r}\right)dr\right](r + \delta r)\, d\theta - \left[E_r + \left(\frac{\partial E_r}{\partial \theta}\right)d\theta\right]dr - E_\theta r d\theta = -j\omega\mu H_z dr\, r\, d\theta$$

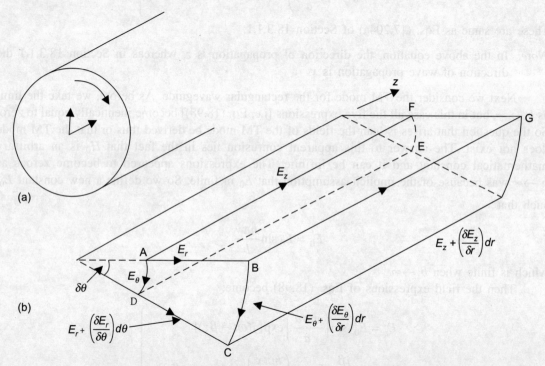

Figure 18.14   A cylindrical waveguide and its elemental section.

or

$$\frac{1}{r}\left[E_\theta + r\left(\frac{\partial E_\theta}{\partial r}\right) - \left(\frac{\partial E_r}{\partial \theta}\right)\right] = -\mu\left(\frac{\partial H_z}{\partial t}\right) \tag{18.127}$$

And similarly from the other equation $\oint \mathbf{H} \cdot d\mathbf{l} = \dfrac{\partial \mathbf{D}}{\partial t}$, we get

$$\frac{1}{r}\left[H_\theta + r\left(\frac{\partial H_\theta}{\partial r}\right) - \left(\frac{\partial H_r}{\partial \theta}\right)\right] = \varepsilon\left(\frac{\partial E_z}{\partial t}\right) \tag{18.128}$$

Note that $(\partial/\partial t) \equiv j\omega$, for sinusoidally time-varying excitations, and hence the operator and the imaginary quantity are interchangeable in these equations.

We again apply the line integral $\oint \mathbf{E} \cdot d\mathbf{l}$ around the contour ADEFA (in the clockwise direction) and obtain

$$E_\theta r\,dr + \left[E_z + \left(\frac{\partial E_z}{\partial \theta}\right)d\theta\right]dz - \left[E_\theta + \left(\frac{\partial E_\theta}{\partial z}\right)dz\right]rd\theta - E_z dz = -j\omega\mu H_r rd\theta dz$$

or

$$\left(\frac{1}{r}\right)\left(\frac{\partial E_z}{\partial \theta}\right) - \left(\frac{\partial E_\theta}{\partial z}\right) = -j\omega\mu H_r \tag{18.129}$$

Similarly applying $\oint \mathbf{H} \cdot d\mathbf{l}$ to the same contour ADEFA, we get

$$\left(\frac{1}{r}\right)\left(\frac{\partial H_z}{\partial \theta}\right) - \left(\frac{\partial H_\theta}{\partial z}\right) = +j\omega\varepsilon E_r \tag{18.130}$$

Next we apply $\oint \mathbf{E} \cdot d\mathbf{l}$ around the contour AFGBA (in the clockwise direction), and get

$$E_z dz + \left[E_r + \left(\frac{\partial E_r}{\partial z}\right)dz\right]dr - \left[E_z + \left(\frac{\partial E_z}{\partial r}\right)dr\right]dz - E_r dr = -j\omega\mu H_\theta dr dz$$

or

$$\frac{\partial E_r}{\partial z} - \frac{\partial E_z}{\partial r} = -j\omega\varepsilon H_\theta \tag{18.131}$$

Similarly applying $\oint \mathbf{E} \cdot d\mathbf{l}$ to the same contour AFGBA, we get

$$\frac{\partial H_r}{\partial z} - \frac{\partial H_z}{\partial r} = j\omega\varepsilon E_\theta \tag{18.132}$$

And we assume $\exp(-\gamma z)$ variation of the field in the z-direction. We then combine Eqs. (18.129) and (18.132),

$$\left(\frac{1}{r}\right)\left(\frac{\partial E_z}{\partial \theta}\right) + \gamma E_\theta = -j\omega\mu H_r$$

$$= -j\omega\mu\left[-j\left(\frac{\omega\varepsilon}{\gamma}\right)E_\theta - \left(\frac{1}{\gamma}\right)\left(\frac{\partial H_z}{\partial r}\right)\right]$$

or

$$E_\theta\left(\gamma^2 + \omega^2\mu\varepsilon\right) = -\left(\frac{\gamma}{r}\right)\left(\frac{\partial E_z}{\partial \theta}\right) + j\omega\mu\left(\frac{\partial H_z}{\partial r}\right)$$

$$\therefore \qquad E_\theta = \left(\frac{1}{k^2}\right)\left[-\left(\frac{\gamma}{r}\right)\left(\frac{\partial E_z}{\partial \theta}\right) + j\omega\mu\left(\frac{\partial H_z}{\partial r}\right)\right] \tag{18.133}$$

where $k^2 = \gamma^2 + \omega^2\mu\varepsilon$.

From Eq. (18.129),

$$H_r = -\left(\frac{1}{j\omega\mu r}\right)\left(\frac{\partial E_z}{\partial \theta}\right) - \left(\frac{\gamma}{j\omega\mu}\right)\left[-\left(\frac{\gamma}{k^2 r}\right)\left(\frac{\partial E_z}{\partial \theta}\right) + j\left(\frac{\omega\mu}{k^2}\right)\left(\frac{\partial H_z}{\partial r}\right)\right]$$

or

$$H_r = \frac{1}{k^2}\left[j\left(\frac{\omega\varepsilon}{r}\right)\left(\frac{\partial E_z}{\partial \theta}\right) - \gamma\left(\frac{\partial H_z}{\partial r}\right)\right] \tag{18.134}$$

From Eqs. (18.130) and (18.131), we get

$$H_\theta = \frac{1}{k^2}\left[-j\omega\varepsilon\left(\frac{\partial E_z}{\partial r}\right) - \left(\frac{\gamma}{r}\right)\left(\frac{\partial H_z}{\partial \theta}\right)\right] \tag{18.135}$$

$$E_r = \frac{1}{k^2}\left[-j\left(\frac{\omega\mu}{r}\right)\left(\frac{\partial H_z}{\partial \theta}\right) - \gamma\left(\frac{\partial E_z}{\partial r}\right)\right] \tag{18.136}$$

We now derive the wave equation for E_z, i.e. from Eq. (18.128),

$$\frac{1}{r}\left[H_\theta + r\left(\frac{\partial H_\theta}{\partial r}\right) - \left(\frac{\partial H_r}{\partial \theta}\right)\right] = j\omega\varepsilon E_z$$

From Eq. (18.135),

$$\frac{\partial H_\theta}{\partial r} = \frac{1}{k^2}\left[-j\omega\varepsilon\left(\frac{\partial^2 E_z}{\partial r^2}\right) + \left(\frac{\gamma}{r^2}\right)\left(\frac{\partial H_z}{\partial \theta}\right) - \left(\frac{\gamma}{r}\right)\left(\frac{\partial^2 H_z}{\partial \theta \partial r}\right)\right]$$

Also from Eq. (18.134),

$$H_r = j\left(\frac{\omega\varepsilon}{k^2 r}\right)\left(\frac{\partial^2 E_z}{\partial \theta^2}\right) - \left(\frac{\gamma}{k^2}\right)\left(\frac{\partial^2 H_z}{\partial r \partial \theta}\right)$$

Substituting from these equations in Eq. (18.128), we have

$$-j\left(\frac{\omega\varepsilon}{k^2}\right)\left(\frac{\partial E_z}{\partial r}\right) - \left(\frac{\gamma}{rk^2}\right)\left(\frac{\partial H_z}{\partial \theta}\right) - j\left(\frac{\omega\varepsilon r}{k^2}\right)\left(\frac{\partial^2 E_z}{\partial r^2}\right) + \left(\frac{\gamma}{k^2 r}\right)\left(\frac{\partial H_z}{\partial \theta}\right) - \left(\frac{\gamma}{k^2}\right)\left(\frac{\partial^2 H_z}{\partial \theta \partial r}\right)$$

$$-j\left(\frac{\omega\varepsilon}{k^2 r}\right)\left(\frac{\partial^2 E_z}{\partial \theta^2}\right) + \left(\frac{\gamma}{k^2}\right)\left(\frac{\partial^2 H_z}{\partial r \partial \theta}\right) = j\omega\varepsilon r E_z$$

Simplifying

$$\left(\frac{\partial^2 E_z}{\partial r^2}\right) + \left(\frac{1}{r}\right)\left(\frac{\partial E_z}{\partial r}\right) + \left(\frac{1}{r^2}\right)\left(\frac{\partial^2 E_z}{\partial \theta^2}\right) + \left(\gamma^2 + \omega^2\mu\varepsilon\right)E_z = 0 \tag{18.137}$$

where $k^2 = \gamma^2 + \omega^2\mu\varepsilon = \gamma^2 + p^2$, $p^2 = \omega^2\mu\varepsilon$.

This is the wave equation in E_z in the cylindrical coordinate system.

To obtain the solution of this wave equation, using the method of separation of variables, let the solution be of the form

$$E_z = RF \exp\left(j\omega t - \gamma z\right) \tag{18.138}$$

where $R \equiv R(r)$, $F = F(\theta)$.

Substituting in Eq. (18.137),

$$R''F + \left(\frac{1}{r}\right) R'F + \left(\frac{1}{r^2}\right) RF'' + (\gamma^2 + p^2) RF = 0$$

where the prime indicates differentiation with respect to its corresponding independent variable. Multiplying this equation by $[r^2/(RF)]$, and rearranging the terms,

$$\frac{r^2 R''}{R} + \frac{rR'}{R} + (\gamma^2 + p^2) = -\frac{F''}{F} \tag{18.139}$$

For this equation to be true for all values of r and θ, both sides must equal constants. Hence,

$$\frac{d^2 F}{d\theta^2} = -n^2 F \tag{18.140}$$

where the constant n^2 is to determine the periodicity in the θ direction. The solution of this equation is

$$F = A \cos n\theta + B \sin n\theta \tag{18.141}$$

where $n = 0, 1, 2, 3, \dots$.

The corresponding r equation is

$$\left(\frac{d^2 R}{dr^2}\right) + \left(\frac{1}{r}\right)\left(\frac{dR}{dr}\right) + \left(\frac{k^2 - n^2}{r^2}\right) R = 0 \tag{18.142}$$

There are three solutions to this equation, which are

$$R = CJ_n(kr) + DY_n(kr) \tag{18.143}$$

where J_n and Y_n are the Bessel's functions of first and second kind (and of the order n) respectively. This is a standing wave solution.

$$R = EH_n^{(1)}(kr) + FH_n^{(2)}(kr) \tag{18.144}$$

where $H_n^{(1)}$ and $H_n^{(2)}$ are Hankel's functions of the first and second kind (and of the order n) respectively. These are Bessel's functions with complex arguments.

$$R = GI_n(jkr) + G'K_n(jkr) \tag{18.145}$$

where I_n and K_n are modified Bessel's functions of the first and second kind (and of order n) respectively. These are Bessel's functions with imaginary arguments.

The behaviour of $J_n(x)$ and $Y_n(x)$ are shown below (approximately) in Figure 18.15.

$$H_n^{(1)}(x) = J_n(x) + jY_n(x) \leftarrow \text{represents an inward travelling wave.}$$
$$H_n^{(2)}(x) = J_n(x) - jY_n(x) \leftarrow \text{represents an outward travelling wave.}$$

The inward and the outward directions refer to the assumptions based on that of $\exp(j\omega t)$ (this is a matter of relative convention. Stratton, in his book uses as reference $\exp(-j\omega t)$, and his notations are reversed).

$H_n^{(1)}(x)$ at the Brewster's angle is a surface wave travelling inwards so that there is no reflection.

So far, we have used the notation

$$k^2 = (\gamma^2 + \omega^2 \mu\varepsilon) = \gamma^2 + p^2, \qquad p^2 = \omega^2 \mu\varepsilon$$
$$= p^2 - \beta^2$$

If k is real, $p^2 - \beta^2$ is +ve; or $\left(\dfrac{2\pi}{\lambda_0} - \dfrac{2\pi}{\lambda_g} \right)$ is +ve; i.e. if k is real, $\lambda_0 < \lambda_g$.

$\therefore$ It is a fast wave, i.e. $v > c$.

For a slow wave, k^2 is $-$ve; $\therefore k = j\ (\ )$.

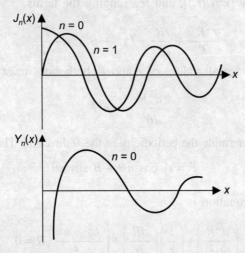

Figure 18.15   Approximate plots of $J_n(x)$ and $Y_n(x)$.

Given below in Figure 18.16 are the plots of the modified Bessel's functions which are non-orthogonal and hence are not oscillatory in nature.

$$I_n(\mu) = j^n J_n(-j\mu) \qquad \text{and} \qquad K_n(\mu) = \left(\frac{\pi}{2} \right) (-j)^{n+1} H_n^{(2)}(-j\mu)$$

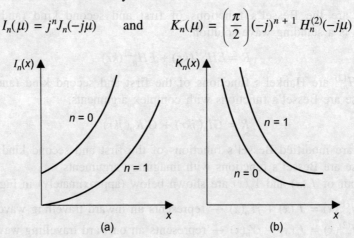

Figure 18.16   Modified Bessel's functions: (a) of the first kind and (b) of the second kind.

Next we consider some examples.

18.3.6.1   *TE wave in cylindrical waveguide*

We assume perfectly conducting wall; and so there is a standing wave. For the TE mode $E_z = 0$. Hence the wave equation solution is for H_z, which is

$$H_z = [CJ_n(kr) + DY_n(kr)](A \cos n\theta + B \sin n\theta) \exp(-j\beta z) \tag{18.146}$$

where $k^2 = \gamma^2 + p^2$, $\gamma = j\beta$.

Since the origin of the coordinate system is inside the guide geometry, $D = 0$ (as $Y_n \to \infty$ at $r = 0$) (see Figure 18.17).

Since the boundary conditions need the electric fields, we determine the E_θ now:

$$E_\theta = j\left(\frac{\omega\mu}{k^2}\right)\left(\frac{\partial H_z}{\partial r}\right)$$

$$= j\left(\frac{\omega\mu}{k^2}\right)kCJ_n'(kr)(A \cos n\theta + B \sin n\theta) \exp(-j\beta z) \tag{18.147}$$

where J_n' is the derivative of J_n with respect to its argument.

The boundary condition is $E_\theta = 0$ at $r = a$;

$$\therefore \quad J_n'(ka) = 0 \tag{18.148}$$

The roots of this equation are

$$(ka)_{01}' = 3.83, \qquad (ka)_{02}' = 7.02$$

$$(ka)_{11}' = 1.84, \qquad (ka)_{12}' = 5.33$$

where the first subscript refers to the value of n, and the second to the order of the root.

$$\therefore \quad \beta^2 = p^2 - k^2 = \omega^2 \mu_0 \varepsilon_0 - \frac{(k_{mn}a)^2}{a^2} \quad \text{(for free space)} \tag{18.149}$$

$$\therefore \quad \text{The cut-off frequency} = \omega_c^2 = \frac{(k_{mn}a)^2}{a^2 \mu_0 \varepsilon_0} \tag{18.150}$$

(Note that the other boundary condition that can be applied is: $H_r = 0$ at $r = a$.)

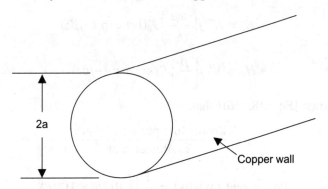

Figure 18.17 A cylindrical waveguide.

The other field components are:

$$E_r = j\left(\frac{\omega\mu n}{k^2 r}\right)A'' J_n(kr) \sin n\theta \tag{18.151a}$$

$$H_\theta = \left(\frac{n\gamma}{k^2 r}\right)A'' J_n(kr) \sin n\theta \tag{18.151b}$$

$$H_r = -\left(\frac{\gamma}{k}\right) A'' J_n'(kr) \cos n\theta \qquad (18.151c)$$

where $A'' = CA$.

It should be noted that when $n = 0$ (i.e. no angular variation), the only nonzero components are E_θ, H_r, H_z. The field patterns are as shown below in Figure 18.18.

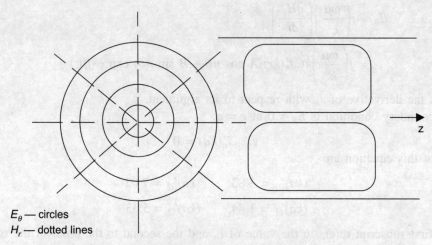

E_θ — circles
H_r — dotted lines

Figure 18.18   Field pattern for circular waveguide when $n = 0$.

18.3.6.2   *Attenuation in TE₁₀ mode in cylindrical waveguide*

The field components are:

$$H_z = A'' J_0(kr) \exp (-j\beta z) \qquad (18.152a)$$

$$E_\theta = A'' j\left(\frac{\omega\mu}{k}\right) J_0'(kr) \exp (-j\beta z) \qquad (18.152b)$$

$$H_z = A'' j\left(\frac{\beta}{k}\right) J_0'(kr) \exp (-j\beta z) \qquad (18.152c)$$

We have already shown [Eq. (18.116)] that:

$$\alpha = \frac{\text{Power lost per unit length}}{2 \times \text{Power sent}}$$

$$\text{Power sent (axially)} = \frac{1}{2} \iint \text{Re}(\mathbf{E} \times \mathbf{H}^*) dS$$

$$= \frac{1}{2} \iint \text{Re}\,(E_r H_\theta^* - E_\theta H_r^*) r\, dr\, d\theta \qquad (18.153)$$

In the above expression, $E_r = 0$.

$$\therefore \quad E_\theta H_r^* = -\frac{\omega\mu\beta}{k^2} \left(A''\right)^2 \left[J_0'(kr)\right]^2$$

$$\therefore \quad 2 \times \text{Power sent} = \int_0^{2\pi} \int_0^a \left(\frac{\omega \mu \beta}{k^2} \right) (A'')^2 \left[J_0'(kr) \right]^2 r \, dr \, d\theta$$

$$= 2\pi \int_0^a \left(\frac{\omega \mu \beta}{k^2} \right) (A'')^2 \left[J_0'(kr) \right]^2 r \, dr \tag{18.154}$$

Note: $J_0' = J_1$; and

$$\int_0^a r \left[J_0'(kr) \right]^2 dr = \left(\frac{1}{2} \right) a^2 \left[\left\{ J_1(ka) \right\}^2 + \left(1 - \frac{1}{k^2 a^2} \right) \left\{ J_1(ka) \right\}^2 \right] \tag{18.155}$$

$$\text{Power lost/metre} = \left(\frac{1}{2} \right) J_\theta R_S \tag{18.156}$$

where J_θ is the linear current density in amperes/metre; and

$$R_S = \sqrt{\frac{\pi \beta \mu}{\sigma}} \tag{18.157}$$

$$\therefore \quad \text{Power lost per metre} = \left(\frac{1}{2} \right) H_z R_S = \left(\frac{1}{2} \right) R_S \ (A'')^2 \ [J_0(ka)]^2 \ 2\pi a l \tag{18.158}$$

(l, being the length of the guide, which in this case is $= 1$.)

$$\therefore \quad \alpha = \frac{dP}{2P} = \left(\frac{R_S}{a Z_0} \right) \left[\frac{1}{\sqrt{1 - \left(\frac{f_c}{f} \right)^2}} \right] \left(\frac{f_c}{f} \right)^2 \tag{18.159}$$

If α is plotted as a function of frequency, then its behaviour is as shown in Figure 18.19, given below.

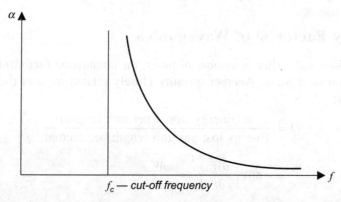

Figure 18.19 Attenuation as a function of the frequency.

We show below the two modes TE_{01} and TE_{11} with their **E** and **H** lines shown in two orthogonal sections (Figure 18.20).

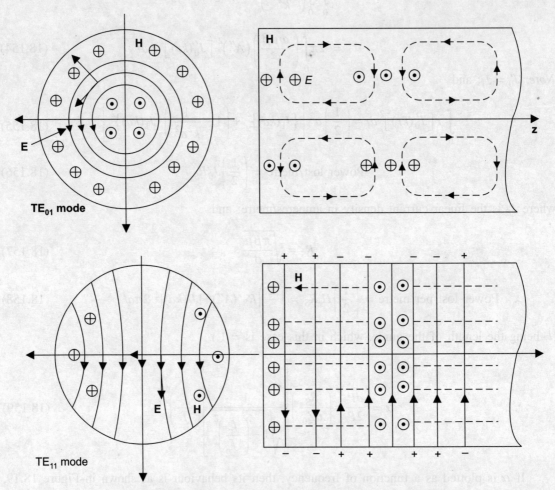

Figure 18.20 TE_{01} and TE_{11} modes in a circular waveguide.

18.3.7 Quality Factor Q of Waveguides

We have already discussed earlier, a number of times, the attenuation factor (or constant) α in the range of propagation of a wave. Another quantity closely related to α is the 'quality factor Q' which is defined as:

$$Q = \frac{\omega \,(\text{Energy stored per unit length})}{\text{Energy lost per unit length per second}} \qquad (18.160)$$

$$= -\omega W \left(\frac{\partial W}{\partial t} \right)^{-1} = \frac{\omega W}{\rho}$$

where W = energy at a time after the initial energy W_0.

The above expression, which is a general one, is applicable to both waveguides and transmission lines.

For a waveguide,

$$\text{Energy transmitted per second} = v_{gr} \times \text{Energy stored per unit length} \qquad (18.161)$$

where v_{gr} is the group velocity which is related to the phase velocity v_{ph} by the relationship

$$v_{gr} = \frac{v_0^2}{v_{ph}}, \qquad \text{where } v_0 = (\mu\varepsilon)^{-\frac{1}{2}} \qquad (18.162)$$

From Eq. (18.161),

$$\text{Energy stored per unit length} = \left(\frac{1}{v_{gr}}\right) \times \text{Power transmitted} \qquad (18.163)$$

∴ Substituting in (18.160),

$$Q = \frac{\left(\dfrac{\omega}{v_{gr}}\right)(\text{Power transmitted})}{\text{Power lost per unit length}}$$

$$= \frac{\omega}{2\alpha v_{gr}} \qquad (18.164)$$

which can also be written in terms of the cut-off frequency as

$$Q = \left(\frac{\omega v_{ph}}{2\alpha v_0^2}\right) = \frac{\omega}{2\alpha\sqrt{1 - \dfrac{\omega_c^2}{\omega^2}}} \qquad (18.165)$$

Because the waveguides have low attenuation factors compared with the transmission lines, it is possible to construct waveguide sections with extremely high Q's, which are used as resonators or waveguide filters.

It should be noted that the Q factor of ordinary resonant circuits is of the order of a few hundreds, and of resonant lines a few thousands.

18.3.8 Dielectric Slab Waveguide

These are generally used in thin film technology. It consists of two layers of dielectrics. The bottom layer dielectric slab is called the 'substrate'. The top layer is a thin layer of another dielectric of higher dielectric constant (compared to that of the substrate) deposited on the substrate. The propagation loss in the top layer is thus much less at the operating frequency. The slab dielectric waveguide is an asymmetrical structure as shown in Figure 18.21.

Simplifying assumptions: (1) *The substrate is infinitely thick.* This is a justifiable assumption, as the field decays rapidly as we move from the dielectric–substrate interface into the dielectric. (2) The y- and z-dimensions are assumed to be infinite, to make it a simple one-dimensional problem.

As discussed earlier in this chapter (Section 18.3.3), the wave is propagating in the $+z$-direction. Also, either E_z or H_z zero would give rise to modal fields for TE and TM modes respectively. Hence these two independent components must satisfy the wave equation (in rectangular Cartesian coordinates)

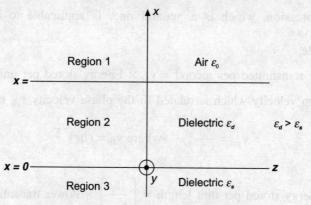

Figure 18.21 Dielectric slab waveguide.

$$\left(\frac{\partial^2}{\partial x^2} + \frac{\partial^2}{\partial y^2} + \frac{\partial^2}{\partial z^2} + \omega^2 \mu \varepsilon\right)(E_z \text{ or } H_z) = 0 \tag{18.166}$$

Since the waves are travelling in the z-direction, the z-variation of the fields will be $\sim \exp(-j\beta z)$ where β, the modal phase constant will be determined from the interface continuity conditions. Also, since the structure extends to infinity in the y-direction, the fields are constant functions of y, i.e. independent of y.

$$\therefore \qquad (E_z, H_z) = X(x)\exp(-j\beta z) \tag{18.167}$$

We will now consider the TE mode for this guide.

A. TE Mode

In this case $E_z = 0$, and all the transverse fields are represented in terms of H_z only. Hence,

$$H_z = X(x)\exp(-j\beta z) \tag{18.168}$$

$\exp(j\omega t)$ being implicit in the above expression. Substituting in Eq. (18.166),

$$\frac{1}{X}\frac{d^2 X}{dx^2} - \beta^2 + \omega^2 \mu \varepsilon = 0$$

This has to be satisfied for all values of x, and so

$$\frac{1}{X}\frac{d^2 X}{dx^2} = \pm k^2 \quad \text{(say, a constant)}$$

$$\therefore \qquad \frac{d^2 X}{dx^2} = \pm k^2 X \tag{18.169}$$

The sign of k will have to be chosen so as to satisfy the interface continuity conditions between the media 1 and 2, and 2 and 3. There will be fields in the three media, but in air (1) and in the substrate (3), the fields would decay rapidly as we move away from the interfaces. So this requirement gives +ve sign of k^2 in the media 1 and 3 and −ve sign in region 2. The equations for the three media can be written as

Region 1
$$\frac{d^2 X_1}{dx^2} = k_1^2 X_1$$

∴
$$k_1^2 - \beta^2 + \omega^2 \mu \varepsilon = 0 \tag{18.170a}$$

Region 2 (X_2)
$$-k_2^2 - \beta^2 + \omega^2 \mu \varepsilon_d = 0 \tag{18.170b}$$

Region 3 (X_3)
$$k_3^2 - \beta^2 + \omega^2 \mu \varepsilon_s = 0 \tag{18.170c}$$

The field then in the regions 1 and 3 will be in terms of exponentials and in the intermediate region 2 it will be in terms of trigonometric functions. The boundary conditions at infinity would simplify the equations further, i.e. as $x \to +\infty$, $H_{z1} \to 0$ in the region 1 and as $x \to -\infty$, $H_{z3} \to 0$ in region 3. Thus the longitudinal component of the magnetic field in the three regions will be

$$H_{z1} = A_1 \exp(-k_1 x) \exp(-j\beta z) \tag{18.171a}$$

$$H_{z2} = (A_3 \cos k_2 x + A_4 \sin k_2 x) \exp(-j\beta z) \tag{18.171b}$$

$$H_{z3} = A_6 \exp(k_3 x) \exp(-j\beta z) \tag{18.171c}$$

β being same in all the three media.

The transverse field components (H_x, H_y, E_x, E_y) in the three regions can be obtained, as shown in Section 18.3.3, Eqs. (18.59) and (18.62). Substituting for H_z and E_z in these equations, we get:

Region 1

$$E_{x1} = 0, \quad E_{y1} = -\frac{j\omega\mu}{k_1} A_1 \exp(-k_1 x) \exp(-j\beta z) \tag{18.172a}$$

$$H_{x1} = -\frac{j\beta}{k_1} A_1 \exp(-k_1 x) \exp(-j\beta z); \quad H_{y1} = 0$$

Region 2

$$E_{x2} = 0; \quad E_{y2} = \frac{j\omega\mu}{k_z} (A_3 \sin k_2 x - A_4 \cos k_2 x) \exp(-j\beta z)$$

$$H_{x2} = \frac{j\beta}{k_2} (A_3 \sin k_2 x - A_4 \cos k_2 x) \exp(-j\beta z) \tag{18.172b}$$

$$H_{y2} = 0$$

Region 3

$$E_{x3} = 0; \quad E_{y3} = \frac{j\omega\mu}{k_3} A_6 \exp(k_3 x) \exp(-j\beta z)$$

$$H_{x3} = \frac{j\beta}{k_3} A_6 \exp(k_3 x) \exp(-j\beta z) \tag{18.172c}$$

The unknowns to be evaluated are A_1, A_3, A_4, A_6, and k_1, k_2, k_3, and β. The interface continuity conditions used for evaluating these unknowns are:

(i) On $x = 0$, $H_{z2} = H_{z3}$ $\rightarrow$ $A_3 = A_6$ (18.173a)

(ii) On $x = 0$, $E_{y2} = E_{y3}$ $\rightarrow$ $\dfrac{-A_4}{k_2} = \dfrac{A_6}{k_3}$ (18.173b)

(iii) On $x = d$, $H_{z1} = H_{z2}$ $\rightarrow$ $A_1 \exp(-k_1 d) = A_3 \cos k_2 d + A_4 \sin k_2 d$ (18.173c)

(iv) On $x = d$, $E_{y1} = E_{y2}$ $\rightarrow$ $\dfrac{-A_1}{k_1} \exp(-k_1 d) = \dfrac{1}{k_2}(A_3 \sin k_2 d - A_4 \cos k_2 d)$ (18.173d)

It should be noted that since there are no surface currents on the dielectric interfaces, the continuity conditions are simplified.

We need three more equations to evaluate k_1, k_2 and k_3, i.e. from Eqs. (18.170a) and (18.170b),

$$k_1^2 + \omega^2 \mu \varepsilon_0 = -k_2^2 + \omega^2 \mu \varepsilon_d$$

or

$$k_1 = \sqrt{[\omega^2 \mu(\varepsilon_d - \varepsilon_s) - k_2^2]}$$ (18.174a)

and from Eqs. (18.170b) and (18.170c),

$$k_3 = \sqrt{[\omega^2 \mu(\varepsilon_d - \varepsilon_s) - k_2^2]}$$ (18.174b)

Equations (18.173a to d) can be written in matrix form to solve for A_1, A_3, A_4, A_6. The characteristic equation of the determinant of the 4×4 coefficient matrix comes out to be:

$$\tan k_2 d = \frac{(k_1 + k_3) k_2}{k_2^2 - k_1 k_3}$$ (18.175)

These three equations can be solved as simultaneous equations by a numerical method, and once k_2 has been evaluated, using Eq. (18.170b), i.e.

$$-k_2^2 + \omega^2 \mu \varepsilon_d = \beta^2$$

β can be evaluated.

Some important points which should be noted are:

1. The characteristic Eq. (18.175) has multiple solutions which represent the propagation of 'discrete modes'.
2. k_1, k_2 and k_3 have to be real. So from Eqs. (18.174a) and (18.174b), we have

$$\omega^2 \mu(\varepsilon_d - \varepsilon_0) > k_2^2 \quad \text{and} \quad \omega^2 \mu(\varepsilon_d - \varepsilon_s) > k_2^2$$ (18.176)

Since k_2^2 is always +ve, this means $\varepsilon_d > \varepsilon_0$ and $\varepsilon_d > \varepsilon_s$. Now $\varepsilon_d > \varepsilon_0$ is always true; and the permittivity of the dielectric slab must be greater than that of the substrate for the propagation of waves to be possible in the slab.

3. For a specified frequency $\omega = 2\pi f$, k_2 must lie between 0 and $\omega\mu(\varepsilon_d - \varepsilon_s)$.

4. When k_2 becomes $> \omega\mu(\varepsilon_d - \varepsilon_s)$, k_3 becomes imaginary and then $\exp(k_3 x)$ does **not** represent an attenuating exponent and now it represents a leakage wave travelling in the $-x$ direction. So this mode is no longer a guided wave mode and is now its cut-off mode. The frequency at which this happens is the cut-off frequency of the guide, i.e.

$$\omega_c = \frac{k_2}{\sqrt{\mu(\varepsilon_d - \varepsilon_s)}} \tag{18.177}$$

18.3.9 Circular (Cylindrical) Dielectric Waveguide

So far, the present discussion has emphasized the mathematics of waveguides with cylindrical geometry. A circular dielectric waveguide is now very commonly used for guiding microwaves as well as millimetre waves. The energy is propagated along the axis of the circular rod made of dielectric material, i.e. glass or silica rod in the form of optical fibres. The operation of the circular waveguide is same as that of dielectric slab metallic waveguide. The modal propagation is a consequence of superposition of totally internally reflected waves inside the dielectric rod. The analysis of this geometry is already explained in Section 18.3.6 and hence without repeating it, the results in terms of field components will be stated now.

A circular dielectric waveguide is shown in Figure 18.22. The rod has a radius a, and permittivity ε_1. To keep the analysis general, let the rod be located in an infinitely large medium of permittivity ε_2. If this is free space, then $\varepsilon_2 = \varepsilon_0$.

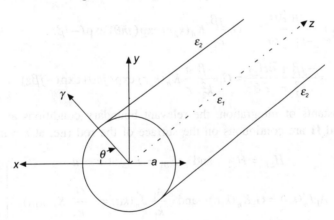

Figure 18.22 Circular dielectric waveguide.

The wave equation for field components will be as derived in Eq. (18.137) and the solutions are given in Eqs. (18.143) to (18.146), So now the TE and TM modes will be considered.

18.3.9.1 Transverse electric mode

For a TE mode, E_z is zero and the longitudinal field H_z is given as

$$H_{z1} = A_1 J_n(k_1 r) \exp(jn\theta) \exp(-j\beta z) \qquad r < a \tag{18.178a}$$

$$H_{z2} = G_1 K_n(k_2 r) \exp(jn\theta) \exp(-j\beta z) \qquad r > a \tag{18.178b}$$

The transverse fields are obtained as:

For $r < a$ (i.e. inside the rod)

$$E_{r1} = \frac{-j\omega\mu}{k_1^2} \frac{1}{r} \frac{\partial H_{z1}}{\partial \theta} = A_1 \frac{\omega\mu}{k_1^2} \frac{n}{r} J_n(k_1 r) \cdot \exp(jn\theta) \cdot \exp(-j\beta z) \tag{18.179a}$$

$$E_{\theta 1} = \frac{j\omega\mu}{k_1^2} \frac{\partial H_{z1}}{\partial r} = A_1 \frac{j\omega\mu}{k_1} J_n'(k_1 r) \exp(jn\theta) \cdot \exp(-j\beta z) \tag{18.179b}$$

$$H_{r1} = -\frac{j\beta}{k_1^2} \frac{\partial H_{z1}}{\partial r} = A_1 \frac{-j\beta}{k_1} J_n'(k_1 r) \exp(jn\theta) \cdot \exp(-j\beta z) \tag{18.179c}$$

$$H_{\theta 1} = -\frac{j\beta}{k_1^2} \frac{1}{r} \frac{\partial H_z}{\partial \theta} = A_1 \frac{\beta}{k_1^2} \frac{n}{r} J_n(k_1 r) \exp(jn\theta) \cdot \exp(-j\beta z) \tag{18.179d}$$

and for $r > a$ (i.e. outside the waveguide)

$$E_{r2} = \frac{-j\omega\mu}{-k_2^2} \frac{1}{r} \frac{\partial H_{z2}}{\partial \theta} = G_1 \frac{-\omega\mu}{k_2^2} \frac{n}{r} K_n(k_2 r) \exp(jn\theta) \exp(-j\beta z) \tag{18.180a}$$

$$E_{\theta 2} = \frac{j\omega\mu}{-k_2^2} \frac{\partial H_{z2}}{\partial r} = G_1 \frac{-j\omega\mu}{k_2} K_n'(k_2 r) \exp(jn\theta) \exp(-j\beta z) \tag{18.180b}$$

$$H_{r2} = \frac{-j\beta}{-k_1^2} \frac{\partial H_{z2}}{\partial r} = G_1 \frac{j\beta}{k_2} K_n'(k_2 r) \exp(jn\theta) \exp(-j\beta z) \tag{18.180c}$$

$$H_{\theta 2} = \frac{-j\beta}{-k_2^2} \frac{1}{r} \frac{\partial H_{z2}}{\partial \theta} = G_1 \frac{-\beta}{k_2^2} \frac{n}{r} K_n(k_2 r) \exp(jn\theta) \exp(-j\beta z) \tag{18.180d}$$

To evaluate the constants of integration, the relevant boundary conditions are that the tangential components of **E** and **H** are continuous on the surface of the rod (i.e. at $r = a$). This gives

$$\left. \begin{array}{c} H_{z1} = H_{z2} \quad \text{and} \quad E_{\theta 1} = E_{\theta 2} \text{ at } r = a \\[2mm] A_1 J_n(ka) = G_1 K_n(k_1 a) \quad \text{and} \quad \dfrac{A_1}{k_1} J_n'(ka) = -\dfrac{G_1}{k_2} K_n'(k_1 a) \end{array} \right\} \tag{18.181}$$

i.e.

Since H_θ is also tangential to the rod surface, we get

$$H_{\theta 1} = H_{\theta 2} \quad \text{or} \quad -\frac{nA_1}{k_1^2} J_n(ka) = \frac{nG_1}{k_2^2} K_n(k_1 a) \tag{18.182}$$

The above equations for H_z and H_θ can be simultaneously satisfied only if β or G_1 or n is made identically equal to zero.

Now G_1 which represents the field amplitude cannot be made zero. Also β cannot be zero because this is a travelling mode.

$$\therefore \qquad n = 0 \text{ is the required condition} \tag{18.183}$$

This means that there is no θ variation, i.e. the field is circularly symmetric.

$$E_{r1} = E_{r2} = 0 \qquad \text{and} \qquad H_{\theta 1} = H_{\theta 2} = 0 \tag{18.184}$$

Hence the resulting field components are:
Inside the waveguide $(r < a)$,

$$H_{z1} = A_1 J_0(k_1 r) \exp(-j\beta z) \tag{18.185a}$$

$$E_{\theta 1} = A_1 \frac{j\omega\mu}{k_1} J_0'(k_1 r) \exp(-j\beta z) \tag{18.185b}$$

$$H_{r1} = -A_1 \frac{j\beta}{k_1} J_0'(k_1 r) \exp(-j\beta z) \tag{18.185c}$$

Outside the waveguide $(r > a)$,

$$H_{z2} = G_1 K_0(k_2 r) \exp(-j\beta z) \tag{18.186a}$$

$$E_{\theta 2} = -G_1 \frac{j\omega\mu}{k_2} K_0'(k_2 r) \exp(-j\beta z) \tag{18.186b}$$

$$H_{r2} = G_1 \frac{j\beta}{k_2} K_0'(k_2 r) \exp(-j\beta z) \tag{18.186c}$$

To eliminate the arbitrary constants, the characteristic equation for the TE mode is obtained from

$$\frac{E_{\theta 1}}{H_{z1}} = \frac{E_{\theta 2}}{H_{z2}} \quad \text{on } r = a,$$

i.e.
$$\frac{J_0'(k_1 a)}{k J_0(k_1 a)} = \frac{K_0'(k_2 a)}{k_1 K_0(k_2 a)} \tag{18.187}$$

This equation has multiple roots, because J_0 is an orthogonal function. A TE mode is designated as TE_{0m} because the suffix 0 corresponds to $n = 0$.

18.3.9.2 *Transverse magnetic mode (TM)*

For the transverse magnetic mode $H_z = 0$, and the transverse fields are expressed in terms of E_z. Following the analysis of the TE mode, it will be seen that the TM mode is also circularly symmetric and hence the corresponding field components are:

$$E_{z1} = A_1 J_0(k_1 r) \exp(-j\beta z) \tag{18.188a}$$

$$E_{z2} = G_1 K_0(k_2 r) \exp(-j\beta z) \tag{18.188b}$$

The corresponding transverse components are:
Inside the waveguide $(r < a)$,

$$E_{r1} = \frac{-j\beta}{k_1^2} \frac{\partial E_{z1}}{\partial r} = \frac{-j\beta}{k_1} A_1 J_0'(k_1 r) \exp(-j\beta z) \tag{18.189a}$$

$$H_{\theta 1} = \frac{-j\omega\varepsilon_1}{k_1^2}\frac{\partial E_{z1}}{\partial r} = \frac{-j\omega\varepsilon_1}{k_1}A_1 J_0'(k_1 r)\exp(-j\beta z) \qquad (18.189b)$$

and outside the waveguide $(r > a)$,

$$E_{r2} = \frac{-j\beta}{-k_2^2}\frac{\partial E_{z2}}{\partial r} = \frac{j\beta}{k_2}G_1 K_0'(k_2 r)\exp(-j\beta z) \qquad (18.190a)$$

$$H_{\theta 2} = \frac{-j\omega\varepsilon_2}{-k_2^2}\frac{\partial E_{z2}}{\partial r} = \frac{j\omega\varepsilon_2}{k_2}G_1 K_0'(k_2 r)\exp(-j\beta z) \qquad (18.190b)$$

Next, the continuity of the tangential components of the fields at the waveguide surface $r = a$ gives

$$E_{z1} = E_{z2} \quad \text{and} \quad H_{\theta 1} = H_{\theta 2} \qquad (18.191)$$

from which we get:

$$A_1 J_0(k_1 a) = G_1 K_0(k_2 a) \quad \text{and} \quad -\frac{\varepsilon_1}{k_1}A_1 J_0'(k_1 a) = \frac{\varepsilon_2}{k_2}G_1 K_0'(k_2 a) \qquad (18.192)$$

Taking the ratios of these two equations,

$$\frac{\varepsilon_1}{k_1}\frac{J_0'(k_1 a)}{J_0(k_1 a)} = -\frac{\varepsilon_2}{k_2}\frac{K_0'(k_2 a)}{K_0(k_2 a)} \qquad (18.193)$$

This is the characteristic equation of the TM mode, which is similar to that of the TE mode. The above equation also has multiple roots. The TM mode is designated as TM_{0m} mode.

18.3.9.3 Cut-off frequencies of TM mode

For the two Bessel functions, i.e. $J_0(k_1 r)$ the Bessel function for the region inside the dielectric rod and $K_0(k_2 r)$ the modified Bessel function for the region outside the rod, K_0 is not oscillatory and is a decaying function as shown in Figure 18.16(b). We also have

$$k_1 = \sqrt{(\omega^2\mu\varepsilon_1 - \beta^2)} \quad \text{and} \quad jk_2 = j\sqrt{(\beta^2 - \omega^2\mu\varepsilon_2)} \qquad (18.194a)$$

$$\therefore \qquad k_1^2 + k_2^2 = \omega^2\mu(\varepsilon_1 - \varepsilon_2) = \text{constant} \qquad (18.194b)$$

for a given waveguide and frequency.

The decaying field outside the rod remains so, so long as k_2 is real. If k_2 were to be imaginary K_0 would be replaced by ordinary Bessel function which is oscillatory in nature and travelling radially away from the axis of the rod—a leaking wave. This then no longer remains a guided mode. Hence the cut-off frequency would be obtained when k_2 is made zero. From Eq. (18.194b), it is obvious that both k_1 and k_2 cannot be made simultaneously equal to zero.

Hence, as $k_2 \to 0$, since k_1 cannot approach zero, $J_0(k_1 a) \to 0$

$\therefore$ $J_0(k_1 a) = 0$ corresponds to the cut-off frequency of TE or TM mode, i.e.

$$k_c a = \chi_{0m} \qquad (18.195a)$$

where χ_{0m} is the mth root of the J_0 Bessel function.

∴ The modal cut-off frequency

$$\omega_c = \frac{\chi_{0m}}{a\sqrt{\mu(\varepsilon_1 - \varepsilon_2)}} \tag{18.195b}$$

The first root of the J_0 function is 2.40, and hence the lowest frequency which can propagate in TE or TM mode is

$$\omega_{c01} = \frac{2.4}{a\sqrt{\mu(\varepsilon_1 - \varepsilon_2)}} \tag{18.195c}$$

18.3.9.4 Hybrid modes

So far it has been seen that in circular dielectric waveguides the TE and TM modes are circularly symmetric, This is so when either $E_z = 0$ or $H_z = 0$, i.e. one field component in the direction of propagation is mode equal to zero. When both E_z and H_z are non-zero, then the mode is neither TE nor TM. Such fields are called 'hybrid modal fields.' When such fields exist, they are not circularly symmetric. The longitudinal fields in the two media can then be written as follows:

For $r < a$, i.e. inside the waveguide

$$E_{z1} = A\, J_n(k_1 r) \exp(jn\theta - j\beta z) \tag{18.196a}$$

$$H_{z1} = B\, J_n(k_1 r) \exp(jn\theta - j\beta z) \tag{18.196b}$$

For $r > a$, i.e. outside the waveguide

$$E_{z2} = C\, K_n(k_2 r) \exp(jn\theta - j\beta z) \tag{18.196c}$$

$$H_{z2} = D\, K_n(k_2 r) \exp(jn\theta - j\beta z) \tag{18.196d}$$

A, B, C, D being the amplitudes of the respective field components.

From these four equations for the z-components of the field, the transverse field expressions can be written down as follows:

Inside the waveguide, $r < a$

$$E_{r1} = \frac{\omega\mu n}{k_1^2 r} B\, J_n(k_1 r) \exp(jn\theta) - \frac{j\beta}{k_1} A\, J_n'(k_1 r) \exp(jn\theta) \tag{18.197a}$$

$$E_{\theta 1} = \frac{j\omega n}{k_1} B\, J_n'(k_1 r) \exp(jn\theta) + \frac{\beta}{k_1^2} \frac{nA}{r} J_n(k_1 r) \exp(jn\theta) \tag{18.197b}$$

$$H_{r1} = -\frac{\omega\varepsilon_1}{k_1^2} \frac{n}{r} A\, J_n(k_1 r) \exp(jn\theta) - \frac{j\beta}{k_1} B J_n'(k_1 r) \exp(jn\theta) \tag{18.197c}$$

$$H_{\theta 1} = \frac{-j\omega\varepsilon_1}{k_1} A\, J_n'(k_1 r) \exp(jn\theta) + \frac{\beta n}{k_1^2 r} B J_n(k_1 r) \exp(jn\theta) \tag{18.197d}$$

Outside the waveguide, $r > a$,

$$E_{r2} = -\frac{\omega\mu}{k_2^2}\frac{n}{r} D K_n(k_2 r) \exp(jn\theta) + \frac{j\beta}{k_2} C K_n'(k_2 r) \exp(jn\theta) \tag{18.198a}$$

$$E_{\theta 2} = -\frac{j\omega\mu}{k_2} D K_n'(k_2 r) \exp(jn\theta) - \frac{\beta}{k_2^2}\frac{n}{r} C K_n(k_2 r) \exp(n\theta) \tag{18.198b}$$

$$H_{r2} = \frac{\omega\varepsilon_2}{k_2^2}\frac{n}{r} C K_n(k_2 r) \exp(jn\theta) + \frac{j\beta}{k_2} D K_n'(k_2 r) \exp(jn\theta) \tag{18.198c}$$

$$H_{\theta 2} = \frac{j\omega\varepsilon_2}{k} C K_n'(k_2 r) \exp(jn\theta) - \frac{\beta}{k_2^2}\frac{n}{r} K_n(k_2 r) \exp(jn\theta) \tag{18.198d}$$

For four unknowns A, B, C, D to be evaluated, the four boundary conditions are:

at $r = a$, $E_{z1} = E_{z2}$, $H_{z1} = H_{z2}$

$\qquad\qquad\qquad E_{\theta 1} = E_{\theta 2}$, $H_{\theta 1} = H_{\theta 2}$

The four equations obtained from these four conditions can be written in a compact matrix form as:

$$\begin{bmatrix} J_n(k_1 a) & 0 & -K_n(k_2 a) & 0 \\ 0 & J_n(k_1 a) & 0 & -K_n(k_2 a) \\ \dfrac{\beta n}{ak_1^2} J_n(k_1 a) & \dfrac{j\omega\mu}{k_1} J_n'(k_1 a) & \dfrac{\beta n}{ak_2^2} K_n(k_2 a) & \dfrac{j\omega\mu}{k_2} K_n'(k_2 a) \\ \dfrac{-j\omega\varepsilon_1}{k_1} J_n'(k_1 a) & \dfrac{\beta n}{ak_1^2} J_n(k_1 a) & \dfrac{-j\omega\varepsilon_2}{k_2} K_n'(k_2 a) & \dfrac{\beta n}{ak_2^2} K_n(k_2 a) \end{bmatrix} \begin{bmatrix} A \\ B \\ C \\ D \end{bmatrix} = 0 \tag{18.199}$$

The characteristic equation of the hybrid mode can be obtained by setting the determinant of the coefficient matrix of the last equation to zero. If then, in the characteristic equation n is made equal to zero, the equation splits into two equations which are

$$\frac{J_0'(k_1 a)}{k_1 J_0(k_1 a)} + \frac{K_0'(k_2 a)}{k_2 K_0(k_2 a)} = 0 \tag{18.200a}$$

and

$$\frac{\varepsilon_1}{k_1}\frac{J_0'(k_1 a)}{J_0(k_1 a)} + \frac{\varepsilon_2}{k_2}\frac{K_0'(k_2 a)}{K_0(k_2 a)} = 0 \tag{18.200b}$$

Equations (18.200a) and (18.200b) are the characteristic equations of TE and TM modes respectively [i.e. Eqs. (18.187) and (18.193)].

18.3.9.5 *Cut-off frequency of a hybrid mode*

Evaluation of the cut-off frequency of a hybrid mode is rather complicated. The recurrence relations of Bessel functions have to be used. The derivatives of Bessel functions are replaced by Bessel functions of higher and lower orders. After a somewhat lengthy algebraic manipulation, it is found that the lowest mode is HE_{11} and for $n = 1$, its cut-off is given by $k_{1c} = 0$. The cut-off frequency for $k_{1c} = 0$ is 0. Hence it means that HE_{11} does not have a cut-off frequency, i.e. it can propagate any frequency up to dc. It is an interesting point to be noted that for direct currents, the fields inside a dielectric rod are hybrid and **not** transverse. So the electrostatic field (which corresponds to dc) must have a field component along the axis of the dielectric rod.

18.4 RESONANT CAVITIES (CAVITY RESONATORS)

A tuned circuit consisting of a coil and a capacitor (i.e. a resonating circuit) acts as an energy storage device, and is an important part of a radio receiver. But at very high frequencies, a simple coil cannot act as an inductor. In the centimetre range of wavelengths (i.e. 100 MHz and above), the dimensions of the circuits are comparable with the operating wavelength and hence unwanted radiation takes place. So, at high frequencies the RLC circuits are replaced by cavity resonators. Such resonant cavities are used in klystron tubes, band-pass filters and wave-meters. Even the microwave oven is an application of a cavity resonator so that the oven is the cavity itself which is supplied by a waveguide feed and a power supply.

In a resonant cavity, the electromagnetic waves are reflected by the conducting walls and thus the resonance is produced in it. A cavity resonator can be of any shape—rectangular, cylindrical or spherical—but an important class is produced by placing end-faces on a finite length (i.e. piece) of cylindrical waveguide.

We will consider a rectangular cavity (or a closed conducting box). It is effectively a rectangular waveguide shorted at both the ends. Now when a metal plate is placed at the end of a waveguide (rectangular), the propagation of the electromagnetic wave is blocked and the wave is reflected. So now there are two waves travelling in opposite directions. A standing wave pattern is produced which must satisfy the boundary conditions at both the ends. The problem can be analysed either (1) by starting with the (say) longitudinal magnetic wave travelling in the direction of propagation for TE_{mn} mode or electric wave for the TM_{mn} mode, or (2) by solving the wave equation for the closed box with appropriate boundary conditions.

18.4.1 TE Mode Waveguide Approach

In the waveguide, the wave is assumed to travel in the z-direction, and for the cavity, the metal plates are placed at $z = 0$ and $z = d$. In this situation, the two waves are travelling in opposite directions (i.e. $+z$ and $-z$). For the TE_{mn} mode, the longitudinal H_z for the travelling wave is given by

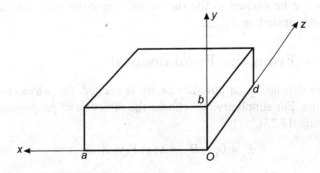

Figure 18.23 A rectangular resonant cavity.

$$H_z = H_0 \cos\frac{m\pi x}{a} \cos\frac{n\pi y}{b} \exp[j(\omega t - \beta z)] \tag{18.201a}$$

For the reflected TE_{mn} wave, let its amplitude be H_0'. Hence

$$H_z' = H_0' \cos\frac{m\pi x}{a} \cos\frac{n\pi y}{b} \exp[j(\omega t + \beta z)] \tag{18.201b}$$

The total H field inside the cavity is then

$$H_Z = H_z + H_z' \tag{18.202}$$

Since H_Z would be perpendicular to the boundaries $z = 0$ and $z = d$, it follows that it should be zero on these two planes.

$$\therefore \qquad \text{at } z = 0, \quad H_z = 0 \quad \rightarrow \quad H_0 = -H_0' \tag{18.203}$$

$$H_z = H_0 \cos\frac{m\pi x}{a} \cos\frac{n\pi y}{b} [\exp(-j\beta z) - \exp(j\beta z)]$$

$$= -2jH_0 \cos\left(\frac{m\pi x}{a}\right) \cos\left(\frac{n\pi y}{b}\right) \sin(\beta z) \tag{18.204}$$

not writing $\exp(j\omega t)$ in these expressions explicitly.

Also on $z = d$, $H_z = 0 \quad \rightarrow \quad \beta d = p\pi, p = 1, 2, 3, \dots$

or

$$\beta = \frac{p\pi}{d} \tag{18.205}$$

Substituting for β from this equation, into Eqs. (18.67) or (18.70), while noting that $\gamma = j\beta$ in the present case,

$$\omega^2 \mu\varepsilon = \left(\frac{m\pi}{a}\right)^2 + \left(\frac{n\pi}{b}\right)^2 + \left(\frac{p\pi}{d}\right)^2$$

or

$$\omega = 2\pi f = \frac{1}{\sqrt{\mu\varepsilon}} \left[\left(\frac{m\pi}{a}\right)^2 + \left(\frac{n\pi}{b}\right)^2 + \left(\frac{p\pi}{d}\right)^2 \right]^{1/2} \tag{18.206}$$

where m, n, p are all integers and hence there will be discrete frequencies at which the electromagnetic fields can be excited inside the cavity. Since the fields are characterized by three indices, this mode is designated as TE_{mnp}.

18.4.2   TE Mode—From the Fundamentals

It should be noted that depending on how the cavity is excited, the wave can propagate in any of the x-, y-, or z- direction. For simplicity, we choose the direction of propagation as $+z$ direction (as in Section 18.4.1, Figure 18.23).

Since

$$E_z = 0, \quad H_z = X(x)\,Y(y)\,Z(z) \tag{18.207}$$

where H_z is the solution of $\nabla^2 \mathbf{H} + k_2 \mathbf{H} = 0$.

$$\left.\begin{array}{l} X(x) = B_1 \cos k_x x + B_2 \sin k_x x \\ Y(y) = B_3 \cos k_y y + B_4 \sin k_y y \\ Z(z) = B_5 \cos k_z z + B_6 \sin k_z z \end{array}\right\} \qquad (18.208)$$

where
$$k^2 = k_x^2 + k_y^2 + k_z^2 \qquad (18.209)$$

The boundary conditions are:

(i) $\quad H_z = 0 \quad$ at $\quad z = 0, d$

(ii) $\quad \dfrac{\partial H_z}{\partial x} = 0 \quad$ at $\quad x = 0, a$

(iii) $\quad \dfrac{\partial H_z}{\partial y} = 0 \quad$ at $\quad y = 0, b.$

From the boundary conditions (ii) and (iii),

$$B_2 = 0, \quad B_4 = 0, \quad \text{and} \quad k_x = \frac{m\pi}{a}, \quad k_y = \frac{n\pi}{b} \qquad (18.210)$$

where $m = 0, 1, 2, 3, \dots$ and $n = 0, 1, 2, 3.$

For the boundary condition (i),

$$B_5 = 0 \quad \text{and} \quad k_z = \frac{p\pi}{d}, \quad \text{where } p = 1, 2, 3, \dots \qquad (18.211)$$

$$\therefore \qquad H_z = H_0 \cos\left(\frac{m\pi x}{a}\right) \cos\left(\frac{n\pi y}{b}\right) \sin\left(\frac{p\pi z}{d}\right) \qquad (18.212)$$

$$\beta^2 = k^2 = \left(\frac{m\pi}{a}\right)^2 + \left(\frac{n\pi}{b}\right)^2 + \left(\frac{p\pi}{d}\right)^2 = \omega^2 \mu\varepsilon$$

$$\therefore \qquad \omega = 2\pi f = \frac{1}{\sqrt{\mu\varepsilon}} \left[\left(\frac{m\pi}{a}\right)^2 + \left(\frac{n\pi}{b}\right)^2 + \left(\frac{p\pi}{d}\right)^2\right]^{1/2} \qquad (18.213)$$

The resonant frequency is same as derived by the other method, i.e. Eq. (18.183). It should be noted that both m and n cannot be zero simultaneously because the field components will be zero if both m and n are zeroes. The 'dominant mode' (i.e. the mode having the lowest resonant frequency is TE_{101} mode $(a > b < c)$. A practical resonant cavity has walls with finite conductivity σ_c, and hence can lose stored energy. The loss is determined by the quality factor Q.

18.4.3 TM Mode—From the Fundamentals

In this case, $H_z = 0$ and hence

$$E_z = X(x)\, Y(y)\, Z(z) \qquad (18.214)$$

$$\therefore \qquad \left.\begin{array}{l} X(x) = A_1 \cos k_x x + A_2 \sin k_x x \\[2mm] Y(y) = A_3 \cos k_y y + A_4 \sin k_y y \\[2mm] Z(z) = A_5 \cos k_z z + A_6 \sin k_z z \end{array}\right\} \qquad (18.215)$$

where
$$k^2 = k_x^2 + k_y^2 + k_z^2 = \omega^2 \mu \varepsilon \qquad (18.216)$$

The boundary conditions are:

(i) $E_z = 0$ at $x = 0, a$

(ii) $E_z = 0$ at $y = 0, b$ $\qquad\qquad (18.217)$

(iii) $E_x = 0, \quad E_y = 0$ at $z = 0, d$

From the boundary conditions (i) and (ii),

$$\left.\begin{array}{c} A_1 = 0, \quad A_3 = 0, \quad k_x = \dfrac{m\pi}{a}, \quad k_y = \dfrac{n\pi}{b} \\[3mm] m = 1,\,2,\,3,\,\dots \qquad n = 1,\,2,\,3,\,\dots \end{array}\right\} \qquad (18.218)$$

where

Next, for the boundary condition (iii), from the two curl equations of Maxwell, i.e.

$$\nabla \times \mathbf{H} = \frac{\partial \mathbf{D}}{\partial t} \qquad \text{and} \qquad \nabla \times \mathbf{E} = -\frac{\partial \mathbf{B}}{\partial t} \qquad (18.218a)$$

we get

$$j\omega\varepsilon E_x = \frac{\partial H_z}{\partial y} - \frac{\partial H_y}{\partial z} \qquad \text{and} \qquad -j\omega\mu H_y = \frac{\partial E_x}{\partial z} - \frac{\partial E_z}{\partial x}$$

Combining these two equations,

$$j\omega\varepsilon E_x = \frac{\partial H_z}{\partial y} + \frac{1}{j\omega\mu}\left(\frac{\partial^2 E_x}{\partial z^2} - \frac{\partial^2 E_z}{\partial x \partial z}\right)$$

Since $H_z = 0$, this simplifies to

$$j\omega\varepsilon E_x = \frac{1}{j\omega\mu}\left(\frac{\partial^2 E_x}{\partial z^2} - \frac{\partial^2 E_z}{\partial z \partial x}\right) \qquad (18.219)$$

and considering E_y and H_x from the same two ($\nabla\times$) equations

$$j\omega\varepsilon E_y = \frac{1}{-j\omega\mu}\left(\frac{\partial^2 E_z}{\partial y \partial z} - \frac{\partial^2 E_y}{\partial z^2}\right) \qquad (18.220)$$

From these two equations [i.e. (18.219) and (18.220)], to satisfy the boundary condition (iii) which states

$$E_x = 0, \quad E_y = 0 \quad \text{at} \quad z = 0, d$$

the requisite condition is

$$\frac{\partial E_z}{\partial z} = 0 \quad \text{at} \quad z = 0 \text{ and } d.$$

$$\rightarrow A_6 = 0 \quad \text{and} \quad \sin k_z d = 0 = \sin p\pi$$

$$\therefore \qquad k_z = \frac{p\pi}{d}, \quad \text{where } p = 0, 1, 2, 3, \dots \qquad (18.221)$$

Substituting for the unknowns in Eqs. (18.214) and (18.215),

$$E_z = E_0 \sin\left(\frac{m\pi x}{a}\right) \sin\left(\frac{n\pi y}{b}\right) \cos\left(\frac{p\pi z}{d}\right) \qquad (18.222)$$

where $E_0 = A_2 A_4 A_5$.

The other field components can be obtained from Eq. (18.222) and the two curl Eqs. (18.218a).

The phase constant comes out to be

$$k^2 = \left(\frac{m\pi}{a}\right)^2 + \left(\frac{n\pi}{b}\right)^2 + \left(\frac{p\pi}{d}\right)^2$$

$$= \omega^2 \mu\varepsilon$$

$$\therefore \qquad \omega = 2\pi f = \frac{1}{\sqrt{\mu\varepsilon}} \sqrt{\left[\left(\frac{m\pi}{a}\right)^2 + \left(\frac{n\pi}{b}\right)^2 + \left(\frac{p\pi}{d}\right)^2\right]} \qquad (18.223)$$

The lowest order TM mode is TM_{110}

18.4.4 Stored Energy and Quality Factor

Considering the TE_{101} mode ($m = 1$, $n = 0$), the longitudinal magnetic field component is [from Eq. (18.204)]

$$H_z = -2j H_0 \cos\left(\frac{\pi x}{a}\right) \sin\left(\frac{\pi z}{d}\right) \qquad (18.224)$$

The other field components come out to be

$$H_x = 2j \frac{a}{d} H_0 \sin\left(\frac{\pi x}{a}\right) \cos\left(\frac{\pi z}{d}\right) \qquad (18.225)$$

$$E_y = -2\omega_0 \mu H_0 \frac{a}{\pi} \sin\left(\frac{\pi x}{a}\right) \sin\left(\frac{\pi z}{d}\right) \qquad (18.226)$$

by suitable substitutions in Eqs. (18.77c) and (18.77b) respectively (for the incident and the reflected waves in the cavity).

The resonant frequency ω_0 for the TE_{101} mode comes out as

$$\omega_0 = 2\pi f_0 = \frac{1}{\sqrt{\mu\varepsilon}}\left[\left(\frac{\pi}{a}\right)^2 + \left(\frac{\pi}{d}\right)^2\right]^{1/2} \tag{18.227}$$

Since every resonant circuit stores electromagnetic energy, we now calculate the stored energy. The average electrical energy stored inside the cavity is

$$W_e = \frac{\varepsilon}{2}\int_{x=0}^{a}\int_{y=0}^{b}\int_{z=0}^{d}\frac{1}{2}\mathrm{Re}\,(\mathbf{E}.\mathbf{E}^*)\,dx\,dy\,dz$$

$$= \varepsilon|H_0|^2\left(\frac{\omega\mu a}{\pi}\right)^2\iiint \sin^2\left(\frac{\pi x}{a}\right)\sin^2\left(\frac{\pi z}{d}\right)dx\,dy\,dz$$

$$= \frac{abd\varepsilon}{4}|H_0|^2\left(\frac{\omega\mu a}{\pi}\right)^2 \tag{18.228}$$

The average magnetic energy stored inside the cavity

$$W_m = \frac{\mu}{2}\int_{x=0}^{a}\int_{y=0}^{b}\int_{z=0}^{d}\frac{1}{2}\mathrm{Re}\,(\mathbf{H}\cdot\mathbf{H}^*)\,dx\,dy\,dz$$

$$= \mu|H_0|^2\int_{x=0}^{a}\int_{y=0}^{b}\int_{z=0}^{d}\left[\left(\frac{a}{d}\right)^2\sin^2\left(\frac{\pi x}{a}\right)\cos^2\left(\frac{\pi z}{d}\right) + \cos^2\left(\frac{\pi x}{a}\right)\sin^2\left(\frac{\pi z}{d}\right)\right]dx\,dy\,dz$$

$$= \frac{abd\mu}{4}|H_0|^2\left[\left(\frac{a}{d}\right)^2 + 1\right] = W_e \qquad \left(\text{since }\left(\frac{a}{d}\right)^2 + 1 = \omega^2\mu\varepsilon a\pi\right) \tag{18.229}$$

which is obtained from Eq. (18.223) or (18.213) by suitable substitutions for m, n, p.

Thus the average stored electrical and magnetic energy are equal for the cavity resonator. This equality is identical with the LC circuit at the resonance.

The quality factor Q, for the resonator, is a measure of loss in the resonator, and is defined as

$$Q = \omega_0\frac{\text{Energy stored in the cavity}}{\text{Power loss in the cavity}} \tag{18.230}$$

$$= \omega_0\frac{W_e + W_m}{\text{Power loss in the cavity}}$$

$$= \frac{2\omega_0 W_e}{\text{Power loss in the cavity}} \tag{18.231}$$

Assuming the loss in the cavity to be small, the field distribution of a lossy cavity is almost same as that of a loss-less cavity. The surface currents on the walls of the waveguide (and the conductor loss) can be obtained from the knowledge of the magnetic field. If the surface resistance is denoted by R_S,

$$R_S = \sqrt{(\omega_0 \mu)/(2\sigma)}, \quad \sigma = \text{conductivity of the cavity walls,}$$

then for the TE_{101} mode,

$$Q_{101} = \frac{\mu^2 \varepsilon(\omega_0 ad)^3 b}{2\pi^2 R_S [2b(a^3 + d^3) + ad(a^2 + d^2)]} \tag{18.232a}$$

$$= \frac{(a^2 + d^2)abd}{\delta[2b(a^3 + d^3) + ad(a^2 + d^2)]} \tag{18.232b}$$

where $\delta = \sqrt{\dfrac{2}{\omega_0 \mu_0 \sigma}}$ = depth of penetration (or skin depth) = $d\sqrt{2}$ of Eq. (15.7).

Note: '*d*' of skin-depth or depth of penetration $(d\sqrt{2})$ of Eq. (15.7) is not to be confused with the dimension d of the cavity. Hence the notation δ has been used here.

18.4.5 Cylindrical Cavity

It is a cylindrical piece of radius R and axial length d, and its walls are assumed to have infinite conductivity. For simplicity, the cavity is asumed to be filled with a loss-less dielectric of characteristics μ, ε. Since the reflections take place on the end-surfaces of the cylinder the relevant expressions for the standing waves (using the cylindrical coordinate system) are:

$$A\sin(kz) + B\cos(kz)$$

Since the two ends of the cylindrical cavity are $z = 0$ and $z = d$, the boundary conditions can be satisfied only if

$$k = \frac{p\pi}{d}, \qquad \text{where } p = 0, 1, 2, 3, \ldots \tag{18.233}$$

For TE modes, the vanishing of H_z at $z = 0$ and $z = d$ requires

$$H_z = \psi(x, y)\sin\left(\frac{p\pi z}{d}\right), \qquad p = 1, 2, 3, \ldots \tag{18.234}$$

For TM modes, the vanishing of E_t at $z = 0$ and $z = d$ requires

$$E_z = \psi(x, y)\cos\left(\frac{p\pi z}{d}\right), \qquad p = 0, 1, 2, 3, \ldots \tag{18.235}$$

where ψ is a scalar function which satisfies the two-dimensional wave equation

$$(\nabla_t^2 + \gamma^2)\psi = 0 \tag{18.236}$$

and ∇_t^2 is the transverse part of the Laplacian operator, i.e.

$$\nabla_t^2 \equiv \nabla^2 - \frac{\partial^2}{\partial z^2} \tag{18.237}$$

In the Cartesian coordinates, the transverse fields for the two modes are obtained as:

TM mode:
$$E_t = -\left[\left(\frac{p\pi}{\gamma^2 d}\right)\sin\left(\frac{p\pi z}{d}\right)\right]\nabla_t \psi \qquad (18.238a)$$

$$H_t = \left[\left(\frac{j\varepsilon\omega}{\gamma^2 c}\right)\cos\left(\frac{p\pi z}{d}\right)\right]\mathbf{i}_z \times \nabla_t \psi \qquad (18.238b)$$

TE mode:
$$E_t = -\left[\left(\frac{j\omega\mu}{\gamma^2 c}\right)\sin\left(\frac{p\pi z}{d}\right)\right]\mathbf{i}_z \times \nabla_t \psi \qquad (18.239a)$$

$$H_t = \left[\left(\frac{p\pi}{\gamma^2 d}\right)\cos\left(\frac{p\pi z}{d}\right)\right]\nabla_t \psi \qquad (18.239b)$$

where the constant
$$\gamma^2 = \left(\frac{\omega^2 \mu\varepsilon}{c}\right) - \left(\frac{p\pi}{d}\right)^2 \qquad (18.240)$$

and ψ can be solved as an eigenvalue problem.

In the cylindrical resonant cavity, the tuning is done with a piston by varying d. For the TM mode, the transverse wave equation for ψ is $= E_z$, subject to the boundary condition that $E_z = 0$ at $r = R$.

The solution for the cavity is

$$\psi(r, \phi) = J_m(\gamma_{mn} r)\exp(\pm jm\phi)$$

where
$$\gamma_{mn} = \frac{x_{mn}}{R} \qquad (18.241)$$

x_{mn}, being the nth root of $J_m(x) = 0$.

The integers m and n have the values

$$m = 0, 1, 2, 3, \ldots; \qquad n = 1, 2, 3, \ldots$$

The resonant frequencies are given by:

$$\omega_{mnp} = \frac{c}{\sqrt{\mu\varepsilon}}\sqrt{\left(\frac{x_{mn}^2}{R^2} + \frac{p^2 \pi^2}{d^2}\right)} \qquad (18.242)$$

For the lowest TM mode, $m = 0$, $n = 1$, $p = 0$, the designation is TM$_{010}$ and its resonance frequency is

$$\omega_{010} = \frac{2.405c}{R\sqrt{\mu\varepsilon}} \qquad (18.243)$$

In general terms, for cavities of a few cm linear dimension with α of about 10^{-4} cm, the Q value is of the order of 10,000

PROBLEMS

18.1 Show that the input impedance of a loaded lossy transmission line is given by

$$Z_{in} = Z_c \left[\frac{Z_L + jZ_c \tanh \gamma l}{Z_c + jZ_l \tanh \gamma l} \right]$$

where

γ = propagation constant

Z_c = characteristic impedance

Z_L = load impedance

l = length of the line.

Hence, for a quarter wavelength line

$$Z_{in} = \frac{Z_c^2}{Z_L}$$

18.2 A coil has a complex impedance of resistance R and self-inductance L. It is connected in parallel with a capacitor of capacitance C with an imperfect dielectric equivalent to a series resistance which is also R. Find (i) a value of R which makes the impedance purely resistive at all values of ω, and (ii) a value of ω which again makes the impedance purely resistive for all R.

Ans.: (i) $R = \sqrt{\dfrac{L}{C}}$, (ii) $\omega = \dfrac{1}{\sqrt{LC}}$

18.3 Rectangular waveguide is often made of brass or steel for economy, and then silver-plated to provide the lowest losses. Assuming operation at 10 GHz with $\sigma = 6.17 \times 10^7$ mho/m for silver, calculate the amount of silver required per mile to provide a three-skin-depths coating on a waveguide with an inner periphery of 10 cm. Density of silver = 10.5 g/cc.

Ans.: 3.25 kg

18.4 Define phase velocity v_{ph} and group velocity v_{gr} of a travelling wave, and show that

$$\frac{1}{v_{ph}} - \frac{1}{v_{gr}} = \frac{\omega}{v_{ph}^2} \frac{dv_{ph}}{d\omega}$$

and that

$$v_{gr} = v_{ph} - \lambda \frac{dv_{ph}}{d\lambda}$$

Hint: Differentiate the modified expression for v_{ph} with respect to β, and $\beta = \dfrac{2\pi}{\lambda}$.

18.5 A transmission-line consists of two parallel strips of copper forming the go and return conductors, their width being six times the separation between them. The dielectric is air. From the Maxwell's equations applied to a TEM wave, show that the ratio of voltage to current in a progressive wave is 20π ohms.

Hint: Calculate L and C of the system, and hence the characteristic impedance.

18.6 Radar signals at 10,000 MHz are to be transmitted and recieved through a polystyrene window ($\varepsilon/\varepsilon_0 = 2.5$) let into the fuselage of an aircraft. Assuming that the waves are incident normally, how would you ensure that no reflections are produced by the window by choosing a particular thickness ($= d$) for the window?

Ans.: d = any integral multiple of 0.95 cm

18.7 By using Maxwell's equations, prove that a TEM wave cannot exist in a single conductor waveguide, such as rectangular or cylindrical waveguides.

19 Radiation and Reception of Electromagnetic Waves

19.1 INTRODUCTION

So far we have studied the propagation of electromagnetic waves in some detail. In Chapters 17 and 18, we studied their propagation in free space, in various dielectric and conducting media (extending to infinity), and then across the interfaces (i.e. planes of discontinuity) between different types of media, which produce the phenomena of reflection and refraction, and then along various guiding structures. But till now, we have not considered how and where such waves are produced and their effects at their destinations. So in the present chapter, we shall study the sources and the receivers of such waves.

The sources of any electromagnetic field are electric charges and currents. When these charges are time-varying, they may produce electromagnetic waves propagating away from the sources (and not returning to them). Such a process is known as 'the radiation of electromagnetic waves'. Theoretically, any time-varying sources of charges and currents radiate certain amount of energy. For example, at power frequency of 50 Hz, the radiation from the power transmission lines does exist in the rigorous sense, but in reality the radiated energy is so small that practically it cannot be detected, and hence justifiably considered as negligible.

In many practical problems, configurations of charges and currents radiating considerable energy to the surrounding space are required; and the science of designing and analyzing the 'radiating systems' has developed as a part of the theory of electromagnetism. Such a topic is highly specialized and complex. In our present introductory text, we intend to consider the basic, fundamental and simple types of radiating systems.

Systems designed for effectively radiating electromagnetic waves, are called antennae, of which there are many types. Once an antenna creates the em wave, the wave travels through the space to its destination where the message contained in the wave has to be extracted. The distance between the transmitting antenna and the receiving point is variable, and can be as much as hundreds of thousands of miles. For such large distances, special antennae which radiate very narrow beams are used. For receiving purposes, structures similar to transmitting antennae are used. These are called receiving antennae. There is a great diversity of such antennae, but their common characteristic is that they behave as generators when the incoming wave hits them and a corresponding emf is induced in them. The analysis of receiving antennae is more complex than that of the transmitting antennae.

To design a radiating system, the information needed would include its wave pattern distribution, its polarization, and the distribution in space of the radiant energy, non-radiative losses, the currents and the charge distributions in the system, and its input impedance. These will depend on impressed frequency and voltage, the system dimensions, geometrical configuration, its materials and those of its surroundings. A complete solution of the problem must give fields which satisfy the Maxwell's equations and also the surface boundary conditions. There are methods of calculating the necessary required quantities with reasonable accuracy. By using the retarded potentials, the fields of charge and current distributions can be obtained. A rough estimate of the distant radiation (the far field) which is dependent on the major features of the source distributions is quite adequate. The ohmic losses can be calculated with sufficient accuracy by taking the real part of the complex Poynting vector.

19.2 THE ELECTRIC DIPOLE ANTENNA (THE HERTZIAN DIPOLE)

The electric dipole antenna or the Hertzian dipole (as it is more commonly known as) is the simplest of all the radiating systems, and is the basis for all types of antennae.

19.2.1 Electromagnetic Field of a Hertzian Dipole

The basic source of an electrostatic field is a point charge; and of magnetic field is a current loop. For an electromagnetic field, the simplest independent source is a *Hertzian Dipole* consisting of a pair of charges $\pm q$, separated by a distance l which is small compared with other distances considered; the charges vary with time, and are connected by a conductor in which is a current i which is

$$i = \frac{dq}{dt}$$

The electric field of the charges is associated, when the charges vary with time, with a displacement current which may be considered to complete the circuit for the element (i, l); alternatively, in terms of conduction currents only, we have a flow of charges which is associated with variation in the positive and negative charges at the termini (Figure 19.1).

Let us consider the field in free space surrounding such a dipole, in which (say) the charges and the current are given by

$$q = f(t) \qquad \text{and} \qquad i = f'(t) \tag{19.1}$$

In Section 13.5, we considered the magnetic vector potential applied to time-varying fields. Therein we have shown that the time-varying fields expressed by the Maxwell's equations can be expressed by the equations in terms of the magnetic vector potential **A** and a scalar electric potential V under the 'Lorentz gauge condition', such that the potential equations are completely separate. [Refer to Eqs. (13.52) to (13.54)]. These general equations reduce to the following form in free space (which we are considering at present), i.e.

$$\nabla \cdot \mathbf{A} + \left(\frac{1}{c^2}\right)\left(\frac{\partial V}{\partial t}\right) = 0 \tag{19.2a}$$

$$\nabla^2 \mathbf{A} - \left(\frac{1}{c^2}\right)\left(\frac{\partial^2 \mathbf{A}}{\partial t^2}\right) = 0 \tag{19.2b}$$

$$\nabla^2 V - \left(\frac{1}{c^2}\right)\left(\frac{\partial^2 V}{\partial t^2}\right) = 0 \tag{19.2c}$$

where $c = (\mu_0 \varepsilon_0)^{-1/2}$, as earlier in connection with the plane waves.

For a current element (i, l) under static conditions, we saw that $\mathbf{A}$ was a vector of magnitude $(\mu_0/4\pi)(il/r)$, parallel to the current element at every point [Ref.: Eq. (13.10) of Section 13.3.1]. It is not to be assumed that this will hold good under non-static conditions, but it will be assumed that the non-static solution still retains two features of the static, i.e.

(a) $\mathbf{A}$ is everywhere parallel to the element; and
(b) $\mathbf{A}$ depends only on the distance r from the element and on time t.

With these assumptions, $\mathbf{A}$ in Eqs. (19.2) has only one component which may be called A_z or just A.

Also,

$$\nabla \cdot \mathbf{A} = \frac{\partial A_z}{\partial z} = \frac{\partial A}{\partial z}$$

and

$$\left|\nabla^2 A\right| = \left(\frac{\partial^2 A}{\partial r^2}\right) + \left(\frac{2}{r}\right)\frac{\partial A}{\partial r} = \left(\frac{1}{r}\right)\left(\frac{\partial^2}{\partial r^2}\right)(rA)$$

These two equations may be proved by considering the flux out of an elementary volume in spherical coordinates.

Moreover with $\mathbf{A}$ being a function of r only, the maximum rate of change is $\left(\dfrac{\partial A}{\partial r}\right)$, and

$$\frac{\partial A}{\partial z} = \left(\frac{\partial A}{\partial r}\right)\cos \theta.$$

The first two equations of the set (19.2), i.e. (b) and (a) therefore become in the reverse order as mentioned above:

$$\left(\frac{1}{r}\right)\left(\frac{\partial^2}{\partial r^2}\right)(rA) - \left(\frac{1}{c^2}\right)\left(\frac{\partial^2 A}{\partial t^2}\right) = 0 \tag{19.3}$$

and

$$\cos \theta \left(\frac{\partial A}{\partial r}\right) + \left(\frac{1}{c^2}\right)\left(\frac{\partial V}{\partial t}\right) = 0 \tag{19.4}$$

It may be verified that Eq. (19.3) is satisfied by

$$A = \left(\frac{1}{r}\right)F\left(t - \frac{r}{c}\right) \tag{19.5}$$

where F is any function.

$$\left[\text{This is because: } \left(\frac{1}{r}\right)\left(\frac{\partial^2}{\partial r^2}\right)(rA) = \left(\frac{1}{rc^2}\right)F'' = \left(\frac{1}{c^2}\right)\left(\frac{\partial^2 A}{\partial t^2}\right)\right]$$

We now compare Eq. (19.5) with the static equation

$$A = \left(\frac{\mu_0}{4\pi} \right) \left(\frac{il}{r} \right), \text{ which now becomes } = \frac{\mu_0 l f'(t)}{4\pi r}$$

when $i = f'(t)$ [Ref.: Eq. (19.1)].

Now c is a large number; thus for small values of r and moderate values of t, $F\left(t - \dfrac{r}{c} \right)$ approximates to $F(t)$. If now we make

$$F(t) = \left(\frac{\mu_0 l}{4\pi} \right) f'(t)$$

then we see that Eq. (19.5) reduces to the static equation (or more accurately, the quasi-static). Hence the solution (19.5), for the more general case, is to be written as

$$A = \frac{\mu_0}{4\pi} \left(\frac{l}{r} \right) f'\left(t - \frac{r}{c} \right) \tag{19.6}$$

Substitution of this value of A in Eq. (19.4) now gives

$$\frac{\partial V}{\partial t} = -c^2 \cos \theta \left(\frac{\partial A}{\partial r} \right)$$

$$= \frac{\mu_0}{4\pi} l c^2 \cos \theta \left[\left(\frac{1}{r^2} \right) f'\left(t - \frac{r}{c} \right) + \left(\frac{1}{cr} \right) f''\left(t - \frac{r}{c} \right) \right] \tag{19.7}$$

whence

$$V = \frac{l \cos \theta}{4\pi \varepsilon_0} \left[\left(\frac{1}{r^2} \right) f\left(t - \frac{r}{c} \right) + \left(\frac{1}{cr} \right) f'\left(t - \frac{r}{c} \right) \right] \tag{19.8}$$

Now $f(t - r/c)$ is the value of the charges q at an instant r/c earlier than the instant at which the value of V is being calculated; similarly $f'(t - r/c)$ is the value of i at an earlier instant. We write these as $[q]$, $[i]$, and call them the *retarded values* of q and i (refer to Section 13.6 on Retarded Potentials). Physically we see that this means that a signal travels from the point O to the point P with a finite velocity c, so that at the time t, an observer at P can only know about the values which q and i had at an earlier instant $(t - r/c)$.

Thus the potentials due to the oscillating dipole are

$$A = \left(\frac{\mu_0 l}{4\pi} \right) \left\{ \frac{[i]}{r} \right\} \tag{19.9}$$

$$V = \left(\frac{l \cos \theta}{4\pi \varepsilon_0} \right) \left\{ \frac{[q]}{r^2} + \frac{[i]}{cr} \right\} \tag{19.10}$$

It should be noted that we did not assume the retarding effect to start with, but proved this to be an essential requirement for the time-varying nature of the radiating sources. If the 'retarding effect' is assumed, then these potentials can be obtained more directly (see Carter: *The Electromagnetic Field*, pp. 301–302). It must however be noted carefully that the field components **E** and **B** *cannot* be obtained by inserting the retarded values of q and i into the static expressions of **E** of the static dipole. It is essential to note that we started from the potentials (and *not* the field expressions) which were shown to require the retarding effects to account for the time-varying nature of the sources.

Note: In our evaluation of the expressions for the two potentials, we have so far disregarded (or to be more precise, we have not been required to use it in our derivations so far) the third of the equations (19.2), i.e. Eq. (19.2c). If we use the Cartesian coordinate system, then:

$$\nabla^2 \equiv \frac{\partial^2}{\partial x^2} + \frac{\partial^2}{\partial y^2} + \frac{\partial^2}{\partial z^2}$$

The first equation (19.2a) is

$$\left(\frac{\partial \mathbf{A}}{\partial z}\right) + \left(\frac{1}{c^2}\right)\left(\frac{\partial V}{\partial t}\right) = 0 \tag{19.2a}$$

The second equation is

$$\left[\nabla^2 - \left(\frac{1}{c^2}\right)\left(\frac{\partial^2}{\partial t^2}\right)\right]\mathbf{A} = 0 \tag{19.2b}$$

Differentiating Eq. (19.2b) with respect to z, we get

$$\left[\nabla^2 - \left(\frac{1}{c^2}\right)\left(\frac{\partial^2}{\partial t^2}\right)\right]\left(\frac{\partial \mathbf{A}}{\partial z}\right) = 0 \tag{19.2b$'$}$$

Combining Eqs. (19.2a) and (19.2b$'$), we get

$$\left[\nabla^2 - \left(\frac{1}{c^2}\right)\left(\frac{\partial^2}{\partial t^2}\right)\right]\left(\frac{\partial V}{\partial t}\right) = 0$$

In other words, Eq. (19.7) is a solution of the equation, and V in Eq. (19.8) is of just the same form except for the different functions of $(t - r/c)$. Hence, we find that V, deduced as before, automatically satisfies Eq. (19.2c).

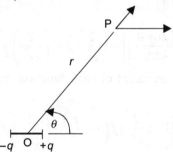

Figure 19.1 An oscillating dipole.

19.2.2 Field Components for the Hertzian Dipole

We use the spherical polar coordinate system with the origin at the centre of the dipole, and the angle θ measured from the axis of the dipole (Figure 19.2). In this coordinate system, a point P is defined by (r, θ, ϕ), and the element of length has the components—δr, $r\delta\theta$, $r \sin \theta\delta\phi$—and

$$\text{grad } V = \nabla V = \mathbf{i}_r\left(\frac{\partial V}{\partial r}\right) + \mathbf{i}_\theta\left(\frac{1}{r}\right)\left(\frac{\partial V}{\partial \theta}\right) + \mathbf{i}_\phi\left(\frac{1}{r \sin \theta}\right)\left(\frac{\partial V}{\partial \phi}\right)$$

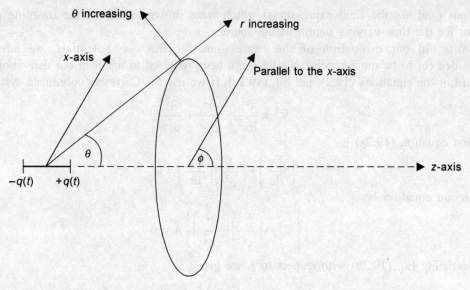

Figure 19.2 Oscillating dipole with spherical polar coordinate system.

In the present problem, V varies with r and θ, but not with ϕ [see Eq. (19.8)].

∴ (grad V) has r and θ components only.

Now,
$$\mathbf{E} = -\left(\frac{\partial \mathbf{A}}{\partial t}\right) - \nabla V$$

where $\mathbf{A}$ and V are given by Eqs. (19.6) and (19.8).

Also, $A_r = A \cos \theta$, and $A_\theta = A \sin \theta$.

$$\therefore \quad E_r = -\left(\frac{\partial A}{\partial t}\right) \cos \theta - \left(\frac{\partial V}{\partial r}\right)$$

$$= \left(\frac{\mu_0 l}{4\pi r}\right) \cos \theta f'' - \left(\frac{l \cos \theta}{4\pi\varepsilon_0}\right)\left[-\left(\frac{2}{r^3}\right)f - \left(\frac{2}{cr^2}\right)f' - \left(\frac{1}{c^2 r}\right)f''\right]$$

where $(t - r/c)$ is understood as the argument of each function; and if we make the substitution: $\mu_0 = 1/(c^2\varepsilon_0)$, we find

$$E_r = \left(\frac{l \cos \theta}{4\pi\varepsilon_0}\right)\left[-\left(\frac{2}{r^3}\right)f\left(t - \frac{r}{c}\right) - \left(\frac{2}{cr^2}\right)f'\left(t - \frac{r}{c}\right)\right] \tag{19.11}$$

Similarly,

$$E_\theta = -\left(\frac{\partial A}{\partial t}\right)\sin \theta - \left(\frac{1}{r}\right)\left(\frac{\partial V}{\partial \theta}\right)$$

$$= \left(\frac{\mu_0 l}{4\pi r}\right)\sin \theta f'' + \left(\frac{l \sin \theta}{4\pi\varepsilon_0 r}\right)\left[\left(\frac{1}{r^2}\right)f + \left(\frac{1}{cr}\right)f'\right]$$

$$= \left(\frac{l \sin \theta}{4\pi\varepsilon_0}\right) \times \left[\left(\frac{1}{r^2}\right)f\left(t - \frac{r}{c}\right) + \left(\frac{1}{cr^2}\right)f'\left(t - \frac{r}{c}\right) + \frac{1}{c^2 r}f''\left(t - \frac{r}{c}\right)\right] \tag{19.12}$$

The lines of force of the magnetic field form circles round the axis of the current (carried by the dipole). Thus B has a ϕ-component only. To evaluate B_ϕ, we consider the contour ABCDA as shown below in Figure 19.3:

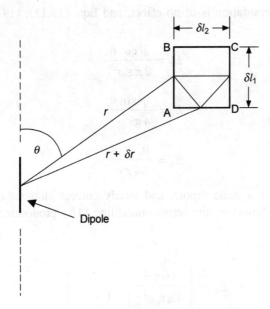

Figure 19.3   Contour for evaluating B_ϕ due to the dipole.

$$B_\phi = \frac{\text{line-integral of } \mathbf{A} \text{ round ABCDA}}{\text{area ABCD}}$$

$$= \frac{\delta l_1 \left[A(r) - A(r + \delta r) \right]}{\delta l_1 \delta l_2} = \left(\frac{1}{\delta l_2} \right) \left(-\frac{\partial A}{\partial r} \right) \delta r$$

Also, $\delta r = \delta l_2 \sin \theta$

$$\therefore \quad \mathbf{B}_\phi = -\left(\frac{\partial \mathbf{A}}{\partial r} \right) \sin \theta$$

Also, $B_\phi = (\nabla \times \mathbf{A})_\phi = \dfrac{\partial A_\theta}{\partial r} + \dfrac{A_\theta}{r} - \left(\dfrac{1}{r} \right) \left(\dfrac{\partial A_r}{\partial \theta} \right)$

with $A_r = A \cos \theta$, $A_\theta = - A \sin \theta$, where A is a function of r only (and of t).

$$\therefore \qquad\qquad B_\phi = \sin \theta \left(-\frac{\partial A}{\partial r} - \frac{A}{r} + \frac{A}{r} \right)$$

$$= -\left(\frac{\partial A}{\partial r} \right) \sin \theta$$

Thus,

$$B_\phi = \left(\frac{\mu_0 l}{4\pi} \right) \sin\theta \left[\left(\frac{1}{r^2} \right) f'\left(t - \frac{r}{c} \right) + \left(\frac{1}{cr} \right) f''\left(t - \frac{r}{c} \right) \right] \tag{19.13}$$

If (r/c) is negligible, the retardation is of no effect, and Eqs. (19.11), (19.12), and (19.13) can be written as

$$E_r = \frac{ql\cos\theta}{2\pi\varepsilon_0 r^3} \tag{19.14a}$$

$$E_\theta = \frac{ql\sin\theta}{4\pi\varepsilon_0 r^3} \tag{19.14b}$$

$$B_\phi = \frac{\mu_0 il\sin\theta}{4\pi r^2} \tag{19.14c}$$

These are the equations for a static dipole, and steady current element respectively.

At a great distance, however, the terms containing $(1/r)$ predominate, and we get (the far field):

$$E_r = 0 \tag{19.15a}$$

$$E_\theta = \left(\frac{l\sin\theta}{4\pi\varepsilon_0 c^2 r} \right) f''\left(t - \frac{r}{c} \right)$$

$$= \left(\frac{\mu_0 l\sin\theta}{4\pi r} \right) f''\left(t - \frac{r}{c} \right) \tag{19.15b}$$

$$B_\phi = \left(\frac{\mu_0 l\sin\theta}{4\pi rc} \right) f''\left(t - \frac{r}{c} \right) \tag{19.15c}$$

Thus the field at this distance consists of electric and magnetic components, perpendicular to each other, and both perpendicular to the radius, and related by the simple relationship:

$$E_\theta = cB_\phi \tag{19.16}$$

This pattern travels outwards with a velocity c, diminishing in proportion to $(1/r)$; it forms, in fact, 'a travelling electromagnetic wave'. It is this waveform, which made the radio-telegraphy and telephony possible. The Poynting vector shows that it is associated with an outward flow of energy into space.

The Hertzian dipole is not in itself an efficient form of transmitting aerial (or antenna), but its field is the 'brick' from which the fields of practical aerials are built up.

19.2.3   Radiated Power of the Hertzian Dipole Calculated by the Poynting Vector, and the Radiation Resistance

We now apply the Poynting vector to find the energy transmitted from an oscillating dipole. As in the previous sections, the dipole is made up of the charges $\pm q$, where $q = f(t)$, and the charges are separated by a distance l.

At a *great* distance r from the dipole, the electric field was found to be in the θ-direction (i.e. a line of longitude on a sphere concentric with the dipole), and given by the expression:

$$E_\theta = \left(\frac{\mu_0 l}{4\pi} \right) \left(\frac{\sin\theta}{r} \right) f'' \left(t - \frac{r}{c} \right) \tag{19.15b}$$

and the magnetic field lies along a parallel of a latitude, i.e.

$$B_\phi = \left(\frac{\mu_0 l}{4\pi c} \right) \left(\frac{\sin\theta}{r} \right) f'' \left(t - \frac{r}{c} \right) \tag{19.15c}$$

$\therefore$ The Poynting vector is radially outwards,

$$\mathbf{S} = \mathbf{E} \times \mathbf{H}, \quad \text{where } H_\phi = \frac{B_\phi}{\mu}$$

And hence the magnitude of the Poynting vector is

$$S = \left(\frac{\mu_0 l^2}{16\pi^2 c} \right) \left(\frac{\sin\theta}{r} \right)^2 \left[f'' \left(t - \frac{r}{c} \right) \right]^2 \tag{19.17}$$

i.e. a travelling wave of energy in which the direction of flow is never reversed (like in a coaxial cable).

To obtain the total outflow of power from the dipole, we have to integrate over the whole surface of the sphere, concentric with the dipole, as shown in Figure 19.4.

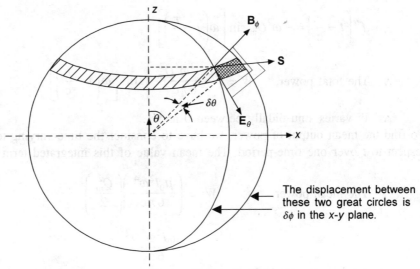

Figure 19.4 Surface of integration around the dipole. Note that the three vectors $\mathbf{E}_\theta$, $\mathbf{B}_\phi$ and $\mathbf{S}$ are mutually orthogonal.

Area of the cross-hatched curvilinear rectangle between the angles θ and $\theta + \delta\theta$, and $\delta\phi$ is $(r\delta\theta)(r\sin\theta\delta\phi)$.

$\therefore$ Area of the circular strip (shown dashed) between the angles θ and $\theta + \delta\theta$, is $(2\pi r \sin\theta)(r\delta\theta)$.

For the complete area covering the whole surface of the enclosing sphere, θ varies from $\theta = 0$ to $\theta = \pi$.

Total power, $\quad W = \int\limits_{\theta=0}^{\theta=\pi} S(2\pi r \sin \theta)(r \, \delta\theta)$

$$= \left(\frac{\mu_0 l^2}{16\pi^2 c}\right)\left[f''\left(t - \frac{r}{c}\right)\right]^2 \int\limits_0^\pi \left(\frac{\sin \theta}{r}\right)^2 2\pi r^2 \sin \theta \, d\theta$$

$$= \left(\frac{\mu_0 l^2}{8\pi c}\right)\left[f''\left(t - \frac{r}{c}\right)\right]^2 \int\limits_0^\pi \sin^3 \theta \, d\theta$$

In this integral, substitute $\cos \theta = x$; $\therefore -\sin \theta \, d\theta = dx$, and the limits are: $\theta = 0 \Rightarrow x = 1$; and $\theta = \pi \Rightarrow x = -1$.

$$\int\limits_0^\pi \sin^3 \theta \, d\theta = \int\limits_{-1}^{+1} (1 - x^2) \, dx = \left(x - \frac{x^3}{3}\right)_{-1}^{+1} = \left(2 - \frac{2}{3}\right) = \frac{4}{3}$$

$$\therefore \qquad\qquad W = \left(\frac{\mu_0 l^2}{6\pi c}\right)\left[f''\left(t - \frac{r}{c}\right)\right]^2$$

Usually $f(t)$ is a function varying sinusoidally with time. Hence, we can write:

$$q = f(t) = Q_m \sin \omega t, \text{ where } Q_m = \text{amplitude of the charge}$$

$$\therefore \quad f''\left(t - \frac{r}{c}\right) = -\omega^2 Q_m \sin\left[\omega\left(t - \frac{r}{c}\right)\right]$$

$\therefore$ The total power, $\quad W = \left(\frac{\mu_0 l^2 \omega^4 Q_m^2}{6\pi c}\right) \sin^2\left[\omega\left(t - \frac{r}{c}\right)\right]$ $\qquad$ (19.18)

$\therefore$ $\quad W$ varies sinusoidally between 0 and 1.

To find the mean output of power, we have to consider the time-varying term and integrate with respect to t over one time-period. The mean value of this integrated term is (1/2).

$\therefore$ The mean power, $\qquad \bar{W} = \left(\frac{\mu_0 l^2 \omega^4}{6\pi c}\right)\left(\frac{Q_m^2}{2}\right)$

$$= \frac{\mu_0 l^2 \omega^4 Q^2}{6\pi c} \qquad\qquad (19.19)$$

where $\left(\dfrac{Q_m}{\sqrt{2}}\right) = Q \leftarrow$ rms value of the time-varying charge.

In the transmitting aerials, it is more common to use the current than the charge. Hence:

The rms (= root mean square) current, $I = \omega Q$

$\therefore$ The mean power, $\qquad \bar{W} = \frac{\mu_0 l^2 \omega^2 I^2}{6\pi c} \qquad\qquad (19.20)$

We substitute for the angular frequency ω,

$$\omega = \frac{2\pi c}{\lambda}, \quad \text{where } \lambda \text{ is the wavelength}$$

$\therefore$ The mean power, $\overline{W} = \left(\frac{\mu_0 l^2}{6\pi c}\right)\left(\frac{4\pi^2 c^2}{\lambda^2}\right) I^2$

$$= \left(\frac{2}{3}\right)\pi Z_0\left(\frac{l^2}{\lambda^2}\right) I^2 = R_e I^2 \tag{19.21}$$

where $\mu_0 c = \sqrt{\mu_0/\varepsilon_0} = Z_0$ (= wave impedance of free space).

R_e (= R_{rad}) is called the *radiation resistance* of the aerial at the wavelength in question.

$$\therefore \quad R_e = \left(\frac{2}{3}\right)\pi Z_0\left(\frac{l^2}{\lambda^2}\right) \tag{19.22}$$

But, $Z_0 = 377\ \Omega$ $\therefore$ $R_e = 790\,\dfrac{l^2}{\lambda^2}$.

Thus the Hertzian dipole is rather inefficient because of the $(l/\lambda)^2$ term as $l \ll \lambda$.

The above expression explains how it is possible for a transmitting aerial to send out power into the surrounding space, and how the process of transmission reacts back upon the source by bringing about an apparent increase in the resistance.

So the Hertz dipole can be considered as a resistance when seen from the input terminals of the antenna [Figure 19.4(a)].

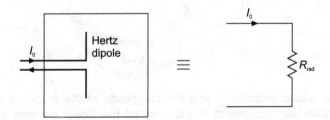

Figure 19.4(a)   Equivalent resistance of the Hertz dipole.

This is quite low for a Hertzian dipole as mentioned above, e.g., for a 0.1λ long dipole, $R_{rad} = 8\ \Omega$ only

Note that E_θ and B_ϕ are in time-phase; and I is not necessarily a constant, but a function of z.

We shall see later that $l = \lambda/2$ is a more efficient choice of an antenna.

19.2.4   Distributions of Potentials, Field Vectors, and the Poynting Vector of the Hertzian Dipole

We have obtained the expressions for the vector and the scalar potentials of the Hertzian dipole (i.e. the oscillating electric dipole) in Section 19.2.1, as:

$$\mathbf{A} = \mathbf{i}_z \left(\frac{\mu_0}{4\pi} \right) \left(\frac{I_0 l}{r} \right) \exp \left[j\omega \left(t - \frac{r}{c} \right) \right] \tag{19.9'}$$

$$V = \left(\frac{l \cos\theta}{4\pi\varepsilon_0} \right) \times \left[\left(\frac{Q_0}{r^2} \right) \exp \left\{ j\omega \left(t - \frac{r}{c} \right) \right\} + \left(\frac{I}{cr} \right) \exp \left\{ j\omega \left(t - \frac{r}{c} \right) \right\} \right] \tag{19.10'}$$

The plots of **A** and V are shown in Figure 19.5. It is seen that the scalar potential V is a maximum at the poles and becomes zero at the equator, where the potentials due to the individual charges $\pm Q$ of the dipole cancel each other. The charge of $+Q$ predominates in the northern hemisphere, and that of $-Q$ in the southern hemisphere. The magnitude of **A** is represented by the sphere marked A (Figure 19.5), and is independent both in direction and magnitude, of the coordinates θ and ϕ.

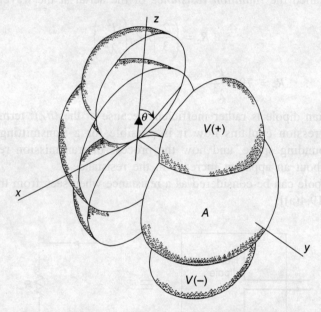

Figure 19.5 The scalar potential V and the magnitude of the magnetic vector potential, i.e. |**A**|, shown as functions of θ and ϕ about the dipole oriented as shown.

The electric lines of force can be obtained on the basis of the consideration that when (r/c) is negligible, the retardation effects can be neglected, and then the **E** vector [i.e. Eqs. (19.11) and (19.12)] collapses to the expressions of the static dipole. Then,

$$\frac{E_r}{dr} = \frac{E_\theta}{r\,d\theta} \tag{19.14'}$$

since an element of a line of force having the components dr and $r\,d\theta$ is parallel to the local **E** having the components E_r and E_θ. To simplify the calculations, an auxiliary vector **C** can be used such that:

$$\mathbf{C} = \mathbf{i}_\phi \left(\frac{Q_0 l}{4\pi\varepsilon_0} \right) \left(\frac{l}{r} + \frac{j\omega}{c} \right) \exp \left[j \left(\omega t - \frac{r}{c} \right) \right] \sin\theta \tag{19.14a'}$$

whence $\mathbf{E} = \nabla \times \mathbf{C}$, so that

$$E_r = \left(\frac{1}{r \sin \theta} \right) \frac{\partial}{\partial \theta} (C \sin \theta) \qquad (19.14b')$$

and

$$E_\theta = \left(-\frac{1}{r} \right) \frac{\partial}{\partial r} (rC) \qquad (19.14c')$$

The differential equation for the lines of force is therefore:

$$\left(\frac{1}{\sin \theta} \right) \frac{\partial}{\partial \theta} (C \sin \theta) = \left(-\frac{1}{r} \right) \frac{\partial}{\partial r} (rC)$$

or

$$\left[\frac{\partial}{\partial \theta} (Cr \sin \theta) \right] d\theta + \left[\frac{\partial}{\partial r} (Cr \sin \theta) \right] dr = 0$$

$$\therefore \quad Cr \sin \theta = \text{constant} \qquad (19.14d')$$

Figure 19.6 shows four families of lines of force of **E** at four instants of time. The magnetic lines of force are much simpler. They are circles, perpendicular to, and centred on the axis of the dipole.

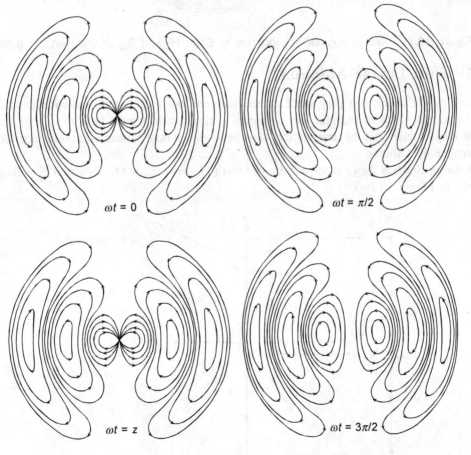

Figure 19.6 Lines of **E** of a Hertzian dipole for $\omega t = 0$, $\pi/2$, π, $3\pi/2$. The dipole is situated at the centre and oriented vertically.

Figure 19.7 shows the polar diagrams (or the angular distributions) of **E** or **H**, and $\mathbf{S}_{av}$ at distances much greater than the dipole wavelength λ. In fact, Eqs. (19.14) and (19.17) show that **E** and **S** vary as $\sin \theta$ and $\sin^2\theta$ respectively; and hence these are effectively plots of these two functions. The Poynting vector varies as $(1/r^2)$, and **E** and **B** vary as $(1/r)$. Since the energy flow varies as $\sin^2\theta$, it is zero along the axis of the dipole, and is maximum in the equatorial plane. So *an electric dipole does not radiate energy along its axis*. Also, the energy flow is radial everywhere.

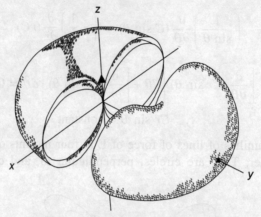

Figure 19.7 Plots of angular distributions of **E** (or **H**) and $\mathbf{S}_{av}$ of the Hertzian dipole.

19.2.5 Thin Linear Antenna

The Hertz dipole which is a very small current element has a very small radiation resistance, and hence is not an efficient radiator. So a logical extrapolation would be a dipole of reasonable physical length, such that the antenna can then be used for both transmission and reception of the electromagnetic radiation.

A linear dipole is then a piece of wire of length $2L$ (say) excited by a current or voltage source as shown in Figure 19.7(a).

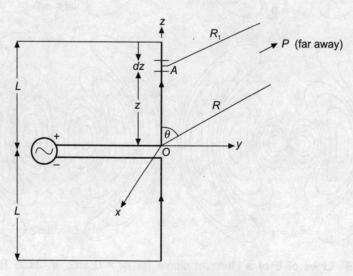

Figure 19.7(a) A linear dipole antenna of length $2L$.

The gap at the centre of the dipole is assumed to be small, and the current spreads over its length only to achieve a steady-state value (or distribution). Finding the current distribution along the antenna is not an easy problem. Once the current distribution is known, the radiation characteristic of the antenna can be predicted. It can be argued that where the wire ends the current will be zero and this antenna can be visualized as a flared-up version of a twin-wire transmission line as shown in Figure 19.7(b).

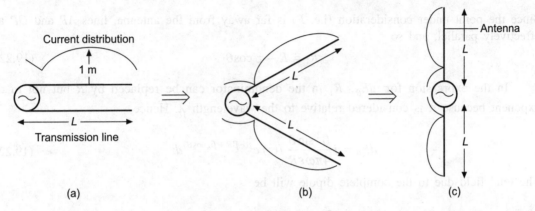

Figure 19.7(b) A dipole antenna as a flared version of a transmission line.

We consider an o.c. section of a transmission line (twin-wire types of length L). The voltage reflection coefficient at the o.c. end is +1, and hence there would be a standing wave along the line. The current at the o.c. end would be zero and its magnitude varies sinusoidally along the length.

The standing wave current distribution on the line

$$\left. \begin{aligned} I(z) &= I_m \sin[\beta(L - |z|)] \\ &= I_m \sin[\beta(L - z)], \quad \text{for } z > 0 \\ I_m &\sin[\beta(L + z)], \quad \text{for } z < 0 \end{aligned} \right\} \tag{19.22a}$$

where

I_m = maximum current amplitude on the line

$\beta = \dfrac{2\pi}{\lambda}$, i.e. the propagation constant in free space

z = distance measured on the line from the generator, +ve on the upper conductor and −ve on the lower conductor.

As the line becomes flared, it becomes a non-uniform transmission line. When the line becomes an antenna, we assume the current distribution to remain unchanged, which rigorously speaking is a questionable assumption. For the analysis, we simplify the current distribution to be sinusoidal [$I \sin(\omega t - \beta r)$]. To evaluate the field due to this linear dipole, the dipole is sub-divided into infinitesimally small current elements, and obtain the field due to each element and then apply the principle of superposition to obtain the field due to the whole dipole. So considering an element dz at a height z with the coordinate system as shown in Figure 19.17(a), the E_θ field can be expressed as [referring to Eq. (19.15b) for the far field components]

$$dE_\theta = j\frac{\beta^2 \sin\theta}{4\pi\omega\varepsilon} \frac{I(z)\,dz\,e^{-j\beta R_1}}{R_1} \qquad (19.22b)$$

and the associated magnetic field

$$dH_\theta = \frac{dE_\theta}{\eta} \qquad (19.22c)$$

Since the point under consideration (i.e. P) is far away from the antenna, lines AP and OP are effectively parallel, and so

$$R_1 = R - z\cos\theta \qquad (19.22d)$$

In the expression for dE_θ, R_1 in the denominator can be replaced by R but not in the exponent because it is considered relative to the wavelength λ. Hence

$$dE_\theta = j\frac{\beta^2 \sin\theta}{4\pi\omega\varepsilon R} I(z)\,e^{j(-\beta R + \beta z\cos\theta)}\,dz \qquad (19.22e)$$

The total field due to the complete dipole will be

$$E_\theta = j\frac{\beta^2 \sin\theta\,e^{-j\beta R}}{4\pi\omega\varepsilon R} \int_{-L}^{L} I(z)\,e^{j\beta z\cos\theta}\,d\theta$$

$$= j60\,I_m\,\frac{e^{-j\beta R}}{R}F(\theta) \qquad (19.22f)$$

where $I(z)$ is as stated earlier, and

$$\frac{\beta^2}{4\pi\omega\varepsilon} = \frac{\omega^2\mu\varepsilon}{4\pi\omega\varepsilon} = \frac{\omega\mu}{4\pi} = \frac{\beta\eta_0}{4\pi} = 30\beta \qquad (19.22g)$$

and

$$F(\theta) = \frac{\cos(\beta L\cos\theta) - \cos(\beta L)}{\sin\theta} \qquad (19.22h)$$

$F(\theta)$ describes the relative variation of the electric field as a function of θ and so it is the E-plane radiation pattern. In the H-plane, E_θ, not being a function of ϕ, is constant. So the H-plane radiation pattern of this dipole is same as that of the Hertzian dipole. But as seen the E-plane pattern is different from that of the Hertzian dipole.

19.3 THE HALF-WAVE ANTENNA

The oscillating dipole discussed so far, is a useful tool for theoretical work, but it is not a practical antenna. The half-wave antenna, shown in Figure 19.8, is simply a straight conductor whose length is half a free-space wavelength. It is fed at the centre (i.e. a current ($I_0 \cos\omega t$) is established at the centre of the dipole) by means of a suitable electronic circuit, and a standing wave is formed along the conductor.

Note: It should be noted that, in many cases, the half-wave antenna is a quarter wavelength mast set vertically on the ground which then behaves like a mirror. The quarter-wave mast and

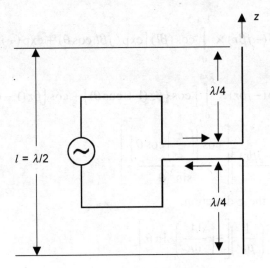

Figure 19.8 Centre-fed half-wave antenna.

its image in the ground then together form a half-wave antenna. Radio broadcast antennae are often of this type. The ground in the neighbourhood of the antenna can be covered with a conducting screen in order to achieve good conductivity.

The standing wave of the current on the conductor is

$$I = I_0 \exp(j\omega t) \cos(\beta l) \tag{19.23a}$$

Each element $(I\,dl)$ of the antenna then radiates an electromagnetic wave similar to that of an electric dipole, and the field at any point in space is the sum of all these fields.

Since the (magnetic) vector potential at any point will be parallel to the direction of the source current in the antenna, the vector potential will have only the z-component (parallel to l).

The vector potential at the point P(r, ϕ, θ) due to the antenna element $(I\,dl)$, at a distance l from the centre-point of the antenna (which is also the origin of our coordinate system) is given by

$$dA_z = \frac{\mu_0 I \exp(-j\beta R)\,dl}{4\pi R} \tag{19.23b}$$

where R is the distance between the point P and the antenna element $(I\,dl)$. Since the distance R to the point of observation is $\gg \lambda$ (we are interested in the far field only), we shall be able to make some simplifications in our analysis as we proceed.

The total vector potential $\mathbf{A}_z$ at P, due to all the current elements in the antenna is

$$A_z = \left(\frac{\mu_0}{4\pi}\right) \int_{-\lambda/4}^{0} I_0 \cos(\beta l) \exp(-j\beta R) \frac{dl}{R} + \left(\frac{\mu_0}{4\pi}\right) \int_{0}^{\lambda/4} I_0 \cos(\beta l) \exp(-j\beta R) \frac{dl}{R} \tag{19.23c}$$

In the denominators, we can approximate $R \approx r$, but for the R in the phase factor of the numerator, the difference between R and r is important. Also, for the large values of R, the two lines R (from the element dl to P) and r (from the centre (the origin) to P) can be considered as parallel lines, and we can write

$$R = r - l \cos\theta \tag{19.24}$$

∴ The above expression for $\mathbf{A}$ simplifies to

$$A_z = \left(\frac{\mu_0 I_0}{4\pi r}\right)\exp(-j\beta r) \times \int_0^{\lambda/4} \cos(\beta l)\left[\exp(j\beta l \cos\theta) + \exp(-j\beta l \cos\theta)\right] dl$$

$$\therefore \qquad A_z = \left(\frac{\mu_0 I_0}{4\pi r}\right)\exp(-j\beta r) \times \int_0^{\lambda/4} \left[\cos\{\beta z(1 + \cos\theta)\} + \cos\{\beta z(1 - \cos\theta)\}\right] dl$$

$$= \left[\frac{\mu_0 I_0 \exp(-j\beta r)}{2\pi\beta r}\right]\left[\frac{\cos\left\{\left(\dfrac{\pi}{2}\right)\cos\theta\right\}}{\sin^2\theta}\right] \qquad (19.25)$$

Since the current is entirely in the z-direction,

$$H_\phi = \left(\frac{1}{\mu_0}\right)\left[-\left(\frac{\partial A_z}{\partial r}\right)\sin\theta\right]$$

$$= \left[\frac{j I_0 \exp(-j\beta r)}{2\pi r}\right]\left[\frac{\cos\left\{\left(\dfrac{\pi}{2}\right)\cos\theta\right\}}{\sin\theta}\right] \qquad (19.26)$$

retaining only $(1/r)$ terms for the larger distances considered.

The electric field strength,

$$E_\theta = Z_0 H_\phi = \left[\frac{j60 I_0 \exp(-j\beta r)}{r}\right]\left[\frac{\cos\left\{\left(\dfrac{\pi}{2}\right)\cos\theta\right\}}{\sin\theta}\right] \qquad (19.27)$$

$\therefore$ The magnitude of the **E** field for the radiation field of a half-wave dipole (or a quarter-wave monopole) is

$$|E_\theta| = \left(\frac{60 I_0}{r}\right)\left[\frac{\cos\left\{\left(\dfrac{\pi}{2}\right)\cos\theta\right\}}{\sin\theta}\right] \qquad \frac{\text{V}}{\text{m}} \qquad (19.28)$$

For $\theta = 0$ and $\theta = \pi$, the expressions for E_θ and H_ϕ become indeterminate, because the trigonometric term becomes $(0/0)$. To evaluate it (using l'Hospital's rule), we get

$$\lim_{\theta \to 0 \text{ or } \pi}\left[\frac{\cos\left\{\left(\dfrac{\pi}{2}\right)\cos\theta\right\}}{\sin\theta}\right] = \frac{\dfrac{d}{d\theta}\left[\cos\left\{\left(\dfrac{\pi}{2}\right)\cos\theta\right\}\right]}{\dfrac{d}{d\theta}(\sin\theta)}\Bigg|_{\theta \to 0 \text{ or } \pi}$$

$$= \frac{\sin\left\{\left(\dfrac{\pi}{2}\right)\cos\theta\right\}\left(\dfrac{\pi}{2}\right)\sin\theta}{\cos\theta}\Bigg|_{\theta \to 0 \text{ or } \pi} \qquad (19.29)$$

$\therefore$ E is zero along the axis of the antenna.

E_θ and H_ϕ are in time-phase, and hence the maximum value (in time) of the Poynting vector is the product of the peak values of E_θ and H_ϕ.

$\therefore$ The average value in time of the Poynting vector (= 1/2 the peak value),

$$\mathbf{S}_{av} = \left(\frac{Z_0 I_0^2}{8\pi^2 r^2}\right)\left[\frac{\cos^2\left\{\left(\dfrac{\pi}{2}\right)\cos\theta\right\}}{\sin^2\theta}\right] \qquad (19.30)$$

It points radially outwards, and varies as $(1/r^2)$, and hence ensures conservation of energy.

The total radiated power is obtained by integrating $\mathbf{S}_{av}$ over a sphere of radius r:

$$W = 9.55\,(I_{rms})^2 \int_0^{2\pi}\int_0^{\pi}\left[\frac{\cos^2\left\{\left(\dfrac{\pi}{2}\right)\cos\theta\right\}}{r^2\sin^2\theta}\right] r^2\sin\theta\, d\theta\, d\phi$$

$$= 60\,(I_{rms})^2 \int_0^{\pi}\left[\frac{\cos^2\left\{\left(\dfrac{\pi}{2}\right)\cos\theta\right\}}{\sin\theta}\right] d\theta \qquad (19.31)$$

by replacing I_0 by its rms value I_{rms}.

In most of the radiation problems, the main difficulty lies in the evaluation of some integral. The above integral can be evaluated in a number of ways. One possible way is to use the substitution,

$$\left(\frac{\pi}{2}\right)\cos\theta = \frac{\alpha}{2} - \frac{\pi}{2} \qquad (19.32)$$

$$\therefore \quad I = \int_0^{\pi}\left[\frac{\cos^2\left\{\left(\dfrac{\pi}{2}\right)\cos\theta\right\}}{\sin\theta}\right] d\theta = \int_0^{2\pi}\left[\frac{1-\cos\alpha}{\alpha(4\pi-2\alpha)}\right] d\alpha \qquad (19.33)$$

Breaking up the fraction:

$$\frac{1}{\alpha(4\pi-2\alpha)} = \left(\frac{1}{4\pi}\right)\left(\frac{1}{\alpha}+\frac{1}{2\pi-\alpha}\right) \qquad (19.34)$$

$$\therefore \quad I = \left(\frac{\pi}{4\pi}\right)\left[\int_0^{2\pi}\left(\frac{1-\cos\alpha}{\alpha}\right) d\alpha + \int_0^{2\pi}\left(\frac{1-\cos\alpha}{2\pi-\alpha}\right) d\alpha\right]$$

$$= \left(\frac{1}{2}\right)\int_0^{2\pi}\left(\frac{1-\cos\alpha}{\alpha}\right) d\alpha = \left(\frac{1}{2}\right)\times 2.4377 \qquad (19.35)$$

by Simpson's rule (numerically).

$$\therefore \quad W = 73.1(I_{rms})^2 \text{ watts} \qquad (19.36)$$

$$R_{rad} = 73.1\ \Omega \qquad (19.37)$$

Thus the radiation resistance of the half-wave antenna is 73.1 Ω, on the basis of the assumption that the current distribution on the antenna is sinusoidal, which however is not quite correct. This is because, the standing wave pattern assumed on the antenna can be truly sinusoidal, only if there is zero energy loss, and hence no radiated wave. But a more rigorous calculation shows nearly the same result as the present approximate idealized calculation. So the present simplified assumption is a justifiable one.

The radiated power by this antenna is also greater in the equatorial plane, compared with the dipole. If we plot the angular distributions of $\mathbf{E}$, $\mathbf{H}$, and the Poynting vector for the half-wave antenna, then the comparable functions are $[\cos\{(\pi/2)\cos\theta\}/\sin\theta]$ for E and $[\cos^2\{(\pi/2)\cos\theta)\}/\sin^2\theta]$ for $\mathbf{S}_{av}$, as against $\sin\theta$ for E and $\sin^2\theta$ for $\mathbf{S}_{av}$ of the Hertzian dipole. The trigonometric functions for the half-wave antenna produce flatter polar diagrams compared with the torii produced by the $\sin\theta$ and $\sin^2\theta$ for the Hertzian dipole (refer to Figure 19.7). The polar diagrams for the half-wave antenna are plotted below in Figure 19.9.

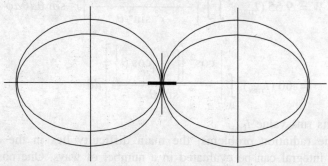

Figure 19.9 Angular plots of $[\cos\{(\pi/2)\cos\theta\}/\sin\theta]$ and $[\cos^2\{(\pi/2)\cos\theta\}/\cos^2\theta]$ showing respectively the angular distributions of $\mathbf{E}$ and $\mathbf{S}_{av}$ for a half-wave antenna at $r \gg \lambda$. The plots are similar to those of the dipole (Figure 19.7) except that these are flatter compared to those of the dipole, indicating a larger fraction of its power in the equatorial plane.

19.3.1 Quarter-wave Monopole Antenna

Since at low frequencies, the wavelength becomes too large, the length of the dipole antenna also becomes large. So at medium frequencies (wavelength approximately hundreds of metres), the dipole antenna is not a viable choice. So a quarter-wave monopole antenna consisting of one-half of a half-wave dipole, normal to a conducting ground plane is used. The base plane is assumed to be infinite and perfectly conducting. A co-axial cable connected to its base, feeds it.

A monopole antenna of length L is shown here, and a voltage has been applied between the bottom of the antenna and the ground. By using the image theory, the infinite, perfectly conducting ground plane is replaced by the image of the monopole. The field produced in the region above the ground plane, by the $\lambda/4$ monopole and its image is same as the field produced by a $\lambda/2$ dipole. For calculating the radiated power, the limit of integration in Eq. (19.31) should be replaced by $\theta = 0$ to $\theta = \pi/2$, as the monopole radiates only through the upper hemispherical surface. Thus the monopole radiates only half the power radiated by the dipole with the same current. Hence

$$P_{rad} = 18.28 I_0^2 \quad \text{and} \quad R_{rad} = \frac{2P_{rad}}{I_0^2} \quad \text{or} \quad R_{rad} = 36.5\ \Omega$$

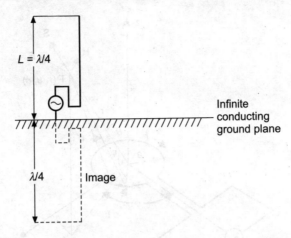

Figure 19.9(a) The monopole antenna. (Its image is also shown in the figure.)

Thus, in spite of the similarity, the following points should be borne in mind while analyzing a monopole antenna.

1. The radiation from a monopole is in the semi-infinite half-space as distinct from a dipole which radiates in the infinite space. Hence the range of θ in the monopole is from 0 to $\pi/2$ and for the dipole θ varies from 0 to π.
2. For identical currents in a monopole and the corresponding dipole, the radiated power by the monopole is only half of that radiated by the corresponding dipole.
3. Since the radiated power of a monopole is half of that radiated by the corresponding dipole for the same current, the input impedance of the monopole is half of the dipole.

19.4   THE MAGNETIC DIPOLE RADIATION

The static magnetic dipole has already been studied in Section 8.2.1, where we considered a circular current loop of radius a, and carrying a current I; and was found to have a vector potential $\mathbf{A}$ at a point $P(r, \phi, \theta)$ from the centre of the dipole, as

$$\mathbf{A}_\phi = \mathbf{i}_\phi \left(\frac{\mu_0 I \pi a^2 \sin \theta}{4 \pi r^2} \right) = \mathbf{i}_\phi \left(\frac{\mu_0 IS \sin \theta}{4 \pi r^2} \right)$$

$$= \mathbf{i}_\phi \left(\frac{\mu_0 m \sin \theta}{4 \pi r^2} \right) = \frac{\mu_0 \mathbf{m} \times \mathbf{u}}{4 \pi r^2} \tag{8.11}$$

where the magnetic moment of the loop (or the dipole) was:

$$\mathbf{m} = \mathbf{i}_z IS, \text{ and } \mathbf{u} = \text{the unit vector in the direction of } \mathbf{r}$$

We now consider a magnetic dipole, as shown in Figure 19.10.

The vector potential at a point $P(r, \theta, \phi)$ or (x, y, z) as shown in Figure 19.10, is the vector sum of the potential due to each element $(I dl)$ of the dipole loop, i.e.

$$\mathbf{A} = \left(\frac{\mu_0 I}{4 \pi} \right) \oint \frac{d\mathbf{l}}{r'} \tag{19.38}$$

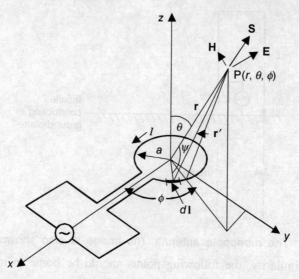

Figure 19.10   Magnetic dipole antenna fed by an oscillator.

where r' is the distance of the point P from the element under consideration. It can be easily seen that, in the loop, for any given value of r', there are two symmetrical $d\mathbf{l}$ vectors, such that their y-components add up and the x-components cancel.

$$\therefore \qquad \mathbf{A} = \left[\left(\frac{\mu_0 I}{4\pi}\right)\int_0^{2\pi}\frac{a\,d\phi'\cos\phi'}{r}\right]\mathbf{i}_\phi \qquad (19.39)$$

where ϕ' is the ϕ-coordinate of the element $(I\,dl)$ under consideration; and ψ is the angle between the radius vector a of the current element $(I\,dl)$ and r' (the distance between the point P and the element under consideration).

Now,
$$r'^2 = r^2 + a^2 - 2ra\cos\psi$$

$$\therefore \qquad \frac{r}{r'} = \left[1 - \frac{a^2}{r'^2} + \frac{2ar}{r^2}\cos\psi\right]^{1/2}$$

$$\simeq 1 - \frac{a^2}{2r'^2} + \frac{a}{r}\cos\psi$$

since $a \ll r'$, and $(r/r') \approx 1$, and hence we can substitute r for r' in the denominators of the two correction terms on the right-hand side. Now consider $(\mathbf{r} \cdot \mathbf{a})$, $\mathbf{a}$ being the vector radius at the element under consideration.

$$(\mathbf{r} \cdot \mathbf{a}) = (\mathbf{i}_x x + \mathbf{i}_y y + \mathbf{i}_z z) \cdot [(a\cos\phi')\mathbf{i}_x + (a\sin\phi')\mathbf{i}_y]$$

$$= xa\cos\phi' + ya\sin\phi' = ra\cos\psi$$

$$\therefore \qquad \cos\psi = \left(\frac{x}{r}\right)\cos\phi' + \left(\frac{y}{r}\right)\sin\phi'$$

$$\therefore \qquad \frac{r}{r'} = 1 - \frac{a^2}{2r^2} + \left(\frac{ax}{r^2}\right)\cos\phi' + \left(\frac{ay}{r^2}\right)\sin\phi' \qquad (19.40)$$

Now, for the 'oscillating magnetic dipole', we have to consider the retardation effect, i.e.

$$A_P = \left(\frac{\mu_0}{4\pi}\right) \int_0^{2\pi} \left(\frac{1}{r'}\right) \left[I_0 \exp\left\{j\omega\left(t - \frac{r'}{c}\right)\right\}\right] a \cos\phi'\, d\phi' \tag{19.41}$$

$$= \frac{\mu_0 a I_0 \exp\left\{j\omega\left(t - \dfrac{r}{c}\right)\right\}}{4\pi} \int_0^{2\pi} \left(\frac{1}{r'}\right) \exp\left(\frac{j\omega(r - r')}{c}\right) \cos\phi'\, d\phi'$$

Since the loop is quite small compared with the wavelength, i.e.

$$|(r - r')| \ll \frac{\lambda}{2\pi}, \text{ then:}$$

$$\exp\left\{\frac{j\omega(r - r')}{c}\right\} \simeq 1 + j\left(\frac{\omega}{c}\right)(r - r')$$

$$\therefore \quad \mathbf{A} = \mathbf{i}_\phi \left[\frac{\mu_0 a I_0 \exp\left\{j\omega\left(t - \dfrac{r}{c}\right)\right\}}{4\pi r}\right] \times \int_0^{2\pi} \left(\frac{r}{r'}\right)\left[1 + j\left(\frac{\omega}{c}\right)(r - r')\right] \cos\phi'\, d\phi'$$

The integral $= \displaystyle\int_0^{2\pi} \left[\frac{r}{r'} + j\left(\frac{\omega r}{c}\right)\left(\frac{r}{r'} - 1\right)\right] \cos\phi'\, d\phi'$

$$= \int_0^{2\pi} \left[\left\{1 - \frac{a^2}{2r^2} + \left(\frac{ax}{r^2}\right)\cos\phi' + \left(\frac{ay}{r^2}\right)\sin\phi'\right\}\right.$$

$$\left. + j\left(\frac{\omega r}{c}\right)\left\{-\frac{a^2}{2r^2} + \left(\frac{ax}{r^2}\right)\cos\phi' + \left(\frac{ay}{r^2}\right)\sin\phi'\right\}\cos\phi'\right]\, d\phi'$$

$$= \left(\frac{ax}{r^2}\right)\pi + j\left(\frac{\omega r}{c}\right)\left(\frac{ax}{r^2}\right)\pi$$

$$\therefore \quad \mathbf{A} = \mathbf{i}_\phi \left(\frac{\mu_0 I_0 \pi a^2}{4\pi r^2}\right) \exp\left\{j\omega\left(t - \frac{r}{c}\right)\right\}\left\{1 + j\left(\frac{\omega r}{c}\right)\right\}\sin\theta \tag{19.42}$$

where $x = r \sin\theta$.

$$\therefore \quad \mathbf{A} = \mathbf{i}_\phi \left[\frac{\mu_0 m_0 \exp\left\{j\omega\left(t - \dfrac{r}{c}\right)\right\}}{4\pi r^2}\right]\left\{1 + j\left(\frac{\omega r}{c}\right)\right\}\sin\theta$$

$$= \mathbf{i}_\phi \left[\frac{\mu_0 [\mathbf{m}_0] \times \mathbf{r}_1}{4\pi r^2}\right]\left\{1 + j\left(\frac{\omega r}{c}\right)\right\} \tag{19.43}$$

where m_0 is the magnetic moment of the dipole $= I_0\pi a^2 = I_0 S$; and $[\mathbf{m}_0]$ is the retarded value of the moment; and $\mathbf{r}_1$ is the unit vector in the direction of r.

When $\omega = 0$, Eq. (19.43) reduces to the magnetic vector potential of the static dipole, i.e.

$$\mathbf{A} = \mathbf{i}_\phi r^2 \left[\left(\frac{\mu_0}{4\pi} \right) \left(\frac{\mathbf{m} \times \mathbf{r}_1}{r^2} \right) \right] \qquad (19.44)$$

Since there is no static charge in the dipole, $V = 0$. $\qquad (19.45)$

And, hence the Lorentz gauge simplifies to:

$$\text{div } \mathbf{A} = \nabla \cdot \mathbf{A} = 0 \qquad (19.46)$$

19.4.1 E and H Vectors of the Oscillating Magnetic Dipole

$$\mathbf{H} = \left(\frac{1}{\mu_0} \right) \nabla \times \mathbf{A}$$

$\therefore \qquad H_r = \left(\frac{1}{\mu_0 r \sin\theta} \right) \left(\frac{\partial}{\partial\theta} \right) (A_\phi \sin\theta)$

$$= \left[\frac{m_0 \exp\left\{ j\omega\left(t - \dfrac{r}{c} \right) \right\}}{2\pi r^3} \right] \left[1 + j\left(\frac{\omega r}{c} \right) \right] \cos\theta \qquad (19.47)$$

$H_\theta = -\left(\frac{1}{\mu_0 r} \right) \left(\frac{\partial}{\partial r} \right) (rA_\phi)$

$$= -\left(\frac{m_0}{4\pi r} \right) \left(\frac{\partial}{\partial r} \right) \left[\exp\left\{ j\omega\left(t - \frac{r}{c} \right) \right\} \left\{ \left(\frac{1}{r} \right) + j\left(\frac{\omega}{c} \right) \right\} \right] \sin\theta$$

$$= -\left(\frac{m_0}{4\pi r} \right) \times \left[-j\left(\frac{\omega}{c} \right) \left\{ \frac{1}{r} + j\left(\frac{\omega}{c} \right) \right\} - \left(\frac{1}{r^2} \right) \right] \left[\exp\left\{ j\omega\left(t - \frac{r}{c} \right) \right\} \right] \sin\theta$$

$$= \left[\frac{m_0 \exp\left\{ j\omega\left(t - \dfrac{r}{c} \right) \right\}}{4\pi r^3} \right] \left[-\left(\frac{\omega^2 r^2}{c^2} \right) + 1 + j\left(\frac{\omega r}{c} \right) \right] \sin\theta \qquad (19.48)$$

$$\mathbf{E} = -\left(\frac{\partial \mathbf{A}}{\partial t} \right) - \nabla V = -\left(\frac{\partial \mathbf{A}}{\partial t} \right)$$

$$= \mathbf{i}_\phi \left[\frac{\mu_0 m_0 \exp\left\{ j\omega\left(t - \dfrac{r}{c} \right) \right\}}{4\pi r^3} \right] \left\{ j\omega - \left(\frac{\omega^2 r}{c} \right) \right\} \sin\theta \qquad (19.49)$$

Since the scalar potential is zero, $\mathbf{E}$ is hence due to the changing magnetic field. $\mathbf{H}$ lies in a plane passing through the z-axis, whereas $\mathbf{E}$ is azimuthal.

At $\omega = 0$, $\mathbf{H}$ reduces to that of a static magnetic dipole, and $\mathbf{E} = 0$.

If we compare the $\mathbf{E}$ and the $\mathbf{H}$ fields of the magnetic and the electric dipoles, it is seen that the fields of the two are similar, except that the expressions for $\mathbf{E}$ and $\mathbf{H}$ are interchanged.

19.4.2   Poynting Vector and the Radiated Power of the Oscillating Magnetic Dipole

For $r \gg \lambda$,

$$H_r = 0 \tag{19.50a}$$

$$H_\theta = -\left[\left(\frac{m_0 \omega^2}{4\pi r c^2}\right) \sin\theta\right] \exp\left\{j\omega\left(t - \frac{r}{c}\right)\right\} \tag{19.50b}$$

$$E_\phi = \left[\left(\frac{\mu_0 m_0 \omega^2}{4\pi r c}\right) \sin\theta\right] \exp\left\{j\omega\left(t - \frac{r}{c}\right)\right\} \tag{19.50c}$$

$$\therefore \quad \overline{\mathbf{S}}_{av} = \mathbf{i}_r \left(\frac{\mu_0 \omega^4 m_0^2}{32\pi^2 r^2 c^3}\right) \sin^2\theta \tag{19.51}$$

The total radiated power W is obtained by integrating $\mathbf{S}_{av}$ over the surface of a sphere of radius r, i.e.

$$W = \frac{\mu_0 \omega^4 m_0^2}{32\pi^2 c^3} \int\limits_0^{2\pi} \int\limits_0^{\pi/2} \left(\frac{\sin\theta}{r^2}\right) r^2 \sin\theta \, d\theta \, d\phi$$

$$= \left(\frac{\mu_0 \omega^4 m_0^2}{32\pi^2 c^3}\right)(2\pi)\left(\frac{4}{3}\right) = \frac{\mu_0 \omega^4 m_0^2}{12\pi c^3}$$

Substituting $\dfrac{\omega}{c} = \dfrac{2\pi}{\lambda}$, and $m_0 = I_0 \pi a^2$,

$$W = \left(\frac{\mu_0 c}{12\pi}\right)\left(\frac{2\pi}{\lambda}\right)^4 (I_0 \pi a^2)^2 = \left(\frac{\mu_0 c\pi}{12}\right)\left(\frac{2\pi a}{\lambda}\right)^4 I_0^2 \tag{19.52}$$

The radiation resistance is the coefficient of $\left(\dfrac{I_0^2}{2}\right)$.

$$\therefore \quad R_{rad} = 197\left(\frac{2\pi a}{\lambda}\right)^4 \Omega, \quad a \ll \frac{\lambda}{2\pi} \tag{19.53}$$

Thus the radiation resistance of the magnetic dipole is proportional to the 4th power of the frequency, whereas that of the electric dipole is proportional to the square of the frequency. This dipole is the basis for loop antenna.

It will be noticed that E_ϕ given by Eq. (19.50) is a maximum, when $\theta = (\pi/2)$, i.e. in the plane of the loop. Hence, by the reciprocity theorem (which we shall study later in this chapter), the signal received by a loop will be a maximum when the plane of the loop passes through the transmitter. This property is used in the loop antenna which is fitted to the aircraft and to the ships to locate their positions by taking bearings on the radio beacons at known places.

19.4.3 Electric and Magnetic Quadrupoles

We now go on to study the more elaborate types of radiation produced by quadrupoles. We first study the linear electric quadrupole which consists of two dipoles of opposite polarity arranged in a line to give three charges $+q$, $-2q$, $+q$, at distances l from each other. The dipole moment of such charge distribution is zero (i.e. $m = \Sigma (Q_m l) = 0$, where $q = f(t) = Q_m \sin \omega t$, Q_m being the amplitude of the charge). Its quadrupole moment is $m_{00} = \Sigma (Q_m l^2) = 2Q_m l^2$.

Since the dipole moment is zero, there will be no dipole radiation, but as there are time-varying charges, there will be radiation of some sort which would be the subject of our investigation. We can proceed exactly as for the electric dipole radiation, and calculate as before the quantities V, A, E, and H. However, it is easier to add the fields of the component dipoles as indicated below; and for simplicity we consider the radiation field components at large distances ($r \gg \lambda$, i.e. the far field). There are two dipoles now, one with the moment $[-m_0 \exp(j\omega t)]$ centred at $(-l/2)$, and another with the moment $[+m_0 \exp(j\omega t)]$ centred at $(+l/2)$. The electric field intensities of the two dipoles can be added vectorially (by the principle of superposition). Since the two dipoles (forming the quadrupole) are located at some distance away from the origin of the coordinate system, their field intensities at a point P(r, θ, ϕ) will differ slightly in direction, in amplitude, and in phase. However for the far field (when $r \gg l$), the differences in direction and in amplitude may easily be neglected, but not in phase. Hence, for each dipole at the origin,

$$\mathbf{E}_\theta = \mathbf{i}_\theta \left[-\left(\frac{m_0 \omega^2}{4\pi\varepsilon_0 c^2 r} \right) \sin\theta \exp\left\{ j\omega\left(t - \frac{r}{c} \right) \right\} \right] \qquad \text{[from Eq. (19.15a)]}$$

For the quadrupole,

$$\mathbf{E}_\theta = \mathbf{i}_\theta \left[-\left(\frac{m_0 \omega^2}{4\pi\varepsilon_0 c^2 r} \right) \sin\theta \exp\left\{ j\omega\left(t - \frac{r}{c} \right) \right\} \right] \times \left[\exp\left\{ j\left(\frac{\omega l}{2c} \right) \right\} \cos\theta - \exp\left\{ -j\left(\frac{\omega l}{2c} \right) \right\} \cos\theta \right]$$

These two exponential functions can be expanded in power series in $(\omega l/c)$ for the far field, and then their sum reduces to $j(\omega l/c) \cos\theta$.

$$\therefore \quad \mathbf{E}_\theta = \mathbf{i}_\theta \left[-j \left(\frac{m_0 \omega^3}{8\pi\varepsilon_0 c^3 r} \right) \sin\theta \cos\theta \exp\left\{ j\omega\left(t - \frac{r}{c} \right) \right\} \right] \quad \text{for } r \gg \lambda \gg l \qquad (19.15a')$$

There can be no radiation along the axis $\theta = 0$ or $= \pi$, where neither of the two dipoles forming the quadrupole radiate energy. Also along the equator $\theta = \pi/2$, there would be zero radiation as the two dipoles produce equal and opposite fields on this plane.

The magnetic field intensity can be found directly from the E field as

$$\mathbf{H}_\phi = \mathbf{i}_\phi \, E_\theta \left(\frac{\mu_0}{\varepsilon_0} \right)^{-1/2}$$

Next, we consider an oscillating magnetic quadrupole which can be formed from two oscillating magnetic dipole loops placed parallel to each other on either side of the origin of the coordinate system. For the simplest case, we assume the distance between the two loops to be equal to the radius (= a) of the loop. The lower dipole is centred at $z = -a/2$ and has a moment, $-m_0 \exp(j\omega t)$, whereas the upper dipole is located at $z = +a/2$ and has a moment, $+m_0 \exp(j\omega t)$. This arrangement is very similar to that of the linear electric quadrupole discussed in the earlier part of this section.

Once again, the fields of the two magnetic dipoles can be added up, neglecting the differences in direction and amplitude, but taking into account the difference in phase or retardation. This is done by multiplying the dipole field by $j(a\omega/2\pi c) \cos \theta$,

$$H_\theta = -\left[j\left(\frac{m_0 a\omega^3}{8\pi^2 rc^3} \right) \sin\theta \cos\theta \right] \exp\left\{ j\omega\left(t - \frac{r}{c} \right) \right\} \tag{19.50b'}$$

$$E_\phi = \left[j\left(\frac{\mu_0 m_0 a\omega^3}{8\pi^2 rc^2} \right) \sin\theta \cos\theta \right] \exp\left\{ j\omega\left(t - \frac{r}{c} \right) \right\} \quad \text{for } r \gg \lambda \gg a \tag{19.50c'}$$

19.4.4 Antenna Characteristics (Radiation Parameters)

So far we have considered the theory of some of the basic elementary antenna types. Now we shall discuss some of the important characteristics of an antenna as radiator of electromagnetic energy. These are stated as below.

(A) An Antenna Pattern (or Radiation Pattern)

This is a three-dimensional plot of its radiation at far field. So this parameter describes the directional dependence of the radiated power of the antenna.

The plot of the amplitude of a specified component of the E-field is called its field pattern, the plot of square of the amplitude of E is its power pattern. A three-dimensional plot can be avoided by plotting separately the normalized $|E|$ against θ for a given ϕ (in spherical polar coordinate system). This is called E-plane pattern or vertical pattern. When $\phi = \pi \times 2$, the pattern is called H-plane pattern or horizontal pattern. The normalization of E is done with respect to maximum value of E.

For Hertzian dipole, from Eqs. (19.14a) and (19.14b), it is seen that

$$f(\theta) = \sin\theta \tag{19.53a}$$

and the polar or angular plot will be as shown in Figures 19.10(a), (b) and (c).

In general, a radiation pattern has a direction of maximum radiation as shown in the polar plot of Figure 19.10(d). This is the main lobe. There are certain directions along which there is no radiation. Such directions are called nulls. There are also certain directions along which the radiation has a local maximum and these are called 'side lobes'.

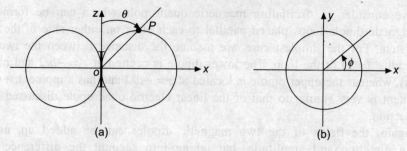

Figure 19.10(a) and (b) Field patterns of the Hertzian dipole:
(a) normalized *E*-plane, $\phi = 0$; (b) normalized *H*-plane, $\theta = \pi/2$.

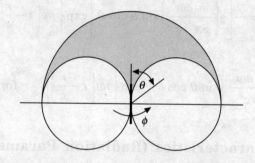

Figure 19.10(c) Three-dimensional pattern.

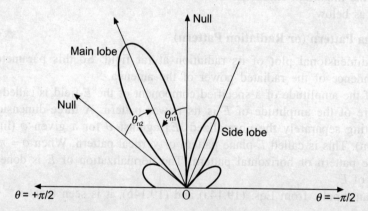

Figure 19.10(d) Radiation pattern as a polar plot.

Direction of the main beam: This is the direction along which the radiation field strength is maximum, and is denoted by Q_{max}.

Half-power beam width (HPBW): The angular region, where the effective radiation from the antenna goes, is the main beam.

The effective width of the main beam = the angular width of the pattern between the points on the radiation pattern where the magnitude of the field reduces to $\dfrac{|E_{max}|}{\sqrt{2}}$, E_{max} being the maximum field.

From Figure 19.10(e),

$$\text{HPBW} = \theta_1 - \theta_2 \tag{19.53b}$$

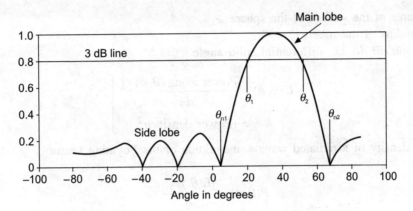

Figure 19.10(e)   Cartesian plot of the radiation pattern.

Since the field in the directions of θ_1 and θ_2 reduces by a factor of $\dfrac{1}{\sqrt{2}}$ of $E_{\max}$, the Poynting vector in these directions reduces to 1/2 or −3 dB compared to its value in the direction of maximum radiation. (HPBW is also referred to as '3 dB beam width' of the antenna). HPBWs are generally measured in the planes of E and H.

Beam width between first nulls (BWFN):   Sometimes, the width of the main beam is measured by the angular separation between the first nulls on either side of the direction of the main lobe.

$$\therefore \qquad\qquad \text{BWFN} = \theta_{n2} - \theta_{n1} \tag{19.53c}$$

However HPBW is a better measure of the effective width of the main beam as the shape of the main beam can change while keeping the null positions unchanged.

Side lobe level (SLL):   Side lobes indicate the leakage of power in the undesired directions. Ideally there should be no radiation outside the main beam. But in any practical antenna, there are side lobes and the total radiated power is not focussed into the main beam. So this leakage is to be kept minimal, i.e. the side lobe amplitude should be kept as small as possible compared to the main beam amplitude. For good satellite antennae, the SLL is generally −30 dB to −40 dB. When we move away from the main beam, the amplitudes of the side lobes decrease and hence the first side lobe usually defines the SLL.

(B)   Radiation Intensity

We know that the radiation pattern (of an antenna) is a three-dimensional surface and the radiation intensity is, in general, a function of θ and ϕ and is given by

$$U(\theta, \phi) = \frac{\text{Power along the direction } (\theta, \phi) \text{ in a solid angle } d\Omega}{\text{Solid angle } (d\Omega)} \tag{19.53d}$$

The solid angle on the surface of a sphere,

$$d\Omega = \frac{dA}{r^2} \tag{19.53e}$$

where

dA = area of the surface of the sphere

r = radius of the sphere

$d\Omega = \sin\theta \, d\theta \, d\phi$, i.e. differential solid angle

$$\therefore \qquad \left. \begin{aligned} U(\theta, \phi) &= \frac{\text{Power along } (\theta, \phi)}{dA} r^2 \\ &= (\text{Power density}) r^2 \end{aligned} \right\} \tag{19.53f}$$

Now, power density of a radiated wave = magnitude of the Poynting vector

i.e. $$P(\theta, \phi) = \frac{\left|E(\theta, \phi)\right|^2}{\eta} \tag{19.53g}$$

(η = intrinsic impedance of the medium)

$$\therefore \qquad U(\theta, \phi) = \frac{\left|E(\theta, \phi)\right|^2}{\eta} r^2 = P(\theta, \phi) r^2 \tag{19.53h}$$

The total power radiated ($= P_{rad}$) can be obtained by integrating the radiation intensity over the total solid angle ($= 4\pi$), i.e.

$$P_{rad} = \iint\limits_{\Omega = 4\pi} U(\theta, \phi) \, d\Omega = \int\limits_{\theta=0}^{\pi} \int\limits_{\phi=0}^{2\pi} U(\theta, \phi) \sin\theta \, d\theta \, d\phi \tag{19.53i}$$

Hence the average radiation intensity

$$U_{av} = \frac{P_{rad}}{4\pi} = \frac{1}{4\pi} \iint U(\theta, \phi) \, d\Omega \tag{19.53j}$$

(C) Directive Gain and Directivity

The radiation focussing capability of an antenna is quantified by the parameter 'directivity'. So as a first step in this process we define a parameter called its 'directive gain'. So, the **Directive Gain** $G_D (\theta, \phi)$ of an antenna is a measure of the concentration of the radiated power in specified direction (θ, ϕ). It is thus the measure of the ability of the antenna to direct the radiated power in a given direction.

So it is the ratio of the radiation intensity in a given direction (θ, ϕ) to the average radiation intensity, i.e.

$$G_D(\theta, \phi) = \frac{U(\theta, \phi)}{U_{av}}$$

$$= \frac{4\pi \, U(\theta, \phi)}{\displaystyle\iint U(\theta, \phi) \, d\Omega} = \frac{4\pi \, U(\theta, \phi)}{P_{rad}} \tag{19.53k}$$

So $P(\theta, \phi)$ can be expressed in terms of the directive gain as

$$P(\theta, \phi) = \frac{G_D}{4\pi r^2} P_{rad} \qquad (19.53l)$$

The directive gain $G_D(\theta, \phi)$ depends on antenna pattern. For Hertzian dipole and also for $\lambda/2$ dipole, $P(\theta, \phi)$ is maximum for $\theta = \pi/2$, and minimum (i.e. = 0) at $\theta = 0$ or π. So the Hertzian dipole radiates power in a direction broadside its length.

In general G_D can vary from 0 to ∞. In the direction of the nulls, $E(\theta, \phi)$ and hence $U(\theta, \phi)$ and $G(\theta, \phi)$ are zero, whereas G_D is maximum in the direction of the main beam.

So now we define directivity:

The directivity D of an antenna is the ratio of the maximum radiation intensity to the average radiation intensity.

Thus the directivity D is the maximum directive gain.

$$\therefore \qquad \left. \begin{array}{l} D = \dfrac{U_{max}}{U_{av}} = G_{D\,max} \\[4mm] \text{or} \\[4mm] D = \dfrac{4\pi\, U_{max}}{P_{rad}} = \dfrac{4\pi\, U_{max}}{\displaystyle\iint U(\theta,\phi)\, d\Omega} \end{array} \right\} \qquad (19.53m)$$

Thus $D = 1$ for an isotropic antenna (which does not exist physically and is an ideal reference).

So,

$$D = \frac{4\pi E_{max}^2}{\displaystyle\int_{\theta=0}^{\pi} \int_{\phi=0}^{2\pi} \left|E_{\theta,\phi}\right|^2 \sin\theta\, d\theta\, d\phi} \qquad (19.53n)$$

Namalizing the radiation pattern as $E_n(\theta, \phi) = \dfrac{E(\theta, \phi)}{E_{max}}$, D can be rewritten as

$$D = \frac{4\pi}{\displaystyle\int_{\theta=0}^{\pi} \int_{\phi=0}^{2\pi} \left|E_n(\theta, \phi)\right| \sin\theta\, d\theta\, d\phi} \qquad (19.53p)$$

For a Hertzian dipole, $\qquad\quad G_D(\theta, \phi) = 1.5 \sin^2\theta, \quad D = 1.5$

For a $\lambda/2$ dipole, $\qquad\quad G_D(\theta,\phi) = \dfrac{\eta}{\pi R_{rad}} f^2(\theta), \quad D = 1.64 \qquad\qquad (19.53q)$

where $\eta = 120\pi$, $\quad R_{rad} = 73\ \Omega$, $\quad$ and $\quad f(\theta) = \dfrac{\cos\left(\dfrac{\pi}{2}\cos\theta\right)}{\sin\theta}$

(D) Antenna Gain or Power Gain

As seen above, the parameter directivity depends totally on the radiation pattern. An implicit assumption in this discussion, has been that the total power radiated P_{rad}, is same as the power supplied to the antenna input. In actual practice, the antennae are made out of conductors having finite resistivity (or conductivity), and so when there is a current flow in the antenna surface, there is an ohmic loss. So a part of the power supplied to the antenna input is lost in the heating of the antenna due to the ohmic loss. So if P_i is the power supplied to the antenna input, then

$$P_i = P_{rad} + P_l \tag{19.53r}$$

where P_l is the ohmic loss in the antenna due to its finite conductivity.

$$\therefore \qquad P_i = \frac{1}{2} |I_{in}|^2 (R_l + R_{rad}) \tag{19.53s}$$

where

I_{in} = current at the input terminals

R_l = loss or ohmic resistance of the antenna.

So we define the power efficiency ($= \eta_r$) of the antenna as

$$\eta = \frac{P_{rad}}{P_i} = \frac{P_i - P_l}{P_i} = \frac{P_{rad}}{P_{rad} + P_l} \tag{19.53t}$$

And the antenna power gain ($= G_P$) is defined as

$$\left. \begin{aligned} G_P(\theta, \phi) &= \frac{U_{max}(\text{actual})}{U_{av} \text{ for a loss-less case}} \\ &= \frac{4\pi U_{max}(\text{actual})}{P_i} \\ &= \frac{4\pi U_{max}(\text{actual})}{P_{rad}} \cdot \frac{P_{rad}}{P_i} = D\eta_r \end{aligned} \right\} \tag{19.53u}$$

Thus

$$\text{Power Gain} = \text{Directivity} \times \text{Efficiency} \tag{19.53v}$$

19.5 ANTENNA ARRAYS

19.5.1 Directional Properties of Antennae

The antennae have two main functions. The first job is to radiate the high frequency energy which has been generated in the transmitter, and then guided to the antenna by the transmission line. In this process, the antenna is acting as an impedance matching device whereby it matches the impedance of the transmission line to that of the free space. The second job of the antenna is to direct the energy to the required directions and to suppress the energy from those directions where it is not required.

In general, a completely omni-directional (i.e. non-directional) radiator radiates energy uniformly in all directions. Such a device is called an isotropic radiator or a unipole, an example of this being a point source of sound. Since all radio antennae have some directivity, there is no isotropic radiator of electromagnetic energy. However, conceptually such a hypothetical source can still be used as a standard of reference for comparing with actual devices.

The radiation pattern of an antenna is a graphical representation of the radiation of the antenna as a function of the direction. The radiation can be expressed either in terms of the field-strength (i.e. **E** in volts/metre) or in terms of the power per unit solid angle. The power pattern is proportional to the square of the field strength pattern. The coordinate system, generally used for specifying the radiation patterns is the spherical polar coordinate system (r, θ, ϕ). The antenna is usually located at or near the origin of the coordinate system, and the field strength is specified at points on the spherical surface of radius r. So long as r is chosen such that $r \gg \lambda$ and also $\gg$ the largest dimension of the antenna system, the shape of the radiation pattern is independent of r. For the radiation field, **E** is always tangential to the spherical surface. For a vertical dipole, **E** is in the θ-direction; and for a horizontal loop, **E** is in the ϕ-direction. In general, there may be both E_θ and E_ϕ components which may or may not be in time-phase. In this case, the characteristics are shown by separate patterns for θ- and ϕ-polarizations, instead of the older vertical and horizontal polarizations respectively. The older denominations were somewhat confusing, because the θ- or the vertical polarization does not rigorously mean that the signal is vertical (though the signal does lie in a vertical plane through the radius vector), whilst the ϕ- or the horizontally polarized signal is always horizontal.

The half-wave wire antenna which we have studied so far, is directive, in the sense that most of its radiation is in the direction for which $\theta > 60°$, but it does not discriminate between the azimuthal directions. To produce a preferred direction in the equatorial plane, it is necessary to replace the single antenna by a group or an array of antennae suitably spaced and excited. So we define an 'antenna array' as a system of similar antennae, similarly oriented. The arrays make use of the wave-interference phenomena which take place between the radiations from the different elements of the array. We shall consider first, the simplest two-element array.

19.5.2 Two Element Array

We consider the simplest array in which two half-wave antennae (with their axes parallel to the z-axis) are spaced apart $\lambda/2$, and are excited in phase. The antennae are parallel and lie in the x-z plane, as shown in Figure 19.11. The point of interest P is (r, θ, ϕ) such that $r \gg \lambda$.

The **E** field due to each antenna is given by Eq. (19.27) which we can rewrite as

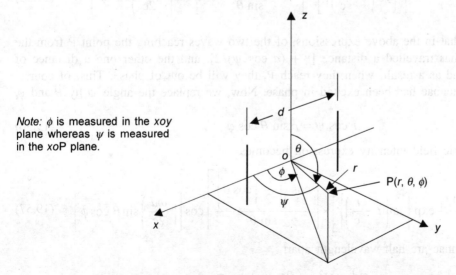

Note: ϕ is measured in the *xoy* plane whereas ψ is measured in the *xoP* plane.

Figure 19.11 A pair of parallel half-wave antennae, *d* metres apart.

$$E_\theta = \left[\frac{j\,60I_0 \exp\left\{j\omega\left(t - \dfrac{r}{c}\right)\right\}}{r}\right]\left[\frac{\cos\left\{\left(\dfrac{\pi}{2}\right)\cos\theta\right\}}{\sin\theta}\right] \tag{19.54}$$

For the array, the resulting E_θ will be

$$E_\theta = j\left(\frac{60I_0}{r}\right)\left[\frac{\cos\left\{\left(\dfrac{\pi}{2}\right)\cos\theta\right\}}{\sin\theta}\right] \times \left[\exp\left\{j\omega\left(t - \frac{r + \dfrac{d\cos\psi}{2}}{c}\right)\right\}\right.$$

$$\left. + \exp\left\{j\omega\left(t - \frac{r - \dfrac{d\cos\psi}{2}}{c}\right)\right\}\right]$$

$$= \left[\frac{j\,60I_0}{r}\exp\left\{j\omega\left(t - \frac{r}{c}\right)\right\}\right]\left[\frac{\cos\left\{\left(\dfrac{\pi}{2}\right)\cos\theta\right\}}{\sin\theta}\right]$$

$$\times \left[\exp\left\{-j\left(\frac{\omega}{c}\right)\left(\frac{d\cos\psi}{2}\right)\right\} + \exp\left\{j\left(\frac{\omega}{c}\right)\left(\frac{d\cos\psi}{2}\right)\right\}\right]$$

$$= \left[\frac{j\,60I_0}{r}\exp\left\{j\omega\left(t - \frac{r}{c}\right)\right\}\right] \times \left[\frac{\cos\left\{\left(\dfrac{\pi}{2}\right)\cos\theta\right\}}{\sin\theta}\right]\cos\left[\left(\frac{\omega d}{2c}\right)\cos\psi\right] \tag{19.55}$$

It should be noted that in the above expressions, of the two waves reaching the point P from the two antennae, one has travelled a distance $[r + (d\cos\psi)/2]$, and the other one a distance of $[r - (d\cos\psi)/2]$, and as a result, when they reach P, they will be out of phase. This, of course, assumes that the antennae had been excited in phase. Now, we replace the angle ψ by θ and ϕ, because:

$$r\cos\psi = r\sin\theta\cos\phi \tag{19.56}$$

$\therefore$ The electric field intensity expression becomes

$$\mathbf{E}_\theta = \mathbf{i}_\theta\left[\frac{j\,120\,I_0}{r}\exp\left\{j\omega\left(t - \frac{r}{c}\right)\right\}\right] \times \left[\frac{\cos\left\{\left(\dfrac{\pi}{2}\right)\cos\theta\right\}}{\sin\theta}\right]\cos\left[\left(\frac{\omega d}{2c}\right)\sin\theta\cos\phi\right] \tag{19.57}$$

When the two antennae are half-wavelength apart,

$$\frac{\omega d}{2c} = \frac{\omega\lambda}{4c} = \left(\frac{2\pi}{\lambda}\right)\left(\frac{\lambda}{4}\right) = \frac{\pi}{2}$$

∴ In the x-y plane, where $\theta = \pi/2$, the variation of the **E** field is proportional to $\cos\left(\dfrac{\pi}{2}\cos\theta\right)$, and hence

$$E = i_\theta \left[\frac{j\,120\,I_0}{r}\exp\left\{j\omega\left(t - \frac{r}{c}\right)\right\}\right]\left[\cos\left\{\left(\frac{\pi}{2}\right)\cos\phi\right\}\right] \tag{19.58}$$

At points where $\phi = 0$ or π, **E** = 0; and where $\phi = \pi/2$, **E** is a maximum, i.e.

$$E_{\text{max}} = i_\theta \left[\frac{j\,120\,I_0}{r}\exp\left\{j\omega\left(t - \frac{r}{c}\right)\right\}\right] \tag{19.59}$$

Thus there is constructive interference along the y-axis; and destructive interference along the x-axis.

In the x-z plane, $\phi = 0$, and hence **E** is

$$E = i_\theta \left[\frac{j\,120\,I_0}{r}\exp\left\{j\omega\left(t - \frac{r}{c}\right)\right\}\right] \times \left[\frac{\cos\left\{\left(\dfrac{\pi}{2}\right)\cos\theta\right\}}{\sin\theta}\right]\left[\cos\left\{\left(\frac{\pi}{2}\right)\sin\theta\right\}\right] \tag{19.60}$$

The first trigonometric term is the angular distribution for a single half-wave antenna. This is zero at $\theta = 0$, and maximum at $\theta = \pi/2$. The second trigonometric term is a consequence of the interference between the two antennae. It is a maximum at $\theta = 0$, and zero at $\theta = \pi/2$.

∴ In the x-z plane, **E** is zero both at $\theta = 0$, and $\theta = \pi/2$.

Finally, we consider the y-z plane where $\phi = \pi/2$.

$$E = i_\theta \left[\frac{j\,120\,I_0}{r}\exp\left\{j\omega\left(t - \frac{r}{c}\right)\right\}\right] \times \left[\frac{\cos\left\{\left(\dfrac{\pi}{2}\right)\cos\theta\right\}}{\sin\theta}\right] \tag{19.61}$$

i.e. **E** on the plane y-z, behaves like the **E** field of a single half-wave antenna.

To obtain the expression for power, we rewrite the expression for the **E** vector, changing its numerical constant to the characteristic impedance, and we have

$$E = i_\theta \left[j\left(\frac{I_0 Z_0}{\pi r}\right)\exp\left\{j\omega\left(t - \frac{r}{c}\right)\right\}\right] \times \left[\frac{\cos\left\{\left(\dfrac{\pi}{2}\right)\cos\theta\right\}}{\sin\theta}\right]\left[\cos\left\{\left(\frac{\omega d}{2c}\right)\sin\theta\cos\phi\right\}\right] \tag{19.62a}$$

$$H = i_\phi \left[j\left(\frac{I_0}{\pi r}\right)\exp\left\{j\omega\left(t - \frac{r}{c}\right)\right\}\right] \times \left[\frac{\cos\left\{\left(\dfrac{\pi}{2}\right)\cos\theta\right\}}{\sin\theta}\right]\left[\cos\left\{\left(\frac{\omega d}{2c}\right)\sin\theta\cos\phi\right\}\right] \tag{19.62b}$$

∴ The average value in time, of the Poynting vector is

$$\overline{S}_{av} = \left(\frac{Z_0 I_0^2}{2\pi^2 r^2}\right) \times \left[\frac{\cos\left\{\left(\dfrac{\pi}{2}\right)\cos\theta\right\}}{\sin\theta}\right]^2 \cos^2\left[\left(\frac{\omega d}{2c}\right)\sin\theta\cos\phi\right] \tag{19.63}$$

This is for the two half-wave antennae spaced a distance d on the x-axis, both excited with the same current and in phase (by the same current, we mean both have currents of the same amplitude). We can generalize further, and if there is a phase difference between the antennae of α, then, we have:

$$\overline{S}_{av} = \left(\frac{Z_0 I_0^2}{2\pi^2 r^2}\right) \times \left[\frac{\cos\left\{\left(\dfrac{\pi}{2}\right)\cos\theta\right\}}{\sin\theta}\right]^2 \cos^2\left[\left(\frac{\omega d}{2c}\right)\sin\theta\cos\phi + \alpha\right] \tag{19.64}$$

This is the 'power per unit solid angle', when $r = 1$.

If the two antennae are in phase, and spaced a distance of half-wavelength, then $\alpha = 0$, $d = \lambda/2$, and $\{\omega d/(2c)\} = \pi/2$, and so:

$$\overline{S}_{av} = \left(\frac{Z_0 I_0^2}{2\pi^2 r^2}\right) \times \left[\frac{\cos\left\{\left(\dfrac{\pi}{2}\right)\cos\theta\right\}}{\sin\theta}\right]^2 \cos^2\left[\left(\frac{\pi}{2}\right)\sin\theta\cos\phi\right] \tag{19.65}$$

The pattern in the plane $\theta = \pi/2$, is shown in Figure 19.12, which indicates that there are two main directions of radiation which are both perpendicular to the line of the array. This is a particular example of a 'broadside array'. If the number of elements is increased, the main beam becomes sharper and small sidelobes appear.

On the other hand, if the two antennae are spaced quarter wavelength, i.e. $d = \lambda/4$, with a phase difference of $\pi/2$, i.e. $\alpha = \pi/2$, then Eq. (19.64) becomes

$$\overline{S}_{av} = \left(\frac{Z_0 I_0^2}{2\pi^2 r^2}\right) \times \left[\frac{\cos\left\{\left(\dfrac{\pi}{2}\right)\cos\theta\right\}}{\sin\theta}\right]^2 \cos^2\left[\left(\frac{\pi}{4}\right)(\sin\theta\cos\phi + 1)\right] \tag{19.66}$$

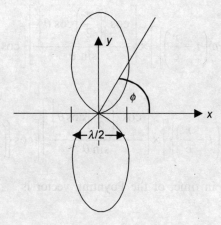

Figure 19.12 Two-element broadside array.

The pattern of this expression is symmetrical about the x-z plane (i.e. $\mathbf{E}$ plane) and about the x-y plane (i.e. $\mathbf{H}$ plane). The power patterns in these two planes are shown in Figure 19.13. It will be seen that only a small portion of the power is radiated to the left of $x = 0$, the main energy going in a broad beam in the direction of the positive x-axis, i.e. the line of the array. This system is an example of an 'end-fire array'.

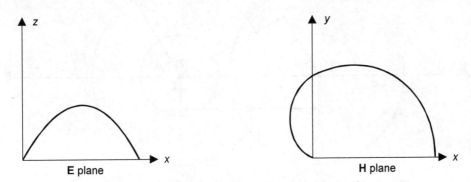

Figure 19.13 Two-element end-fire array.

As mentioned earlier, the factor $[\cos \{(\pi/2) \cos \theta\}/\sin \theta]^2$ in Eqs. (19.65) and (19.66) represents the pattern due to an element of the array. The factors $\cos^2 [(\pi/2) \cos \theta]$ and $\cos^2 [(\pi/4) (\sin \theta \cos \phi + 1)]$ characterize the broadside and the end-fire arrays respectively, and are called 'array factors'. The broadside array factor is like a toroid with a directive pattern in any plane through the x-axis. The end-fire array has a pattern like a pencil beam possessing directivity in both the planes through x- and y-axes. These arguments hold for the arrays containing more than two elements. The end-fire arrays usually have a higher gain than the broadside arrays of the same size. More highly directive systems can be designed by combining the two types which we have discussed now.

19.5.2.1 *Two element array (of isotropic antennae)*

So far we have described a two-element array of half-wave dipoles which is a practical one. Now we will discuss a two-element array made up of isotropic antennae. An isotropic antenna does not exist in real life and is a hypothetical one. But its use helps us in understanding the principle of the arrays, and we will show that an array of non-isotropic elements can be derived very easily from this analysis of isotropic element array.

Since we are considering an array of isotropic elements, this means that each antenna is a 'point source'. Let the two such antennae be separated by a distance d, and be excited by the currents $I_1 \angle \delta_1$ and $I_2 \angle \delta_2$ where I_1 and I_2, and δ_1, δ_2 are the amplitudes and phases of the excitation current in the two antennae respectively. The line joining the two elements is the axis of the array [i.e. line AB in Figure 19.13(a)]. All the angles measured from the axis of the array are ϕ which should not be confused with the spherical polar coordinate variable (r, θ, ϕ). As the antenna elements are point sources, the radiation pattern of the array would be axi-symmetric about the axis AB. So the section of the radiation pattern in a plane passing through this axis [e.g. (say) the plane of the paper] would generate the total pattern by rotating the section about AB. Since we are interested in the far field, let P be such a point at which the total $\mathbf{E}$ field has to be evaluated. The distance of the point P from the array is specified as r, as shown in Figure 19.13(a). This distance r is >> than the dimensions of the array.

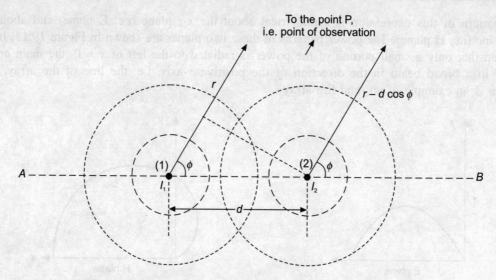

Figure 19.13(a)   A two-element array of isotropic antennae.

∴   **E** field at the point P, due to the antenna (1) is

$$E_1 = \frac{C\,I_1 e^{j\delta_1}}{r} e^{-j\beta r} \tag{19.66a}$$

where C is a constant dependent on the parameters of the medium. Similarly the field E_2 at P due to the antenna (2) is

$$E_2 = \frac{C\,I_2 e^{j\delta_2}}{(r - d\cos\phi)} e^{-j\beta(r - d\cos\phi)} \tag{19.66b}$$

Since $d \ll r$, it can be neglected in the denominator of the amplitude term, but not in the phase term.

∴ $$E_2 = \frac{C\,I_2\,e^{j\delta_2}}{r} e^{-j\beta(r - d\cos\phi)} \tag{19.66c}$$

Since the two isotropic antennae are identical, the directions of E_1 and E_2 will be same.

∴ $$E_T = E_1 + E_2$$

$$= \frac{C\,e^{-j\beta r}}{r} \left(I_1 e^{j\delta_1} + I_2 e^{j\delta_2}\, e^{j\frac{2\pi d}{\lambda}\cos\phi} \right)$$

For a specified r, $\dfrac{C\,e^{-j\beta r}}{r} = \text{constant} = C_0$ (say)

∴ $$E_T = C_0 I_1 e^{j\delta_1} \left(1 + \frac{I_2}{I_1} e^{j(\delta_2 - \delta_1)} e^{j2\pi\left(\frac{d}{\lambda}\cos\phi\right)} \right) \tag{19.66d}$$

A plot of E_T as a function of ϕ gives the radiation pattern of the array in the plane containing the axis. From this equation, the radiation pattern can be controlled by the following three parameters.

1. $\dfrac{d}{\lambda}$ (i.e. the ratio of the distance between the two antennae to the wavelength).

2. $(\delta_2 - \delta_1)$ (= phase difference between the two elements).

3. $\dfrac{I_2}{I_2}$ (i.e. the ratio of the amplitudes of the currents).

(A) Effect of Phase Difference on Radiation Pattern

Let $\dfrac{I_2}{I_1} = 1$ and $I_2 = I_1 = I$; then

$$E_T = C_0\, I\, e^{j\delta_1}\left(1 + e^{j(\delta_2 - \delta_1)}\, e^{j\frac{2\pi d}{\lambda}\cos\phi}\right) \tag{19.66e}$$

Since the radiation pattern is a plot of $|E|$ against the angle ϕ, we have

$$|E_T| = |C_0\, I|\left|\left(1 + e^{j(\delta_2 - \delta_1)}e^{j\frac{2\pi d}{\lambda}\cos\phi}\right)\right| \tag{19.66f}$$

Let the antenna 1 be the reference element, i.e. $\delta_1 = 0$ and the phase difference $\delta_1 - \delta_2 = \delta$. So, we get

$$|E_T| = |C_0 I|\left|\left(1 + e^{j\left(\delta + \frac{2\pi d}{\lambda}\cos\phi\right)}\right)\right|$$

$$= 2\,|C_0 I|\left|\cos\left\{\frac{1}{2}\left(\delta + \frac{2\pi}{\lambda}\cos\phi\right)\right\}\right| \tag{19.66g}$$

For maximum E_t, from the above equation,

$$\frac{1}{2}\left(\delta + \frac{2\pi}{\lambda}\cos\phi\right) = m\pi, \quad m \text{ being} = 0, 1, 2, \ldots \tag{19.66h}$$

The direction of maximum radiation is obtained from the principal value of m, i.e.

$$\left.\begin{array}{c} \delta + \dfrac{2\pi}{\lambda}\cos\phi = 0 \\[3mm] \phi_{max} = \cos^{-1}\left(\dfrac{-\delta\lambda}{2\pi}\right) \end{array}\right\} \tag{19.66j}$$

$\therefore$

When the spacing between the elements and the wavelength of operation are specified, the direction of maximum radiation is a function of δ. So the direction of maximum radiation changes as the phase difference δ changes, i.e. when $\delta = 0$ and the two elements have the same phase, then $\phi_{max} = \cos^{-1}(0) = \pi/2$; or when $\delta = -\beta d = -\dfrac{2\pi d}{\lambda}$, $\phi_{max} = \cos^{-1}(1) = 0$.

From the expression for ϕ_{max}, it is seen that as δ changes from $-\beta d$ to βd, ϕ_{max} changes from $0°$ to $180°$, i.e. this is the range of variation of the direction of maximum radiation. So the inter-element phase difference is an important parameter to control the direction of maximum radiation.

(B) Inter-element Spacing (= d)

Let $I_1 = I_2 = I$ and $\delta_1 = \delta_2$ so that $\delta = 0$. The radiation pattern then becomes

$$|E_T| = 2|C_0 I|\left|\cos\left(\frac{\pi d}{\lambda}\cos\phi\right)\right| \tag{19.66k}$$

where $\dfrac{d}{\lambda}$ is the spacing normalized with respect to the wavelength.

$\therefore$ The condition for maximum radiation is

$$\pi\frac{d}{\lambda}\cos\phi = m\pi, \qquad m = 0, 1, 2, \ldots \text{ (integers only)}$$

$\therefore$

$$\phi_{max} = \cos^{-1}\left(\frac{m\lambda}{d}\right) \tag{19.66l}$$

When $\dfrac{m\lambda}{d} \leq 1$, the corresponding values of ϕ_{max} will be physically realizable, i.e. for all $m \leq \dfrac{d}{\lambda}$, the radiation is maximum. There will be discrete number of directions of maximum radiation ($= N$).

$\therefore N$ = maximum permitted value of m = floor $\left(\dfrac{d}{\lambda}\right) + 1$ where floor (x) represents the highest integer $< x$.

Next, for null directions, i.e. directions along which there is no radiation, we use the same equation, allowing the cosine function to be zero and thus we get:

$$\frac{\pi d}{\lambda}\cos\phi_{null} = \left(m + \frac{1}{2}\right)\pi \qquad m = 0 \text{ and integers} \tag{19.66m}$$

So it follows that the directions of nulls and the directions of maximum radiation appear alternately [Figure 19.13(b)].

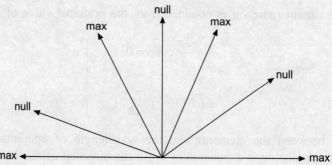

Figure 19.13(b) Maxima and nulls in a radiation pattern of a two-element array.

Thus the inter-element spacing $\dfrac{d}{\lambda}$ splits the radiation pattern into angular zones.

(C) Effect of Amplitude Ratio

Considering the general case, i.e. Eq. (19.66d),

$$|E| = |C_0 I_1| \left| \left\{ 1 + \frac{I_2}{I_1} e^{j\left(\delta + \frac{2\pi}{\lambda} d \cos\phi\right)} \right\} \right| \qquad (19.66d)$$

let us discuss the effect of the ratio $R = \dfrac{I_2}{I_1}$ on the radiation pattern, allowing R to vary over the whole range 0 to ∞.

When $R = 0$, there is no excitation to the second element, and when $R \to \infty$, there is no excitation to the first element.

In both these cases, there will be no array and the radiation patterns will be those of individual antenna (i.e. isotropic in both the cases). The maximum array effect is thus realized when $I_1 = I_2$, i.e. equal excitation to both the elements. In general, the array elements are excited with equal magnitude but with different phases. There are special cases where the amplitudes of the currents have to be varied.

Thus combining the effects of these three parameters, i.e. δ, $\dfrac{d}{\lambda}$ and $\dfrac{I_1}{I_2}$ (each having different effect on the radiation pattern) a derived radiation pattern of high complexity can be achieved.

So far this analysis has been based on the assumption of isotropic antenna which is of course not physically realizable. All available antennae are non-isotropic in nature. Even the basic Hertzian dipole is non-isotropic with zero radiation along its axis and the maximum on the normal central plane. So when the elements have non-identical patterns, the radiation pattern in each plane through the array axis has to be computed, and the three-dimensional pattern would be a collection of such planar patterns.

We now consider a two-element array of non-isotropic but identical antennae, with its axis lying in the plane of the paper (say). Let the individual pattern be $f(\phi)$ in the plane of the paper. Let the two antennae be oriented identically with respect to the array axis and the excitation currents be $I_1 \angle 0$ and $I_2 \angle \delta$. The far fields at a point P, due to these two elements can be expressed as

$$\left. \begin{aligned} E_1 &= \frac{C\, I_1\, e^{-j\beta r}}{r} f(\phi) \\[2mm] E_2 &= \frac{C\, I_2\, e^{j\delta} e^{-j\beta r}}{r} f(\phi) \end{aligned} \right\} \qquad (19.66n)$$

Hence the total field at the point P will be

$$E_T = \frac{C\, e^{-j\beta r} I_1}{r} f(\phi) \left(1 + \frac{I_2}{I_1} e^{j\delta} e^{j\beta d \cos\phi} \right) \qquad (19.66p)$$

by analysis on similar lines as in the case of isotropic elements.

It should be noticed that Eq. (19.66p) is identical with Eq. (19.66d), except that now there is a multiplying factor $f(\phi)$.

Hence it can be stated that:

Radiation pattern of a non-isotropic array

= (Pattern of each element) × (Radiation pattern of array of isotropic elements)

        ↑   ↑

This is also known as   This is defined by array parameters and is called
Primary Pattern or   Array Factor (AF).
Unit Pattern.

= Element Radiation Pattern × Array Factor (= Group Pattern)   (19.66q)

This is known as Pattern Multiplication.

Thus, it is possible to draw by inspection, the pattern of an array by pattern multiplication

While the 'Unit Pattern' depends on the type of the element, the 'Group Pattern' is independent of the element type so long as d, δ and orientation of the element in the array remain the same.

Note: These points which have been mentioned in general terms here, can be checked specifically for a two-element half-wave antenna discussed in Section 19.5.2 by referring to Eqs. (19.60) to (19.66).

19.5.3 Linear Arrays

When the communication has to be made from one point to another (i.e. point-to-point communication), the requisite radiation pattern is a single narrow lobe or a beam. Such a characteristic can be achieved by a multi-element linear array. An array is said to be linear, when the elements of the array are spaced equally along a straight line. A linear array is said to be uniform, when the elements are fed with currents of equal magnitude and progressive phase-shift along the line.

The pattern of such an array can be obtained by the vector addition of the field-strengths of each of the elements. For a uniform array of non-directional elements, the field-strength will be

$$E_T = E_0[1 + \exp(j\psi) + \exp(j2\psi) + \cdots + \exp(j(n-1)\psi)] \qquad (19.67)$$

where

E_0 = field-strength due to the first element of the array, or due to an isolated element

$$\psi = \beta d \cos\phi + \alpha \qquad (19.67a)$$

with

α = progressive phase-shift between two successive elements

d = distance between two successive elements in the array

$\beta d = 2\pi/\lambda$—path difference in radians

From Eq. (19.67),

$$\frac{E_T}{E_0} = \left| \frac{1 - \exp\{j(n\psi)\}}{1 - \exp(j\psi)} \right|$$

$$= \left| \frac{\sin\left(\dfrac{n\psi}{2}\right)}{\sin\left(\dfrac{\psi}{2}\right)} \right| \tag{19.68}$$

The maximum value of this expression is n, and this occurs when $\psi = 0$. This is the 'principal maximum' of the array. This occurs, when [from Eq. (19.67a)]:

$$\cos \phi = \frac{-\alpha}{\beta d} \tag{19.69}$$

A broadside array is one whose array factor has an absolute maximum in directions perpendicular to the axis of the array. (In our present notations, in this section, this means $\phi = \pi/2$.) This means that $\alpha = 0$ for this condition. The half-power width, the full angle in which the power radiated in any direction is not less than half the maximum value, is $102°/n$, the approximation improving as n increases.

When the (currents in the) elements in an array are all in phase, but the amplitudes decrease uniformly from the central element, such an array is called a 'gabled array'. If a is the ratio of the sidelobe maximum to the main maximum of an array in which the currents are uniform, then for the corresponding gabled array, this ratio will be a^2 (as its factor is square of the uniform one). Hence the sidelobes are reduced, but the main beam is now broader, and has a half-power width of about $146°/n$ for n elements.

An end-fire array is one, which has a maximum in the direction of the axis of the array. This happens when $\phi = 0$, and hence,

$$\alpha = -\beta d \tag{19.70}$$

For this type, Eq. (19.68) is zero, when

$$\frac{n\psi}{2} = \pm k\pi, \quad k = 1, 2, 3, \ldots \tag{19.71}$$

These are the nulls of the pattern. The secondary maxima occur approximately between the zeroes or nulls, i.e.

$$\frac{n\psi}{2} = \pm (2m + 1)\,\frac{\pi}{2}, \quad m = 1, 2, 3, \ldots \tag{19.72}$$

Numerous graphs and details of the function (E_T/E_0) can be found in any book specifically dealing with detailed study and design of antennae (e.g. Jordan and Balmain, *Electromagnetic Waves and Radiating Systems*, 2nd Edition, Prentice-Hall of India, 2000).

Another type of linear array has elements which are called 'parasitic elements'. These elements are not connected to a generator, instead the currents in the parasitic elements are induced by the currents in the driven elements. The resultant radiation pattern is the vector sum of the patterns produced by all these elements.

A very familiar type of a linear array with parasitic elements is the Uda-Yagi array, shown in Figure 19.14. A rigorous analysis of such a system is highly complex. The distances d_1, d_2, d_3 are determined experimentally. The driven element is approximately $\lambda/2$ long, the reflector being slightly longer, and the directors shorter. The directors can be two or more.

The Uda-Yagi antenna is most often used as a receiving antenna. So far we have discussed some of the basic points of some of the fundamental types and simple and familiar types of antennae. The subject is a complex one, and for greater details and in-depth study, the interested readers are recommended texts on the subject, such as Jones, D.S., Jordan and Balmain, etc.

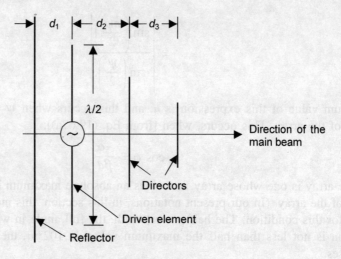

Figure 19.14 An Uda-Yagi array.

It should be noted that Eq. (19.68) is the Array Factor of the uniform linear array, i.e.

$$AF = \frac{E_T}{E_0} = \frac{\sin \dfrac{n\psi}{2}}{\sin \dfrac{\psi}{2}} \qquad (19.68)$$

(or sometimes, $AF = \dfrac{E_T}{nE_0}$, where n is the number of elements in the array)

19.5.3.1 *Direction of maximum radiation*

The total phase difference between the fields due to any adjacent elements in the uniform linear array is

$$\psi = \beta d \cos\phi + \alpha \qquad (19.67a)$$

where

$\beta d \cos\phi$ is the space phase, being a function of the direction ϕ (βd—the path difference in radians $= 2\pi/\lambda$),

α = the electrical phase – the progressive phase shift between the two successive elements, independent of the direction ϕ.

For the direction of maximum radiation, $\psi = 0$

$$\therefore \qquad \cos\phi_{max} = -\frac{\alpha}{\beta d}$$

or

$$\phi_{max} = \cos^{-1}\left(-\frac{\alpha}{\beta d}\right) = \cos^{-1}\left(\frac{-\alpha\lambda}{2\pi d}\right) \qquad (19.72a)$$

This is same as Eq. (19.66j).

It is to be noticed that the direction of maximum radiation is independent of the number of elements in the uniform array. Hence as in the case of the two-element array, the direction of maximum radiation is made to vary from $\phi = 0$ to $\phi = \pi$ by allowing α to change from $-\beta d$ to $+\beta d$.

When $\phi = 0$ or $\phi = \pi$, the direction of the maximum radiation appears along the array axis, and such an array is called the 'End-fire Array'. When the direction of the maximum radiation is orthogonal to the array axis, i.e. $\phi = \pi/2$, the array is called the 'Broadside Array' [Figure 19.14(a)].

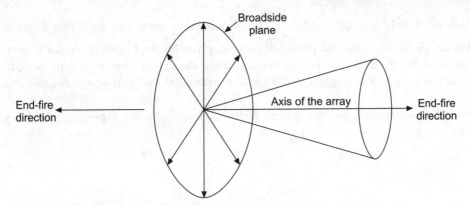

Figure 19.14(a)   Broadside and end-fire directions of an antenna array.

Substituting for α (or δ of the earlier equations) in Eq. (19.67a),

$$\psi = \beta d(\cos\phi - \cos\phi_{max}) \tag{19.67b}$$

19.5.3.2 Direction of nulls

This is the direction in which there is no radiation, i.e. the electric field is zero. Hence the required condition from Eq. (19.68) is

$$\sin\left(\frac{n\psi}{2}\right) = 0$$

or

$$\frac{n\psi}{2} = \pm m\pi, \qquad m = 1, 2, 3, \ldots$$

$$\therefore \qquad \psi = \pm \frac{2m\pi}{n}, \qquad m = 1, 2, 3, \ldots \tag{19.72b}$$

$\therefore$ If ϕ_{null} denotes the direction of null

$$\psi = \beta d\cos\phi_{null} + \alpha = \pm \frac{2m\pi}{n}$$

or

$$\beta d(\cos\phi_{null} - \cos\phi_{max}) = \pm \frac{2m\pi}{n} \tag{19.72c}$$

$$\therefore \qquad \cos\phi_{null} = \cos\phi_{max} \pm \frac{2m\pi}{\beta dn} = \cos\phi_{max} \pm \frac{m\lambda}{dn} \tag{19.72d}$$

It should be noted that m is to be an integer $\neq 0$ because $m = 0$ corresponds to $\psi = 0$ representing maximum radiation and *not* a null. To obtain the directions of null, the integral values of m must be such that the RHS of Eq. (19.72d) must lie within the range ± 1. So there will be finite number of nulls. Also the maximum value of m with +ve and −ve signs can be different depending on the value of ϕ_{max}.

19.5.3.3   Half-power beam width (HPBW)

This has been defined while discussing the radiation parameters of an antenna. This is the angular separation between two directions, one on either side of the direction of maximum radiation, along which the E field has reduced to $\dfrac{1}{\sqrt{2}}$ of its maximum value. Let these two directions be ϕ_1 and ϕ_2 [Figure 19.14(b)]. Since the power density, as given by the Poynting Vector is proportional to the square of the E field, the power density along these two directions will be half of that along the direction ϕ_{max}. The angular width $(\phi_2 - \phi_1)$ is called the 'half-power beam-width' of the array.

The half-power angles ϕ_1 and ϕ_2 can be calculated from the expression for $|E|$ given in Eq. (19.68)

$$\frac{1}{n}\left|\frac{\sin\dfrac{n\psi}{2}}{\sin\dfrac{\psi}{2}}\right| = \frac{1}{\sqrt{2}} \tag{19.72e}$$

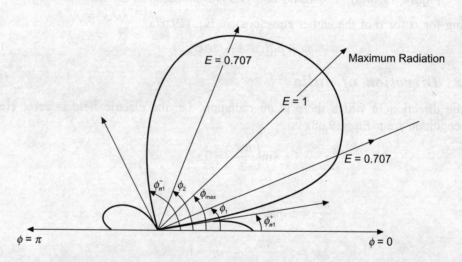

Figure 19.14(b)   Half-power beam-width of a radiation pattern.

This equation has to be solved numerically to obtain the half-power angles ϕ_1 and ϕ_2, which then gives the exact value for HPBW.

Next, we have the following quick and approximate method of calculating HPBW of a large array (when an accurate answer is not required).

Note that the beam width between the first nulls (BWFN) is approximately twice the half-power beam-width (HPBW).

We assume that the first nulls are approximately symmetric with respect to the direction of maximum radiation, then

$$\left.\begin{array}{l} \phi_{HPBW} = \phi_2 - \phi_1 \simeq \dfrac{1}{2}\left(\phi_{n1}^+ - \phi_{n1}^-\right) \\[2mm] \qquad\quad \simeq \left(\phi_{n1}^+ - \phi_{max}\right) \\[2mm] \qquad\quad \simeq \left(\phi_{max} - \phi_{n1}^-\right) \end{array}\right\} \tag{19.72f}$$

Here the implicit assumption is $\phi_{max} \simeq \frac{1}{2}(\phi_{n1}^+ + \phi_{n1}^-)$

It should be appreciated that depending on the location of ϕ_{max}, there may be cases when ϕ_{n1}^+ or ϕ_{n1}^- may not be visible in the polar plot of the radiation pattern, i.e. when ϕ_{max} approaches π, the null ϕ_{n1}^+ may not be visible, or when ϕ_{max} approaches 0, ϕ_{n1}^- may not be visible. In such cases, the suitable expression from Eq. (19.72f) should be used.

Let us first consider the case

$$\phi_{HPBW} \simeq \phi_{n1}^+ - \phi_{max} \tag{19.72g}$$

then

$$\cos\phi_{n1}^+ = \cos\phi_{max} - \frac{\lambda}{nd} \qquad \text{from Eq. (19.72d) with } m = 1$$

or

$$\cos\phi_{n1}^+ - \cos\phi_{max} = -\frac{\lambda}{nd} \tag{19.72h}$$

or

$$2\sin\left(\frac{\phi_{n1}^+ - \phi_{max}}{2}\right)\sin\left(\frac{\phi_{n1}^+ + \phi_{max}}{2}\right) = \frac{\lambda}{nd}$$

or

$$2\sin\left(\frac{\phi_{HPBW}}{2}\right)\sin\left(\frac{2\phi_{max} + \phi_{PBW}}{2}\right) = \frac{\lambda}{nd} \tag{19.72k}$$

Expanding the trigonometric function, and considering a large array for which $n \gg 1$ and using the approximations $\sin x \rightarrow x$, $\cos x \rightarrow 1$ $(x \ll 1)$ the above equation can be reduced to the following quadratic

$$\phi_{HPBW}^2 (\cos\phi_{max}) + (2\sin\phi_{max})\phi_{HPBW} - \frac{2\lambda}{nd} = 0 \tag{19.72l}$$

Solving this quadratic,

$$\phi_{HPBW} = \frac{-\sin\phi_{max} + \sqrt{\left(\sin^2\phi_{max} + \frac{2\lambda}{nd}\cos\phi_{max}\right)}}{\cos\phi_{max}} \tag{19.72m}$$

i.e. as ϕ_{max} increases from 0 to $\pi/2$, the beam width ϕ_{HPBW} decreases monotonically.

When $\phi_{max} = 0$—the end-fire array, HPBW is maximum.

When $\phi_{max} = \pi/2$—the broadside array, HPBW is minimum.

For these two limiting cases, from Eq. (19.72l), for the broadside array ($\phi_{max} = \pi/2$)

$$\phi_{HPBW} = \frac{\lambda}{nd} = \frac{\lambda}{\text{length of the array}} \tag{19.72n}$$

For the end-fire array ($\phi_{max} = 0$),

$$\phi_{HPBW} = \sqrt{\frac{2\lambda}{nd}} = \sqrt{\frac{2\lambda}{\text{length of the array}}} \tag{19.72p}$$

The length of the array is $(n-1)d$, but when $n \gg 1$, the length $= nd$ (approx).

19.5.4 Directivity of Uniform Array

In Section 19.4.4 subsection (C), the directivity of an antenna has been defined as its power focussing capability and from the radiation pattern of an antenna, the directivity can be calculated using Eq. (19.53p).

∴ The directivity for an N-element uniform array,

$$D = \frac{4\pi}{\displaystyle\iint_{\theta\;\phi} |AF|^2 \, d\Omega} \tag{19.72q}$$

where AF (= the normalized radiation pattern of the array) is given by Eq. (19.68).

For a general uniform array, this expression has to be solved numerically. For a large array, approximations are possible for the integral in the denominator. The integral can be replaced by the solid angle within the half-power beam-width of the array.

Considering the two limiting cases, i.e. broadside and end-fire arrays, and denoting their HPBW by ϕ_{BS} and ϕ_{EF} respectively.

$$\phi_{BS} = \frac{\lambda}{nd} \quad \text{and} \quad \phi_{EF} = \sqrt{\frac{2\lambda}{nd}} \tag{19.72r}$$

The solid angle for the broadside array is approximately

$$\Omega_{BS} \simeq 2\pi\phi_{BS};$$

and for the end-fire array is

$$\Omega_{EF} \simeq \pi\left(\frac{\phi_{EF}}{2}\right)^2 \tag{19.72s}$$

The directivity of the two arrays, thus, are

$$D_{BS} = \frac{4\pi}{2\pi\phi_{BS}} = \frac{2nd}{\lambda}$$

$$D_{EF} = \frac{4\pi}{\pi\left(\dfrac{\phi_{EF}}{2}\right)^2} = \frac{16}{\left(\dfrac{2\lambda}{nd}\right)^2} = \frac{8nd}{\lambda} \tag{19.72t}$$

i.e. the directivity of the end-fire array is about four times that of the broadside array of same length.

On the other hand, comparing HPBWs.

$$\frac{\phi_{BS}}{\phi_{EF}} = \frac{\lambda}{nd}\sqrt{\frac{nd}{2\lambda}} = \sqrt{\frac{\lambda}{2nd}} \tag{19.72u}$$

Since $(nd) \gg 1$ for large arrays, the conclusion is $\phi_{BS} \gg \phi_{EF}$. This implies that the broadside array has high directivity as it has a narrower beam compared to the end-fire array.

So one has to be careful using only a planar radiation pattern. It is more important to develop the capability of visualizing the three-dimensional patterns (as three-dimensional solids).

19.6 THE RECEIVING ANTENNA

So far we have been discussing only the transmitting antennae. The task of a receiving antenna is to extract the energy from an electromagnetic wave, together with the signal carried by the wave, and deliver it to a receiver. This mechanism can be described qualitatively in simple terms. The time-varying **E** field of the wave which surrounds the antenna, induces currents and charges in the body of the conducting antenna. A certain voltage is thus developed across the antenna terminals; this voltage varying with time as per the inducing wave. This voltage is fed into the receiver which amplifies it, and then converts it into the required form which can be sound (e.g. in radio, and the corresponding audio signals of the televisions) and/or optical (e.g. optical signals in televisions, and in radars).

Though the geometrical shape of a receiving antenna is less diverse than that of a transmitting antenna, they are functionally interchangeable. But it must be remembered that the working conditions of the two types are not the same. For the transmitter, the external **E**-field wave acts only between the antenna terminals; whilst for the receiver, the external **E**-field exists all over the antenna surface. The resulting currents and the charge distributions for the two cases will be quite different.

But even then, it can be shown that the most important characteristics of the receiving antenna (which are its directive properties and its impedance) are identical to those of a transmitting antenna. In our present discussions, we shall consider the two dipoles as the two basic receiving antennae. (For further detailed information, interested readers are referred to the specialized texts mentioned earlier.)

We have seen so far that from the input side, an antenna appears as an impedance in general, the resistive part of the impedance corresponds to the power radiated by the antenna. So, for a transmitting antenna, we can say that the current (of the antenna) is the cause and the electromagnetic radiation is the effect. But for a receiving antenna the cause and the effect get reversed, i.e. the cause is the incoming electromagnetic radiation, and the effect is the current induced in the antenna surface, and the voltage induced between the antenna terminals. There are two important points to be understood regarding the receiving behaviour of the antenna: (1) Variation of the terminal voltage as a function of the direction and polarization of the incoming radiation. (2) The maximum power that can be received by the load connected to the antenna. Also of interest are the relationship between the antenna parameters in its two modes, i.e. transmitting and receiving.

The antenna is a reciprocal device (i.e. an antenna has identical radiation and circuit characteristics in transmitting and receiving modes). This follows from the reciprocity theorem which has been proved in Section 19.7.

19.6.1 The Electric and the Magnetic Dipoles (Oscillating) as Receiving Antennae

Figure 19.15 shows the electric (Hertzian) and the oscillating magnetic dipoles as the receiving antennae.

The tangential component of the incident **E** field induces currents in the wire, such that they re-radiate the energy and produce a voltage V across the load resistance R. It can be justifiably assumed that the effects of these currents on the transmitting antenna are negligible. The voltage across R can be measured by some suitable electronic voltmeter.

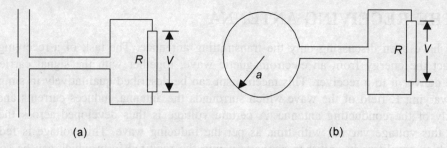

(a)   (b)

Figure 19.15 Oscillating electric and magnetic dipoles used as receiving antennae.

For the Hertzian dipole, it can be shown that,

$$V = E_t l = \mathbf{E} \cdot \mathbf{l} \ (= El \cos \alpha) \tag{19.73}$$

where

E_t = tangential component of $\mathbf{E}$ (i.e. tangential to the antenna)

l = length of the dipole antenna

V is maximal when $\mathbf{E}$ is parallel to the antenna (i.e. $\alpha = 0$).

Hertzian dipoles (or almost Hertzian dipoles) are used as receiving antennae of television receivers, portable radios, or car radios, etc.

For the magnetic dipole, the induced emf is given by

$$V = \oint_C \mathbf{E} \cdot d\mathbf{l} = \oint_C -\left(\frac{\partial \mathbf{A}}{\partial t} + \nabla V \right) \cdot d\mathbf{l}$$

$$= \iint_S -\left(\nabla \times \frac{\partial \mathbf{A}}{\partial t} + \nabla \times \nabla V \right) \cdot d\mathbf{S} \tag{19.74}$$

where S is any surface bounded by the contour C of the loop.

Now, $\nabla \times \nabla V = 0$ (a vector identity)

Also, we can interchange the order of the operators of time and space on the first term on the right. Hence, we have

$$V = \oint_C \mathbf{E} \cdot d\mathbf{l} = -\left(\frac{\partial}{\partial t} \right) \iint_S (\nabla \times \mathbf{A}) \cdot d\mathbf{S} = -\left(\frac{\partial}{\partial t} \right) \iint_S \mathbf{B} \cdot d\mathbf{S} \tag{19.75}$$

Hence, the induced emf in the loop is equal to the time-rate of change of the flux linking the loop. This is a maximum, when the normal to the loop is parallel to the local $\mathbf{B}$. V is zero, when $\alpha = \pi/2$. Either of these two conditions can be used to determine the direction of the wave, and locate, say, a clandestine broadcasting station. Usually $\alpha = \pi/2$ condition is used, because the zero of V can be detected more accurately than a maxima. With two or more search loops, the location of a transmitting antenna can be determined with a high degree of accuracy (Figure 19.16).

It should be noted that when $R \to \infty$, then the voltage V is not necessarily the induced emf, because the circuit may be excited in the electric dipole mode. For a symmetrical loop as shown in Figure 19.15(b), when the $\mathbf{E}$ vector is in the plane of the loop, but is perpendicular to the pair of the wires leading to the loop, an extra voltage appears on R which comes from the dipole excitation and adds to the induced emf. But if the co-planar $\mathbf{E}$ is parallel to the two wires leading to R, then the charge oscillates from one end of the wire to the other end, and V is not affected by the dipole oscillation, and so Eq. (19.75) is correct.

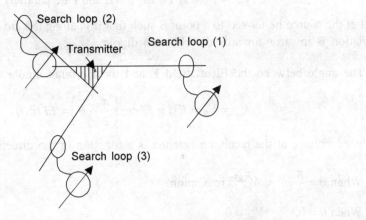

Figure 19.16 Locating a transmitter by search loop antennae.

19.6.2 Hertzian Dipole Parameters as a Receiving Antenna

(A) Radiation Pattern and Polarization

We consider a Hertzian dipole, which of course is a small length of wire with an infinitesimal gap at the centre, placed in an incoming radiation field. The dipole is located at the origin of the coordinate system, its axis being along the z-axis. A source of an electromagnetic wave is located at a very large distance R from the dipole which generates an electromagnetic wave linearly polarized in the plane of the paper.

Let this source be located at A [Figure 19.17(a)] on the y-axis (i.e. along the centre of the dipole orthogonal to its axis, i.e. $\theta = \pi/2$. So the $\mathbf{E}$ field will be polarized along the z-direction and hence parallel to the Hertz dipole.

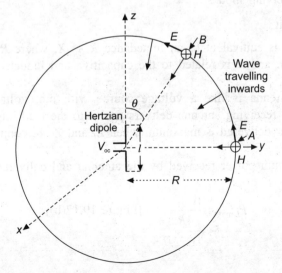

Figure 19.17(a) Hertzian dipole as a receiving antenna.

The o.c. voltage between the terminals of the dipole will be

$$V_{oc} = V_A = \mathbf{E} \cdot \mathbf{l} = El \qquad (\mathbf{E} \text{ and } \mathbf{l} \text{ are parallel}) \tag{19.75a}$$

Let the source be moved to a point B such that it is along the arc of radius R and the direction of radiation is inwards towards the Hertzian dipole.

The angle between the Elect. field $\mathbf{E}$ and the Hertzian dipole $= \dfrac{\pi}{2} - \theta$

$$V_{oc} = V_B = \mathbf{E} \cdot l = El \cos\left(\frac{\pi}{2} - \theta\right) = El \sin\theta \tag{19.75b}$$

$\therefore$ Induced voltage at the receiving antenna is a function of the direction of incoming radiation θ.

When $\theta = \dfrac{\pi}{2}$, V_{oc} is maximum

When $\theta = 0$, $V_{oc} = 0$

Thus $\sin\theta$ is the factor of dependence for V_{oc} (for a given polarization).

It should be remembered that the radiation pattern for a transmitting Hertzian dipole is $\sin\theta$. So the Hertzian dipole shows the same directional dependence for both the transmitting and the receiving mode. This is true for any radiating system, i.e. the radiation pattern for an antenna is identical for both transmitting and receiving.

We have kept the orientation of $\mathbf{E}$ unchanged in the movement of source so far. If the polarization of $\mathbf{E}$ is changed by moving the point A to the x-axis, the terminal voltage of the Hertz dipole changes and becomes zero when $\mathbf{E}$ is oriented in the x-direction. So the o.c. voltage is also a function of the polarization of the incoming radiation.

For the Hertzian dipole, V_{oc} will be maximum when $\mathbf{E}$ is along θ-direction, i.e. $\mathbf{E} = \mathbf{i}_\theta E_\theta$. So an antenna responds maximally to that polarization in the receiving mode, which it generates in the transmitting mode, i.e. the state polarization of a receiving antenna is same as that which it is capable of generating. Thus the radiation pattern and the polarization of an antenna are identical in transmitting and receiving modes.

(B)   Equivalent Circuit

A transmitting antenna is equivalent to an impedance $R + jX$, where R is related to the power radiated by the antenna, and X is related to the capacitive and inductive fields surrounding the antenna.

The receiving antenna is like a voltage source with o.c. voltage V_{oc} and an internal impedance $R + jX$. The receiving antenna delivers power to the load impedance Z_L connected to its terminals. The power delivered is maximum when Z_L and Z are conjugates of each other, i.e. $Z_L = R - jX$.

Hence, the maximum power received by the antenna and delivered to the load is then

$$P_{L\max} = \frac{|V_{oc}|^2}{4R} \qquad \text{[Figure 19.17(b)]} \tag{19.75c}$$

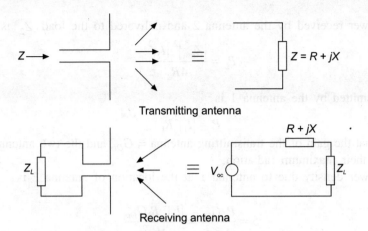

Figure 19.17(b)   Equivalent circuits of the antenna.

(C)   Effective Aperture (or Area)

Let the Poynting vector of the incident radiation on the receiving antenna be **S**.

∴   Power density of the incident wave = S watts/m^2

This antenna taps a power P_L from the wave.

∴   The effective aperture of the antenna $= A_e = \dfrac{P_L}{S}$ (19.75d)

This parameter is special to the receiving antenna and it gives the power capturing ability of a receiving antenna.

(D)   Directive Gain

A system as shown in Figure 19.17(c) consists of a transmitting antenna 1 and a receiving antenna 2 separated by a distance r. Let the antennae 1 and 2 have internal impedances Z_1 and Z_2 respectively where antenna 2 has been connected to a conjugate load Z_2^*. From circuit considerations the two antennae would interact through a mutual impedance Z_{mu}.

Hence V_{oc} can be expressed as

$$V_{\text{oc}} = Z_{\text{mu}}I_1 \tag{19.75e}$$

Figure 19.17(c)   Transmitting and receiving antennae system.

∴ The power received by the antenna 2 and delivered to the load Z_2^* is

$$P_L = \frac{|Z_{mu}|^2 |I_1|^2}{4R_2} \qquad (19.75f)$$

The power transmitted by the antenna 1 is

$$P_t = |I_1|^2 R_1 \qquad (19.75g)$$

Let us assume that the gain of the transmitting antenna $= G_{Dt}$, and the two antennae are aligned in the direction of their maximum radiation.

∴ The power density due to antenna 1 at the location of antenna 2 is

$$S = \frac{P_t G_{Dt}}{4\pi r^2} = \frac{|I_1|^2 R_1 G_{Dt}}{4\pi r^2} \qquad (19.75h)$$

If the effective aperture of the antenna 2 is A_{e2}, then the power received by antenna 2

$$P_r = SA_{e2} = \frac{|I_1|^2 R_1 G_{Dt}}{4\pi r^2} A_{e2} \qquad (19.75j)$$

Since this is same as the power delivered to the load P_L,

then $$P_L = P_r \rightarrow \frac{|Z_{mu}|^2 |I_1|^2}{4R_2} = \frac{|I_1|^2 R_1 G_{Dt}}{4\pi r^2} A_{e2} \qquad (19.75k)$$

∴ $$|Z_{mu}|^2 = \frac{R_1 R_2 G_{Dt} A_{e2}}{\pi r^2} \qquad (19.75l)$$

By the reciprocity theorem, since the two antennae are reciprocal, so

$$|Z_{mu}|^2 = \frac{R_1 R_2 G_{Dr} A_{e1}}{\pi r^2} \qquad (19.75m)$$

∴ From Eqs. (19.75l) and (19.75m),

$$G_{Dt} A_{e2} = G_{Dr} A_{e1} \qquad (19.75n)$$

or $$\frac{G_{Dt}}{A_{e1}} = \frac{G_{Dr}}{A_{e2}} = K \text{ (a constant)} \qquad (19.75p)$$

Since in this Section (D) no specific antenna was mentioned, Eq. (19.75p) will hold $\left(\text{i.e. the ratio } \frac{G}{A_e}\right)$ only if it is a constant, which is to say that K does not depend on any type of antenna.

(E)   K for the Hertzian Dipole

First we calculate G for the Hertzian dipole

$$E(\theta) = \sin\theta$$

For a loss-less dipole,

$$G_D = D = \frac{4\pi}{\int\limits_{\theta=0}^{\pi} \int\limits_{\phi=0}^{2\pi} \sin^2\theta \sin\theta \, d\theta \, d\phi} = \frac{3}{2} \tag{19.75q}$$

Let the Hertz dipole be of length l, and be located in a radiation electric field specified as E

$$\therefore \qquad \text{Power density of the wave} = S = \frac{|E|^2}{\eta} = \frac{|E|^2}{120\pi} \tag{19.75r}$$

Maximum o.c. voltage developed at the antenna terminals,

$$V_{oc} = El$$

Note: Radiation resistance of the Hertzian dipole $= R_{rad} = \dfrac{80\pi^2 l^2}{\lambda^2}$

$\therefore$ Maximum power delivered (to the matched load)

$$P_L = \frac{V_{oc}^2}{4R_{rad}} = \frac{|E|^2 l^2}{4 \times 80\pi^2}\left(\frac{\lambda^2}{l^2}\right) \tag{19.75s}$$

$\therefore$ The effective aperture for the Hertz dipole

$$A_e = \frac{P_L}{S} = \frac{3\lambda^2}{8\pi} \tag{19.75t}$$

$\therefore$ Effective aperture of Hertzian dipole is not dependent on its length and is a function of the operating wavelength only.

$$\therefore \qquad K = \frac{G_D}{A_e} = \frac{4\pi}{\lambda^2} \tag{19.75u}$$

For a general antenna, $\qquad G_D = \dfrac{4\pi A_e}{\lambda^2} \tag{19.75v}$

It should be noted that the 'Directive Gain' is a parameter of a transmitting antenna, whereas the 'Effective Aperture' is a parameter of a receiving antenna. So for an antenna which can operate in both modes (by the theorem of reciprocity), these two parameters, G_D and A_e, are directly proportional, i.e. if an antenna has high gain while transmitting, its effective aperture will also be high while in receiving mode.

Referring back to 2-antennae system of (D), from Eq. (19.75h), we have

$$P_t = \frac{4\pi r^2 S}{G_{Dt}}$$

From Eq. (19.75d),

$$P_L = A_{e2} S = P_r$$

which combined with Eq. (19.75v), gives

$$P_r = S \cdot \frac{\lambda^2}{4\pi} G_{Dr}$$

$$\therefore \qquad \frac{P_r}{P_t} = \frac{S\lambda^2 G_{Dr}/(4\pi)}{4\pi r^2 S} = G_{Dt} \, G_{Dr} \left(\frac{\lambda}{4\pi r}\right)^2$$

$$\therefore \qquad P_r = G_{Dt} G_{Dr} \left(\frac{\lambda}{4\pi r}\right)^2 P_t \qquad\qquad (19.75w)$$

This is known as 'Friis Transmission Formula' relating the power received by one antenna to the power transmitted by another provided that the two antennae are separated by a distance $r > 2d^2/\lambda$ where d is the largest dimension of either antenna. So care must be taken to see that the two antennae are in the far field of each other.

19.7 THE RECIPROCITY THEOREM

It is known, in the theory of electrostatics, that certain relations exist between two possible potential and charge distributions on a given system of conductors (see Appendix 3). Such relations are commonly known as the 'reciprocity theorems', and similar theorems exist for the harmonic electromagnetic field. Each component of the field vector satisfies the harmonic wave equation,

$$\nabla^2 \phi + k^2 \phi = 0 \qquad\qquad (19.76)$$

However, we start by discussing a more general equation, which can be written as

$$\text{Div} \, (a \, \text{grad} \, f) + k^2 f = 0 \qquad\qquad (19.77)$$

where a and k are known functions. When $a = 1$, this equation reduces to Eq. (19.76). Let T be the volume enclosed by a closed surface S, and let f_1 and f_2 be any two solutions of the Eq. (19.77) which satisfy the same boundary conditions at any boundaries within T.

$\therefore$ It follows from the divergence theorem, that

$$\oiint_S a \left\{ f_1 \left(\frac{\partial f_2}{\partial n}\right) - f_2 \left(\frac{\partial f_1}{\partial n}\right) \right\} dS = 0 \qquad\qquad (19.78)$$

provided that the integrand is continuous across all boundaries within T.

The boundary conditions of this type are:

1. f and $(a \, \partial f/\partial n)$ are continuous, or
2. (af) and $(\partial f/\partial n)$ are continuous.

The more general boundary condition containing both these conditions is:

$a\{(\partial f/\partial n) + \alpha f\}$ and $\{\beta \, (\partial f/\partial n) + f\}$ are continuous, where α and β are continuous, and such that $(\alpha \beta) \neq 1$.

The continuity of the integrand with these conditions can be seen by writing it in the form:

$$\left(\frac{a}{1-\alpha\beta}\right)\left[\left\{f_1 + \beta\left(\frac{\partial f_1}{\partial n}\right)\right\}\left\{\left(\frac{\partial f_2}{\partial n}\right) + \alpha f_2\right\} - \left\{f_2 + \beta\left(\frac{\partial f_2}{\partial n}\right)\right\}\left\{\left(\frac{\partial f_1}{\partial n}\right) + \alpha f_1\right\}\right]$$

This theorem holds also if the boundary condition is $f = 0$ or $(\partial f/\partial n) = 0$ or more generally $(\partial f/\partial n) + \sigma f = 0$. Equation (19.78), which is valid under the appropriate boundary conditions, is one form of the reciprocity theorem. This form does not include the sources in the region. A different form of the theorem is for when the sources are present in the region under consideration, i.e. inside T. In this case, let $f_1(R)$ and $f_2(R)$ satisfy the equations,

$$\text{div} (a \text{ grad } f_1) + k^2 f_1 = -\delta(R - R_1) \tag{19.79a}$$

$$\text{div} (a \text{ grad } f_2) + k^2 f_2 = -\delta(R - R_2) \tag{19.79b}$$

where $R_1 \neq R_2$, and R_1 and R_2 are points of T. Then

$$\oiint_S a\left[f_1\left(\frac{\partial f_2}{\partial n}\right) - f_2\left(\frac{\partial f_1}{\partial n}\right)\right] dS = f_2(R_1) - f_1(R_2) \tag{19.80}$$

provided f_1 and f_2 satisfy the boundary conditions of the type mentioned earlier. If, in addition,

$$\frac{\partial f_1}{\partial n} + \sigma f_1 = 0, \quad \frac{\partial f_2}{\partial n} + \sigma f_2 = 0, \quad \text{on } S,$$

then

$$f_1(R_2) = f_2(R_1) \tag{19.81}$$

Under these conditions, the reciprocity theorem states that:

The field produced at the second source by the first source is the same as that produced at the first source by the second.

In case Eqs. (19.77) and (19.79) are not satisfied inside S, but valid outside, then the reciprocity theorems (19.78), (19.80), and (19.81) are still valid provided f_1 and f_2 satisfy suitable radiation conditions at infinity.

The corresponding theorems for the electromagnetic fields are obtained in a similar manner.

This theorem when applied to electromagnetic waves states that 'the current in a detector divided by the voltage at the source remains constant when the source and the detector are interchanged, so long as the frequency and all the impedances remain unchanged'.

This theorem is very widely used for investigating circuits as well as antennae. Here we shall prove the generalized form by using the Maxwell's equations.

To start with, we have a pair of loop antennae, one of which is being used as a transmitter, and the other is used as a receiver, as shown in Figure 19.18 shown below.

The conductors and the medium of propagation are assumed to be isotropic. The source connected to the left-hand antenna supplies a voltage V, and the detector is connected to the right-hand antenna and measures a current I.

By the reciprocity theorem, (I/V) remains unchanged, if the source and the detector are interchanged, as shown in Figure 19.19. We now consider the field a (i.e. $\mathbf{E}_a$, $\mathbf{H}_a$) that is obtained when the antenna a is the transmitter on being connected to the oscillator (the top part of the Figure 19.19), and then the different field b (i.e. $\mathbf{E}_b$, $\mathbf{H}_b$) when the antenna b is made the transmitter by connecting it to the oscillator as shown in the lower part of Figure 19.19. We assume the frequency and the impedances to remain unchanged for these two arrangements.

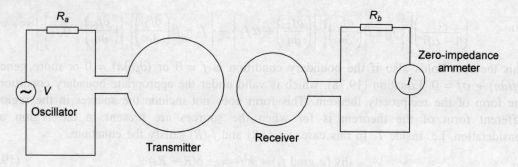

Figure 19.18 A pair of loop antennae. The one on the left (transmitter) is excited by an oscillator, supplying a voltage V. The other (receiver) is connected to a load resistance R_b through a zero-impedance ammeter, measuring the current I.

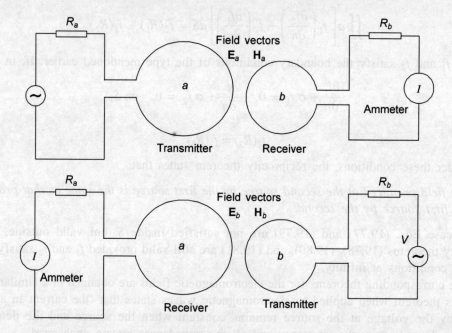

Figure 19.19 A pair of loop antennae with the source in a at the top, and then in b (bottom). The frequency and the impedances remain unchanged.

Then for any point in the space which includes the antennae as well as the source, the following vector identity holds:

$$\nabla \cdot (\mathbf{E}_a \times \mathbf{H}_b - \mathbf{E}_b \times \mathbf{H}_a) = \mathbf{H}_b \cdot (\nabla \times \mathbf{E}_a) - \mathbf{E}_a \cdot (\nabla \times \mathbf{H}_b) - \mathbf{H}_a \cdot (\nabla \times \mathbf{E}_b) - \mathbf{E}_b \cdot (\nabla \times \mathbf{H}_a) \quad (19.82)$$

Using the Maxwell's equations,

$$\nabla \cdot (\mathbf{E}_a \times \mathbf{H}_b - \mathbf{E}_b \times \mathbf{H}_a) = -\mathbf{H}_b \cdot \left(\frac{\partial \mathbf{B}_a}{\partial t} \right) - \mathbf{E}_a \cdot \left(\mathbf{J}_{fb} + \frac{\partial \mathbf{D}_b}{\partial t} \right)$$

$$+ \mathbf{H}_a \cdot \left(\frac{\partial \mathbf{B}_b}{\partial t} \right) + \mathbf{E}_b \cdot \left(\mathbf{J}_{fa} + \frac{\partial \mathbf{D}_a}{\partial t} \right) \quad (19.83)$$

Since we are considering the time-harmonic fields, $\dfrac{\partial}{\partial t} \equiv j\omega$,

and on simplifying, this equation reduces to:

$$\nabla \cdot (\mathbf{E}_a \times \mathbf{H}_b - \mathbf{E}_b \times \mathbf{H}_a) = \mathbf{E}_b \cdot \mathbf{J}_{fa} - \mathbf{E}_a \cdot \mathbf{J}_{fb} \qquad (19.84)$$

For points outside the source, $\mathbf{J}_f = \sigma\mathbf{E}$ (assuming that the Ohm's law holds). But within the source there is another electric field intensity $\mathbf{E}_s$, and hence, in general:

$$\mathbf{J}_{fa} = \sigma(\mathbf{E}_a + \mathbf{E}_{sa}) \qquad (19.85a)$$

$$\mathbf{J}_{fb} = \sigma(\mathbf{E}_b + \mathbf{E}_{sb}) \qquad (19.85b)$$

The quantities $\mathbf{E}_{sa}$ and $\mathbf{E}_{sb}$ are the applied field intensities within the source when it is in the loop a, and when it is in the loop b, respectively.

$\mathbf{J}_{fa}$ = the current density at any point in space, when the source is in a
$\mathbf{J}_{fb}$ = the current density at any point in space, when the source is in b.

∴ Substituting these in Eq. (19.84), we obtain

$$\nabla \cdot (\mathbf{E}_a \times \mathbf{H}_b - \mathbf{E}_b \times \mathbf{H}_a) = \mathbf{E}_{sa} \cdot \mathbf{J}_{fb} - \mathbf{E}_{sb} \cdot \mathbf{J}_{fa} \qquad (19.86)$$

In general, the right-hand side of the equation is not equal to zero.

This above relationship holds for any pair of electromagnetic fields at any points in space, including the region inside the sources. Hence, integrating over the whole space,

$$\iiint_\infty \nabla \cdot (\mathbf{E}_a \times \mathbf{H}_b - \mathbf{E}_b \times \mathbf{H}_a)\, dv = \iiint_\infty (\mathbf{E}_{sa} \cdot \mathbf{J}_{fb} - \mathbf{E}_{sb} \cdot \mathbf{J}_{fa})\, dv \qquad (19.87)$$

By applying the divergence theorem,

$$\oiint_\infty (\mathbf{E}_a \times \mathbf{H}_b - \mathbf{E}_b \times \mathbf{H}_a)\, d\mathbf{S} = \iiint_\infty (\mathbf{E}_{sa} \cdot \mathbf{J}_{fb} - \mathbf{E}_{sb} \cdot \mathbf{J}_{fa})\, dv \qquad (19.88)$$

If the sources are now constrained to a finite volume, the surface of integration on the left-hand side is infinitely away from them, and then there is a plane wave with $\mathbf{E}$ and $\mathbf{H}$ orthogonal and transverse.

∴ $$\mathbf{E} \times \mathbf{H} = \mathbf{r}_1 EH \qquad (19.89)$$

where $\mathbf{r}_1$ is the unit radial vector.

∴ $$\mathbf{H}_a = \left(\frac{1}{Z_0}\right)\mathbf{r}_1 \times \mathbf{E}_a \quad \text{and} \quad \mathbf{H}_b = \left(\frac{1}{Z_0}\right)\mathbf{r}_1 \times \mathbf{E}_b \qquad (19.90)$$

∴ The integrand on the left-hand side of Eq. (19.88) is

$$(\mathbf{E}_a \times \mathbf{H}_b - \mathbf{E}_b \times \mathbf{H}_a) = \left(\frac{1}{Z_0}\right)[\mathbf{E}_a \times (\mathbf{r}_1 \times \mathbf{E}_b) - \mathbf{E}_b \times (\mathbf{r}_1 \times \mathbf{E}_a)] = 0 \qquad (19.91)$$

at points infinitely remote from the sources.

∴ The integral on the right-hand side of Eq. (19.88) must also be zero, i.e.

$$\iiint_{\infty} (\mathbf{E}_{sa} \cdot \mathbf{J}_{fb} - \mathbf{E}_{sb} \cdot \mathbf{J}_{fa}) \, dv = 0 \qquad\qquad (19.92)$$

The integration is extended to all space, but it can be restricted to the sources, since $\mathbf{E}_{sa}$ and $\mathbf{E}_{sb}$ are zero elsewhere.

$$\therefore \qquad \iiint_{\infty} (\mathbf{E}_{sa} \cdot \mathbf{J}_{fb}) \, dv = \iiint_{\infty} (\mathbf{E}_{sb} \cdot \mathbf{J}_{fa}) \, dv \qquad\qquad (19.93)$$

where the integrals are evaluated over the regions where $\mathbf{E}_{sa}$ and $\mathbf{E}_{sb}$ are non-zeroes.

Physically what this equation means, can be explained in terms of the pair of the loop antennae a and b, i.e.

$$\iiint_{a} (\mathbf{E}_{sa} \cdot \mathbf{J}_{fb}) dv = \iiint (\mathbf{E}_{sa} \cdot d\mathbf{l})(\mathbf{J}_{fb} \cdot d\mathbf{S}) = V_{sa} I_{b \text{ in } a}$$

where V_{sa} is the voltage supplied by the source in a, and $I_{b \text{ in } a}$ is the current in the same loop a when b is energized.

Similarly,

$$\iiint_{b} (\mathbf{E}_{sb} \cdot \mathbf{J}_{fa}) \, dv = \iiint (\mathbf{E}_{sb} \cdot d\mathbf{l}) (\mathbf{J}_{fa} \cdot d\mathbf{S}) = V_{sb} I_{a \text{ in } b}$$

$$\therefore \qquad V_{sa} I_{b \text{ in } a} = V_{sb} I_{a \text{ in } b}$$

$$\therefore \qquad \frac{I_{a \text{ in } b}}{V_{sa}} = \frac{I_{b \text{ in } a}}{V_{sb}}$$

i.e. the physical interpretation is:

The current induced in b when a is energized, divided by the voltage applied on a is equal to the current induced in a when b is energized, divided by the applied voltage on b (keeping the frequency and the impedances unchanged).

This is the reciprocity theorem. It is valid for any pair of antennae. It should also be noted that this theorem is concerned only with the ratio (I/V), and does not say anything about the power expended by the source (which usually changes when the source is moved from one position to the other).

PROBLEMS

19.1 The field near to a Hertzian dipole of length l has the following principal components in spherical polar coordinates:

$$E_r = \frac{ql \cos \theta}{2\pi \varepsilon_0 r^3}; \qquad E_\theta = \frac{ql \sin \theta}{4\pi \varepsilon_0 r^3}; \qquad B_\phi = \frac{\mu_0 il \sin \theta}{4\pi r^2}$$

If i is oscillating and equal to $I\sqrt{2} \cos \omega t$, prove that the predominant energy flow in this region is likewise oscillatory, being such that a quantity of energy given by

$$W = \frac{i^2 l^2}{6\pi\varepsilon_0 \omega^2 r^3}$$

flows out and back from a sphere of radius r, twice in each cycle of the dipole current.

19.2 Show that the phase velocity of **H** field of an oscillating dipole is

$$v_\phi = c\left(1 + \frac{c^2}{\omega^2 r^2}\right)$$

Show also that the phase velocities of r- and θ-components of **E** field are:

$$v_r = c\left(1 + \frac{c^2}{\omega^2 r^2}\right), \quad \text{and} \quad v_\theta = c\left[\frac{(\omega r/c)^4 - (\omega r/c)^2 + 1}{(\omega r/c)^4 - 2(\omega r/c)^2}\right] \text{ respectively}.$$

(The charges of the dipole are $\pm Qe^{j\omega t}$.)

19.3 The symmetry of Maxwell's equations in free space implies that any system of travelling waves defined by the field vectors **E**, **B**, has a dual in which $\mathbf{E}' = -c\mathbf{B}$, $\mathbf{B}' = \mathbf{E}/c$. What source would produce a field which is the dual of that set up by a Hertzian dipole?

19.4 Discuss and draw the image of a horizontal dipole antenna above a perfectly conducting plane, and show that the current in the image and the current in the antenna flow in *opposite* directions.

Discuss and draw again the image of a vertical dipole (antenna) above a perfectly conducting plane, and show that in this case, the current in the image as well as in the dipole flow in the *same* direction.

19.5 Considering the far fields of the electric dipole and the magnetic dipole, show that they are duals of each other.

19.6 The field of a magnetic dipole is such that $V = 0$ and $\mathbf{A} \neq 0$. Is it possible to have a radiation field which has $V \neq 0$, $\mathbf{A} = 0$?

19.7 A sealed plastic box contains a transmitting antenna radiating electromagnetic waves. How would you identify whether it is a magnetic or electric dipole?

20 Electromagnetism and Special Relativity

20.1 INTRODUCTION

So far, in our study of electromagnetism, whenever we have distinguished the 'electrostatic' field of stationary charges from the 'electromagnetic' field of moving charges, we have made a tacit assumption that the earth is fixed, and 'stationary' means at rest relative to the earth's surface. But the earth is not fixed in any absolute sense, and the dominant factor is whether there exists rest or motion with respect to a particular observer. Electromagnetic observations, made by two observers in relative motion, will differ. However before we apply the relativistic concepts to the electromagnetic phenomena, we shall have a look at the concepts of relativity in the context of classical mechanics.

Furthermore, if we have a look at the historical sequence of the scientific developments, we find that Maxwell's electromagnetic theory (1855–1865) was based on the experimental laws of Coulomb, Ampere, and Faraday. The special theory of relativity was enunciated in 1904–1905. It was L. Page, who in 1912 said that 'if the principle of special relativity had been enunciated before the date of Oersted's discovery of the magnetic effects of electric currents, then the fundamental relations of Maxwellian electrodynamics could have been predicted on theoretical grounds as a direct consequence of the fundamental laws of electrostatics, extended so as to apply to charges in relative motion, as well as to charges at rest'.

We shall try to show in this chapter that starting from electrostatics (i.e. Coulomb's law), and applying the transformations of special relativity, we can derive Ampere's, Faraday's laws, and the generalization into Maxwell's equations.

This will give us a better insight and deeper understanding of all aspects of the electromagnetic theory, and thereby lay the groundwork for more advanced study of electrodynamics in moving media. It will also help us in finding correct solutions for indeterminate or ambiguous problems caused by the flux-cutting rule. Finally, various isolated laws will appear as different facets of a single comprehensive theory. However, before we apply the concepts of relativity to electromagnetic phenomena, we shall have a look at some of the simpler phenomena in classical mechanics so as to be clear about the 'relative velocity'.

20.2 GALILEIAN RELATIVITY (GALILEO GALILEI)

This is the simplest case in classical mechanics, so much so that it is applied without any conscious thought process.

Let us consider a boat, on a river moving downstream with a velocity v relative to the water of the river, and that the river water has a velocity u (in the same direction).

Hence the velocity of the boat relative to a stationary observer on the bank of the river = v + u.

And (to an observer sitting on the boat), the observer on the bank appears to move with a velocity equal to = −(v + u).

∴   The position of the boat can be specified with respect to:

1. a fixed point on the bank of the river, or
2. a point on the river—moving with the water, i.e. a drifting bouy.

So now we choose a coordinate system S fixed to a point which is fixed on the bank, and another coordinate system S' whose origin is fixed on the drifting bouy (Figure 20.1).

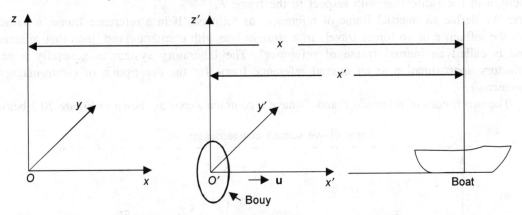

Figure 20.1 Coordinate systems S and S'.

Hence,

x = the position of the boat with respect to the coordinate system S; and
x' = the position of the boat with respect to the coordinate system S'; then we can write:

$$x' = x - ut \qquad (20.1)$$

This equation expresses the position of the boat relative to the drifting bouy in terms of the position and the time measured by an observer fixed on the bank.

Or, we could equally well have written this relationship in the form

$$x = x' + ut', \quad (t = t') \qquad (20.2)$$

where the position of the boat relative to the bank has now been expressed in terms of the position and the time measured by an observer sitting on the bouy and drifting along with it.

This transformation from one coordinate system to another as given by Eq. (20.1) or (20.2) is known as the Galilean transformation, named after Galileo Galilei. In classical Newtonian mechanics, the basic hypothesis is that the laws of motion hold equally in all rigid coordinate frames moving with uniform rectilinear velocity with respect to each other. The equations of motion remain unchanged in the two systems by using the two transformation relations mentioned above. This invariance of the laws of mechanics under a Galilean transformation is called the 'Galilean relativity'. There are certain assumptions implicit in this transformation. They are that the mass and the dimensions remain same at rest as under motion. Also, it is important to note that the variation of time is at the same rate for both moving and fixed observers. As we shall see later, that these assumptions are valid only when the velocities under consideration are much smaller when compared with the velocity of light (= c), i.e. v << c. These laws become different when we have much higher velocities, i.e. the velocities comparable to that of the light velocity.

20.3 ELECTROMAGNETIC PHENOMENA AS VIEWED BY DIFFERENT OBSERVERS

We have two inertial frames of reference F and F' where the frame F' moves with a constant velocity u in the x-direction with respect to the frame F.

(*Note:* We define an 'inertial frame of reference' as follows: 'If in a reference frame, a particle under the influence of no forces travels in a straight line with constant speed, then that reference frame is called an inertial frame of reference'. The laboratory system is generally a very satisfactory approximation to an inertial reference frame for the description of electromagnetic phenomena.)

The two frames of reference F and F' have a common x-axis as shown in Figure 20.2 below.

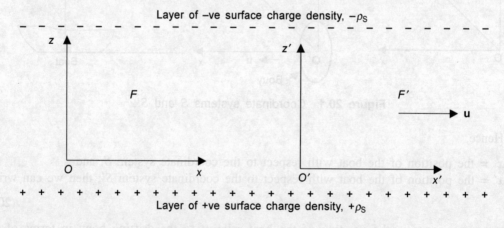

Figure 20.2 Parallel layers of electric charge.

There exist two layers of electric charges parallel to the x-y plane, y-axis being normal (into) the plane of the paper. We consider an observer making measurements at O, a point between the two sheets of charges (as shown above) of densities $\pm \rho_S$ per unit area. Since the electric field is stationary in this frame, the observer will detect an electric field having one component given by

$$E_z = \frac{\rho_S}{\varepsilon_0}$$

(20.3)

and no magnetic field.

In the other frame of reference F' with the axes $O' x' y' z'$, moving relatively to F with the velocity u in the direction Ox, an observer (sitting at O') will also detect the electric field E_z, but for him the charges are gliding backwards with the velocity u, and so the upper charge-sheet appears as a current-sheet of $(\rho_S u)$ amps/metre directed in the direction $O'x'$ whilst the lower charge-sheet appears as a similar current-sheet in the reverse direction. The diagram (Figure 20.3)

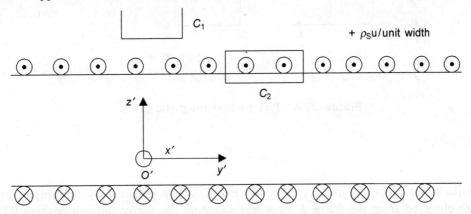

Figure 20.3 End-view of the charge-sheets as seen by an observer in the moving frame of reference F'.

shows the end-view of these currents. At infinity they seem coincident, so produce no magnetic field, and hence a magnetic circuit such as C_1 shows that there exists no magnetic field anywhere outside the currents, while the circuit C_2 shows that between them (the current-sheets—as they appear to the observer in the moving frame of reference), there exists a magnetic field in the direction $O'y'$, which is given by

$$H'_y = u\rho_S = -J'_{Sx} \tag{20.4}$$

or

$$B'_y = \mu_0 \rho_S u = \mu_0 \varepsilon_0 u E_z = \left(\frac{u}{c^2}\right) E_z \tag{20.5}$$

Thus the observer O' in the frame F' observes this magnetic field as well as the electric field which the observer O in the frame F discerns, i.e.

$$E'_z = E_z \tag{20.6}$$

Let the charge-sheets now be replaced by iron poles with respect to which the frame F is at rest. Let the magnetic field between these poles be observed from F as B_z (Figure 20.4).

If the frame F' carried a conductor along the axis $O'y'$, then an emf (uB_z) would be found to be induced in it in the direction $O'y'$. This emf is a sign that if the conductor were absent, there would be an electric field given by

$$E'_y = -uB_z \tag{20.7}$$

The observer in the frame F' will observe this field in addition to the magnetic field B_z.

The magnetic flux density B'_y given by the Eq. (20.5), introduced into the observations on the moving frame F' by its relative motion to the frame F, is got by multiplying (F)'s electric field E_z by (u/c^2) and swinging the vector through negative 90° about the direction of u. If (F)'s field had contained a component E_y, the same rule would give

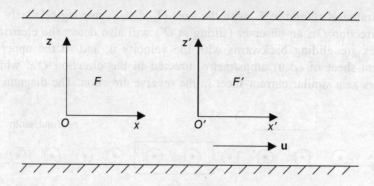

Figure 20.4 Two parallel magnetic poles.

$$B'_z = -\left(\frac{u}{c^2}\right)E_y \tag{20.8}$$

Similarly the electric force E'_y given by Eq. (20.7) is obtained by multiplying the flux density B_z observed from the frame F by u and swinging the vector through positive 90° about the direction of u. So by similar arguments [as we had for Eq. (20.8)], if the frame (F)'s field had contained a component B_y, then the same rule (mentioned before in this paragraph) would give

$$E'_z = uB_y \tag{20.9}$$

But the components in the x-direction (i.e. the direction of motion) would be observed equally from both the frames. Hence

$$E'_x = E_x \quad \text{and} \quad B'_x = B_x \tag{20.10}$$

Thus building up a general field by superposition of perpendicular components. we find that the general relation between the vectors $\mathbf{E}$, $\mathbf{B}$ in the frame F and $\mathbf{E}'$, $\mathbf{B}'$ in the frame F' which has a relative motion u with respect to F in the direction Ox, is contained in these equations:

$$E'_x = E_x, \qquad E'_y = E_y - uB_z, \qquad E'_z = E_z + uB_y \tag{20.11a}$$

$$B'_x = B_x, \qquad B'_y = B_y + \left(\frac{u}{c^2}\right)E_z, \qquad B'_z = B_z - \left(\frac{u}{c^2}\right)E_y \tag{20.11b}$$

These equations have been derived with the assumption of uniform fields, but with fields which vary from place to place, they are still true at the instant when the frames F and F' coincide. Equations (20.11) can be written in compact vector form as:

$$\mathbf{E}' = \mathbf{E} + (\mathbf{u} \times \mathbf{B}) \tag{20.12a}$$

$$\mathbf{B}' = \mathbf{B} - \left(\frac{1}{c^2}\right)(\mathbf{u} \times \mathbf{E}) \tag{20.12b}$$

As a first application, we may get the formula for the force on a moving charge. Let the charge q move with a velocity v = u in the frame F in which exists both an electric field $\mathbf{E}$ and a magnetic field $\mathbf{B}$. Let q move with the origin of F', it is then static in F', and so the force on it is given by

$$\mathbf{P}' = q\mathbf{E}' \tag{20.13}$$

Transforming to the frame F, and assuming:

1. q is same for both the frames (true);
2. $\mathbf{P} = \mathbf{P}'$ (true for the order of the accuracy here considered),

we get [from Eq. (20.12)]

$$\mathbf{P} = q[\mathbf{E} + (\mathbf{u} \times \mathbf{B})] \tag{20.14}$$

This is the important *Lorentz Force Formula*, which we had used to define the magnetic flux density vector **B**.

20.4 TRANSFORMATION OF ELECTRIC AND MAGNETIC FIELDS

Equations (20.11) were derived from the Galilean relativity which is applicable to the Newtonian mechanics.

∴ Similar to these principles, the physical results obtained should be independent, whether the frame F or F' is regarded as fixed, i.e. it is valid to consider F' as fixed and F moving in the x' direction with a velocity $(-u)$.

∴ The unprimed fields should be obtained from the primed fields by a set of relations corresponding exactly to Eqs. (20.11) with the primed and the unprimed quantities interchanged, and u replaced by $(-u)$.

∴ Equations (20.11) should transform to

$$E_x = E'_x, \qquad E_y = E'_y + uB'_z, \qquad E_z = E'_z - uB'_y \tag{20.15a}$$

$$B_x = B'_x, \qquad B_y = B'_y - \left(\frac{u}{c^2}\right)E'_z, \qquad B_z = B'_z + \left(\frac{u}{c^2}\right)E'_y \tag{20.15b}$$

But, if Eqs. (20.11) are solved to obtain the unprimed field quantities, then the following set of relations is obtained by the steps which are obtained from Eqs. (20.12), i.e. Eqs. (20.12) can be re-written as

$$\mathbf{E} = \mathbf{E}' - (\mathbf{u} \times \mathbf{B})$$

$$= \mathbf{E}' - (\mathbf{u} \times \mathbf{B}') - \left(\frac{1}{c^2}\right)[\mathbf{u} \times (\mathbf{u} \times \mathbf{E})]$$

If **u** has only x-component, the components of $(\mathbf{u} \times \mathbf{E})$ are $0, -uE_z, uE_y$; and of $[\mathbf{u} \times (\mathbf{u} \times \mathbf{E})]$ are $0, -u^2E_y, -u^2E_z$.

Thus the equations for **E** and **B** in terms of **E**' and **B**' are

$$E_x = E'_x \tag{20.16a}$$

$$E_y = \frac{E'_y + uB'_z}{1 - \dfrac{u^2}{c^2}} \tag{20.16b}$$

$$E_z = \frac{E'_z - uB'_y}{1 - \dfrac{u^2}{c^2}} \tag{20.16c}$$

and

$$B_x = B_x' \tag{20.17a}$$

$$B_y = \frac{B_y' - \left(\dfrac{u}{c^2}\right)E_z'}{1 - \dfrac{u^2}{c^2}} \tag{20.17b}$$

$$B_z = \frac{B_z' + \left(\dfrac{u}{c^2}\right)E_y'}{1 - \dfrac{u^2}{c^2}} \tag{20.17c}$$

which can be written in the compact form

$$E_x = E_x', \qquad E_y = \beta^2(E_y' + uB_z'), \qquad E_z = \beta^2(E_z' - uB_y') \tag{20.18a}$$

$$B_x = B_x', \qquad B_y = \beta^2\left[B_y' - \left(\frac{u}{c^2}\right)E_z'\right], \qquad B_z = \beta^2\left[B_z' + \left(\frac{u}{c^2}\right)E_y'\right] \tag{20.18b}$$

where $\beta^2 = \left(1 - \dfrac{u^2}{c^2}\right)^{-1}$.

Then, how do we explain this lack of self-consistency in these equations? That is, they do not transform properly into a similar set when solved with primed and unprimed quantities interchanged and u replaced by −u. We have to look for the reasons for this inconsistency.

This inconsistency implies that something is wrong with the underlying principles of this above analysis, i.e. either with Newtonian mechanics and Galilean relativity, or with classical electromagnetics, or with both. Historically, this was the difficulty faced by the physicists towards the end of the nineteenth century. The uncertainty and the controversy were associated with the correct formulation of the velocity of light, and was eliminated by the special (or the restricted) principle of relativity.

What we have been saying so far has been that:

The laws of nature are same referred to all frames of reference, which are in uniform translation with respect to one another (i.e. there is no meaning in absolute velocity).

So, we consider, as before, two frames of reference F and F'. The coordinates of a point, in the frame F, are (x, y, z), and in the frame F' are $(x - ut, y, z)$; i.e. a particle with velocity u_1 in the x-direction with respect to the frame F, will appear to have a velocity $(u_1 - u)$ in the frame F'.

This, in fact, conflicts with the observation of constant velocity of light in both the frames of reference.

We shall not go into the historical details of this controversy regarding the velocity of light. Suffice it to say that the root of the conflict was the question of existence of an 'aether'. We have seen that Maxwell showed light to be an electromagnetic phenomenon, and that the velocity of light was given by $c = (\mu\varepsilon)^{-1/2}$—a characteristic of the medium, and presumably the velocity is measured relative to the medium. Under these circumstances, if the frame F is assumed to be stationary in the medium, the frame F' moves through the medium with a velocity u in the +x-direction. Then a light wave travelling in the medium with a velocity c in the

+x-direction, should appear to have a velocity (c − u) to an observer in the frame F', moving along with it. This result conflicts with our results as we obtained in Eqs. (20.18), as the factor $(1 - u^2/c^2)$ obtrudes itself. Admittedly, c is a very large velocity, and so this factor is very small; but even so its presence raises doubts about the validity of the whole theory. It is not difficult to cook Eq. (20.11) in such a way as to remove this anomaly. For example, if it could be shown that the true equation for $\mathbf{E}'$ were

$$E'_x = E_x \qquad (20.19a)$$

$$E'_y = \beta(E_y - uB_z) \qquad (20.19b)$$

$$E'_z = \beta(E_z + uB_y) \qquad (20.19c)$$

where

$$\beta = \left(1 - \frac{u^2}{c^2}\right)^{-1/2} \qquad (20.20)$$

with a similarly modified set of equations for $\mathbf{B}'$, i.e.

$$B'_x = B_x \qquad (20.19d)$$

$$B'_y = \beta\left[B_y + \left(\frac{u}{c^2}\right)E_z\right] \qquad (20.19e)$$

$$B'_z = \beta\left[B_z - \left(\frac{u}{c^2}\right)E_y\right] \qquad (20.19f)$$

the process of solution would give

$$E_x = E'_x \qquad (20.21a)$$

$$E_y = \frac{E'_y + uB'_z}{\beta\left(1 - \dfrac{u^2}{c^2}\right)} = \beta(E'_y + uB'_z) \qquad (20.21b)$$

$$E_z = \frac{E'_z - uB'_y}{\beta\left(1 - \dfrac{u^2}{c^2}\right)} = \beta(E'_z - uB'_y) \qquad (20.21c)$$

and so forth, so that the new equations would have the same form as Eqs. (20.19) except that the sign of u has been changed. It should be noted in passing that Eqs. (20.19) cannot be expressed directly in vector form, because the factor β does not multiply every component.

However, the mere fact that β makes the answer come true (right) does not justify us in inserting it. There must be some much more solid argument for its presence. To explain it, we need a fundamental enquiry into the relation between the physical quantities as measured in the two frames of reference; not merely of electromagnetic quantities, but of length and time, and—ultimately—of mass. For the two frames of reference having a relative motion, which is linear and uniform, this inquiry is the province of the 'Special Theory of Relativity'.

20.5 THE RELATIVITY OF SPACE AND TIME

The 'relativity' of electromagnetic measurements to a particular observer is a consequence of the elementary electromagnetic principles, but the more subtle considerations lead to a similar 'relativity' about the fundamental measures of mass, length, and time. We shall consider first the last two.

We have proved that the electromagnetic waves travel with the velocity $c = (\mu_0 \varepsilon_0)^{-1/2}$ in free space. Since the field equations on which this deduction is based are relative to a particular observer, we do not expect the velocity as observed by an observer in a 'moving' frame of reference to be the same. Experiments [especially those of Michaelson and Morley (1887)] show that *the velocity of light or other electromagnetic signals is the same for all observers.*

This means a departure from the normal kinematic ideas; if a particle has a velocity (U, V, W) with respect to the frame of reference F, it is assumed to have the velocity (U − u, V, W) with respect to the moving frame F', and so it cannot have the same velocity with respect to both. In order that the light may have the same velocity c with respect to both F and F', we find it necessary to introduce a scheme wherein *the measures of length l and time t are relative to a particular observer.*

Let F and F' be the frames of reference having relative motion u, and let them coincide at $t = 0$. An *event* is defined as something happening at a specified place and time—e.g. a flash of light or a pulse of radiation occurring at a place (x, y, z) and time (t). In ordinary or classical Newtonian mechanics, an event (x, y, z, t) observed from the frame F will have the coordinates

$$x' = x - ut, \qquad y' = y, \qquad z' = z, \qquad t' = t \tag{20.22}$$

observed from the frame F'. These are linear relationships, but we have seen that they cannot satisfy the 'constant velocity of light' condition.

The path of a particle in either F or F' is a sequence of events. If a particle is acted on by no forces, it moves (we assume) with uniform velocity in a straight line with respect to either F or F'; its path may be represented by a straight line with time members uniformly spread along it. In order that this may be true, the relations between (x, y, z, t) and (x', y', z', t') must be linear.

A flash of light occurring at the origin, at the instant when the two frames F and F' coincide, will spread out so that at the time t an observer in F sees it as having reached the sphere

$$x^2 + y^2 + z^2 = c^2 t^2$$

and, in F'

$$x'^2 + y'^2 + z'^2 = c^2 t'^2$$

Hence the relation between (x, y, z, t) and (x', y', z', t') must be such that

$$x'^2 + y'^2 + z'^2 - c^2 t'^2 = x^2 + y^2 + z^2 - c^2 t^2 \tag{20.23}$$

and this combination of coordinates is said to be *invariant*.

We find it possible to satisfy [Eq. (20.23)] with $y' = y$, $z' = z$, and x', t' linear functions of x, t such that

$$x'^2 - c^2 t'^2 = x^2 - c^2 t^2 \tag{20.24}$$

Let those functions be (since $x = 0$, $t = 0 \rightarrow x' = 0$, $t' = 0$)

$$x' = Ax + Bt, \; t' = Cx + Dt; \text{ then from (20.24)}$$

$$(Ax + Bt)^2 - c^2(Cx + Dt)^2 = x^2 - c^2 t^2$$

whence

$$A^2 - c^2 C^2 = 1, \qquad c^2 D^2 - B^2 = c^2, \qquad AB - c^2 CD = 0 \qquad (20.25)$$

Now $x' = y' = z' = 0$ is moving with the velocity u with respect to F.

$$\therefore \qquad \frac{B}{A} = -u \qquad (20.26)$$

and Eqs. (20.25) and (20.26) give four equations for A, B, C, D.

Substituting from Eq. (20.26) in Eqs. (20.25),

$$c^2 C^2 = A^2 - 1 \qquad \text{and} \qquad c^2 D^2 = u^2 A^2 + c^2; \text{ thus}$$

$$(A^2 - 1)(u^2 A^2 + c^2) - u^2 A^4 = 0$$

whence (taking the positive root),

$$A = \left(1 - \frac{u^2}{c^2}\right)^{-1/2} = \beta \qquad (20.27a)$$

$$B = -u\beta; \qquad C = \pm \frac{\beta u}{c^2}; \qquad D = \beta \qquad (20.27b)$$

Assimilation to Eq. (20.22) requires the lower signs, and the relations are:

$$x' = \beta(x - ut), \qquad y' = y, \qquad z' = z, \qquad t' = \beta\left(t - \frac{ux}{c^2}\right) \qquad (20.28)$$

This is called the *Lorentz transformation*.

20.6 CONSEQUENCES OF THE LORENTZ TRANSFORMATION

1. Events which occur simultaneously, but at different places in one frame, are not simultaneous in the other frame. This is a consequence of $t' = \beta\left(t - \frac{ux}{c^2}\right)$.

2. If the equations are solved for x', t' in terms of x and t, we get the same relation with the sign of u changed.

3. *Contraction of lengths.* Let x'_1, x'_2 be points on the x'-axis in the frame F'; and x_1, x_2 their coordinates in the other frame F. Then,

$$x'_2 - x'_1 = \beta(x_2 - x_1) \qquad (20.29)$$

when measured at a particular time t with respect to the frame F.

Hence an observer in F sees a length divided by β, a number > 1. (This is Fitzgerald contraction.)

It should be noted that there is no contraction perpendicular to the line of motion.

4. *Dilatation of time.* Let a clock at the origin of the frame F' tick at $t' = t'_1$ and $t' = t'_2$. With respect to the frame F, we have

$$x_1 - ut_1 = 0, \qquad x_2 - ut_2 = 0, \qquad t'_1 = \beta\left(t_1 - \frac{ux_1}{c^2}\right), \qquad t'_2 = \beta\left(t_2 - \frac{ux_2}{c^2}\right)$$

i.e.
$$t_1' = \beta\left(1 - \frac{u^2}{c^2}\right)t_1 = \frac{t_1}{\beta}, \qquad t_2' = \frac{t_2}{\beta}$$

and the time-interval measured from the frame F is

$$t_2 - t_1 = \beta(t_2' - t_1') \tag{20.30}$$

—a longer time—i.e. the ticks seem to occur at a longer interval. This leads to the famous *clock paradox*.

5. *Transformation of velocities.* Let a particle have the velocity (v_x, v_y, v_z) in the frame F, and (v_x', v_y', v_z') in the frame F', where

$$v_x^2 + v_y^2 + v_z^2 = v^2 \quad \text{and} \quad v_x'^2 + v_y'^2 + v_z'^2 = v'^2$$

If the coordinates of the particle in the two frames are (x, y, z, t) and (x', y', z', t') respectively, then:

$$v_x' = \frac{dx'}{dt'} = \frac{\beta(dx - u\,dt)}{\beta\left(dt - \frac{u\,dx}{c^2}\right)} = \frac{v_x - u}{1 - \frac{uv_x}{c^2}} \tag{20.31a}$$

$$v_y' = \frac{dy'}{dt'} = \frac{dy}{\beta\left(dt - \frac{u\,dx}{c^2}\right)} = \frac{v_y}{\beta\left(1 - \frac{uv_x}{c^2}\right)} \tag{20.31b}$$

$$v_z' = \frac{dz'}{dt'} = \frac{dz}{\beta\left(dt - \frac{u\,dx}{c^2}\right)} = \frac{v_z}{\beta\left(1 - \frac{uv_x}{c^2}\right)} \tag{20.31c}$$

Similarly,

$$v_x = \frac{dx}{dt} = \frac{v_x' + u}{1 + \frac{v_x'u}{c^2}} \tag{20.31d}$$

$$v_y = \frac{dy}{dt} = \frac{v_y'}{\beta\left(1 + \frac{v_x'u}{c^2}\right)} \tag{20.31e}$$

$$v_z = \frac{dz}{dt} = \frac{v_z'}{\beta\left(1 + \frac{v_x'u}{c^2}\right)} \tag{20.31f}$$

It should be noted that if the two systems have a relative velocity $u = c$, and if a point in the F'-system has a velocity $v_x' = c$, then the value of u_x is still c.

By similarly differentiating these six equations with respect to t and t', we get

$$\frac{dv_x}{dt} = \left[\beta\left(1 + \frac{v_x'u}{c^2}\right)\right]^{-3}\frac{dv_x'}{dt'} \tag{20.31g}$$

and
$$\frac{dv_{y,z}}{dt} = \left[\beta\left(1 + \frac{v'_x u}{c^2}\right)\right]^{-2}\frac{dv'_{y,z}}{dt'} - \frac{v'_{y,z}}{\beta^2}\frac{u}{c^2}\left(1 + \frac{v'_x u}{c^2}\right)\frac{du'_x}{dt'} \qquad (20.31h)$$

The corresponding expressions for $\dfrac{du'_x}{dt'}$ and $\dfrac{du'_{y,z}}{dt'}$ can be obtained by interchanging the primed and unprimed quantities and replacing +u by −u. A point to be noted is that a constant acceleration in the F'-system does not, in general, imply a constant acceleration in the F-system. Thus,

$$c^2 - v'^2 = c^2 - \frac{\beta^2(v_x - u)^2 + v_y^2 + v_z^2}{\beta^2\left(1 - \dfrac{uv_x}{c^2}\right)^2}$$

$$= c^2 - \frac{(v_x - u)^2 + \left(1 - \dfrac{u^2}{c^2}\right)(v_y^2 + v_z^2)}{\left(1 - \dfrac{uv_x}{c^2}\right)^2}$$

$$= \frac{\left(c^2 - 2uv_x + \dfrac{u^2 v_x^2}{c^2}\right) - \left(v_x^2 - 2v_x u + u^2\right) - \left(1 - \dfrac{u^2}{c^2}\right)(v_y^2 + v_z^2)}{\left(1 - \dfrac{uv_x}{c^2}\right)^2}$$

$$= \frac{\left(1 - \dfrac{u^2}{c^2}\right)(c^2 - v^2)}{\left(1 - \dfrac{uv_x}{c^2}\right)^2}$$

i.e.

$$c^2 - v'^2 = \frac{c^2 - v^2}{\beta^2\left(1 - \dfrac{uv_x}{c^2}\right)^2} \qquad (20.32)$$

∴ If v = c, then v′ = c; the 'addition' of (u, 0, 0) to (v_x, v_y, v_z), then gives the same velocity.

If we write $(1 - v^2/c^2) = (\beta_v)^{-2}$, then $(1 - v'^2/c^2) = (\beta'_v)^{-2}$
then Eq. (20.32) becomes:

$$(\beta'_v)^2 = \left(1 - \frac{uv_x}{c^2}\right)\beta\beta_v \qquad (20.33)$$

6. *Transformation of mass and momentum.* (a) We postulate for the mechanics of interacting particles, as a general law of nature, the conservation of mass and momentum.

In the system F', two equal perfectly elastic particles, moving with velocities v and −v along $O'x'$, collide and rebound. ('Equal' means that they have identical properties with respect to an observer at rest relative to them.)

The frame F' moves relative to the frame F, parallel to Ox with the velocity u, and it will be shown that the masses of the particles depend on their velocities. Relative to F, let the velocities before the collision be w_1 and w_2, and let the masses be m_1, m_2. Let M be the sum of the masses at the moment of collision when they are relatively at rest—at rest relative to F', but having velocity u relative to F.

Then, for F:

$$m_1 + m_2 = M \qquad \text{(conservation of mass)} \tag{20a}$$

$$m_1 w_1 + m_2 w_2 = Mu \qquad \text{(conservation of momentum)} \tag{20b}$$

Also,

$$w_1 = \frac{u + v}{1 + \dfrac{uv}{c^2}}, \qquad w_2 = \frac{u - v}{1 - \dfrac{uv}{c^2}} \tag{20c}$$

From Eqs. (20a) and (20b),

$$m_1 = \frac{M(u - w_2)}{w_1 - w_2} \qquad \text{and} \qquad m_2 = \frac{M(w_1 - u)}{w_1 - w_2}$$

$$\frac{m_1}{m_2} = \frac{u - w_2}{w_1 - u} = \frac{1 + \dfrac{uv}{c^2}}{1 - \dfrac{uv}{c^2}}, \qquad \text{by (Eq. 20c)}$$

but by Eq. (20c),

$$1 - \frac{w_1^2}{c^2} = \frac{1 - (u + v)^2}{c^2 \left(1 + \dfrac{uv}{c^2}\right)^2}$$

$$= \frac{\left(1 - \dfrac{u^2}{c^2}\right)\left(1 - \dfrac{v^2}{c^2}\right)}{\left(1 + \dfrac{uv}{c^2}\right)^2}$$

Thus,

$$1 + \frac{uv}{c^2} = \left[\frac{\left(1 - \dfrac{u^2}{c^2}\right)\left(1 - \dfrac{v^2}{c^2}\right)}{1 - \dfrac{w_1^2}{c^2}} \right]^{1/2} \tag{20d1}$$

and

$$1 - \frac{uv}{c^2} = \left[\frac{\left(1 - \dfrac{u^2}{c^2}\right)\left(1 - \dfrac{v^2}{c^2}\right)}{1 - \dfrac{w_2^2}{c^2}} \right]^{1/2} \tag{20d2}$$

$$\therefore \quad \frac{m_1}{m_2} = \left(\frac{1 - \dfrac{w_2^2}{c^2}}{1 - \dfrac{w_1^2}{c^2}} \right)^{1/2} \tag{20d3}$$

Hence, the masses of the two particles, which by hypothesis have the same mass—m_0, say, when at rest, are inversely proportional to $(1 - w^2/c^2)^{1/2}$ when moving with the velocity w. So the mass m of a particle moving with the velocity w is

$$m = \frac{m_0}{\left(1 - \dfrac{w^2}{c^2} \right)^{1/2}}$$

where m_0 is called its *rest-mass* or *proper-mass*. Therefore, the mass m increases with velocity. By Eq. (20a),

$$M = m_1 + m_2 = \frac{m_0}{\left(1 - \dfrac{w_1^2}{c^2} \right)^{1/2}} + \frac{m_0}{\left(1 - \dfrac{w_2^2}{c^2} \right)^{1/2}}$$

$$= \frac{m_0 \left[\left(1 + \dfrac{uv}{c^2} \right) + \left(1 - \dfrac{uv}{c^2} \right) \right]}{\sqrt{\left(1 - \dfrac{u^2}{c^2} \right)\left(1 - \dfrac{v^2}{c^2} \right)}} \qquad \text{by Eqs. (20d),}$$

$$= \frac{2\,m_0}{\sqrt{\left(1 - \dfrac{u^2}{c^2} \right)\left(1 - \dfrac{v^2}{c^2} \right)}}$$

$$> \frac{2\,m_0}{\sqrt{\left(1 - \dfrac{u^2}{c^2} \right)}}, \quad \text{since} \ \left(1 - \dfrac{v^2}{c^2} \right) < 1, \quad \text{when} \ v \neq 0.$$

But M is the total mass at the instant of collision, when the particles are relatively at rest—the instant of greatest deformation. u is their common velocity at this instant (with respect to F); $2m_0$ is their total (undeformed) rest-mass.

Hence the total mass M at the instant of greatest deformation is greater than the mass with respect to F as calculated from the total undeformed rest-mass. This suggests that the mass must be ascribed to the potential energy of the elastic deformation, if the laws of conservation of mass and momentum are to be preserved.

(b) We consider next a simple hypothetical experiment devised by Tolman.

As before we consider two frames of reference F and F' where F' moves with a constant velocity u in the x-direction with respect to the frame F (also they have a common x-axis). At the instant of time when the origins of the two frames are coincident, the frame F' projects a sphere with a velocity v from B' toward O', and the frame F projects one from A parallel to y with a velocity v. The lengths OA and OB are so chosen that these two spheres collide when their centres are aligned in the y-direction. The collisions as observed by F and F' are shown in Figure 20.4(a).

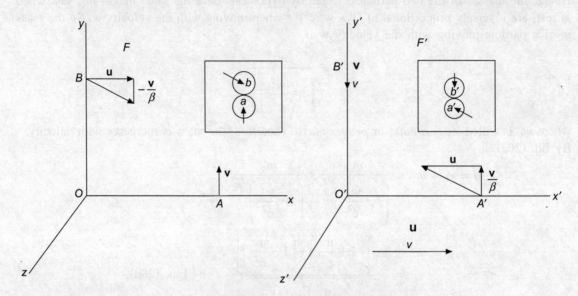

Figure 20.4(a)   Experiment with colliding spheres.

The masses of the spheres have been so chosen that when they are at rest with respect to **any** observer, both have (for the observer), the mass m_0. It is assumed that the mass is a function of the magnitude of the velocity, so that

$$m = f(v^2) \qquad \text{and} \qquad m_0 = f(0) \tag{20.d4}$$

From the formulae of last section,

For F | | For F'
$$v_{ax} = 0, \qquad v_{ay} = v \qquad\qquad v'_{ax} = -u \qquad v'_{ay} = \frac{v}{\beta}$$

$$v_{bx} = u \qquad v_{by} = -\frac{v}{\beta} \qquad\qquad v'_{bx} = 0 \qquad v'_{by} = -v \tag{20.d5}$$

Let the velocities after the impact be denoted by bars on the top.

Neither of the observers in the two frames will see any transfer of the x-component of the momentum (as a consequence of the impact of smooth spheres),

Hence F observes that $\qquad m_b u = \bar{m}_b u$,

or

$$uf\left(u^2 + \frac{v^2}{\beta^2}\right) = uf\left(u^2 + \frac{\bar{v}_b^2}{\beta^2}\right)$$

which requires $\qquad \bar{v}_b = -v \qquad$ and $\qquad \therefore \qquad \bar{m}_b = m_b \tag{20.d6}$

The –ve sign has been chosen, since it is to be correct for small velocities where $\beta = 1$.

For the y-component, the observation of F is

$$vf(v^2) - \frac{m_b v}{\beta} = \overline{v}_a f(\overline{v}_a^2) - \frac{\overline{m}_b \, \overline{v}_b}{\beta}$$

Since we saw above that $\overline{m}_b = m_b$ and also the known result when u = 0, this equation can be satisfied, only if $\overline{v}_a = -v$, and so the above equation becomes:

$$f(v^2) = m_a = \frac{m_b}{\beta} \tag{20.d7}$$

If the velocity of projection v becomes very small, then

$$m_b = f\left(u^2 + \frac{v^2}{\beta^2}\right) \to f(u^2) \quad \text{and} \quad m_a = f(v^2) \to f(0) = m_0 \tag{20.d8}$$

Thus the mass of an object in motion having a velocity u with respect to a given observer appears to him to be increased by a factor

$$\beta = \left\{1 - \left(\frac{u}{c}\right)^2\right\}^{-1/2} \tag{20.d9}$$

over its mass at rest.

At this stage, two new symbols are introduced, i.e. β_1 and β_1' which are defined as:

$$\beta_1 = \left(1 - \frac{v_x^2 + v_y^2 + v_z^2}{c^2}\right)^{-1/2} \tag{20.d10}$$

$$\beta_1' = \left(1 - \frac{v_x'^2 + v_y'^2 + v_z'^2}{c^2}\right)^{-1/2} \tag{20.d11}$$

where v_x, v_y, v_z are the components of the velocity of a particle as seen by an observer in the frame F, and v_x', v_y', v_z' are the components of the velocity of the same particle as seen by the observer in the frame F'.

Using Eqs. 20.31(a) to (f), we get

$$\beta_1 = \beta\beta_1'\left(1 + \frac{v_x' u}{c^2}\right) \tag{20.d12}$$

and

$$\beta_1' = \beta\beta_1\left(1 - \frac{v_x u}{c^2}\right) \tag{20.d13}$$

7. *Transformation of charge density amd current density.* (If ρ_C and **J** are the values measured from the frame F, what are the corresponding values measured from the frame F'?)

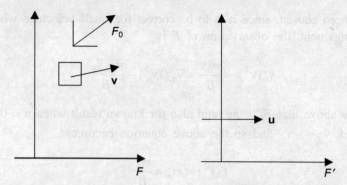

Figure 20.5 Charge density and current in the two frames of reference F and F'.

We consider a volume element δv with respect to the frame F, containing $(n_v \delta v)$ charges, all moving with the same velocity $\mathbf{v}$ ($= v_x, v_y, v_z$). Let F_0 be a frame of reference moving with the charges; and if an observer in F_0 sees $(n_0 \delta v_0)$ charges occupying the volume δv_0, then the observer in the frame F sees:

$$\delta v = \delta v_0 \sqrt{\left(1 - \frac{v^2}{c^2}\right)}, \quad \text{and since } (n_v \delta v) = (n_0 \delta v_0),$$

$$n_v = \frac{n_0}{\sqrt{\left(1 - \dfrac{v^2}{c^2}\right)}} \tag{20.34}$$

If each charge is q (assumed absolute), we have

$$\rho_C = \Sigma (q n_v) \tag{20.35}$$

and

$$J_x = \Sigma (q n_v v_x), \quad \text{and similarly } J_y \text{ and } J_z, \text{ so that:}$$

$$\mathbf{J} = \Sigma (q n_v \mathbf{v}) \tag{20.36}$$

where the summation is over all the velocities.

Similarly, an observer in the frame F' sees the density:

$$n_v' = \frac{n_0}{\sqrt{\left(1 - \dfrac{v'^2}{c^2}\right)}} \tag{20.37}$$

$$\rho_C' = \Sigma (q n_v') \tag{20.38}$$

$$\mathbf{J}' = \Sigma (q n_v' \mathbf{v}') \tag{20.39}$$

The components of $\mathbf{v}'$ are given by Eq. (20.31), and in the notation of Eq. (20.33), Eqs. (20.34) and (20.37) are to be written in the form:

$$n_v = \beta_v n_0, \quad n_v' = \beta_v' n_0 \tag{20.40}$$

$$\therefore \quad n_v' = \left(\frac{\beta_v'}{\beta_v}\right) n_v = \beta \left(1 - \frac{u v_x}{c^2}\right) n_v \quad \text{[from Eq. (20.33)]} \tag{20.41}$$

Thus,

$$\rho'_C = \Sigma \, (qn'_v) = \Sigma \left[q\beta \left(1 - \frac{uv_x}{c^2} \right) n_v \right]$$

$$= \beta \left(\rho_C - \frac{uJ_x}{c^2} \right) \tag{20.42}$$

$$J'_x = \Sigma \, (qn'_v v'_x) = \Sigma \left[q\beta \left(1 - \frac{uv_x}{c^2} \right) \frac{v_x - u}{1 - \dfrac{uv_x}{c^2}} \, n_v \right]$$

$$= \beta \, (J_x - \rho_C u) \tag{20.43}$$

$$J'_y = \Sigma \, (qn'_v v'_y) = \Sigma \left[q\beta \left(1 - \frac{uv_x}{c^2} \right) \frac{v_y \, n_v}{\beta \left(1 - \dfrac{uv_x}{c^2} \right)} \right]$$

$$= J_y \tag{20.44}$$

and

$$J'_z = J_z \tag{20.45}$$

These are similar to the Lorentz transformation of t, x, y, z.
   When $\beta \to 1$, they tend to vector equations:

$$\rho'_C = \rho_C - \left(\frac{1}{c^2} \right) (\mathbf{u} \cdot \mathbf{J}) \tag{20.46}$$

$$\mathbf{J}' = \mathbf{J} - \rho_C \mathbf{u} \tag{20.47}$$

8. *Moving conductors.* The charge and the current density transformations derived in Eqs. (20.42)–(20.45) can be expressed in the compact matrix form as

$$\begin{bmatrix} J_x \\ J_y \\ J_z \\ jc\rho_C \end{bmatrix} = \begin{bmatrix} \beta & 0 & 0 & -j\,(\beta u/c) \\ 0 & 1 & 0 & 0 \\ 0 & 0 & 1 & 0 \\ j\,(\beta u/c) & 0 & 0 & \beta \end{bmatrix} \begin{bmatrix} J'_x \\ J'_y \\ J'_z \\ jc\rho'_C \end{bmatrix} \tag{20.48}$$

(a)   **Charged body not carrying conduction current**

   If $J'_x = J'_y = J'_z = 0$, then we get $J_x = (\beta u \rho'_C)$, $\rho_C = \beta \rho'_C$.

   The latter is increased due to the Fitzgerald contraction. The former, equivalent to $J_x = (u\rho_C)$, is a convection current.

(b)   **Current-carrying body not charged**

   If $\rho'_C = 0$, we get $J_x = \beta J'_x$, $J_y = J'_y$, $J_z = J'_z$, $\rho_C = \left(\dfrac{\beta u}{c^2} \right) J'_x$.

$\mathbf{J}'$ is entirely the conduction current (the movement of equal +ve and −ve charges). Ohm's law ($\mathbf{E}' = \rho'\mathbf{J}'$) is obeyed.

(Note that ρ' is the conductivity of the conductor, whereas ρ_C and ρ'_C are the charge densities.)

From the fixed frame, the +ve and −ve charges no longer appear equal, and the current (density vector) $\mathbf{J}$ is part conduction, and part convection; and in fact:

$$\mathbf{J} = \mathbf{J} + \rho_C \mathbf{u} \tag{20.49}$$

Ohm's law applies to conduction current only. We thus have

$$J_{Cx} = J_x - \rho_C u = \beta J'_x - \left(\frac{\beta u^2}{c^2}\right) J'_x = \frac{J'_x}{\beta}$$

Also, $J_{Cy} = J_y = J'_y$, $J_{Cz} = J'_z$.

Let the electric and the magnetic fields in the fixed frame F be $\mathbf{E}$, $\mathbf{B}$ respectively. The effective electric force driving the current through the conductor is $[\mathbf{E} + (\mathbf{u} \times \mathbf{B})]$; so if the effective resistivities are ρ_x, ρ_y, ρ_z, then

$$E_x = \rho_x J_{Cx}, \qquad E_y - u B_z = \rho_y J_{Cy}, \qquad E_z + u B_y = \rho_z J_{Cz}.$$

But $E_x = E'_x = \rho' J'_x$, $\qquad E_y - u B_z = \dfrac{E'_y}{\beta} = \rho' \dfrac{J'_y}{\beta}, \qquad E_z + u B_y = \rho' \dfrac{J'_z}{\beta}.$

∴ Substituting for J_{Cx}, J_{Cy}, J_{Cz}, we get

$$\rho' J'_x = \frac{\rho_x J'_x}{\beta} \quad \text{or} \quad \rho_x = \beta \rho' \tag{20.50a}$$

$$\frac{\rho' J'_y}{\beta} = \rho_y J'_y \quad \text{or} \quad \rho_y = \frac{\rho'}{\beta} \tag{20.50b}$$

$$\frac{\rho' J'_z}{\beta} = \rho_z J'_z \quad \text{or} \quad \rho_z = \frac{\rho'}{\beta} \tag{20.50c}$$

Thus ρ (= the resistivity) appears to have increased in the direction of motion, and reduced in the perpendicular directions.

20.6.1 The Transformation Equations for Force

We define the force as the rate of change of momentum (and not as the product of mass by acceleration, which can then change the nature of these equations). Then,

$$\mathbf{F} = \frac{d}{dt}(m\mathbf{v}) = m_0 \frac{d}{dt}(\beta_1 \mathbf{v}) \tag{20.50d}$$

When the components of this equation are written down, it is seen that with this definition, the force and the acceleration, in general, are not in the same direction. Carrying out the differentiation in the above equation,

$$\mathbf{F} = m\frac{d\mathbf{v}}{dt} + \mathbf{v}\frac{dm}{dt} = m_0 \beta_1 \frac{d\mathbf{v}}{dt} + m_0 \beta_1^3 \, \mathbf{v} \frac{\mathbf{v}}{c^2} \frac{dv}{dt}$$

$$\left[\frac{dm}{dt} = \frac{d}{dt}(m_0 \, \beta_1), \quad \beta_1 = \left(1 - \frac{v_x^2 + v_y^2 + v_z^2}{c^2}\right)^{-1/2} = \left(1 - \frac{v^2}{c^2}\right)^{-1/2} \right.$$

$$= m_0 \left(\frac{d\beta_1}{dt}\right) = m_0 \left\{ -\frac{1}{2}\left(1 + \frac{v^2}{c^2}\right)^{-\frac{1}{2}-1}\left(-\frac{2v}{c^2}\right)\frac{dv}{dt} \right\} = \left. m_0 \beta_1^3 \frac{v}{c^2} \cdot \frac{dv}{dt} \right]$$

$$\therefore \qquad \mathbf{F} = m_0 \beta_1^3 \left[\left(1 - \frac{v^2}{c^2}\right) \frac{d\mathbf{v}}{dt} + \frac{\mathbf{v}\mathbf{v}}{c^2} \frac{dv}{dt} \right] \qquad (20.50e)$$

If the force applied is in the direction $\mathbf{v}_1$ of v ($\mathbf{v}_1$ = unit vector in the direction of $\mathbf{v}$), then

$$\mathbf{v} = \mathbf{v}_1 v \quad \text{and} \quad \frac{d\mathbf{v}}{dt} = \mathbf{v}_1 \frac{dv}{dt}$$

then

$$\mathbf{F}_l = m_0 \beta_1^3 \frac{d\mathbf{v}}{dt} = m_l \frac{d\mathbf{v}}{dt} \qquad (20.50f)$$

where $\mathbf{F}_l$ is the longitudinal component of the force, and $m_l = m_0 \beta_1^3$ = longitudinal mass of the particle.

If $\dfrac{d\mathbf{v}}{dt} = 0$, i.e. the velocity changes in direction, but not in magnitude, then Eq. (20.50e) shows that the force is again in the direction of acceleration (which is perpendicular to $\mathbf{v}$) and hence,

$$\mathbf{F}_t = m_0 \beta_1 \frac{d\mathbf{v}}{dt} = m_t \frac{d\mathbf{v}}{dt} \qquad (20.50g)$$

where $\mathbf{F}_t$ is the transverse component of the force, and $m_t = m_0 \beta_1$ = transverse mass of the particle.

The components of the force $\mathbf{F}$ can be obtained as:

$$F_x = m_0 \frac{d}{dt}(\beta_1 v_x) \qquad \text{[from Eq. (20.50d)]}$$

$$= m_0 \left(1 + \frac{v_x' u}{c^2}\right)^{-1} \frac{d}{dt'}\{\beta_1'(v_x' + u)\}$$

$$= F_x' + m_0 u \left(1 + \frac{v_x' u}{c^2}\right)^{-1} \left[\left(1 - \frac{v_x'^2}{c^2}\right)\frac{d}{dt'}\beta_1' - \frac{\beta_1' v_x'}{c^2}\frac{d}{dt'}v_x'\right] \qquad (20.50h)$$

and so on.

20.6.2 Energy of a Charged Moving Particle

The energy given to a charged particle by the action of a force is defined as the work done on it.

If in an infinitesimal interval of time dt, a particle moves a distance $\mathbf{dr} = \mathbf{v}dt$, then the work done on it,

$$dW = \mathbf{F} \cdot \mathbf{dr} = F_l dr = m_0 \beta_1^3 \frac{dv}{dt} dr \qquad \text{[from Eq. (20.50f)]}$$

$$= m_0 \beta_1^3 \, dv \qquad\qquad (20.50j)$$

Substituting for β_1 and integrating from 0 to v, we get

$$W = \int_0^v dW = \int_0^v m_0 \beta_1^3 \, dv$$

$$= (m_t - m_0)c^2 = (\beta_1 - 1)m_0 c^2 \qquad\qquad (20.50k)$$

i.e. an energy increase is equivalent to a mass increase.

20.7 THE PRINCIPLE OF SPECIAL RELATIVITY

The theory of special relativity is concerned with the frames of reference for which the relative velocity is uniform and in a straight line. The *principle of special relativity* states that:

> *The laws of nature are the same referred to all frames of reference in uniform translation relative to each other.*

As a consequence of applying this to the law of conservation of momentum, it has been shown that a particle whose mass is m_0 with respect to a frame in which it is at rest, has a mass $m = \beta m_0$ with respect to a frame in which it has a velocity u. Thus, *moving bodies become heavier.* This *relativistic increase of mass* must be taken into account in designing high-energy particle accelerators.

Note that all these effects tend to a limit, as u $\rightarrow$ c—moving rod contracts to zero, moving clock goes infinitely slowly, moving mass becomes infinite.

The velocity c of light in free space is deduced from the Maxwell's equations. Since this velocity applies to both the frames, we expect the Maxwell's equations to transform into themselves, or to be *invariant under a Lorentz transformation.* We shall verify this later.

20.8 FIRST ORDER RELATIVISTIC EFFECTS IN ELECTROMAGNETISM

In the exact equations relating $\mathbf{E}'$, $\mathbf{B}'$ to $\mathbf{E}$, $\mathbf{B}$, the factor β appears in the equations for the transverse components only. This means that they cannot be written in the vector form without the use of a highly artificial 'transverse stretching operator'. However if we write $\beta = 1$ [so neglecting the (u^2/c^2) term], we get a *first-order relativity* which cannot be entirely self-consistent, but this nevertheless throws light on a number of electromagnetic phenomena. In this (simplified, approximate, first-order) theory, $\mathbf{E}'$, and $\mathbf{B}'$ are related to $\mathbf{E}$ and $\mathbf{B}$ by:

$$\mathbf{E}' = \mathbf{E} + (\mathbf{u} \times \mathbf{B}) \qquad\qquad (20.51a)$$

$$\mathbf{B}' = \mathbf{B} - \left(\frac{1}{c^2}\right)(\mathbf{u} \times \mathbf{E}) \qquad\qquad (20.51b)$$

There is no loss of generality, if we take the direction of the relative velocity of the frames **u** as the *x*-axis; so that the coordinates are now related by the classical equations:

$$x' = x - ut, \qquad y' = y, \qquad z' = z, \qquad t' = t$$

A charge density ρ_C at rest in the frame F is observed as moving with a velocity $(-\mathbf{u})$ in the frame F'; thereby constituting a convection current density $(-\rho_C \mathbf{u})$; Thus the current densities $\mathbf{J}$ and $\mathbf{J}'$ are related by the equation:

$$\mathbf{J}' = \mathbf{J} - \rho_C \mathbf{u} \tag{20.52}$$

It is not so easily obvious physically that a current density in the frame F gives rise to a charge density when viewed from the moving frame F'; this however is a consequence of the first equation of Eq. (20.51a), as we shall see. Let there be a steady current density $\mathbf{J}$ in the frame F; this creates a magnetic field which is such that it satisfies the equation:

$$\text{curl } \mathbf{H} = \nabla \times \mathbf{H} = \mathbf{J}$$

Let the currents and the charges be in free space; then the first equation of Eq. (20.51), when multiplied by ε_0, can be written in the form:

$$\mathbf{D}' = \mathbf{D} + \left(\frac{1}{c^2}\right)(\mathbf{u} \times \mathbf{H}) \tag{20.53}$$

Now, in the frame F',

$$\rho_C' = \frac{\partial \mathbf{D}_x'}{\partial x'} + \frac{\partial \mathbf{D}_y'}{\partial y'} + \frac{\partial \mathbf{D}_z'}{\partial z'}$$

$$= \frac{\partial \mathbf{D}_x'}{\partial x} + \frac{\partial \mathbf{D}_y'}{\partial y} + \frac{\partial \mathbf{D}_z'}{\partial z}$$

since t is independent of the space coordinates.

Also, $D_x' = D_x,$ $\qquad D_y' = D_y - \left(\dfrac{u}{c^2}\right)H_z,$ $\qquad D_z' = D_z + \left(\dfrac{u}{c^2}\right)H_y,$

so that

$$\rho_C' = \left(\frac{\partial \mathbf{D}_x}{\partial x} + \frac{\partial \mathbf{D}_y}{\partial y} + \frac{\partial \mathbf{D}_z}{\partial z}\right) - \left(\frac{u}{c^2}\right)\left(\frac{\partial \mathbf{H}_z}{\partial y} - \frac{\partial \mathbf{H}_y}{\partial z}\right)$$

$$= \rho_C - \left(\frac{u}{c^2}\right)J_x \tag{20.54}$$

This is generalized as:

$$\rho_C' = \rho_C - \left(\frac{1}{c^2}\right)(\mathbf{u} \cdot \mathbf{J}) \tag{20.55}$$

A physical explanation of the last term of Eq. (20.55) can be offered in terms of the Fitzgerald contraction. Let us imagine a conductor of unit cross-section, carrying a longitudinal current J. and let this consist of positive charges moving to the right (as shown in Figure 20.6) with velocity u, and stationary negative charges. The charge density viewed from a frame F fixed in the conductor, must be $(\pm J/u)$. If there are N charges, each $(-q)$, in each metre of the conductor, then: $Nq = J/u$.

The N positive charges $(+q)$ must also occupy a metre when viewed from the frame F, and hence β metres when viewed from the moving frame F'; because their (i.e. the moving charges) space undergoes a Fitzgerald contraction when viewed from any frame other than that moving with the charges.

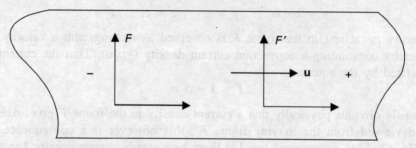

Figure 20.6 Section of a conductor of unit cross-section.

Let us now move to the frame F', and look back at the negative charges, and we observe that their space has undergone a contraction as is now $(1/\beta)$ metres. The negative charges have now become denser, and

$$\text{the apparent charge density is} = -\left(\frac{J}{u}\right)\left(\beta - \frac{1}{\beta}\right) = -\left(\frac{\beta J}{u}\right)\left(\frac{u^2}{c^2}\right)$$

To the first-order approximation, we now put $\beta = 1$. and thereby obtain a charge density (as viewed from the frame F') of $= -(uJ/c^2)$. This is identical with the term $-(1/c^2)(\mathbf{u} \cdot \mathbf{J})$ in Eq. (20.55).

This explanation given above is not a completely satisfactory one. This is because of the fact that the second-order Fitzgerald contraction has to be invoked to explain Eq. (20.55) which is derived from the first-order Eq. (20.51), and thus does indicate the difficulty of defining the border-line between the first- and the second-order effects in such a way that the first-order effects form a closed and self-consistent set.

It is not quite clear that the last term is of such an order as to be retained; but it is essential in order to be consistent with the field equations. It represents the source of the electric part, as viewed from the frame F', of the electromagnetic field which corresponds with a purely magnetic field as seen from the frame F.

In free space, Eqs. (20.51) may be rewritten as

$$\mathbf{D}' = \mathbf{D} + \left(\frac{1}{c^2}\right)(\mathbf{u} \times \mathbf{H}) \tag{20.56a}$$

$$\mathbf{H}' = \mathbf{H} - (\mathbf{u} \times \mathbf{D}) \tag{20.56b}$$

Through the Maxwell's equations,

$$\text{div } \mathbf{D} = \nabla \cdot \mathbf{D} = \rho_C$$

and

$$\text{curl } \mathbf{H} = \nabla \times \mathbf{H} = \mathbf{J} + \frac{\partial \mathbf{D}}{\partial t}$$

these above equations (20.56) are related to the charge and the current densities. If the transformations (20.52) and (20.55) hold good in all media—and it seems likely that the transformations of charge and current will be independent of the medium in which they are found—it follows that Eqs. (20.56) must apply to all media, not merely to free space.

20.9 THE FIELD OF A MOVING CHARGE

Let a charge q, momentarily at the origin of the frame F, be moving with respect to F with a velocity u, and let the frame F' move with the charge. Then, since the field in F' is electrostatic,

$$E' = -\left(\frac{q}{4\pi\varepsilon_0}\right) grad\left(\frac{1}{r'}\right)$$ (20.57a)

$$B' = 0$$ (20.57b)

Transferring to the frame F, and noting that $r = r'$ at the instant stated, we get

$$E = -\left(\frac{q}{4\pi\varepsilon_0}\right) grad\left(\frac{1}{r'}\right)$$ (20.58)

$$B = \left(\frac{1}{c^2}\right)(u \times E') = -\left(\frac{q}{4\pi\varepsilon_0 c^2}\right)\left[u \times grad\left(\frac{1}{r}\right)\right]$$

or

$$B = \frac{\left(\dfrac{\mu_0 q}{4\pi}\right)(u \times r_1)}{r^2}$$ (20.59)

where r_1 is the unit vector in the direction r, because:

$$grad\left(\frac{1}{r}\right) = -\frac{r_1}{r^2}$$

This magnetic vector is perpendicular to u and to r, the rotation from u to r being right-handed about it; and also its magnitude is

$$\frac{\mu_0 q u \sin\theta}{4\pi r^2}$$

where θ is the angle between u and r. This is in strict accord with Biot–Savart.

If we have an element δs of a circuit of wire of cross-section S (Figure 20.7), N charges per unit volume moving with velocity u, the above formula gives

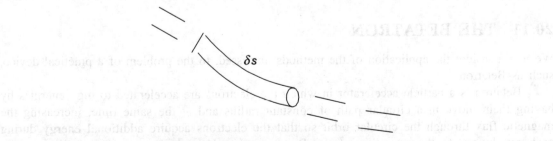

Figure 20.7 A circuit element δs.

$$\mathbf{B} = \frac{\left(\dfrac{\mu_0 N S q \delta s u}{4\pi}\right)(\mathbf{u} \times \mathbf{r}_1)}{r^2}$$

$$= \frac{\mu_0 i(\delta \mathbf{s} \times \mathbf{r}_1)}{4\pi r^2}, \qquad \text{à la Biot–Savart} \qquad (20.60)$$

20.10   THE FORCE ON A MOVING CHARGE (RELATIVISTIC CALCULATION)

If a particle is momentarily at rest in a frame F' and has the force $\mathbf{P}' = (P'_x, P'_y, P'_z)$ upon it, the components of the force measured from the frame F can be shown to be

$$P_x = P'_x, \qquad P_y = \frac{P'_y}{\beta}, \qquad P_z = \frac{P'_z}{\beta} \qquad (20.61)$$

Let us consider now a charge q at rest in the frame F', so that

$$\mathbf{P}' = q\mathbf{E}'$$

or

$$P'_x = qE'_x, \qquad P'_y = qE'_y, \qquad P'_z = qE'_z$$

Transferring to the frame F, we get

$$P_x = qE_x, \qquad \beta P_y = \beta q(E_y - uB_z), \qquad \beta P_z = \beta q(E_z + uB_y)$$

The β's cancel, and we are left with the three equations which are equivalent to the vector equation

$$\mathbf{P} = q[\mathbf{E} + (\mathbf{u} \times \mathbf{B})] \qquad (20.62)$$

which is of course the *Lorentz formula*, which is thus seen to hold good for any velocity. Both parts of it are known from elementary considerations, but the deduction of the magnetic half from the force on a current-carrying wire is of doubtful validity, and the relativistic proof is the sound one.

Note that the magnetic force $[q(\mathbf{u} \times \mathbf{B})]$ cannot change the energy of the particle.

20.11   THE BETATRON

We now consider the application of the methods discussed, to the problem of a practical device, such as Betatron.

Betatron is a particle accelerator in which the electrons are accelerated to high energies by having them move in a circular path of constant radius and at the same time, increasing the magnetic flux through the circular orbit so that the electrons acquire additional energy during each revolution. In the operation of the Betatron, the electrons from a heated filament are injected into the circular or doughnut-shaped tube by applying a difference of potential between the filament and a plate P, whilst the electrons are focused by a grid, placed in between the two. The alternating magnetic field is applied parallel to the axis of the tube. As a result, two effects are produced, i.e. an emf is produced in the electron orbit by the changing magnetic field which gives the electrons additional energy; and secondly, a radial force is produced by the action of the magnetic field whose direction is perpendicular to the electron velocity. thus keeping the electron moving in a circular orbit. The magnetic flux through the orbit has to be chosen in such a way that the electrons will move in a stable orbit of fixed radius R. The electrons make several hundred thousand revolutions in this circular path while the alternating magnetic field is increasing from zero to a maximum in a quarter of a cycle.

The electron accelerator is like a transformer with its secondary replaced by an evacuated glass tube containing an electron source. The core is shaped as shown in the Figure 20.8, to provide at the electron orbit a field to keep the electrons in circular motion.

The equation of motion in orbit (neglecting relativity) is

$$m\left(\frac{du}{dt}\right) = \left(\frac{e}{2\pi R}\right)\left(\frac{d\Phi}{dt}\right)$$

So an electron starting with negligible velocity when $\Phi = 0$, subsequently has the velocity:

$$u = \left(\frac{e}{2\pi Rm}\right)\Phi \qquad (20.63)$$

Let the flux density at the orbit be B. Then, the inward radial force $= euB$. This must equal mu^2/R.

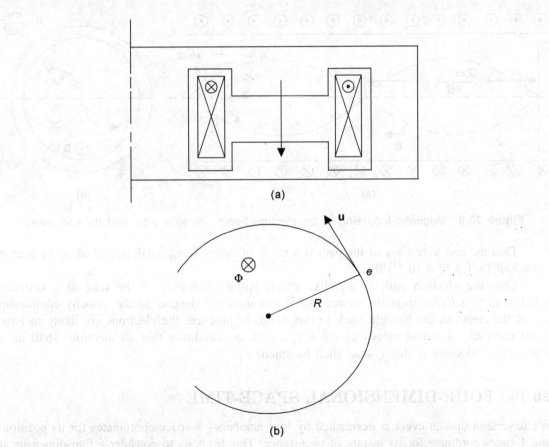

(a)

(b)

Figure 20.8 (a) Section of a Betatron and (b) the orbital path of electrons in a Betatron.

$$\therefore \quad B = \frac{mu}{eR} \qquad (20.64)$$

$$\therefore \quad B = \frac{\Phi}{2\pi R^2} = \left(\frac{1}{2}\right) \text{(Mean flux density within the orbit)} \qquad (20.65)$$

The whole acceleration takes place in a quarter cycle of the supply voltage, during which time the electrons my describe 10^5 orbits. The relativistic increase of mass is used to get them out; they spiral outwards till they hit a target.

20.12   MAGNETIC FOCUSSING OF ELECTRON BEAM BY AXIAL FIELD

Let the electrons be emitted with axial and radial velocities u_0, v_0 respectively (as shown in Figure 20.9), in an axial magnetic field B, and let the subsequent velocities be u, v. Only v cooperates with B to produce a force (evB) perpendicular to the component of velocity at right angles to the axis; it should be noted that *neither component changes if there is no electric field*. In absence of the electric field E, ($u^2 + v^2$) is constant, since B can produce no force in its direction; therefore, for all time, $u = u_0$, and $v = v_0$.

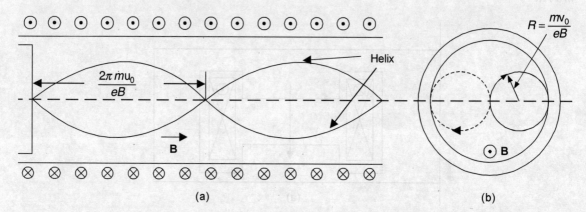

Figure 20.9   Magnetic focussing of an electron beam: (a) side view and (b) end view.

Thus the end-wise view of the path is a circle of radius $[mv_0/(eB)]$, described in the time = $[2\pi m/(eB)] = [(3.57 \times 10^{-11})/B]$ sec.

Thus the electron path is a helix, which crosses the axis of the tube at a distance equal to $[2\pi m u_0/(eB)]$ from the source. Since this does not depend on the velocity component v_0, all the electrons are brought back to this point. In practice, the electrons are likely to have equal energies, i.e. equal values of ($u_0^2 + v_0^2$); thus the condition that all electrons shall have equal axial velocities is that (v_0/u_0) shall be small.

20.13   FOUR-DIMENSIONAL SPACE-TIME

We have seen that an event is designated by four numbers—3 space-coordinates for its position. and 1 time-coordinate for its instant of occurrence. This leads us to consider a four-dimensional coordinate system, i.e. x, y, z, $\omega = ct$; by dropping z, we can picture the rest as a three-dimensional system. A cross-section of this system in the plane $Ox\omega$ is shown below in Figure 20.10.

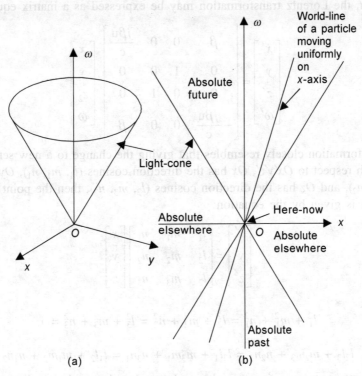

Figure 20.10 (a) Three-dimensional representation and (b) two-dimensional section of the four-dimensional space-time.

A pulse of light at $t = 0$ at O (the origin) spreads out as

$$x^2 + y^2 + z^2 + \omega^2 = 0 \tag{20.66}$$

if z is dropped, this is the equation of a cone; and so in four-dimensions we may call it a *hyper-cone*; it is also known as *light-cone*. In this four-space, each particle, moving in space and durable in time, is represented by a line which is called its *world-line*. In particular, a particle moving uniformly along the x-axis is represented by a straight world-line which must lie (since its velocity is necessarily $< c$) within the light-cone. If the point O (in Figure 20.10) represents *here-now*, then the line points from the past to the future. It can be shown that all the events in the upper-half of the cone are future, and all the events in the lower-half of the cone are past, with respect to O, in all reference systems; and so these regions are labeled as *absolute future* and *absolute past*.

To go from O to the region outside the cone, a particle would need to travel faster than light; this being impossible, these points are *absolute elsewhere* with respect to O. Two events can be related causally if the latter lies within the light-cone of the earlier.

20.14 FOUR-SPACE ASPECT OF THE LORENTZ TRANSFORMATION

Writing ω for ct, the Lorentz transformation may be expressed as a matrix equation:

$$
\begin{bmatrix} x' \\ y' \\ z' \\ \omega' \end{bmatrix} = \begin{bmatrix} \beta & 0 & 0 & \dfrac{j\beta u}{c} \\ 0 & 1 & 0 & 0 \\ 0 & 0 & 1 & 0 \\ -\dfrac{j\beta u}{c} & 0 & 0 & \beta \end{bmatrix} \begin{bmatrix} x \\ y \\ z_2 \\ \omega \end{bmatrix} \tag{20.67}
$$

This linear transformation closely resembles that giving the change to a new set of axes in three-space, i.e. if with respect to $Ox'y'z'$, Ox has the direction cosines (l_1, m_1, n_1), Oy has the direction cosines (l_2, m_2, n_2), and Oz has the direction cosines (l_3, m_3, n_3), then the point (x, y, z) becomes (x', y', z') which is given by the equation:

$$
\begin{bmatrix} x' \\ y' \\ z' \end{bmatrix} = \begin{bmatrix} l_1 & m_1 & n_1 \\ l_2 & m_2 & n_2 \\ l_2 & m_3 & n_3 \end{bmatrix} \begin{bmatrix} x \\ y \\ z \end{bmatrix} \tag{20.68}
$$

In this equation,

$$
l_1^2 + m_1^2 + n_1^2 = l_2^2 + m_2^2 + n_2^2 = l_3^2 + m_3^2 + n_3^2 = 1 \tag{20.68a}
$$

and

$$
l_2 l_3 + m_2 m_3 + n_2 n_3 = l_3 l_1 + m_3 m_1 + n_3 n_1 = l_1 l_2 + m_1 m_2 + n_1 n_2
$$

$$
= m_1 n_1 + m_2 n_2 + m_3 n_3 = n_1 l_1 + n_2 l_2 + n_3 l_3 = l_1 m_1 + l_2 m_2 + l_3 m_3 = 0 \tag{20.68b}
$$

This means that, with respect to $Oxyz$, Ox' has the direct cosines (l_1, l_2, l_3), Oy' has the direction cosines (m_1, m_2, m_3), and Oz' has the direction cosines (n_1, n_2, n_3). This is because $Oxyz$ are mutually perpendicular. Equations (20.67) do not have the corresponding properties; but by a simple alteration they can be made to have such a property. This is by taking the time coordinate as 'imaginary', so that these four are then:

$$
x_1 = x, \quad x_2 = y, \quad x_3 = z, \quad x_4 = jct \tag{20.69}
$$

This is rather inconvenient for visualizing, because the light-cone is now imaginary; but the Lorentz transformation now becomes:

$$
\begin{bmatrix} x_1' \\ x_2' \\ x_3' \\ x_4' \end{bmatrix} = \begin{bmatrix} \beta & 0 & 0 & \dfrac{j\beta u}{c} \\ 0 & 1 & 0 & 0 \\ 0 & 0 & 1 & 0 \\ -\dfrac{j\beta u}{c} & 0 & 0 & \beta \end{bmatrix} \begin{bmatrix} x_1 \\ x_2 \\ x_3 \\ x_4 \end{bmatrix} \tag{20.70}
$$

The sum of the squares of the terms in each row and column is now 1; and the sum of the products in any pair of rows and columns is zero. Hence the Lorentz transformation is simply a rotation of the axes in the four-dimensional space described by (x_1, x_2, x_3, x_4).

20.15 FOUR-DIMENSIONAL VECTOR ALGEBRA

A vector having the components A_1, A_2, A_3, A_4 along the four mutually perpendicular axes is called a *4-vector* or *world-vector*. x_1, x_2, x_3, x_4 are themselves the components of a 4-vector—the radius 4-vector; the rules of addition and transformation for any other 4-vector are the same as for x_1, x_2, x_3, x_4. If $\mathbf{i}_1$, $\mathbf{i}_2$, $\mathbf{i}_3$, $\mathbf{i}_4$ are the unit vectors in the 4 directions, then a world-vector $\mathbf{A}$ is given by:

$$\mathbf{A} = \mathbf{i}_1 A_1 + \mathbf{i}_2 A_2 + \mathbf{i}_3 A_3 + \mathbf{i}_4 A_4 \tag{20.71}$$

and, since $\mathbf{i}_1 \cdot \mathbf{i}_1 = \mathbf{i}_2 \cdot \mathbf{i}_2 = \mathbf{i}_3 \cdot \mathbf{i}_3 = \mathbf{i}_4 \cdot \mathbf{i}_4 = 1$, the scalar product of the 4-vectors would be:

$$\mathbf{A} \cdot \mathbf{B} = A_1 B_1 + A_2 B_2 + A_3 B_3 + A_4 B_4 \tag{20.72}$$

It should be noted that $\mathbf{i}_1$, $\mathbf{i}_2$, $\mathbf{i}_3$, $\mathbf{i}_4$ are ordinary vectors, and the scalar product of any two of them, only involves two dimensions. Just as 3 mutually perpendicular vectors add up to a vector in 3-space, so the adding up of four mutually perpendicular vectors give a 'vector' in 4-space or 4-vector.

It should be further noted that 'vector products' cannot be formed in 4-space; if $(\mathbf{i}_1 \times \mathbf{i}_2)$ is perpendicular to $\mathbf{i}_1$ and $\mathbf{i}_2$, it could be anywhere in the plane $(\mathbf{i}_3, \mathbf{i}_4)$.

If, on the analogy of the vector product, we formed the products of the form $(A_i B_j - A_j B_i)$, we should get *six* components, and hence the analogue of $(\mathbf{A} \times \mathbf{B})$ (of 3-dimensions) will not be a 4-vector in 4-dimensions. Thus the mode of generalizing from 3- to 4-dimensions is found by writing

$$A_i B_j - A_j B_i = C_{ij} = -C_{ji} \tag{20.73}$$

and representing the vector product by the anti-symmetric matrix:

$$\begin{bmatrix} 0 & C_{12} & C_{13} \\ C_{21} & 0 & C_{23} \\ C_{31} & C_{32} & 0 \end{bmatrix}$$

By analogy, we can then say:

$$\mathbf{A} \times \mathbf{B} = \begin{bmatrix} 0 & C_{12} & C_{13} & C_{14} \\ C_{21} & 0 & C_{23} & C_{24} \\ C_{31} & C_{32} & 0 & C_{34} \\ C_{41} & C_{42} & C_{43} & 0 \end{bmatrix} \tag{20.74}$$

By analogy with the vector operator del ∇, we introduce the corresponding 4-vector operator:

$$\Box \equiv \mathbf{i}_1 \left(\frac{\partial}{\partial x_1} \right) + \mathbf{i}_2 \left(\frac{\partial}{\partial x_2} \right) + \mathbf{i}_3 \left(\frac{\partial}{\partial x_3} \right) + \mathbf{i}_4 \left(\frac{\partial}{\partial x_4} \right) \tag{20.75}$$

We then define:

$$\text{grad } \phi = \Box \phi = \mathbf{i}_1 \left(\frac{\partial \phi}{\partial x_1} \right) + \mathbf{i}_2 \left(\frac{\partial \phi}{\partial x_2} \right) + \mathbf{i}_3 \left(\frac{\partial \phi}{\partial x_3} \right) + \mathbf{i}_4 \left(\frac{\partial \phi}{\partial x_4} \right) \tag{20.76}$$

$$\text{div } \mathbf{A} = \Box \cdot \mathbf{A} = \frac{\partial A_1}{\partial x_1} + \frac{\partial A_2}{\partial x_2} + \frac{\partial A_3}{\partial x_3} + \frac{\partial A_4}{\partial x_4} \tag{20.77}$$

However, if curl $\mathbf{A} = \square \times \mathbf{A}$, it is not a 4-vector, but an anti-symmetric matrix:

$$\text{curl } \mathbf{A} = \square \times \mathbf{A} = \begin{bmatrix} 0 & F_{12} & F_{13} & F_{14} \\ F_{21} & 0 & F_{23} & F_{24} \\ F_{31} & F_{32} & 0 & F_{34} \\ F_{41} & F_{42} & F_{43} & 0 \end{bmatrix} = [F_{ij}] \tag{20.78}$$

where
$$F_{12} = \frac{\partial A_2}{\partial x_1} - \frac{\partial A_1}{\partial x_2}, \ldots, \text{ and so on} \tag{20.79}$$

In 3-dimensions, the components of curl $\mathbf{A}$ are of the above form and satisfy the identity div curl $\mathbf{A} = 0$. Corresponding to this in 4-dimensions, there are four identities which may be expressed in the general form,

$$\frac{\partial F_{jk}}{\partial x_i} + \frac{\partial F_{ki}}{\partial x_j} + \frac{\partial F_{ij}}{\partial x_k} = 0 \tag{20.80}$$

where i, j, k, are any 3 of the 4 numbers 1, 2, 3, 4.

A matrix whose components transform in a certain way when the axes are rotated is called a 'tensor'. $[F_{ij}]$ is one of such tensors, it is a 'four-tensor of the second rank'.

20.16 FOUR-DIMENSIONAL ELECTROMAGNETISM

We have seen that the charge density ρ_C and the components of the current density $\mathbf{J}$ transformed in the Lorentz transformation in the same way as t, x, y, z. Hence it follows that the quantity defined by

$$\mathbf{J} = \mathbf{i}_1 J_x + \mathbf{i}_2 J_y + \mathbf{i}_3 J_z + \mathbf{i}_4 j c \rho_C \tag{20.81}$$

is a 4-vector. It is called the 'current 4-vector'. In the same way, the three components of the magnetic vector potential $\mathbf{A}$ combine with the electric scalar potential ϕ to form the *4-potential*:

$$\mathbf{A} = \mathbf{i}_1 A_x + \mathbf{i}_2 A_y + \mathbf{i}_3 A_z + \mathbf{i}_4 \left(\frac{j}{c} \right) \phi \tag{20.82}$$

In both the cases, the dimensional uniformity is preserved by inserting c in the expressions.

We have $\square \times \mathbf{A} = [F_{ij}]$ as defined in Eqs. (20.78) and (20.79).

If, now, we examine the components of $[F_{ij}]$, we find

$$F_{23} = \frac{\partial A_3}{\partial x_2} - \frac{\partial A_2}{\partial x_3} = \frac{\partial A_z}{\partial y} - \frac{\partial A_y}{\partial z} = B_x \tag{20.83}$$

and

$$F_{41} = \frac{\partial A_4}{\partial x_1} - \frac{\partial A_1}{\partial x_4} = -\left(\frac{j}{c} \right) \left(\frac{\partial A_x}{\partial t} \right) - \left(\frac{j}{c} \right) \left(\frac{\partial \phi}{\partial x} \right)$$

$$= \left(\frac{j}{c} \right) E_x \tag{20.84}$$

using respectively curl $\mathbf{A} = \mathbf{B}$ and $-\text{grad } \phi - \left(\dfrac{\partial A}{\partial t} \right) = \mathbf{E}$.

Thus all the components of $[F_{ij}]$ are proportional to the components of the electromagnetic field; in fact:

$$[F_{ij}] = \begin{bmatrix} 0 & B_3 & -B_3 & -\dfrac{jE_1}{c} \\[2ex] -B_3 & 0 & B_1 & -\dfrac{jE_2}{c} \\[2ex] B_2 & -B_1 & 0 & -\dfrac{jE_3}{c} \\[2ex] \dfrac{jE_1}{c} & \dfrac{jE_2}{c} & \dfrac{jE_3}{c} & 0 \end{bmatrix} \tag{20.85}$$

The components of $\mathbf{E}$ and $\mathbf{B}$ are thus all contained in this 'electromagnetic field tensor'.

Next, we have a look at the identities of Eq. (20.80), and substituting $i, j, k = 1, 2, 3$, respectively, we get

$$\frac{\partial B_x}{\partial x} + \frac{\partial B_y}{\partial y} + \frac{\partial B_z}{\partial z} = 0 \quad \text{i.e. div } \mathbf{B} = 0 \tag{20.86}$$

and with $i, j, k = 2, 3, 4$, respectively, we get

$$-\left(\frac{j}{c} \right)\left(\frac{\partial E_z}{\partial y} - \frac{\partial E_y}{\partial z} \right) - \left(\frac{j}{c} \right)\left(\frac{\partial B_x}{\partial t} \right) = 0$$

which is the x-component of the equation:

$$\text{curl } \mathbf{E} = -\left(\frac{\partial \mathbf{B}}{\partial t} \right) \tag{20.87}$$

Thus, these two among the four Maxwell's equations are implied when the field components are expressed in the form:

$$[F_{ij}] = \square \times \mathbf{A} \tag{20.88}$$

This is quite natural and logical; because they are also implied by the underlying equations:

$$\mathbf{E} = -\text{grad } \phi - \left(\frac{\partial \mathbf{A}}{\partial t} \right) \quad \text{and} \quad \mathbf{B} = \text{curl } \mathbf{A}$$

The development of the electromagnetic theory in free space is simplified, if $\mathbf{A}$ is made to satisfy the condition:

$$\text{div } \mathbf{A} + \left(\frac{1}{c^2} \right)\left(\frac{\partial \phi}{\partial t} \right) = 0 \quad \text{(i.e. Lorentz gauge)} \tag{20.89}$$

It is easily verified that in 4-space, this is equivalent to:

$$\square \cdot \mathbf{A} = 0 \tag{20.90}$$

The other two Maxwell's equations,

$$\text{div } \mathbf{D} = \rho_C \tag{20.91}$$

and

$$\text{curl } \mathbf{H} - \left(\frac{\partial \mathbf{D}}{\partial t}\right) = \mathbf{J} \tag{20.92}$$

contain $\mathbf{D}$, $\mathbf{H}$, and the components of the 4-current. So writing in the Cartesian form with numbered components, we get

$$\left(\frac{\partial H_3}{\partial x_2}\right) - \left(\frac{\partial H_2}{\partial x_3}\right) - (jc)\left(\frac{\partial D_1}{\partial x_4}\right) = J_1 \tag{20.93a}$$

$$\left(\frac{\partial H_1}{\partial x_3}\right) - \left(\frac{\partial H_3}{\partial x_1}\right) - (jc)\left(\frac{\partial D_2}{\partial x_4}\right) = J_2 \tag{20.93b}$$

$$\left(\frac{\partial H_2}{\partial x_1}\right) - \left(\frac{\partial H_1}{\partial x_2}\right) - (jc)\left(\frac{\partial D_3}{\partial x_4}\right) = J_3 \tag{20.93c}$$

$$(jc)\left(\frac{\partial D_1}{\partial x_1} + \frac{\partial D_2}{\partial x_2} + \frac{\partial D_3}{\partial x_3}\right) = J_4 (= jc\rho_C) \tag{20.93d}$$

If, now, we define a second field tensor

$$[G_{ij}] = \begin{bmatrix} 0 & H_3 & -H_2 & -jcD_1 \\ -H_3 & 0 & H_1 & -jcD_2 \\ H_2 & -H_1 & 0 & -jcD_3 \\ jcD_1 & jcD_2 & jcD_3 & 0 \end{bmatrix} \tag{20.94}$$

then Eqs. (20.93) reduce to the form:

$$\frac{\partial G_{11}}{\partial x_1} + \frac{\partial G_{12}}{\partial x_2} + \frac{\partial G_{13}}{\partial x_3} + \frac{\partial G_{14}}{\partial x_4} = J_1, \text{ and so on.}$$

Or, in a more compact form:

$$\sum_{j=1,2,\cdots}^{4} \left(\frac{\partial G_{ij}}{\partial x_j}\right) = J_i \quad (i = 1, 2, 3, 4) \tag{20.95}$$

The 4-space approach thus enables the four field vectors $\mathbf{E}$, $\mathbf{B}$, $\mathbf{D}$, and $\mathbf{H}$ to be replaced by two field tensors $[F_{ij}]$ and $[G_{ij}]$; the four Maxwell's equations to be replaced by two sets of equations (20.80) or (20.78) and (20.95), the vector and the scalar potentials by a single 4-potential; the two equations $\mathbf{E} = -\text{ grad}\,\phi - (\partial \mathbf{A}/\partial t)$ and $\mathbf{B} = \text{curl } \mathbf{A}$ by the single Eq. (20.88). Finally, the continuity equation

$$\text{div } \mathbf{J} + \frac{\partial \rho_C}{\partial t} = 0 \tag{20.96}$$

is implicit in Eqs. (20.91) and (20.92), and these take the single form

$$\square \cdot \mathbf{J} = 0 \tag{20.97}$$

20.17 INVARIANCE OF MAXWELL'S EQUATIONS UNDER THE LORENTZ TRANSFORMATION

From the Maxwell's equations, together with the relations $\mathbf{D} = \varepsilon_0 \mathbf{E}$ and $\mathbf{B} = \mu_0 \mathbf{H}$, we conclude that the electromagnetic waves travel in free space with velocity c. The Lorentz transformation assures the truth of this statement for all inertial frames of reference. It is therefore to be expected that Maxwell's equations will hold good in all inertial frames, i.e. they will be invariant under a Lorentz transformation.

A direct proof of this statement is possible, which is rather laborious, by writing the equations in Cartesian coordinates, and then transforming them to the 'primed' system. A more fundamental approach starts from the 4-dimensional field tensors. Comparison of Eqs. (20.85) and (20.94) shows that, in free space, the terms of the tensors $[F_{ij}]$ and $[G_{ij}]$ are proportional:

$$F_{ij} = \mu_0 G_{ij} \tag{20.98}$$

Thus, Eq. (20.95) may be rewritten as

$$\sum_{j=1,2,\cdots}^{4} \left(\frac{\partial F_{ij}}{\partial x_j} \right) = \mu_0 J_i \quad (i = 1, 2, 3, 4) \tag{20.99}$$

Substituting,

$$F_{ij} = \frac{\partial A_j}{\partial x_i} - \frac{\partial A_i}{\partial x_j}, \quad \text{from Eq. (20.79), we get}$$

$$\sum_{j=1,2,\cdots}^{4} \left(\frac{\partial^2 A_j}{\partial x_j \partial x_i} \right) - \sum_{j=1,2,\cdots}^{4} \left(\frac{\partial^2 A_i}{\partial x_j^2} \right) = \mu_0 J_i \tag{20.100}$$

and the first term is

$$\left(\frac{\partial}{\partial x_i} \right) (\square \cdot \mathbf{A}) = 0$$

when we assume that

$$\text{div } \mathbf{A} + \left(\frac{1}{c^2} \right) \left(\frac{\partial \phi}{\partial t} \right) = 0 \quad \text{[see Eqs. (20.89) and (20.90)]}$$

Thus Eq. (20.100) reduces to the four equations,

$$\sum_{j=1,2,\cdots}^{4} \left(\frac{\partial^2 A_i}{\partial x_j^2} \right) = -\mu_0 J_i$$

or

$$\square \cdot \square A_i = -\mu_0 J_i \quad (i = 1, 2, 3, 4) \tag{20.101}$$

Here A_i is treated as a set of 4 scalars. If a Lorentz transformation is performed, A_i and J_i transform in the same way, and the transformed components obey the same equation.

If we substitute the components A_i and J_i from Eqs. (20.81) and (20.82), we find that the first three of Eqs. (20.101) are

$$\nabla^2 \mathbf{A} - \left(\frac{1}{c^2} \right) \left(\frac{\partial^2 \mathbf{A}}{\partial t^2} \right) = -\mu_0 \mathbf{J} \tag{20.102a}$$

and the fourth

$$\nabla^2 \phi - \left(\frac{1}{c^2}\right)\left(\frac{\partial^2 \phi}{\partial t^2}\right) = -\frac{\rho_C}{\varepsilon_0} \qquad (20.102b)$$

These are the equations which give rise to the waves propagating with the velocity c; their similarity, surprising in a 3-dimensional approach, is here quite natural.

Thus the Maxwell's equations in free space have led to a set of invariant equations (20.101), which lead in turn to waves that propagated with velocity c. Maxwell's equations transcend the Lorentz transformation, and are so built deeply into the world structure. They are, more fundamental, for example, than the Newton's second law of motion, which is usually stated in a form which assumes constancy of mass.

20.18   RELATIVISTIC ASPECTS OF ELECTROMAGNETIC INDUCTION

We shall conclude our discussion of the relativistic approach to electromagnetic field theory, by considering the practical problem of 'electromagnetic induction'.

When induction occurs in a magnetic field of constant pattern but varying intensity (as in a transformer), we have the so called *transformer induction* which is a sign of the fact that every varying magnetic field is accompanied by an electric field (also varying). This is expressed in the Maxwell's equation:

$$\text{curl } \mathbf{E} = -\left(\frac{\partial \mathbf{B}}{\partial t}\right)$$

When we have a field pattern, which moves but remains constant in intensity (e.g. that set up by rotating magnetic poles in an alternator), we have the *motional induction*, and find it convenient to apply the *flux-cutting method*. This is a relativistic phenomenon. In Figure 20.11, in the frame F' (which is attached to the rotating pole), we have only a magnetic field; but in the frame F (attached to the stator), we have also an electric field, which makes itself known as an emf induced in a winding in that frame F.

The emf can equally well be calculated by the flux-linking approach $[\mathscr{E} = -(d\Lambda/dt)]$, which is equivalent to the flux-cutting ($\mathscr{E} = Blu$). But the equivalence seems to break down when we have *homopolar generator*, with no passage from N (north pole) to S (south pole) poles.

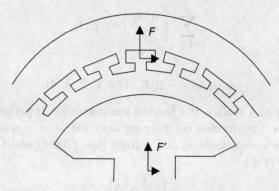

Figure 20.11   Stator and rotor of a rotating alternator.

20.18.1 Electromagnetic Induction by Flux-cutting

This phenomenon takes a new aspect when viewed relativistically. For instance, the train of arguments describing the operation of a dynamo with its field (winding) on the stator becomes:

1. The field winding sets up B with respect to the stator (frame F).
2. Both E' and B' are potentially present in the rotor (frame F').
3. E' is short-circuited by the rotor conductors, and is reduced to zero by the movement of the charges to the ends of the conductors, just as when a metal rod is placed in an electrostatic field.
4. The reduction of E' to zero brings into being an electric field E with respect to the stator (the frame F). The sources of the field are the charges aforementioned. Its magnitude is given by:

$$E = -(\mathbf{u} \times \mathbf{B}') = -(\mathbf{u} \times \mathbf{B}), \qquad \text{to first order} \qquad (20.103)$$

This gives with respect to (the frame) F, a potential difference between the ends of the conductor; but $\mathbf{E} \cdot d\mathbf{l} = 0$ for a fixed circuit with no change of flux-linkage, and so we get an equal and opposite contribution across a measuring instrument. The flux-cutting action is shown diagrammatically in Figure 20.12.

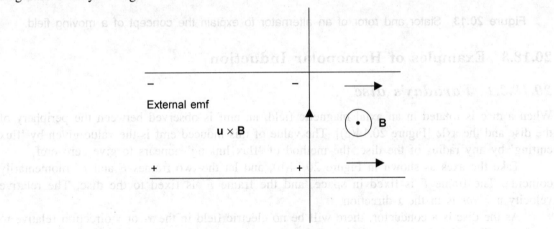

Figure 20.12 Flux-cutting emf.

20.18.2 The Concept of a Moving Field

There is no way in which the ideas of 'fixity' or 'motion' can be ascribed to a field. The velocity $\mathbf{u}$ in the Lorentz formula is not 'velocity relative to the field' but 'velocity relative to the observer'; for another observer with relative motion, $\mathbf{E}$, $\mathbf{B}$, and $\mathbf{u}$ would be different, yet in such a way as to make $\mathbf{F}$ (the Lorentz force) the same. What, then, are we doing when we make use of the idea of a moving or gliding field, for example in an ac machine?

We now consider the induction of emf in the stator coil of an alternator (Figure 20.13). We could calculate it by flux-linkage, but in fact we usually use flux cutting. regarding the flux as glued to the magnetic pole. This is equivalent to changing from a frame F which is fixed with respect to the stator, in which the flux density at any point is changing, to a frame F', fixed with respect to the rotor, in which the flux pattern is practically unchanging. Relative to the frame F', the stator conductors are moving through an unchanging field—a fair case for a flux-cutting method.

We are not necessarily ascribing to the field the same motion as that of the coils which produce it. Thus the words 'the velocity of the field' must be taken to mean 'the velocity of a frame of reference, with respect to which the field pattern is unchanging'. In an induction motor, the frame F' (with respect to which the field is unchanging) glides round at synchronous speed, which is not the speed of any material portion of the motor. When the field is pulsating, whatever the frame of reference we may choose, the 'moving field' idea has reached its limit of usefulness.

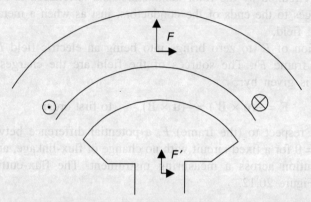

Figure 20.13　Stator and rotor of an alternator to explain the concept of a moving field.

20.18.3　Examples of Homopolar Induction

20.18.3.1　Faraday's disc

When a disc is rotated in an axial magnetic field, an emf is observed between the periphery of the disc and the axle [Figure 20.14(a)]. The value of this induced emf is the value given by 'flux cutting' by any radius of the disc; the method of 'flux linking' appears to give zero emf.

Take the axes as shown in Figure 20.14(b), and let the two frames F and F' momentarily coincide. The frame F is fixed in space, and the frame F' is fixed to the disc. The relative velocity u = ωr is in the x-direction.

As the disc is a conductor, there will be no electric field in the x- or y-direction relative to the frame F' (which is fixed to the disc).

$$\therefore \qquad E'_x = E'_y = 0 \qquad\qquad (20.104)$$

But
$$E'_x = E_x \qquad \text{and} \qquad E'_y = E_y - uB_z \qquad\qquad (20.105)$$

where B_z is the axial, imposed magnetic field.

Hence, with respect to the frame F (which is fixed in space),

$$E_x = 0 \qquad \text{and} \qquad E_y = uB_z \qquad\qquad (20.106)$$

$\therefore$　The emf across the radius PQ [Figure 20.14(a)] is

$$= \int_{r=0}^{r=a} \omega r\, B_z\, dr = \left(\frac{1}{2}\right)\omega a^2 B_z \qquad\qquad (20.107)$$

where a is the radius of the disc. This emf value is measured by the meter.

The *amendment* to the 'flux-cutting' rule which will make it cover this and similar cases is that the circuit must be such that at no place are the particles of the material moving across it. Such a circuit is shown in Figure 20.14(c), and it gives the correct answer when the flux-linking rule is applied.

The answer to this question is, yes, since "a synchronous rotating magnet" nevertheless we should get the same answer – before, we assume it or not.

If the field is stationary the induction occurs across the Faraday disc. If the field rotates, we get an induced emf in the external circuit. It can be seen that the two magnetic pictures give only the same polarity as also of the same magnitude.

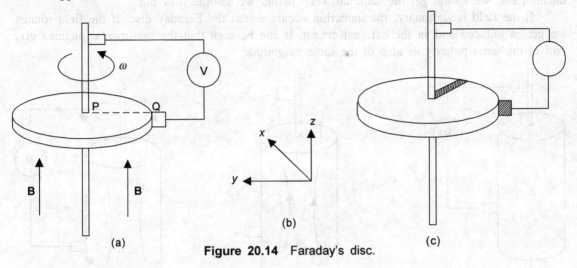

(a)

(b)

(c)

Figure 20.14 Faraday's disc.

20.18.3.2 *Faraday's disc with rotating magnet*

This is a slight modification of the previous configuration, as shown in Figure 20.15. The question now is: 'if the Faraday's disc is excited by a cylindrical bar magnet, which rotates with it, what result is expected?'

Actually, the induced emf is unaffected by the rotation of the magnet. This is because the term 'rotating field' is fundamentally meaningless when the field pattern is symmetrical.

The Faraday disc generator for a monopolar or cyclic generator, with its details, is shown in Figure 20.17. The applied flux density B is constant, and the shaft is driven at constant velocity (angular) ω. The material or the disc is homogeneous, isotropic and electrically linear, with material constants σ, μ, ϵ_0. The dimensions are defined in Figure 20.17. We shall derive the expressions for the terminal voltage under a current for a load resistance R under steady-state operation.

It should be noted that the current in the disc is radial, and the current density is uniform around the periphery at any radius. The magnetic field generated by the current density, the tangential and has to effect on the impressed voltage, the field due to the current in the disc is neglected.

In the cylindrical coordinate system, subject to the symmetry and the uniformity of the problem show that we can write

$$\frac{\partial}{\partial\theta} = 0$$

and the only variation is along the radius (r) h.

If the total output current I (radial component of the current density) in the disc (at a radial distance r) is given b.

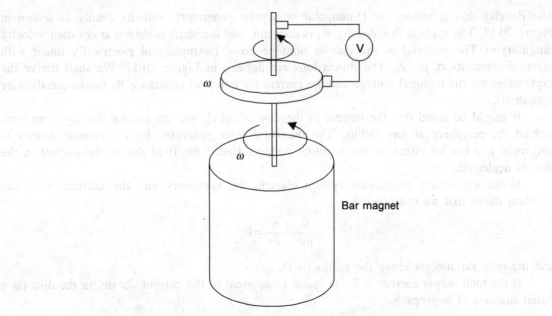

Bar magnet

Figure 20.15 Faraday's disc with rotating cylindrical bar magnet.

20.18.3.3 *Induction in a rotating cylindrical bar magnet*

This problem is akin to the last one. Here, do we expect an induced emf? (Figure 20.16)

The answer to this question is, yes. Since a symmetrical rotating magnetic field is meaningless, we should get the same answer whether we assume it or not.

If the field is stationary, the induction occurs across the Faraday disc. If the field rotates, we get an induced emf in the external circuit. It can be seen that the two mental pictures give emf of the same polarity as also of the same magnitude.

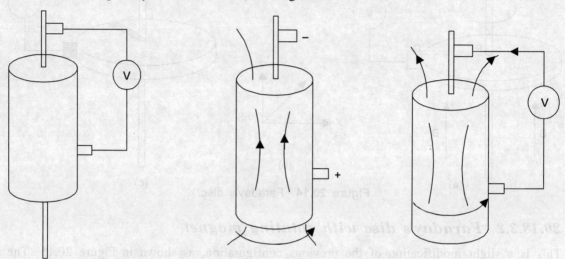

Figure 20.16 A rotating bar magnet.

20.18.3.4 *Current, terminal voltage, and power in a Faraday disc generator*

The Faraday disc generator (or Homopolar or acyclic generator), with its details, is shown in Figure 20.17. The applied flux density B_0 is constant, and the shaft is driven at constant velocity (angular) ω. The material of the disc is homogeneous, isotropic and electrically linear with material constants σ, μ_0, ε_0. The dimensions are defined in Figure 20.17. We shall derive the expressions for the terminal voltage and the current for any load resistance R_L (under steady-state operation).

It should be noted that the current in the disc is radial, and the current density is uniform around the periphery at any radius. The magnetic field generated by the current density is tangential and has no effect on the terminal voltage. Hence the field due to the current in the disc is neglected.

In the cylindrical coordinate system chosen, the symmetry and the uniformity of the problem shows that we can assume

$$\frac{\partial}{\partial \phi} = \frac{\partial}{\partial z} = 0$$

and the only variation is along the radius $(= r)$.

If the total output current is I, the radial component of the current density in the disc (at a radial distance r) is given by

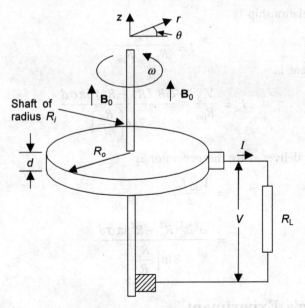

Figure 20.17 Faraday's disc generator, connected to a load resistor.

$$J_r = \frac{I}{2\pi rd} \tag{20.108}$$

By Ohm's law for a grain of matter at a radius r, we get the relationship

$$J_r = \sigma(E_r + \omega r B_0) \tag{20.109}$$

where B_0 is the magnitude of the externally applied magnetic field, and E_r the radial component of the electric field intensity.

The tangential component of **B** (the flux density B_ϕ due to the current flow in the disc) is parallel to the material velocity, and hence does not contribute to the $(\mathbf{v} \times \mathbf{B})$ term above. Thus the neglect of this component of **B** generated by the current flow in the disc is justified.

$$\therefore \qquad E_r = \frac{I}{2\pi rd\sigma} - \omega r B_0 \tag{20.110}$$

Since there is no time-rate of change of **B** in the fixed reference frame, the terminal voltage is

$$V = -\int\limits_{r=R_i}^{r=R_o} E_r dr = -\left(\frac{I}{2\pi\sigma d}\right)\ln\left(\frac{R_o}{R_i}\right) + \left(\frac{\omega B_0}{2}\right)\left(R_o^2 - R_i^2\right) \tag{20.111}$$

In the above expression, if we let $R_L \to \infty$, then the open-circuit voltage is

$$V_{\text{oc}} = \left(\frac{\omega B_0}{2}\right)\left(R_o^2 - R_i^2\right) \tag{20.112}$$

and the internal resistance of the generator is

$$R_{\text{int}} = \frac{\ln\left(\dfrac{R_o}{R_i}\right)}{2\pi\sigma d} \tag{20.113}$$

Hence the terminal relationship is

$$I = \frac{V_{oc}}{R_L + R_{int}} \tag{20.114}$$

The short-circuit current is

$$I_{sc} = \frac{V_{oc}}{R_{int}} = \frac{\omega B_0 (R_o^2 - R_i^2) 2\pi \sigma d}{2 \ln\left(\dfrac{R_o}{R_i}\right)} \tag{20.115}$$

The maximum power delivered by the generator is

$$P_{max} = \frac{V_{oc} I_{sc}}{4}$$

$$= \frac{\omega^2 B_0^2 (R_o^2 - R_i^2) \pi \sigma d}{8 \ln\left(\dfrac{R_o}{R_i}\right)} \tag{20.116}$$

20.18.4 Herring's Experiment

This experiment is one in which the terminals of a galvanometer are connected to a pair of springy metal strips, as shown in Figure 20.18, which are held apart at one end by an insulating block. But the strips are so shaped that their springiness makes them snap together (bringing them in contact) at the free end, thus short-circuiting the galvanometer.

In the experiment, the free ends of the strips are forced apart by pushing a permanent magnet (say, of cylindrical cross-section) between them side-ways; when the magnet has been completely pushed in, the contacts spring together again, with the magnetic flux from the magnet now linking the circuit.

The question is: do we expect an induced emf, when the cylindrical bar magnet is pushed between the clips?

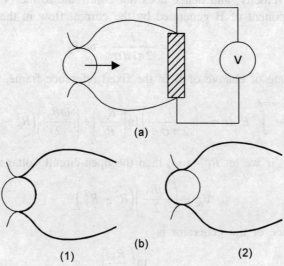

Figure 20.18 Herring's experiment.

The answer is: there is no reading in the galvanometer. The reason is that as in the previous case of the Faraday's disc, the flux-linkage must be calculated in a circuit *across which the material particles are not moving*. Two such circuits are shown in the Figure 20.18(b); and in neither is there any change in the flux-linkage.

It will be found that when the idea of a *moving field* is successfully employed; we are really talking about a *moving field pattern*. This means transference from a frame of reference in which the field is unchanging to another in which the field-pattern moves without variation of shape or magnitude. If no frame exists in which the field is unchanging, the concept of a moving field is a snare.

20.18.5 The Cullwick Experiment

A piece of steel tubing R (as shown in Figure 20.19) is coaxial with a long wire C carrying a direct current I. The tubing moves with a uniform velocity u in the direction opposite to that of the current flow.

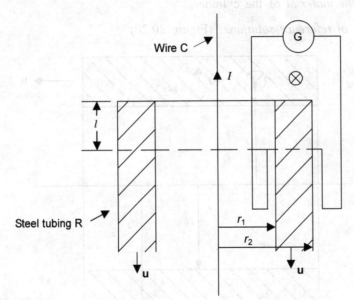

Figure 20.19 The Cullwick experiment.

The questions in this experiment are:

1. What is the induced emf (in the loop or the contour shown in Figure 20.19)?
2. Does the emf change, if the steel tubing is replaced by a brass tubing (of identical shape and size)?

A. Direct solution. We consider the emf in the loop shown in Figure 20.19, comprising a path round the edge of the cylinder.

In air,

$$B = \frac{\mu_0 I}{2\pi r} \qquad (20.117)$$

If the cylinder has fallen through a height l in the time T, the extra flux in the length $l = \left(\dfrac{\mu_0 I l}{2\pi}\right) \ln\left(\dfrac{r_2}{r_1}\right)$ (20.117a)

Since this fall has taken place in the time T,

the induced emf $= \left(\dfrac{\mu_0 I l}{2\pi T}\right) \ln\left(\dfrac{r_2}{r_1}\right)$ (20.118)

and

the current in the loop $= \left(\dfrac{\mu_0 I l}{2\pi R T}\right) \ln\left(\dfrac{r_2}{r_1}\right)$ (20.119)

where R is the resistance of the loop.

And

the charge $= \left(\dfrac{\mu_0 I l}{2\pi R}\right) \ln\left(\dfrac{r_2}{r_1}\right)$ (20.120)

This is *independent of the material* of the cylinder.

 B. *Moving frame of reference solution.* (Figure 20.20)

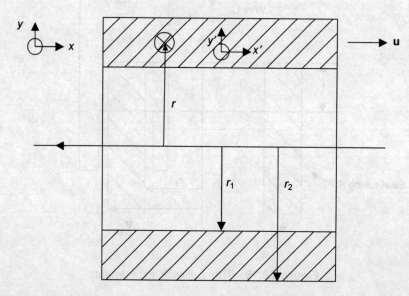

Figure 20.20 The Cullwick experiment, showing the frames of reference.

In the stationary frame F

$$H = H_\phi = \frac{I}{2\pi r} \quad (= -H_z)$$ (20.121)

In the moving frame F', there is potentially

$$D' = \left(\frac{1}{c^2}\right)(\mathbf{u} \times \mathbf{H})$$ (20.122)

which gives

$$D'_y = \frac{uI}{2\pi c^2 r} \quad \text{or} \quad E'_y = \left(\frac{\mu_0}{2\pi}\right)\left(\frac{uI}{r}\right)$$ (20.123)

This is short-circuited by the conductor, giving rise to an emf:

$$\mathscr{E} = \int_{r=r_1}^{r=r_2} E'_y \, dr = \left(\frac{\mu_0 uI}{2\pi}\right) \ln\left(\frac{r_2}{r_1}\right) \tag{20.124}$$

If the velocity $u = \dfrac{dx}{dt}$, this gives a charge:

$$= \int_0^T \left(\frac{\mathscr{E}}{R}\right) dt = \left(\frac{\mu_0 I}{2\pi R}\right) \ln\left(\frac{r_2}{r_1}\right) \int_0^T \left(\frac{dx}{dt}\right) dt$$

$$= \left[\left(\frac{\mu_0 I}{2\pi R}\right) \ln\left(\frac{r_2}{r_1}\right)\right] \times \text{distance moved} \tag{20.125}$$

where R is the resistance of the circuit.

This argument is independent of the material of the cylinder.

PROBLEMS

20.1 A car with 2 metre long bumper is travelling at 100 km/h. Find the potential drop produced in the bumper due to earth's magnetic field of 3.2×10^{-5} webers/m^2 and the angle of dip of $64°9'$.

Ans.: 1.6 mV

20.2 The differential form of Faraday's law when applied to a system moving with a velocity **u** can be written as:

$$\nabla \times \mathbf{E} = -\frac{\partial \mathbf{B}}{\partial t} + \nabla \times \mathbf{u} \times \mathbf{B}$$

A rectangular loop is located in the field of a long current-carrying straight wire as shown below.

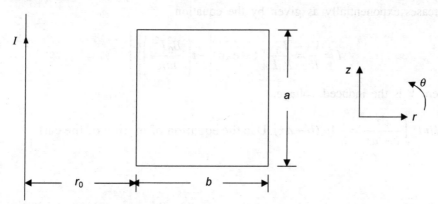

Using the above expression, evaluate:

(i)   The induced voltage in the loop if it is fixed in space but I varies as $I_0 \cos \omega t$.

(ii) The magnitude and the direction of the induced voltage as a function of r when $I = I_0$ and is constant, but the loop moves towards the wire with a velocity **u**.

(iii) The induced voltage in the loop when it moves towards the long conductor with a velocity **u** and the current varies as $I = I_0 \cos \omega t$.

Ans.: (i) $\dfrac{\mu_0 \omega I_0}{2\pi} a \ln \dfrac{r_0 + b}{r_0} \cdot \sin \omega t$; (ii) $-\dfrac{\mu_0 u I_0 a}{2\pi}\left(\dfrac{1}{r_0} - \dfrac{1}{r_0 + b} \right)$;

(iii) $\dfrac{\mu_0 I_0 a}{2\pi}\left\{ \omega \ln \dfrac{r_0 + b}{r_0} \cdot \sin \omega t - \mu_0 \left(\dfrac{1}{r_0} - \dfrac{1}{r_0 + b} \right) \cos \omega t \right\}.$

20.3 The electric and magnetic fields in a region are $\mathbf{E} = \mathbf{i}_y E_0$ and $\mathbf{B} = \mathbf{i}_z B_0$ respectively, where E_0 and B_0 are constants. A small test charge Q having a mass m starts from rest at the origin at the instant $t = 0$.

Using the Lorentz force equation

$$\mathbf{F} = q(\mathbf{E} + \mathbf{v} \times \mathbf{B})$$

and the equation of motion, show that the velocity components of the charge will be:

$$v_x = \frac{E_0}{B_0}(1 - \cos \omega_c t)$$

$$v_y = \frac{E_0}{B_0} \sin \omega_c t$$

where $\omega_c = Q \dfrac{B_0}{m}$.

What will be the electric field as seen by an observer moving with the test charge?

20.4 A metal vehicle travels round a set of perfectly conducting rails which form a large circle. The rails are L metres apart and there is a uniform magnetic field B_0 normal to their plane as shown in the figure below. The mass of the vehicle is m, and it is driven by a rocket engine having a constant thrust F_0. The system acts as a dc generator whose output is fed into a load resistance R. Show that the output current I from the system increases exponentially as given by the equation

$$I = \frac{V}{R} = \frac{F_0}{B_0 L}\left[1 - \exp \left\{ -t \left(\frac{B_0^2 L^2}{mR} \right) \right\} \right]$$

where V is the induced voltage.

$$\left\{ Hint: \int \frac{dx}{b - ax} = \frac{1}{a} \ln (b - ax). \text{ Use the equation of motion of the cart.} \right\}$$

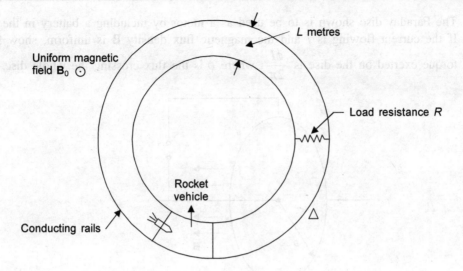

Uniform magnetic field $\mathbf{B}_0$ ⊙

L metres

Load resistance R

Rocket vehicle

Conducting rails

20.5 Faraday's law when applied to a system moving with a velocity v can be written as

$$\mathscr{E} = \oint_C \mathbf{E} \cdot d\mathbf{l} = -\frac{\partial}{\partial t} \iint_S \mathbf{B} \cdot d\mathbf{S} + \oint_C (\mathbf{v} \times \mathbf{B}) \cdot d\mathbf{l}$$

Hence or otherwise, find the emf induced in a rectangular loop, one side of which moves with a constant acceleration g across a flux-density field **B** which increases linearly in the direction of motion of the conductor and periodically with time. The direction of the motion and of the magnetic field are shown in the figures below.

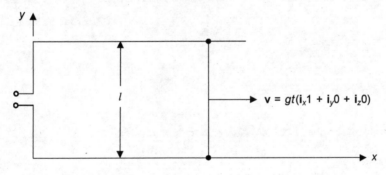

$\mathbf{v} = gt(\mathbf{i}_x 1 + \mathbf{i}_y 0 + \mathbf{i}_z 0)$

$\mathbf{B} = bxe^{j\omega t}(\mathbf{i}_x \sin\theta + \mathbf{i}_z \cos\theta)$

$\therefore \dfrac{\partial \mathbf{B}}{\partial t} = j\omega bxe^{j\omega t}(\mathbf{i}_x \sin\theta + \mathbf{i}_z \cos\theta); \quad d\mathbf{S} = \mathbf{i}_z \, d_x d_y$

Ans.: $= -e^{j\omega t} \, bl\cos\theta \, \dfrac{g^2 t^3}{2}\left(1 + \dfrac{j\omega t}{4}\right)$

20.6 The Faraday disc shown is to be used as a motor by including a battery in the circuit. If the current flowing is I and the magnetic flux density **B** is uniform, show that the torque exerted on the disc is $\dfrac{\phi I}{2\pi}$, where ϕ is the flux crossing the whole disc.

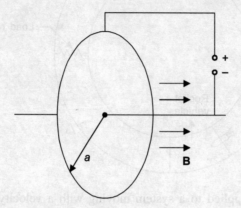

Find I if the battery emf is $\mathscr{E}$, the resistance of the circuit is R, and ω is the angular velocity of the disc in rads/sec.

Ans.: $I = \mathscr{E} - \dfrac{\phi\omega/2\pi}{R}$

21 Numerical Methods for and Computer Solutions of Electromagnetic Field Problems

21.1 INTRODUCTION

So far in our study of electromagnetic field theory, our main emphasis has been on the proper understanding of the underlying physical concepts of the theory, so that correct mathematical techniques may be applied to solve practical problems. In most of the practical problems, the main difficulty lies not in the selection of the mathematical method, but in the representation of the correct boundary conditions. The interpretation of the physical boundaries, and finding their correct mathematical equivalents, is in fact, the first critical step in solving such problems. This is the reason as to why we have emphasized so strongly on the need for a deep insight into the physics of most electromagnetic phenomena. Having completed the mathematical analysis of the problem, again re-interpreting the mathematical solution in terms of its physics depends very much on the earlier step mentioned above. Hence the correct formulation of the boundary conditions for a specified problem is a very critical step in solving it.

We have discussed earlier in a number of chapters (i.e. Chapters 4, 5, 9), the different methods of solving electrostatic, magnetostatic, and quasi-static magnetic field problems, apart from the various problems (including electrostatic, magnetostatic, and electromagnetic) discussed and solved in different other chapters in this book. It has also been pointed out earlier in this book that whilst the electrostatic and the magnetostatic problems are mostly Laplacian and Poissonian in nature, the electromagnetic problems (i.e. eddy currents and wave problems) are more complex in nature, though under special simplified and idealized conditions, these can be reduced to simpler equations (i.e. Laplace and Poisson). However it should also be remembered that in all these operating differential equations, there is the Laplace's operator ($\equiv \nabla^2$) as the main spatial operator on their left-hand side. Hence the basic methods of solving the general electromagnetic field problems would apply to the static problems, as these can be considered as restricted cases of the more general class.

We have already discussed a number of eddy current and wave problems in the Chapters 15–18, for which we have obtained (mostly) analytical closed-form solutions, using a number of analytical methods. But these are, by and large, idealized problems. So in this chapter, we shall not go into further details of such methods. This is not to imply that we have covered the complete range of such problems solved by these analytical methods. But since this is an introductory textbook on the subject of electromagnetism, we shall not go into the details of those more complex problems, which, of course, would be the subject matter of more specialized texts. Of the other methods which have been discussed earlier, the numerical methods are being increasingly used to solve more and more problems because of the rapid development of more powerful and faster computers. While describing the applications of the numerical methods (i.e. the finite difference method = F.D.M., and the finite element method = F.E.M.), we have pointed out that both these methods are being widely used to solve electrostatic problems. Whilst F.E.M. has gained wide popularity in solving electromagnetic, magnetostatic, and quasi-static magnetic field problems, the F.D.M. has been in significant use for solving electrostatic (and heat transfer) problems, because in electrostatics, there are quite a large range of problems with open boundaries. For such problems, F.D.M. is found to have significant advantages, and the geometry of electrostatic problems (in a large number of cases) permits the use of regular and graded meshes without taking too much computer time. Since we have already discussed in fair detail the methods of F.D.M. (while considering the solutions of electrostatic problems), we do not propose to go into the details of this method for solving magnetic and electromagnetic problems, as the techniques of solving such problems are identical with those for the electrostatic problems. This is true particularly for two-dimensional problems, because even though the vector potential is being used for these problems, the potential usually has only one component (though some of the magnetic field vectors can have more than one component) and hence the treatment is similar to thar of the scalar potential (which is the usual operating variable used in most of the electrostatic problems).

Similar arguments may apply to the use of the F.E.M., though of course, the formulation of the 'functional' would be different for (say) the magnetostatic fields (being a resticted case) from that for the electromagnetic eddy current fields to electromagnetic wave patterns. So we shall now discuss the functionals for various types of electromagnetic field problems, using the concept of magnetic vector potential.

21.2 FINITE ELEMENT METHOD APPLIED TO TWO-DIMENSIONAL ELECTROMAGNETIC FIELD PROBLEMS (INVOLVING EDDY CURRENTS)

As mentioned earlier, F.E.M. is a popular numerical method based on the variational principle for solving any boundary-value field problem. A 'functional' is an integral expression involving a function dependent on the unknown variable and its derivatives. The functional is identified, and minimized with respect to the unknown variables, subject to the boundary conditions specified. This process results in the required solution to the field equations. Let the functional be defined as follows:

$$\Gamma = \iint F(x, y, A, A_x, A_y)\, dx\, dy \qquad (21.1)$$

where
$$A_x = \frac{\partial A}{\partial x}, \quad A_y = \frac{\partial A}{\partial y}$$

Notes

1. It should be carefully noted that here the suffices x and y in A_x, A_y respectively represent the derivatives of A with respect to those independent variables, and *not* the vector components.

2. Also this G should not be confused with the reflection coefficient of waveguides, even though the same symbol is used for both.

As stated before, we are restricting ourselves to two-dimensional problems with the magnetic vector potential having one component only, and the present derivation is in Cartesian coordinate system (though this is not a restriction imposed on the method).

Since the functional is an area integral in terms of the variables x and y within the specified boundaries of the problem, the variations can be effected in A only. Let A be changed by a small quantity δA. The value of the functional then changes to:

$$\Gamma' = \iint F(x, y, A + \delta A, A_x + \delta A_x, A_y + \delta A_y)dx\, dy$$

$\therefore$ The change in the functional is given by:

$$\delta\Gamma = \iint F(x, y, A + \delta A, A_x + \delta A_x, A_y + \delta A_y)dx\, dy - \iint F(x, y, A, A_x, A_y)dx\, dy$$

The first term can be expanded by the Taylor series; and then for sufficiently small values of δA, we can neglect the terms containing higher orders of δA.

$$\therefore \quad \delta\Gamma = \iint \left(\frac{\partial F}{\partial A}\right)\delta A\, dx\, dy + \iint \left(\frac{\partial F}{\partial A_x}\right)\delta A_x\, dx\, dy + \iint \left(\frac{\partial F}{\partial A_y}\right)\delta A_y\, dx\, dy$$

$$= \iint \left(\frac{\partial F}{\partial A}\right)\delta A\, dx\, dy + \iint \left(\frac{\partial F}{\partial A_x}\right)d\left(\frac{\partial A}{\partial x}\right) dx\, dy + \iint \left(\frac{\partial F}{\partial A_y}\right)d\left(\frac{\partial A}{\partial y}\right) dx\, dy \quad (21.2)$$

From Eq. (21.1),

$$\delta\Gamma = \iint \left(\frac{\partial F}{\partial A}\right)\delta A\, dx\, dy + \iint \left(\frac{\partial F}{\partial A_x}\right)\left(\frac{\partial}{\partial x}\right)(\delta A)\, dx\, dy + \iint \left(\frac{\partial F}{\partial A_y}\right)\left(\frac{\partial}{\partial y}\right)(\delta A)\, dx\, dy$$

But the total differential of δA is given by:

$$d(\delta A) = \left(\frac{\partial}{\partial x}\right)(\delta A)\, dx + \left(\frac{\partial}{\partial y}\right)(\delta A)\, dy \tag{21.3}$$

$\therefore$
$$\delta\Gamma = \iint \left(\frac{\partial F}{\partial A}\right)\delta A\, dx\, dy + \int\left[\int \left(\frac{\partial F}{\partial A_x}\right)\left(\frac{\partial}{\partial x}\right)(\delta A)\, dx\right] dy$$

$$+ \int\left[\int \left(\frac{\partial F}{\partial A_y}\right)\left(\frac{\partial}{\partial y}\right)(\delta A)\, dy\right] dx \tag{21.4}$$

In Eq. (21.4), for the bracketed term in the second integral, the integration is with respect to x, keeping y constant, which implies that $dy = 0$ in Eq. (21.3), and so for this condition, we get

$$d(\delta A) = \left(\frac{\partial}{\partial x}\right)(\delta A)\, dx$$

and for the third integral, the bracketed term is integration with respect to y keeping x constant, which reduces Eq. (21.3) to

$$d(\delta A) = \left(\frac{\partial}{\partial y}\right)(\delta A)\, dy$$

So Eq. (21.4) becomes

$$\delta\Gamma = \iint \left(\frac{\partial F}{\partial A}\right)\delta A\, dx\, dy + \int\left[\int \left(\frac{\partial F}{\partial A_x}\right)d(\delta A)\right] dy + \int\left[\int \left(\frac{\partial F}{\partial A_y}\right)d(\delta A)\right] dx \tag{21.5}$$

The second and the third integrals can be integrated by parts, i.e.

$$\int \left[\int \left(\frac{\partial F}{\partial A_x} \right) d(\delta A) \right] dy = \int \left[\left(\frac{\partial F}{\partial A_x} \right) \delta A - \int \delta A \, d\left(\frac{\partial F}{\partial A_x} \right) \right] dy \qquad (21.6)$$

But

$$d\left(\frac{\partial F}{\partial A_x} \right) = \left(\frac{\partial}{\partial x} \right)\left(\frac{\partial F}{\partial A_x} \right) dx + \left(\frac{\partial}{\partial y} \right)\left(\frac{\partial F}{\partial A_x} \right) dy$$

$$= \left(\frac{\partial}{\partial x} \right)\left(\frac{\partial F}{\partial A_x} \right) dx$$

since, as before $dy = 0$ as this integration is with respect to x.

Substituting in Eq. (21.6),

$$\int \left[\int \left(\frac{\partial F}{\partial A_x} \right) d(\delta A) \right] dy = \int \left(\frac{\partial F}{\partial A_x} \right) \delta A \, dy - \iint \delta A \left(\frac{\partial}{\partial x} \right)\left(\frac{\partial F}{\partial A_x} \right) dx \, dy \qquad (21.7)$$

Similarly the third term of Eq. (21.5) would reduce to

$$\int \left[\int \left(\frac{\partial F}{\partial A_y} \right) d(\delta A) \right] dx = \int \left(\frac{\partial F}{\partial A_y} \right) \delta A \, dx - \iint \delta A \left(\frac{\partial}{\partial y} \right)\left(\frac{\partial F}{\partial A_y} \right) dx \, dy \qquad (21.8)$$

Substituting from Eqs. (21.7) and (21.8) in Eq. (21.5), the incremental change in the functional is obtained as

$$\delta \Gamma = \iint \left[\delta A \left(\frac{\partial F}{\partial A} \right) - \delta A \left(\frac{\partial}{\partial x} \right)\left(\frac{\partial F}{\partial A_x} \right) - \delta A \left(\frac{\partial}{\partial y} \right)\left(\frac{\partial F}{\partial A_y} \right) \right] dx \, dy$$

$$+ \left[\int \delta A \left(\frac{\partial F}{\partial A_x} \right) dy + \int \delta A \left(\frac{\partial F}{\partial A_y} \right) dx \right] \qquad (21.9)$$

The above expression is called the first variation of the functional for sufficiently small values of δA. The necessary condition for the functional to attain its minimum is obtained when this variation is set to zero, i.e.

$$\delta \Gamma = 0 \qquad (21.10)$$

If, in this expression, as shown in Eq. (21.9), the second (line) integral is set to zero, we are left with the first integral which also must be made equal to zero to satisfy the above condition (21.10). The implication of the line integral setting to zero will be discussed later when we discuss the boundary conditions, with the actual functional for specific problems.

For the first integral, since $\delta A \neq 0$, we are left with the following equation:

$$\delta \Gamma = \left(\frac{\partial F}{\partial A} \right) - \left(\frac{\partial}{\partial x} \right)\left(\frac{\partial F}{\partial A_x} \right) - \left(\frac{\partial}{\partial y} \right)\left(\frac{\partial F}{\partial A_y} \right) = 0 \qquad (21.11)$$

This is called the Euler equation of the functional Γ. Thus the minimization of the functional requires that the Euler equation of the functional be satisfied along with the boundary integral being set to zero. Thus, if for a given functional, the above equation turns out to be the original partial differential equation which we seek to solve and force the boundary conditions so as to make the line integrals to be zero, then the minimization of the functional will yield the solution of the partial differential equation. So now we shall select the functional for electromagnetic eddy current problems with time-harmonic variations.

The appropriate functional for solving Eq. (21.11) for the type of electromagnetic field, as specified just above, is one containing all energy terms expressed as functions of the variables which are the magnetic vector potential and the space (i.e. the coordinate variables). The required functional for two-dimensional electromagnetic eddy-current, time-harmonic field problems is

$$\Gamma = \int \left[\int_R \left(\frac{1}{2} \right)(v \, B \, dB) - (\mathbf{J} \cdot \mathbf{A}) \, dA + \left(\frac{1}{2} \right)(j\omega\sigma A^2) \right] dS \qquad (21.12)$$

where

R is the region of analysis
v is the reluctivity (reluctance)
$\mathbf{J}$ is the current density
B is the flux density
$\mathbf{A}$ is the magnetic vector potential
ω is the angular frequency
σ is the conductivity of the medium.

The first term represents the stored energy in the system; whilst the second term denotes the input energy to the system. The third term represents the reaction of the induced field; i.e. the losses in the system. Thus the functional represents the energy balance of the complete system. If the variable vector potential is changed by a small value, there will be a corresponding resulting change in the functional. This change will be 'zero' only if the functional is at its minimum. If the medium is linear, then the functional can be simplified to:

$$\Gamma = \iint \left[\left(\frac{1}{2} \right)(v \, B^2) - (\mathbf{J} \cdot \mathbf{A}) + \left(\frac{1}{2} \right)(j\omega\sigma A^2) \right] dS$$

$$= \iint \left[\left(\frac{1}{2} \right)v \, (B_x^2 + B_y^2) - (\mathbf{J} \cdot \mathbf{A}) + \left(\frac{1}{2} \right)(j\omega\sigma A^2) \right] dS$$

Writing $\mathbf{B}$ in terms of the vector potential $\mathbf{A}$, i.e.

$$B_x = \frac{\partial A}{\partial y} = A_y, \quad B_y = - \frac{\partial A}{\partial x} = - A_x$$

$$\therefore \qquad \Gamma = \iint \left[\left(\frac{1}{2} \right)v \, (A_x^2 + A_y^2) - (\mathbf{J} \cdot \mathbf{A}) + \left(\frac{1}{2} \right)(j\omega\sigma A^2) \right] dS \qquad (21.13)$$

The Euler equation of the above functional is given by

$$\left(\frac{\partial F}{\partial A} \right) - \left(\frac{\partial}{\partial x} \right)\left(\frac{\partial F}{\partial A_x} \right) - \left(\frac{\partial}{\partial y} \right)\left(\frac{\partial F}{\partial A_y} \right) = 0 \qquad (21.14)$$

where

$$F = \left[\left(\frac{1}{2} \right)v \, (A_x^2 + A_y^2) - (\mathbf{J} \cdot \mathbf{A}) + \left(\frac{1}{2} \right)(j\omega\sigma A^2) \right] \qquad (21.15)$$

Substituting for F in the Euler equation, and differentiating

$$(-J + j\omega\sigma A) - v\left(\frac{\partial}{\partial x}\right)A_x - v\left(\frac{\partial}{\partial y}\right)A_y = 0$$

or

$$(-J + j\omega\sigma A) - v\left(\frac{\partial}{\partial x}\right)\left(\frac{\partial A}{\partial x}\right) - v\left(\frac{\partial}{\partial y}\right)\left(\frac{\partial A}{\partial y}\right) = 0$$

or

$$\frac{\partial^2 A}{\partial x^2} + \frac{\partial^2 A}{\partial y^2} = -\mu(J + j\omega\sigma A) \tag{21.16}$$

This is the governing equation for two-dimensional field problems expressed in terms of the magnetic vector potential. Thus the minimization of the functional indirectly gives the solution of the equation itself.

The line-integral of the equation is given by

$$\int \delta A\left(\frac{\partial F}{\partial A_x}\right)dy + \int \delta A\left(\frac{\partial F}{\partial A_y}\right)dx = 0$$

Substituting for F in Eq. (21.15),

$$\int \delta A \, A_x \, dy + \int \delta A \, A_y \, dx = 0$$

or

$$\int \delta A\left(\frac{\partial A}{\partial x}\right)dy + \int \delta A\left(\frac{\partial A}{\partial y}\right)dx = 0$$

Replacing dx and dy by $(ds \cos \alpha)$ and $(ds \sin \alpha)$ respectively,

$$\int \left[\left(\frac{\partial A}{\partial x}\right)\sin \alpha + \left(\frac{\partial A}{\partial y}\right)\cos \alpha\right]\delta A \, ds = 0$$

Now, we have

$$\left(\frac{\partial A}{\partial n}\right) = \left(\frac{\partial A}{\partial x}\right)\left(\frac{dx}{dn}\right) + \left(\frac{\partial A}{\partial y}\right)\left(\frac{dy}{dn}\right)$$

However,

$$\frac{dx}{dn} = \sin \alpha \quad \text{and} \quad \frac{dy}{dn} = \cos \alpha$$

∴   We get

$$\int \left[\left(\frac{\partial A}{\partial n}\right)\delta A\right]ds = 0 \tag{21.17}$$

The above condition derived by Eq. (21.17) is satisfied on the boundary, if either of the following statements given below is true:

1. $\delta A = 0$. This makes the boundary an equipotential line or a flux line.

2. $\dfrac{\partial A}{\partial n} = 0$. This requires the normal derivative of the vector potential to be zero, or the flux lines to cross this boundary normally.

Thus, in the process of minimization of the functional, we have obtained the Euler equation of the functional (which, of course, comes out to be the original pde), and the boundary conditions, such as the continuity of the flux density vector across the boundary, are automatically satisfied, while the specified potentials on the boundaries have to be imposed in the solution process.

To minimize the functional over the region, the variable (i.e. the vector potential over the whole region) is represented as a discrete quantity. To do this the whole region is sub-divided into a number of elements in any desired manner ensuring that all the material interfaces (i.e. all the iron–air–conducvtor boundaries) coincide with the sides of the elements. The number, shape, and size of the elements can be chosen in any arbitrary manner. An approximate distribution of the vector potential is assumed within each element, such that it is a function of the coordinates of the nodes of the element and the nodal values of the potentials at its vertices. Thus an approximate distribution of the vector potential is obtained by taking the above values together. These potentials are now varied until the functional given by Eq. (21.13) reaches its minimum. The resulting vector potential distribution gives the best possible result in the 'least square' sense, since the functional contains terms involving the second order of the vector potential. A variety of approximate descriptions for A within the element are possible. One of the simplest is triangular element with linear variation of A inside, which gives sufficiently accurate results. The treatment of such a triangular element is similar to that described in Section 5.6 with reference to electrostatic problems. The only difference is that instead of the scalar potential V of the static problems, we now use A—the vector potential, which we write as (referring to Figure 5.13):

$$A (x, y) = ax + by + c \tag{21.18}$$

The constants a, b, c can be obtained in terms of the nodal values of A and their coordinates, to give:

$$A(x, y) = \sum_{i=1,2,3} \left(\frac{p_i + q_i x + r_i y}{2\Delta} \right) A_i \tag{21.19}$$

where

Δ = area of the triangle, i, j, k being the vertices of the triangle

$p_i = (x_j y_k - x_k y_j)$

$q_i = (y_j - y_k)$

$r_i = (x_k - x_j)$

A_i = vector potential at the node i.

The flux density within the triangle is given by

$$B_x = \left(\frac{\partial A}{\partial y} \right) = \sum_{i=1,2,3} \left(\frac{r_i A_i}{2\Delta} \right) \tag{21.20a}$$

$$B_y = - \left(\frac{\partial A}{\partial x} \right) = - \sum_{i=1,2,3} \left(\frac{q_i A_i}{2\Delta} \right) \tag{21.20b}$$

[compare with Eq. (5.83)]

In this case, the flux density, and hence the permeability inside a triangle is constant, for the first order elements.

As in Eqs. (5.84) and (5.85), we can now express A in terms of area coordinates (or shape functions), i.e.

$$A(x, y) = \sum_{i=1,2,3} c_i A_i \qquad (21.21)$$

c_i, c_j, c_k being the area coordinates for the nodes i, j, and k respectively.

$$c_i = \frac{p_i + q_i x + r_i y}{2\Delta} \qquad (21.22)$$

The properties of these functions have already been described in Section 5.6, and so there is no need to repeat them here. The only difference is that the functional is now

$$\Gamma = \sum_{k=1,2,\ldots,n} \int \left[\left(\frac{1}{2} \right) v B_k^2 - \mathbf{J}_k \cdot \mathbf{A}_k + \left(\frac{1}{2} \right) j \omega \sigma A_k^2 \right] dS_k \qquad (21.23)$$

where

n is the number of elements
dS_k is the area of the kth element.

Rest of the treatment is similar to what has been discussed earlier in Section 5.6, and so the final global matrix is now given by

$$[S] [A] + [T] [A] = - [J] \qquad (21.24)$$

The points regarding the Dirichlet boundary condition are also same as before, and the final matrix equation, containing the set of simultaneous equations, is solved by the Gaussian Elimination method.

21.3 FINITE ELEMENT METHOD FOR EDDY CURRENT PROBLEMS

We have seen earlier (Sections 15.1, 15.4, and 15.5) that the current distribution within the section of a conductor is affected by its own field, when the current is alternating. The result is that the final distribution of the current density over the conductor cross-section is non-uniform, producing higher losses which shows up as increased apparent resistance of the conductor. Thus the effects of the induced currents cannot be neglected for evaluating the losses and the current densities correctly.

The governing equation for the fields in a linear conducting region, with the excitation having sinusoidal time-variation is

$$\nabla^2 A - j\omega\mu\sigma A = - \mu J_s$$

or

$$\nabla^2 A = - \mu (J_s - j\omega\sigma A) \qquad (21.25)$$

The first term on the right-hand side is the uniform source current density within the section of the conductor, whilst the second term represents the effects of the induced currents, or the reaction field due to the eddy currents. More generally, the second term reflects the combined effects of the boundaries and other conductors (i.e. combined skin-effects as well as proximity effects). Thus the solution obtained corresponds to the current density distribution given by the right-hand side of Eq. (21.25), or for the total current which is

$$I' = \int (J_s - j\omega\sigma A) \, dS \qquad (21.26)$$

For a linear case, subject to the same boundary conditions, the resultant distribution of A, obtained, remains unchanged, except for the magnitude and the phase for any other value of the total current in that conductor. Hence the field distribution for any specified current I in a single conductor, the final value of A is given by

$$A = A' \left(\frac{I}{I'} \right) \qquad (21.27)$$

where

 A' is the vector potential values obtained by feeding an arbitrary current I' (corresponding to a uniform direct current density J_s)
 I' is the resultant final current given by Eq. (21.26)
 I is the specified current in the conductor.

The current density at any point within the conductor section is

$$J = (J_s - j\omega\sigma A) \qquad (21.28)$$

where J_s is the uniform source current density.

The total current is

$$I = \int (J_s - j\omega\sigma A)\, dS \qquad (21.29)$$

It should be noted that all the quantities like A, J_s, etc. are complex.

21.3.1 Single Circular Conductor in Open Space

We apply the above method to obtain the solution for a single circular conductor carrying an alternating current, and hence having induced eddy currents in it. An analytical, closed-form solution exists for this problem (Sections 15.5 and 15.5.1), and hence has been chosen to show the effectiveness of the F.E. method, and compare the accuracy of the F.E. results with the numerical values obtained from the analytical solution. The results are presented graphically in Figure 21.1,

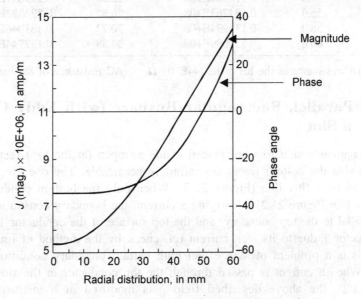

Figure 21.1 Current density distribution inside a circular conductor.

and numerically tabulated in Table 21.1. Figure 21.1 shows the current density amplitudes and its phases presented as a function of the radial distance from the centre of the circular conductor. Graphically, the results obtained by the two methods are practically coincident; and as shown in Table 21.1, the numercal values obtained, agree remarkably for the first two places of decimals, which can be considered to be very good.

Table 21.1 Current density distribution inside a circular conductor

Radius of conductor = 60.0 mm, current = 10000.0 amps
Conductivity = 5.8E+07, Frequency = 50.0 Hz
Average current density = 0.885118E+07 amps/m^2

Sr. No.	Radius	Analytical solution		FEM solution	
		J (mag.)	Phase	J (mag.)	Phase
1	0.0	0.756377E+07	−56.08	0.757594E+07	−56.00
2	8.0	0.756630E+07	−53.98	0.757869E+07	−53.90
3	12.0	0.756661E+07	−51.36	0.758918E+07	−52.80
4	16.0	0.760428E+07	−47.70	0.761703E+07	−47.70
5	20.0	0.766237E+07	−43.04	0.767522E+07	−43.00
6	24.0	0.776708E+07	−37.41	0.777990E+07	−37.90
7	28.0	0.793702E+07	−30.91	0.794965E+07	−30.90
8	32.0	0.819206E+07	−23.66	0.820429E+07	−23.70
9	36.0	0.855192E+07	−15.83	0.856353E+07	−15.80
10	40.0	0.903479E+07	−7.58	0.904555E+07	−7.60
11	42.0	0.932738E+07	−3.36	0.933765E+07	−3.40
12	44.0	0.965642E+07	0.91	0.966614E+07	0.90
13	46.0	0.100235E+08	5.19	0.100326E+08	5.20
14	48.0	0.104299E+08	9.45	0.104385E+08	9.50
15	50.0	0.108772E+08	13.78	0.108851E+08	13.70
16	52.0	0.113665E+08	18.05	0.113737E+08	18.00
17	54.0	0.118991E+08	22.30	0.119057E+08	22.30
18	56.0	0.124763E+08	26.52	0.124822E+08	26.50
19	58.0	0.130994E+08	30.72	0.131046E+08	30.70
20	60.0	0.137699E+08	34.88	0.137744E+08	34.90

DC resistance of the bar = 1.5244E–05 Ω   AC resistance of the bar = 1.9486E–05 Ω

21.3.2 Parallel, Rectangular Busbars (with Eddy Currents) Inside a Slot

Two rectangular conductors are placed inside an open (at the top) rectangular slot whose side-walls (as also the bottom floor) are infinitely permeable. The open top boundary of the slot is assumed to be a flux line (Figure 21.2). When only the bottom conductor in the slot (i.e. the conductor 1 in Figure 21.2) is carrying a current, the boundary constraints force all the flux lines to be parallel to the top boundary, and the top surface of the conductor 1. There is no field below the conductor 1 due to its own current (cf. check by the method of images; and also up to this stage, this is a problem of skin effect with certain boundary conditions imposed in the finite region). When a current is passed through the top conductor in the slot (i.e. the conductor 2 in Figure 21.2), the above described field gets modified in a manner which depends on the magnitude and the phase of the current in the conductor 2 (the current distributions in the two

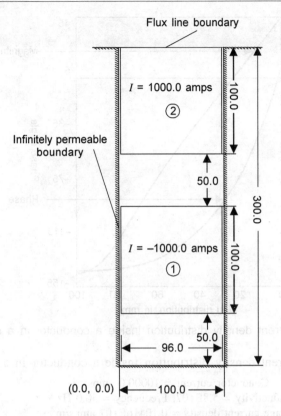

Figure 21.2   Conductors in a slot.

conductors are now a consequence of the skin effect as well as the proximity effect; and of course the superimposed effects of the boundaries in the finite region). The current density **J** and the flux density **B** distributions can be obtained by analytical method as well as the F.E.M. described earlier in this chapter. For the analytical solution, the interested reader is recommended to refer to *Foundations of Electrical Engineering* by K. Simonyi, for the solution of a similar problem of a rectangular conductor in an open rectangular slot. The current density and the flux density distributions for the top conductor in the slot have been ontained by both the analytical method as well as by the F.E.M. The results of the two methods have been compared in Figure 21.3 (i.e. the current density magnitudes at different vertical heights in the slot and the corresponding phase of the current in the top conductor in the slot), and tabulated in Table 21.2, for equal and opposite currents in the two conductors. The agreement between the two sets of results is excellent, indicating the validity of the method. Also, the magnetic flux is confined to the space between the top of the top conductor (i.e. the conductor 2) and the bottom of the lower conductor (i.e. the conductor 1). The resultant field is shown in Figure 21.4. For the calculations, the dimensions are as indicated in Figure 21.2, and the conductivity σ of the conductors $= 5.8 \times 10^6$ mhos/metre.

   For the top conductor, it is found that

$$\frac{R_{ac}}{R_{dc}} = 3.322$$

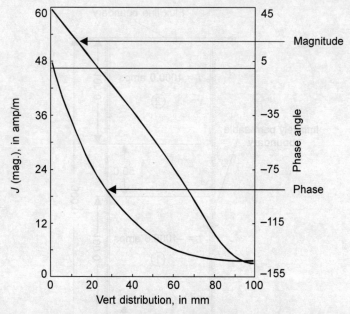

Figure 21.3   Current density distribution inside a conductor in a slot.

Table 21.2   Current density distribution inside a conductor in a slot

Conductor current = 10000.0 amps
Conductivity = 5.8E+07, Frequency = 50.0 Hz
Average current density = 0.10416E+07 amps/m^2

Sr. No.	Dist.	Analytical solution		FEM solution	
		J (mag.)	Phase	J (mag.)	Phase
1	0.8	0.47682E+07	43.43	0.47353E+07	42.90
2	4.2	0.42617E+07	36.99	0.42386E+07	36.50
3	5.8	0.40423E+07	33.96	0.40104E+07	33.20
4	9.2	0.36129E+07	27.53	0.35911E+07	26.80
5	11.7	0.33264E+07	22.82	0.33058E+07	22.20
6	18.3	0.26734E+07	10.41	0.26512E+07	9.40
7	21.7	0.23877E+07	4.04	0.23736E+07	3.00
8	28.3	0.19143E+07	−8.29	0.18997E+07	−9.60
9	34.2	0.15668E+07	−19.30	0.15594E+07	−20.90
10	39.2	0.13184E+06	−28.69	0.13129E+07	−30.40
11	44.2	0.11060E+07	−38.22	0.11021E+06	−40.00
12	49.2	0.92493E+06	−48.02	0.92238E+06	−49.80
13	54.2	0.77215E+06	−58.28	0.77079E+06	−60.20
14	59.2	0.64565E+06	−69.20	0.64543E+06	−71.10
15	68.3	0.47961E+06	−91.17	0.48033E+06	−93.10
16	78.3	0.38575E+06	−116.60	0.38820E+06	−118.20
17	84.2	0.36407E+06	−129.46	0.36681E+06	−130.80
18	89.2	0.35720E+06	−137.65	0.35942E+06	−138.60
19	94.2	0.35541E+06	−142.86	0.35673E+06	−143.40
20	99.2	0.35526E+06	−144.93	0.35540E+06	−145.00

DC resistance of the bar = 1.7959E−05 Ω   AC resistance of the bar = 5.9776E−05 Ω

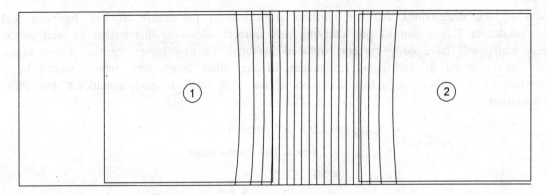

Figure 21.4 Conductor in a slot with eddy currents—FEM solution—analysis in *x-y* coordinates at *t* = 0.

21.3.3 Number of Parallel Busbars Enclosed in a Rectangular Conducting Box

The F.E.M. described has been used to analyze the field distribution of eight, parallel, rectangular, copper busbars enclosed in a rectangular box (whose sides are also parallel to the length dimension of the busbars), made up of a conducting material of finite resistivity and permeability. Only half the section of the box has been considered for analysis, because of the symmetry considerations. Figure 21.5 shows the half-section of the box (or the tank), containing the busbars

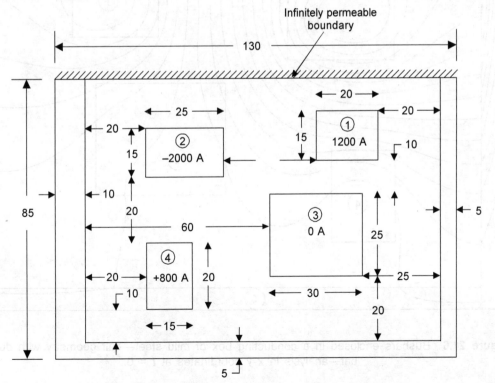

Figure 21.5 Busbars enclosed in a conducting box.

with all the dimensions and the currents indicated on the figure. It will be seen that the conductor 3 is a dummy one carrying zero current. However this busbar as well as the tank walls will have eddy currents induced in them, causing losses therein. These losses will be reflected as additional resistances in the other conductors, which would be a function of the other conductors and also of the tank walls to each conductor. For these calculations,

$$\sigma_{\text{busbars}} = 5.0 \times 10^{+7} \text{ mhos/metre}$$

$$\sigma_{\text{tank walls}} = 1.666 \times 10^{+7} \text{ mhos/metre}$$

$$\mu_{\text{r, tank wall}} = 50$$

The resultant field distribution obtained is shown in Figure 21.6 at the instant of time $t = 0$, when the currents are at their peak values. The flux distribution at the instant of time $t = \pi/2$, when the currents are passing through their zeroes is shown in Figure 21.7. This picture shows the flux due to the induced currents. When the ac resistances of the different conductors are calculated, it is found that the ratio $(R_{\text{ac}}/R_{\text{dc}})$ is different for the different conductors.

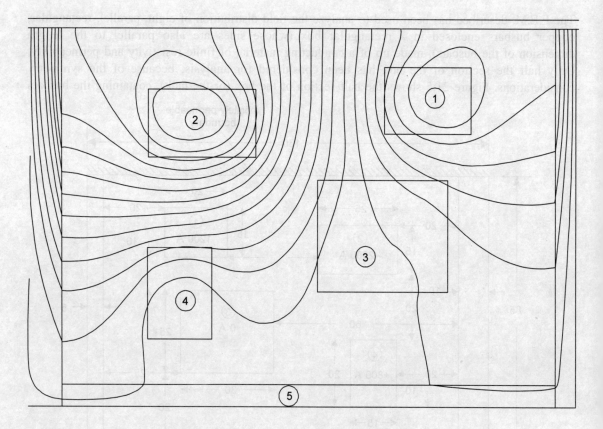

Figure 21.6 Busbars enclosed in a conducting box of mild steel—half geometry with dummy bar—analysis in x-y coordinates at $t = 0$.

Figure 21.7 Busbars enclosed in a conducting box of mild steel—half geometry with dummy bar—analysis in x-y coordinates at $t = \frac{\pi}{2}$.

21.4 APPLICATION OF THE F.E.M. TO TRANSFORMERS AND DC MACHINES

The method of calculating the magnetic field and the eddy current distributions has been successfully applied to all types of rotating machines and other allied electrical devices. Figures 21.8 and 21.9 show the flux distributions in the two orthogonal sections of a generator transformer, and Figures 21.10 to 21.13 show the flux density distributions in the core section (of the armature, field pole and the yoke of the stator of the machine over one pole-pitch) of a DC motor, under different load conditions, i.e. 50%, 100%, 200%, and 300%. Figures 21.14 and 21.15 show the flux distributions in the rotor region of a squirrel cage induction motor. It should be noted that for the DC motor, the field has no eddy currents and its analysis has been treated as a magnetostatic field problem.

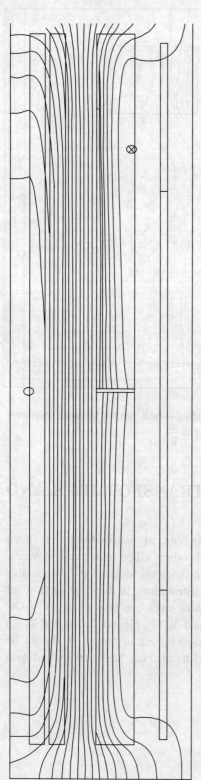

Figure 21.8 250 MVA 220 kV generator transformer window section—analysis in r-z coordinates.

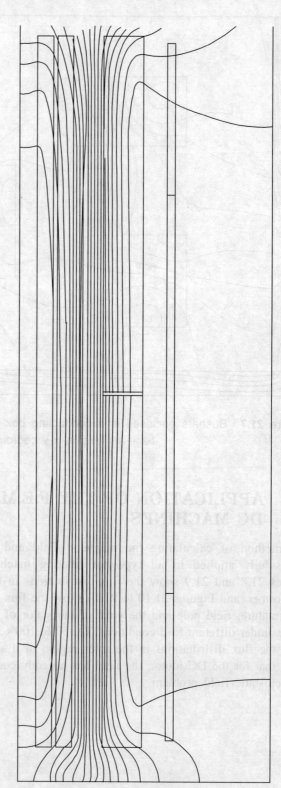

Figure 21.9 250 MVA 220 kV generator transformer—orthogonal section—analysis in r-z coordinates.

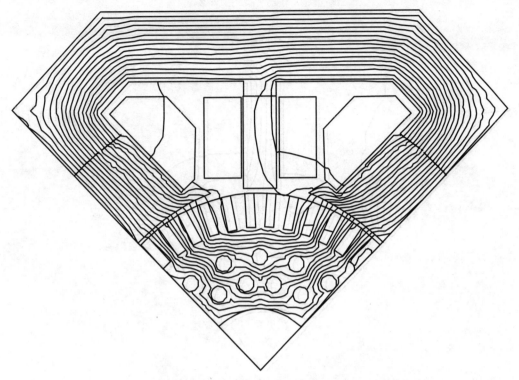

Figure 21.10 DC machine—flux distribution on 50% load.

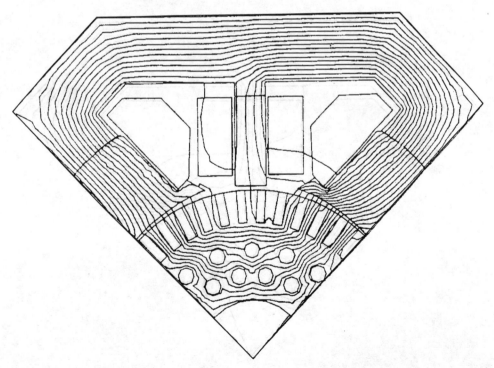

Figure 21.11 DC machine—flux distribution on 100% load.

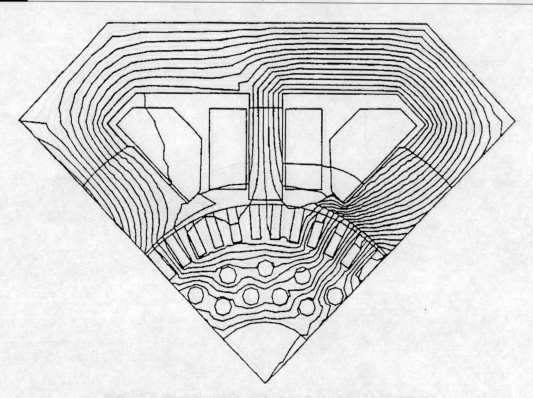

Figure 21.12 DC machine—flux distribution on 200% load.

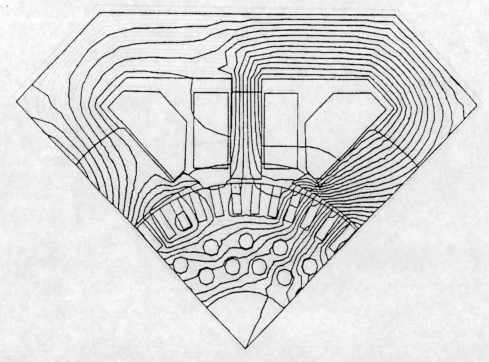

Figure 21.13 DC machine—flux distribution on 300% load.

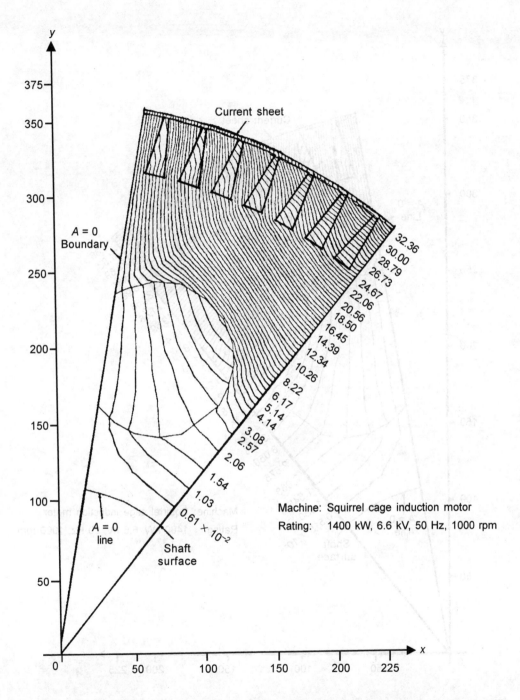

Figure 21.14 Magnetic flux distribution in the rotor region for circular ventilating hole, without shaft.

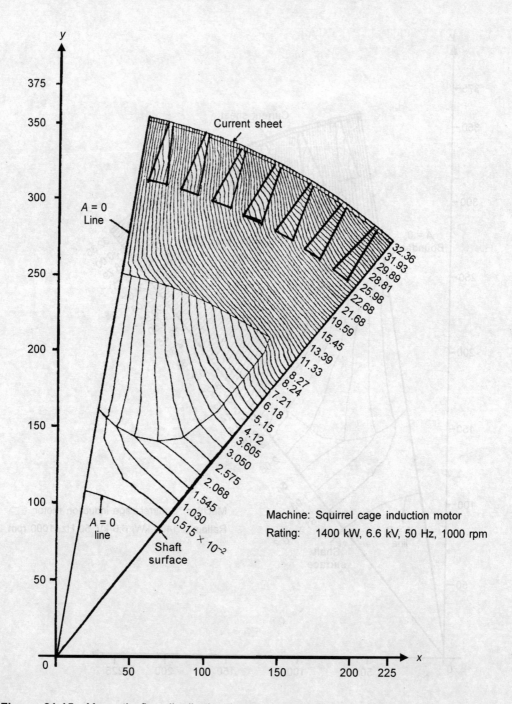

Figure 21.15 Magnetic flux distribution in the rotor region for modified shape ventilating hole, without shaft.

21.5 SOME PARTIAL DIFFERENTIAL EQUATIONS AND THEIR FUNCTIONALS

We now list some of the other very commonly met PDEs and their functionals in electromagnetic problems.

(a) Poisson's equation (scalar)

$$v\nabla^2 A = -J, \qquad \text{and}$$

$$F = \left(\frac{v}{2}\right) \int_\Omega |\nabla A|^2 \, d\Omega - \int_\Omega (\mathbf{J} \cdot \mathbf{A}) \, d\Omega$$

(b) Diffusion equation (and/or Eddy current equation)

$$v\nabla^2 A = j\,\omega\,\sigma A - J, \qquad \text{and}$$

$$F = \left(\frac{v}{2}\right) \int_\Omega |\nabla A|^2 \, d\Omega + \left(\frac{j\omega\sigma}{2}\right) \int_\Omega A^2 \, d\Omega - \int_\Omega (\mathbf{J} \cdot \mathbf{A}) \, d\Omega$$

(c) Vector Poisson's equation

$$\nabla \times v\nabla \times \mathbf{A} = \mathbf{J}, \qquad \text{and}$$

$$F = \left(\frac{v}{2}\right) \int_\Omega |\nabla \times A|^2 \, d\Omega - \int_\Omega (\mathbf{J} \cdot \mathbf{A}) \, d\Omega$$

(d) Nonlinear Poisson's equation

$$v(A)\,\nabla^2 A = -J, \qquad \text{and}$$

$$F = \int_\Omega \left[\int_0^B vb \, db - (\mathbf{J} \cdot \mathbf{A}) \right] d\Omega$$

(e) Inhomogeneous Helmholtz equation

$$\nabla \cdot (p\nabla u) + k^2 u = g \qquad (g = \text{constant, invariant with position})$$

This simplifies to

Laplace's equation $\nabla^2 u = 0$ {charge free region}

and also to Poisson's equation

$$\nabla \cdot (\varepsilon \nabla u) = -\rho$$

where ε is the permittivity which varies with position
and also to two-dimensional Helmholtz equation for TE mode in waveguides

$$\nabla_T^2 H_z + k_c^2 H_z = 0$$

∇_T^2 = Transverse Laplacian operator $\dfrac{\partial^2}{\partial x^2} + \dfrac{\partial^2}{\partial y^2}$,

k_c = cut-off wave number

$$F(u) = \frac{1}{2} \int_{\Omega} [p(\nabla u)^2 - k^2(u^2 + 2gu)] \, d\Omega$$

(f) For waveguides

$$\nabla_T^2 E_z + (k^2 - \beta^2) E_z = 0$$

$$F(E_z) = \frac{1}{2} \int_{\Omega} [(\nabla E_z)^2 - (k^2 - \beta^2) E_z^2] \, dx \, dy$$

(g) Co-axial transmission line with central conductor at potential V_1 completely surrounded by a conductor at potential V_2

$$F(u) = \frac{1}{2} \int_{\Omega} \varepsilon(\nabla u)^2 \, d\Omega$$

which reduces to

$$F(u) = \frac{1}{2} \int \varepsilon(x, y)[\nabla u(x, y)^2 \, dx \, xy$$

(h) Open line pair

$$F(u) = \frac{1}{2} \int_{\Omega} \varepsilon(\nabla u)^2 \, d\Omega + \frac{1}{2} \int_{E} \varepsilon(\nabla u) \, dE$$
$$\uparrow$$

for region external to the box

(i) Problem using scalar magnetic potential {armature of a motor}

$$F(Q) = \frac{1}{2} \int_{\Omega} \mu_0(\nabla Q)^2 \, d\Omega$$

(j) Problem using vector magnetic potential, reducing to scalar two-dimensional equation

$$\nabla \cdot (v \, \nabla A) = -J$$

$$F(u) = \int_{\Omega} \left[v \frac{(\nabla u)^2}{2} - Ju \right] d\Omega$$

(k) Acoustic problem {longitudinal pressure variation}

$$\nabla^2 p = \frac{1}{c^2} \frac{d^2 p}{dt^2}$$

$$F(p) = \frac{1}{2} \int [(\nabla p)^2 - k^2 p^2] \, d\Omega$$

(l) Scalar Laplace and Helmholtz equations in three-dimensions

$$F(u) = \frac{1}{2} \int_{\Omega} \sigma(\nabla u)^2 \, d\Omega$$

So far all these two-dimensional problems have been arrived at from three-dimensional problems by means of **translational** symmetry.

(m) Axi-symmetric potential problems

$$dΩ = 2πr \, dr \, dz$$

$$F(u) = \frac{1}{2} \int_Ω ε(r, z)[\nabla u(r, z)]^2 \, 2πr \, dr \, dz$$

(n) Axi-symmetric system with non-linear magnetic material
For linear case:

$$F_E = \int \left[\frac{1}{2} v \left\{ \left(\frac{\partial A}{\partial z} \right)^2 + \frac{1}{r^2} \left(\frac{\partial}{\partial r}[rA] \right)^2 \right\} - jA \right] 2πr \, dr \, dz$$

$$F = \sum_E F_E$$

(o) Axi-symmetric scalar fields.
Inhomogeneous (but isotropic media) Helmholtz equation

$$\nabla \cdot (p \, \nabla \, u) + k^2 u = g$$

p = local value of permittivity reluctivity, conductivity, etc.

In r–z plane,

$$F(u) = \iint 2πr(p\nabla u \cdot \nabla u - k^2 u^2 + 2ug) dr \, dz$$

This functional differs from its planar counterpart in having the intergrand weighted by the radial variable r.

(p) Axi-symmetric vector fields.
The vector Helmholtz equation is of the form

$$(\nabla^2 + k^2) \, \mathbf{A} = \mathbf{B}$$

The functional is:

$$F(\mathbf{u}) = \int (\nabla \times \mathbf{u} \cdot \nabla \times \mathbf{u} - \mathbf{u} \cdot \nabla\nabla \cdot \mathbf{u} - k^2 \mathbf{u} \cdot \mathbf{u} + 2\mathbf{B} \cdot \mathbf{u}) \, d\Omega$$

$$- \oint \mathbf{u} \times \nabla \times \mathbf{u} \cdot d\mathbf{S}$$

minimized by the vector $\mathbf{u}$, nearest to the correct solution $\mathbf{A}$, provided $\nabla\nabla \cdot \mathbf{u} = 0$.

For the most common types of boundary conditions occuring in practice, the surface integral term vanishes, i.e.

$$\oint \mathbf{u} \times \nabla \times \mathbf{u} \cdot d\mathbf{S} = 0$$

For those axi-symmetric problems in which $\mathbf{B}$ and $\mathbf{A}$ have a single component which is in azimuthal direction, the functional becomes

$$F(\mathbf{u}) = 2π\int \left\{ r \left[\left(\frac{\partial u_\phi}{\partial z} \right)^2 + \left(\frac{\partial u_\phi}{\partial r} \right)^2 - k^2 u_\phi^2 + 2B_\phi u_\phi \right] + 2u_\phi \frac{\partial u_\phi}{\partial r} + \frac{u_\phi^2}{r} \right\} d\Omega$$

where the differentiations and the integrations refer to r – z plane only.

The difference between the translational symmetry of two-dimensional simplification and the rotational symmetry of the axi-symmetric two-dimensional simplification would be carefully noted as this is the cause for change in the form of the functionals.

21.5.1 Open-boundary Problems by F.E.M.

There are a number of ways by which open-boundary problems can be solved. In all these methods the common idea is that the open region {infinitely extending} is subdivided into two regions: (a) interior and (b) exterior, so that the interior part contains the structure and the fields of main interest {$= \Omega^{(p)}$}. An artificial and somewhat arbitrary boundary Γ_0 is placed around this region of interest $\Omega^{(p)}$ and separates the inner region from the rest of the region $\Omega^{(e)}$. The interior region is finite in extent and is treated and analysed normally by the F.E.M. The rest of the region (i.e. the exterior region {$\Omega^{(E)}$} can be dealt in a number of different ways, i.e. (i) baloon boundary {or algorithm}, (ii) Infinite element method, (iii) boundary element method, (iv) absorbing boundary condition, and so on.

Baloon boundary method

In this method, the interior region is treated normally and the problem is to construct a valid representation of the outside region, i.e. an infinite element—where interior edge would match both the shape and the type of approximating functions of the interior model, thus making the complete geometrical model smooth (i.e. seamless) and the potential continuous across Γ_0. The initial step attempts to make the solution to cover a larger (though still finite) region by attaching to $\Omega^{(p)}$ a border of additional elements, which satisfy the following three requirements:

1. The interior edge Γ_0 of the bordering region matches the boundary of $\Omega^{(p)}$ with regard to node number and potential variation.
2. The exterior edge Γ_l of this bordering region is an enlarged and scaled geometrical replica of the interior edge Γ_0.
3. The element subdivision within this bordering region is such that the approximating function is same on both the exterior boundary Γ_l end the interior boundary Γ_0.

The border {$= \Omega^{(l)}$} can then be regarded as a finite element which is a defined geometric region with well-defined approximating functions associated with nodes, but this super element does contain unwanted interior nodes which can be eliminated by a condensation process.

Then the bordering region is enlarged by making an enlarged copy $\Omega^{(ie)}$ of the first border region $\Omega^{(i)}$, such that the inner edge of the new border region coincides with Γ_l. The element materiels applicable to $\Omega^{(ie)}$ are derived from those of $\Omega^{(i)}$ and the interior nodes of this region are again eliminated by condensation. The whole process is repeated from the region $\Omega^{(i)}$ to $\Omega^{(ie)}$, for $i = 1, 2, 3, \ldots$. At great distance, the process is terminated by setting the potentials on the external boundary Γ_i to zero. The process is computational highly efficient and is not accompanied by growth in matrix size.

21.6 GENERAL COMMENTS

We have shown only a very limited set of applications of the F.E.M. to eddy current problems. This method has also been widely used for solving electromagnetic wave problems. We have not discussed such problems here as there is quite a lot of similarity between the magnetic diffusion equation and the wave equation, and the solutions would have significant points of similarity. The main difference is due to the fact that the wave equation contains a term with double derivative of time (as distinct from the diffusion equation where the equivalent term is a single derivative of time). The consequence of this difference is that for time-harmonic excitations, the eddy current equation becomes complex (due to the imaginary j) whereas the wave equation remains one in real variables.

We have not included in the present text any solutions of three-dimensional problems. Though F.E.M. has been successfully used to solve three-dimensional static problems, its application to three-dimensional eddy current problems still remains a controversial point, and is an important topic of research.

21.7 FINITE ELEMENT METHOD (PROCEDURE DETAILS)

The finite element analysis has been so widely accepted as a successful numerical method for solving a wide range of engineering problems, that it has now become an integral part of 'Computer Aided Engineering' (CAE). It is now extensively used in the analysis and design of many complex real-life engineering systems. Though originally it started as a tool for structural analysis, its application to electromagnetic field problems (amongst many other branches as well) is very well-established. So far in our discussions (i.e. in Chapter 4 Section 5.4–5.6.5, and in this Chapter 21) we have given a strong emphasis on the 'variational' basis of this method; and we will end our present discussion of this method by describing the actual steps used in applying the F.E.M to solve a typical two-dimensional problem in electromagnetism (including electrostatics, magnetostatics, electromagnetics, or in fact any two-dimensional problem).

The main steps of the F.E. method are:

1. Choose a suitable formulation of the problem, i.e. whether to use vector or scalar potential, a combination of both, interpretation of the boundaries, etc.
2. Discretization of the region under consideration (i.e. problem domain or solution region) into a finite number of sub-regions which are called 'elements'.
3. Deriving the governing equations, for a typical 'element' in the solution region.
4. Assembling all element equations in the solution region (in the global form).
5. Solving the global linear system of equations so obtained.

21.7.1 Formulation of the Problem

This is in fact a mental process. For a two-dimensional problem, based on the physical aspects, it has to be decided whether a scalar potential or a vector potential is a better choice. If it is an electrostatic field problem, then of course it can be solved by a scalar potential. On the other hand for a magnetic field problem, if the solution region does not contain any current sources, the scalar potential can be used. But if there are current-carrying regions in the solution domain then the vector potential is an obvious choice. When the source current (volume or line) is normal to the plane surface under consideration the vector potential will have only one component (e.g. in a two-dim Cartesian geometry problem in x-y plane). When the vector potential has only one component (i.e. z–component), only then the single component of **A** is similar to the scalar potential $\{\Omega\}$. This is **not** to say that A_z is identical with Ω, it is only similar to Ω because the field vectors H_x, H_y (or B_x, B_y) are in fact $B_x = -\mu \dfrac{\partial \Omega}{\partial x}, B_y = -\mu \dfrac{\partial \Omega}{\partial y}$ from the scalar potential and

$B_x = \dfrac{\partial A_z}{\partial y}$ and $B_y = -\dfrac{\partial A_z}{\partial x}$ from the vector potential. Furthermore, if the source current is a line current, then it can be accounted for in the domain only if it is normal to the plane of the domain (i.e. if it is in the z-direction for a x-y plane problem). A line current in x-y plane cannot be correctly represented in a two-dimensional x-y domain because if it is so drawn then it (the line section) represents a section of a current sheet where width is in either x-z plane or y-z plane and does not represent a line current. In fact, a line current lying in the x-y plane of the solution region would produce a field pattern which would be three-dimensional in nature and hence cannot be treated as a two-dimensional problem.

The boundaries of any two-dimensional problem would be basically straightforward, i.e. Dirichlet-type or Neumann type or Mixed type. For multi-region problems, the interface continuity conditions need some care, in case there are surface currents on the interfaces.

21.7.2 Finite Element Discretization

The solution region is sub-divided into a number of 'finite elements' as shown in Figure 21.16.

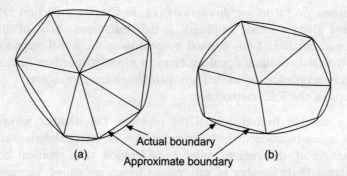

Figure 21.16 Typical irregular domain, sub-divided into (a) triangular elements only and (b) a combination of triangular and quadrilateral elements.

Region (a) has 7 triangular elements and 8 nodes.
Region (b) has 3 triangular and two quadrilateral elements and 8 nodes.
For simplicity, we consider an electrostatic field problem.

Note: If it is a multi-region problem with different material characteristics (i.e. permittivity in E.S. fields, permeability and conductivity in electromagnetic fields, etc.), then the material interface (or interfaces) should coincide with the element sides. This process ensures the continuity of normal boundary conditions across the interface.

We start by taking an approximate value for the potential in a typical element of the domain. Let the potential be V_e (say) within the element e, and then inter-relate the potential distribution in various elements, such that the potential is continuous across the inter-element boundaries. The approximate solution for the potential in the region is then,

$$V(x, y) = \sum_{e=1}^{N} V_e(x, y) \qquad (21.30)$$

where

N = number of elements into which the whole domain has been subdivided

V_e = approximate potential within the element e.

It should be clearly understood that the point (x, y) in the element is 'any point' in the element e and is not restricted to a specific point. This is one of the important differences between the F.E.M. and the F.D.M. (i.e. finite difference method). In the F.D.M., once the region has been discretized (say, for example, the rectangular mesh), we deal with the potential values at the 'nodes only' and the inter-nodal spaces are ignored. This is very obvious when the P.D.E. under consideration is reduced to the corresponding algebraic equation by using the 'Taylor series expansion method'. But when the 'line integral method' is used to derive the discretized equation, the implicit assumption is that the potential values vary linearly along the mesh arms.

The simplest and the most common form of approximation for V_e in a triangular element is the first-order polynomial approximation, i.e.

$$V_e(x, y) = a + bx + cy \tag{21.31}$$

And for a quadrilateral element, the corresponding approximation is

$$V_e(x, y) = a + bx + cy + dxy \tag{21.32}$$

The potential V_e is non-zero within the element e and is zero outside e. It is difficult to approximate the boundary of the problem domain by quadrilateral elements; and for the present problem we have used triangular elements only.

The assumption of linear variation of the potential within the triangular element (as given by Eq. (21.31) is equivalent to assuming uniform electric field within the element, i.e.

$$\mathbf{E}_e = -\nabla V_e = -\left(\mathbf{i}_x \frac{\partial V_e}{\partial x} + \mathbf{i}_y \frac{\partial V_e}{\partial y} \right)$$

$$= -\mathbf{i}_x b - \mathbf{i}_y c \tag{21.33}$$

On the other hand, for the quadrilateral element, it amounts to saying that the components of $\mathbf{E}_e$ vary linearly within the element, i.e.

$$E_e = -\nabla V_e$$

$$= \mathbf{i}_x(b + dy) - \mathbf{i}_y(c + dx) \tag{21.34}$$

21.7.3 Element Governing Equation

For a typical triangular element, as shown in Figure 21.17, the potentials V_{e1}, V_{e2}, and V_{e3} at the nodes 1, 2, and 3 respectively are given by [using the first-order polynomial relation of Eq. (21.31)]

(The local node numbering sequence 1–2–3 must be in the counterclockwise sense.)

$$\begin{bmatrix} V_{e1} \\ V_{e2} \\ V_{e3} \end{bmatrix} = \begin{bmatrix} 1 & x_1 & y_1 \\ 1 & x_2 & y_2 \\ 1 & x_3 & y_3 \end{bmatrix} \begin{bmatrix} a \\ b \\ c \end{bmatrix} \tag{21.35}$$

written in compact matrix form.

The coefficients a, b, c of the polynomial representation can be determined by inverting the 3×3 matrix above, i.e.

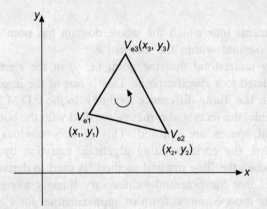

Figure 21.17 A typical triangular element.

$$\begin{bmatrix} a \\ b \\ c \end{bmatrix} = \begin{bmatrix} 1 & x_1 & y_1 \\ 1 & x_2 & y_2 \\ 1 & x_3 & y_3 \end{bmatrix}^{-1} \begin{bmatrix} V_{e1} \\ V_{e2} \\ V_{e3} \end{bmatrix} \qquad (21.36)$$

$$= \frac{1}{2\Delta} \begin{bmatrix} x_2 y_3 - x_3 y_2 & x_3 y_1 - x_1 y_3 & x_1 y_2 - x_2 y_1 \\ y_2 - y_3 & y_3 - y_1 & y_1 - y_2 \\ x_3 - x_2 & x_1 - x_3 & x_2 - x_1 \end{bmatrix} \begin{bmatrix} V_{e1} \\ V_{e2} \\ V_{e3} \end{bmatrix}$$

$$= \frac{1}{2\Delta} \begin{bmatrix} a_1 & a_2 & a_3 \\ b_1 & b_2 & b_3 \\ c_1 & c_2 & c_3 \end{bmatrix} \begin{bmatrix} V_{e1} \\ V_{e2} \\ V_{e3} \end{bmatrix} \qquad (21.37)$$

where

$$a_1 = x_2 y_3 - x_3 y_2 \qquad a_2 = x_3 y_1 - x_1 y_3 \qquad a_3 = x_1 y_2 - x_2 y_1$$

$$b_1 = y_2 - y_3 \qquad b_2 = y_3 - y_1 \qquad b_3 = y_1 - y_2$$

$$c_1 = x_3 - x_2 \qquad c_2 = x_1 - x_3 \qquad c_3 = x_2 - x_1$$

and Δ is the area of the triangular element e, i.e.

$$\Delta = \frac{1}{2} \begin{vmatrix} 1 & x_1 & y_1 \\ 1 & x_2 & y_2 \\ 1 & x_3 & y_3 \end{vmatrix}$$

$$= \frac{1}{2}[(x_2 y_3 - x_3 y_2) + (x_3 y_1 - x_1 y_3) + (x_1 y_2 - x_2 y_1)]$$

$$= \frac{1}{2}[(x_2 - x_1)(y_3 - y_1) - (x_3 - x_1)(y_2 - y_1)] = \frac{1}{2}(b_2 c_3 - b_3 c_2)$$

$$= \frac{1}{2}[(y_1 - y_2)(x_3 - x_2) - (y_2 - y_1)(x_2 - x_1)] = \frac{1}{2}(b_3 c_1 - b_1 c_3)$$

$$= \frac{1}{2}[(y_2 - y_3)(x_1 - x_3) - (y_3 - y_1)(x_3 - x_2)] = \frac{1}{2}(b_1 c_2 - b_2 c_1) \qquad (21.38)$$

Substituting the values of a, b, c from Eq. (21.36) or (21.37) into Eq. (21.31), and writing it in matrix form:

$$V_e = \begin{bmatrix} 1 & x & y \end{bmatrix} \frac{1}{2\Delta} \begin{bmatrix} x_2 y_3 - x_3 y_2 & x_3 y_1 - x_1 y_3 & x_1 y_2 - x_2 y_1 \\ y_2 - y_3 & y_3 - y_1 & y_1 - y_2 \\ x_3 - x_2 & x_1 - x_3 & x_2 - x_1 \end{bmatrix} \begin{bmatrix} V_{e1} \\ V_{e2} \\ V_{e3} \end{bmatrix}$$

This can be written in further compact form as

$$V_e(x, y) = \sum_{i=1}^{3} N_i(x, y) \, V_{ei} \tag{21.39}$$

where N_i are the interpolation (or shape) functions used to interpolate the values of the field variable at an interior point in the element, from its value at certain key points (i.e. nodes) in the element, and are given by:

$$N_1(x, y) = \frac{1}{2\Delta} \left[(x_2 y_3 - x_3 y_2) + (y_2 - y_3)x + (x_3 - x_2)y \right]$$

$$= \frac{1}{2\Delta}(a_1 + b_1 x + c_1 y) \tag{21.40a}$$

$$N_2(x, y) = \frac{1}{2\Delta}(a_2 + b_2 x + c_2 y) \tag{21.40b}$$

$$N_3(x, y) = \frac{1}{2\Delta}(a_3 + b_3 x + c_3 y) \tag{21.40c}$$

Expanding Eq. (21.39),

$$V_e(x, y) = \frac{1}{2\Delta} \left[(a_1 + b_1 x + c_1 y)V_{e1} + (a_2 + b_2 x + c_2 y)V_{e2} + (a_3 + b_3 x + c_3 y)V_{e3} \right]$$

Also, it can be checked,

$$N_i(x_j, y_j) = \delta_j^i = \begin{cases} 1, & i = j; \\ 0, & i \neq j. \end{cases} \tag{21.41a}$$

↑
Kronecker Delta

[Check:
$i = j = 1$

$$N_1(x_1, y_1) = \frac{1}{2\Delta} \left[(x_2 y_3 - x_3 y_2) + (y_2 - y_3)x_1 + (x_3 - x_2)y_1 \right]$$

$$= \frac{2\Delta}{2\Delta} = 1$$

and $(i = 1) \neq (j = 2)$

$$N_1(x_2, y_2) = \frac{1}{2\Delta} \left[(x_2 y_3 - x_3 y_2) + (y_2 - y_3)x_2 + (x_3 - x_2)y_2 \right]$$

$$= 0]$$

Since the shape functions N_i satisfy the Kronecker Delta function, it follows that the sum of the shape functions for the triangular element would equal unity, i.e.

$$\sum_{i=1}^{3} N_i(x, y) = 1 \tag{21.41b}$$

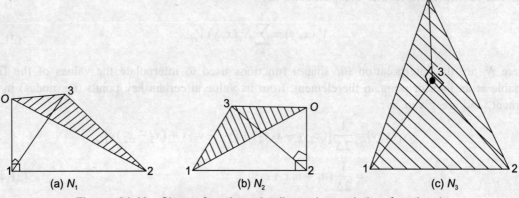

(a) N_1 (b) N_2 (c) N_3

Figure 21.18 Shape functions (or linear interpolation functions) for the triangular element 1–2–3.

Note: Length $O1$, $O2$, $O3$ are unit lengths normal to the plane of the triangular element 1–2–3. Geometrically, the element triangle (1–2–3) is the projection of the shape function triangles on the x-y plane.

Next, we consider the electrostatic energy (per unit length) associated with the element under consideration (i.e. the element e) is given by Eq. (3.4) as:

$$W_e = \frac{1}{2} \iint \varepsilon |\mathbf{E}|^2 \, ds = \frac{1}{2} \iint \varepsilon |\nabla V_e|^2 \, dS \tag{21.42}$$

where a two-dimensional, charge-free ($\rho_0 = 0$) solution region has been assumed.

Using Eq. (21.38), we get:

$$\nabla V_e(x, y) = \sum_{i=1}^{3} V_{ei} \, \nabla N_i(x, y) \tag{21.43}$$

(Since V_{ei} are fixed potentials at the nodes of the element.)

Substituting Eq. (21.43) in Eq. (21.42),

$$W_e = \frac{1}{2} \sum_{i=1}^{3} \sum_{j=1}^{3} \varepsilon V_{ei} \left[\iint (\nabla N_i) \cdot (\nabla N_j) \, dS \right] V_{ej} \tag{21.44}$$

Defining the surface integral term in the above Eq. (21.44) as

$$C_{ij}^{(e)} = \iint (\nabla N_i) \cdot (\nabla N_j) dS \tag{21.45}$$

then W_e [in Eq. (21.44)] can be written down in the matrix form as

$$W_e = \frac{1}{2} \varepsilon [V_e]^T \, [C^{(e)}] [V_e] \tag{21.46}$$

where

$$[V_e] = \begin{bmatrix} V_{e1} \\ V_{e2} \\ V_{e3} \end{bmatrix}$$

(21.47a)

$$[C^{(e)}] = \begin{bmatrix} C_{11}^{(e)} & C_{12}^{(e)} & C_{13}^{(e)} \\ C_{21}^{(e)} & C_{22}^{(e)} & C_{23}^{(e)} \\ C_{31}^{(e)} & C_{32}^{(e)} & C_{33}^{(e)} \end{bmatrix}$$

(21.47b)

↑

The element coefficient matrix

Each term (i.e. matrix element) $C_{ij}^{(e)}$ represents the coupling beween the nodes i and j. Its value can be obtained from Eq. (21.45), e.g.

$$C_{12}^{(e)} = \iint (\nabla N_1) \cdot (\nabla N_2) dS$$

$$= \frac{1}{2\Delta} \left[\mathbf{i}_x (y_2 - y_3) + \mathbf{i}_y (x_3 - x_2) \right] \cdot \frac{1}{2\Delta} \left[\mathbf{i}_x (y_3 - y_1) + \mathbf{i}_y (x_1 - x_3) \right] \iint dS$$

[from Eqs. (21.40) and (21.38)]

$$= \frac{1}{4\Delta^2} \left[(y_2 - y_3)(y_3 - y_1) + (x_3 - x_2)(x_1 - x_3) \right] \Delta$$

$$= \frac{1}{4\Delta} \left[(y_2 - y_3)(y_3 - y_1) + (x_3 - x_2)(x_1 - x_3) \right]$$

(21.48a)

Similarly,

$$C_{11}^{(e)} = \frac{1}{4\Delta} \left[(y_2 - y_3)^2 + (x_3 - x_2)^2 \right]$$

(21.48b)

$$C_{13}^{(e)} = \frac{1}{4\Delta} \left[(y_2 - y_3)(y_1 - y_2) + (x_3 - x_2)(x_2 - x_1) \right]$$

(21.48c)

$$C_{22}^{(e)} = \frac{1}{4\Delta} \left[(y_3 - y_1)^2 + (x_1 - x_3)^2 \right]$$

(21.48d)

$$C_{23}^{(e)} = \frac{1}{4\Delta} \left[(y_3 - y_1)(y_1 - y_2) + (x_1 - x_3)(x_2 - x_1) \right]$$

(21.48e)

$$C_{33}^{(e)} = \frac{1}{4\Delta} \left[(y_1 - y_2)^2 + (x_2 - x_1)^2 \right]$$

(21.48f)

and

$$C_{21}^{(e)} = C_{12}^{(e)}, \quad C_{31}^{(e)} = C_{13}^{(e)}, \quad C_{32}^{(e)} = C_{23}^{(e)}$$

(21.48g)

These calculations would be easier, if the following notations are used, i.e.

and

$$\left. \begin{array}{l} P_1 = (y_2 - y_3), \quad P_2 = (y_3 - y_1), \quad P_3(y_1 - y_2); \\[2mm] Q_1 = (x_3 - x_2), \quad Q_2 = (x_1 - x_3), \quad Q_3 = (x_2 - x_1) \end{array} \right\}$$

(21.49a)

By using P_i and Q_i ($i = 1, 2, 3$ the local node numbers), each term of the element coefficient matrix is obtained as

$$C_{ij}^{(e)} = \frac{1}{4\Delta} (P_i P_j + Q_i Q_j) \tag{21.49b}$$

where

$$\Delta = \frac{1}{2}(P_2 Q_3 - P_3 Q_2) \tag{21.49c}$$

From Eqs. (21.49a), it should be noted that

$$P_1 + P_2 + P_3 = 0 = Q_1 + Q_2 + Q_3 \tag{21.50a}$$

$$\therefore \quad \sum_{i=1}^{3} C_{ij}^{(e)} = 0 = \sum_{j=1}^{3} C_{ij}^{(e)} \tag{21.50b}$$

This serves as a check for these calculations.

21.7.4 Assembling All Element Equations

Having considered a typical element so far, we next move on to take into account all such elements in the solution region.

Hence the energy associated with the collection of all the elements in the solution region comes out to be

$$W = \sum_{e=1}^{N} W_e = \sum_{e=1}^{N} \frac{1}{2} \varepsilon [V]^T [C] [V] \tag{21.51}$$

where

$$[V] = \begin{bmatrix} V_1 \\ V_2 \\ \vdots \\ V_n \end{bmatrix} \tag{21.52}$$

n being the number of nodes, N the number of elements, and $[C]$ = the global (or the overall) coefficient matrix, being the collection of the individual coefficient matrices.

The main problem here is the derivation of $[C]$ from $[C^{(e)}]$. This process is best explained by considering an actual example. So we consider a finite element mesh (a very simple one) as shown in Figure 21.19, consisting of three elements which are interconnected.

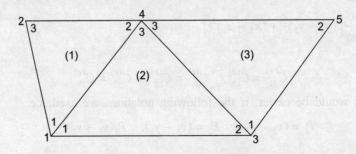

Figure 21.19 A collection of three elements.

There are three elements and five nodes. The numbering of the nodes 1–2–3–4–5 (as shown on the outside of the elements) is called the 'global' numbering. The numbering i-j-k, called the 'local' numbering (shown inside each element) corresponds to the sequence 1–2–3 for each of the elements. Note that in Figure 21.19, the global numbering 3–5–4 of the element (3) corresponds to the local numbering 1–2–3 respectively of that element. It to be noted that the local numbering for each element must be the counterclockwise sense whilst there is no such restriction on the global numbering, and instead of 3–5–4 it is possible to choose 5–4–3 or 3–5–4 to correspond with the local numbering of 1–2–3. It would be seen that whatever the sense of the global numbering sequence, the global coefficient matrix [C] finally obtained, would be the same in all cases. Since there are 5 nodes in our present problem, the (C) matrix will be a 5×5 matrix of the form given as below:

$$[C] = \begin{bmatrix} C_{11} & C_{12} & C_{13} & C_{14} & C_{15} \\ C_{21} & C_{22} & C_{23} & C_{24} & C_{25} \\ C_{31} & C_{32} & C_{33} & C_{34} & C_{35} \\ C_{41} & C_{42} & C_{43} & C_{44} & C_{45} \\ C_{51} & C_{52} & C_{53} & C_{54} & C_{55} \end{bmatrix} \tag{21.53}$$

As in the case of the element coefficient matrix, C_{ij} represents the coupling between the nodes i and j.

C_{ij} is evaluated by using the fact that 'the potential disribution across the inter-element boundaries must be continuous'.

The contribution to the position i–j in the [C] matrix comes from all the elements which contain the nodes i and j. As an example, to evaluate C_{11}, from Figure 21.19, the global node 1 belongs to the elements (1) and (2) and it also happens to be the local node 1 in both the elements. Hence

$$C_{11} = C_{11}^{(1)} + C_{11}^{(2)} \tag{21.54a}$$

For C_{22} it belongs only to the element (1) and is same as the local node 3, and hence

$$C_{22} = C_{33}^{(1)} \tag{21.54b}$$

Similarly for C_{55}, it belongs to the element (3) only, and is same as the local node 2, and so

$$C_{55} = C_{22}^{(3)} \tag{21.54c}$$

Considering the global node 3, it belongs to elements (2) and (3) and is the local node 2 of element (2) and the local node 1 of the element (3). Thus,

$$C_{33} = C_{22}^{(2)} + C_{11}^{(3)} \tag{21.54d}$$

The global node 4 belongs to all the three elements (1), (2) and (3); and is the local node 2 of the element (1), the local node 3 of the element (2) as well as the local node 3 of the element (3); and hence

$$C_{44} = C_{22}^{(1)} + C_{(33)}^{(2)} + C_{33}^{(3)} \tag{21.54e}$$

There is no direct link (or coupling) between

    (a)   the global nodes 2 and 3, and hence $C_{23} = 0 = C_{32}$
    (b)   the global nodes 1 and 5, and hence $C_{15} = 0 = C_{51}$
    (c)   the global nodes 2 and 5, and so $C_{25} = 0 = C_{52}$. $\left.\begin{matrix} \\ \\ \\ \end{matrix}\right\} \tag{21.55a}$

For C_{12} the global link 12 is same as the local link 13 of the element (1)

$$\therefore \qquad C_{12} = C_{13}^{(1)} \qquad (21.56a)$$

and similarly for C_{21}, the global link 21 is same as the local link 31 of the element (1)

$$\therefore \qquad C_{21} = C_{31}^{(1)} \qquad (21.56b)$$

For C_{13}, the global link 13 coincides with the local link 12 of the element (2)

$$\therefore \qquad C_{13} = C_{12}^{(2)} \qquad (21.56c)$$

For C_{31}, the same argument holds except that the linking direction is reversed.

$$\therefore \qquad C_{31} = C_{21}^{(2)} \qquad (21.56d)$$

For C_{14}, the global link 14 coincides with the local link 12 of the element (1) and the local link 13 of the element (2). Hence

$$\therefore \qquad C_{14} = C_{12}^{(1)} + C_{13}^{(2)} \qquad (21.56e)$$

For C_{41}, only the linking direction is reversed in the above Eq. (21.56e)

$$\therefore \qquad C_{41} = C_{21}^{(1)} + C_{31}^{(2)} \qquad (21.56f)$$

Similar arguments for the remaining links will give

$$C_{34} = C_{(23)}^{(2)} + C_{13}^{(3)} \qquad (21.56g)$$

$$C_{43} = C_{(32)}^{(2)} + C_{31}^{(3)} \qquad (21.56h)$$

$$C_{35} = C_{12}^{(3)} \quad \text{and} \quad C_{53} = C_{21}^{(3)} \qquad (21.56k)$$

$$C_{54} = C_{23}^{(3)} \quad \text{and} \quad C_{45} = C_{32}^{(3)} \qquad (21.56l)$$

$$C_{42} = C_{23}^{(1)} \quad \text{and} \quad C_{24} = C_{32}^{(1)} \qquad (21.56m)$$

Having thus obtained all the terms of the global coefficient matrix, it can now be written as:

$$[C] = \begin{bmatrix} C_{11}^{(1)} + C_{11}^{(2)} & C_{13}^{(1)} & C_{12}^{(2)} & C_{12}^{(1)} + C_{13}^{(2)} & 0 \\ C_{31}^{(1)} & C_{33}^{(1)} & 0 & C_{32}^{(1)} & 0 \\ C_{21}^{(2)} & 0 & C_{22}^{(2)} + C_{11}^{(3)} & C_{23}^{(2)} + C_{13}^{(3)} & C_{12}^{(3)} \\ C_{21}^{(1)} + C_{31}^{(2)} & C_{23}^{(1)} & C_{32}^{(2)} + C_{31}^{(3)} & C_{22}^{(1)} + C_{33}^{(2)} + C_{33}^{(3)} & C_{32}^{(3)} \\ 0 & 0 & C_{21}^{(3)} & C_{23}^{(3)} & C_{22}^{(3)} \end{bmatrix} \qquad (21.57)$$

In the global coefficient matrix $[C]$, there are 27 terms, i.e. 9 for each of the 3 elements, and the element coefficient matrices overlap at those nodes which are shared by the elements.

The properties of the global coefficient matrix are:

1. It is symmetric, i.e. $C_{ij} = C_{ji}$ like the element coefficient matrix.
2. $[C]$ is sparse and banded.
   The reason for sparseness is that $C_{ij} = 0$ for those values of i and j where no coupling exists between the two nodes.
3. It is singular.

21.7.5 Solving the Resulting Global Equations

From the discussion of the variational basis of FEM in Chapter 5 and the earlier part of this chapter (Chapter 5, Sections 5.6.1–5.6.5, and Chapter 21, Section 21.2), we know that the Laplace's equation (or to be more general the Poisson's equation as the Laplace's equation is a degenerate case of Poisson), is satisfied when the total energy of the problem domain is minimized. This implies that the partial derivatives of W (= the total energy) with respect to each nodal value of the potential (V_i, $i = 1, 2,..., n$) are zero, i.e.

$$\frac{\partial W}{\partial V_1} = \frac{\partial W}{\partial V_2} = ... = \frac{\partial W}{\partial V_n} = 0$$

or

$$\frac{\partial W}{\partial V_k} = 0, \qquad k = 1, 2, ..., n \tag{21.58}$$

As an example, to evaluate $\dfrac{\partial W}{\partial V_1}$ for the three element mesh of Figure 21.19, W is given in

Eq. (21.51) where N (the number of elements) = 3 and n the number of nodes) is 5, i.e.

$$W = \sum_{e=1}^{N} \frac{1}{2} \varepsilon [V]^T [C][V] \tag{21.51}$$

Since the partial differentiation is with respect to V_1, only these terms of C which contain the node 1 effect will give non-zero values, the rest of the derivatives will be zeroes. i.e.

$$\frac{\partial W}{\partial V_1} = V_1 C_{11} + V_2 C_{12} + V_3 C_{13} + V_4 C_{14} + V_5 C_{15}$$

$$+ V_1 C_{11} + V_2 C_{21} + V_3 C_{31} + V_4 C_{41} + V_5 C_{51} = 0$$

Since $C_{ij} = C_{ji}(j \neq i)$, the above equation simplifies to

$$V_1 C_{11} + V_2 C_{12} + V_3 C_{13} + V_4 C_{14} + V_5 C_{15} = 0 \tag{21.59}$$

$\therefore$ In general
$$\frac{\partial W}{\partial V_k} = 0;$$

gives
$$\sum_{i=1}^{n} V_i C_{ik} = 0 \tag{21.60}$$

n being the number of nodes in the mesh.

This equation [i.e. (21.60)] can be written for all the nodes $k = 1, 2,...,n$ ($n = 5$ in the present case) and thus a set of simultaneous equations are obtained from which the solution of

$$[V]^T = [V_1, V_2,..., V_n]$$

can be found. This can be done by any of the two methods briefly described below.

1. Iteration Method

This method is similar to that used in F.D.M. Let the node 1 (of Figure 21.19) be a free node. The potential at the node 1 can be obtained from Eq. (21.59) by writing it as

$$V_1 = \frac{1}{C_{11}} \sum_{i=2}^{5} V_i C_{1i} \qquad (21.61)$$

In general, if the kth node is made free, then

$$V_k = \frac{1}{C_{kk}} \sum_{i=1, i \neq k}^{n} V_i C_{ik} \qquad (21.62)$$

This equation is applied iteratively to all the free nodes in the mesh which of course contains n nodes. But if the node k is not directly linked with the node i, then $C_{ki} = 0$. So only these nodes, which are directly linked with the node k, would contribute to V_k in the above Eq. (21.62).

Thus the potential of the node k, i.e. V_k can be determined by using Eq. (21.62), provided the potentials at the nodes, which are connected to the node k, are known. So the iteration process is started by setting the potentials at the free nodes to 'zero' or to the average potential which is

$$V_{av} = \frac{1}{2}(V_{min} + V_{max}) \qquad (21.63)$$

where V_{max} and V_{min} are the maximum and minimum values of the prescribed (or defined) potentials at the fixed nodes. Using these as the initial values, the potentials at the free nodes are calculated from Eq. (21.62). When the first iteration is complete, the calculated new value of potentials at all the free nodes become the starting values for the second iteration. This process is repeated till the change between the subsequent iterations becomes negligible, i.e. for the pth and $(p + 1)$th iteration.

$$\left| V_k^{p+1} - V_k^p \right| < \varepsilon, \qquad \text{for } k = 1, 2, 3,..., n$$

where ε can be made as small as possible (e.g. $\varepsilon \sim .0001$ or 1×10^{-7}, depending on the accuracy requirements).

2. Band Matrix Method

In this method, all the free nodes are numbered first and the fixed nodes last, so that Eq. (21.5l) can be rewritten as

$$W = \frac{1}{2} \varepsilon [v_f \quad v_p] \begin{bmatrix} C_{ff} & C_{fp} \\ C_{pf} & C_{pp} \end{bmatrix} \begin{bmatrix} V_f \\ V_p \end{bmatrix} \qquad (21.64)$$

where the subscripts f and p refer to nodes with free (floating) and prescribed (a fixed) potentials. As V_p is constant (since it consists of known fixed values), the differentiations will be only with respect to V_f. Thus applying Eqs. (21.58) to (21.64), the result is

$$C_{ff}V_p + C_{fp}V_p = 0 \qquad (21.65)$$

or, as we are dealing with matrices, this is

$$[C_{ff}][V_f] = -[C_{fp}][V_p] \qquad (21.66)$$

This equation can be expressed in the form

$$[A][V] = [B] \qquad (21.67a)$$

or

$$[V] = [A]^{-1}[B] \qquad (21.67b)$$

where $[V] = [V_f]$, $[A] = [C_{ff}]$,   and $[B] = -[C_{fp}][V_p]$

[A] is, in general, non-singular, and hence the potential at the free nodes can be evaluated by using Eq. (21.66). In Eq. (21.67a), [V] can be solved for by Gaussian elimination. [V] in the equation (21.67b) can be solved by matrix inversion, provided the matrix to be inverted is not large.

21.7.6   Areal Coordinate System and 2D Linear Triangular Elements

21.7.6.1   Areal coordinate system

We will first define this coordinate system.

Let *ABC* be a triangle and *P* be any point (either inside or outside the triangle). Then the areal coordinates of the point *P* with reference to the triangle *ABC* are defined as the ratios

$$\frac{\Delta PBC}{\Delta ABC}, \quad \frac{\Delta PCA}{\Delta BCA}, \quad \frac{\Delta PAB}{\Delta CAB} \qquad (21.68)$$

Let these three ratios be denoted by *X, Y, Z* respectively. It is obvious that if *P* lies within the triangle *ABC*, then

$$X + Y + Z = 1 \qquad (21.69)$$

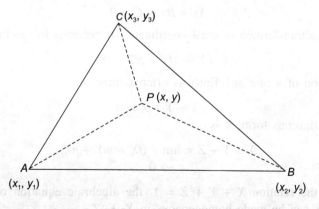

Figure 21.20 Triangle *ABC* to define the areal coordinate system.

But the location of P is not a necessary constraint for Eq. (21.69), and this relationship holds wherever the point P may be in the plane of the triangle ABC (either inside or outside of ΔABC). For this the signs of the areas of the triangles have to be accounted for. If P and A are on the same side of line BC, then both the areas PBC and ABC have the same sign and the ratio X will be +ve. But if P and A are on the opposite side of BC, then the ratio of the areas will be –ve.

Thus X will be +ve or –ve according as P and A are on the same or opposite sides of BC. Similarly Y will be +ve or –ve according as P and B are on the same or opposite sides of CA.

And also Z will be +ve or –ve according as P and C are on the same or opposite sides of AB.

It should be noted that the three denominators for the three coordinates X, Y, Z are the same both in magnitude and sign, e.g.

$$\Delta ABC = \Delta BCA = \Delta CAB$$

the cyclic order of the letters being the same in all. (anticlockwise rotation, referring to Figure 21.20). Hence,

$$\Delta PBC + \Delta PCA + \Delta PAB = \Delta ABC$$

whatever be the position of the point P.

$$\therefore \qquad\qquad X + Y + Z = 1 \qquad\qquad (21.69a)$$

Next, without going into rigorous mathematical derivations, we will now state some important and interesting results pertaining to this coordinate system.

1. If (x_1, y_1), (x_2, y_2), (x_3, y_3) be the Cartesian coordinates referred to any axes (rectangular or oblique) in its plane of the vertices of the triangle ABC, and (x, y) the Cartesian coordinates of the point P in its plane, then

$$\begin{aligned} x &= x_1 X + x_2 Y + x_3 Z \\ y &= y_1 X + y_2 Y + Y_3 Z \end{aligned} \qquad (21.70)$$

where X, Y, Z are the areal coordinates of the point P referred to the triangle ABC.

2. The general equation of a straight line in Cartesian coordinates is

$$Ax + By + C = 0 \qquad\qquad (21.71a)$$

which when transformed to areal coordinates, it becomes of the form

$$LX + MY + NZ = 0 \qquad\qquad (21.71b)$$

3. The equation of a line at infinity is often written as

$$X + Y + Z = 0 \qquad\qquad (21.72a)$$

though in rigorous form, it is

$$X + Y + Z = \lim_{\varepsilon \to 0} \varepsilon \, (lX + mY + nZ) \qquad (21.72b)$$

4. By using the relation $X + Y + Z = 1$, the algebraic equation of any curve in areal coordinates can be made homogeneous in X, Y, Z.

Note: Areal coordinates are only a particular case of a general system of 'homogeneous coordinates'.

In the general homogeneous coordinates, (X, Y, Z) the coordinates of the point P whose Cartesian coordinates are (x, y) would have the relationship

$$\left.\begin{array}{l} x = \lambda_1 X + \mu_1 Y + v_1 Z \\ y = \lambda_2 X + \mu_2 Y + v_2 Z \end{array}\right\} \qquad (21.73)$$

where X, Y, Z are related by the equation

$$1 = \alpha X + \beta Y + \gamma Z \qquad (21.74)$$

(in areal coordinates, $\alpha = \beta = \gamma = 1$)

Now
$$X = \frac{1}{\alpha} \frac{\Delta PBC}{\Delta ABC}, \quad Y = \frac{1}{\beta} \frac{\Delta PCA}{\Delta BCA}, \quad Z = \frac{1}{\gamma} \frac{\Delta PAB}{\Delta CAB} \qquad (21.75)$$

The detailed discussion and derivation of both the coordinate systems would be found in E.H. Askwith's *Analytical Geometry of the Conic Sections.*

21.7.6.2 *Shape functions and 2D linear triangular element*

In two-dimensional F.E.M., triangle has been used as the basic element shape and a suitable trial function based on this element has to be obtained. Consider the triangle of Figure 21.21, where

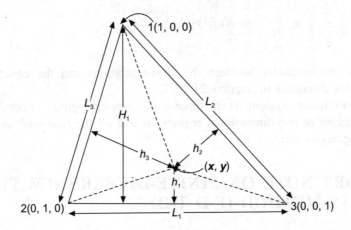

Figure 21.21 Triangular element with its shape function dimensions.

$$N_i = \frac{h_i}{H_i}, \quad i = 1, 2, 3 \qquad (21.76)$$

and (x, y) corresponds to (N_1, N_2, N_3). $\qquad (21.77)$

The natural first order interpolation to be used within the triangle is

$$\phi(x, y) = N_1 \phi_1 + N_2 \phi_2 + N_3 \phi_3 \qquad (21.78)$$

The relationship which shows the interdependence of the three N's can be determined by adding up the areas of the three triangles formed by joining the vertices of the triangular element to the point (x, y) as shown in Figure 21.21, i.e.

$$\frac{1}{2}h_1L_1 + \frac{1}{2}h_2L_2 + \frac{1}{2}h_3L_3 = A \tag{21.79}$$

where A is the total area of the triangle.

Replacing h_1, h_2 and h_3 the trial functions given in Eq. (21.76), we obtain

$$\frac{1}{2}N_1H_1L_1 + \frac{1}{2}N_2H_2L_2 + \frac{1}{2}N_3H_3L_3 = A \tag{21.80}$$

But for every $i = 1, 2, 3$

$$A = \frac{1}{2}H_1L_1 = \frac{1}{2}H_2L_2 = \frac{1}{2}H_3L_3 \tag{21.81}$$

Combining Eqs. (21.80) and (21.81), we get

$$N_1 + N_2 + N_3 = 1 \tag{21.82}$$

Two more relations between the triangular coordinates can be obtained in terms of the Cartesian coordinates. Since (x, y) is of order one, these coordinates may be fitted exactly, with no inherent approximation, by the interpolation of (21.82), so that

$$x_1N_1 + x_2N_2 + x_3N_3 = x \tag{21.83a}$$

and

$$y_1N_1 + y_2N_2 + y_3N_3 = y \tag{21.83b}$$

Note:

1. Compare the similarity between the above relations and the equations of the areal coordinates discussed in Section 21.7.6.1.
2. Areal coordinate system is a three-axis, non-orthogonal, coordinate system for representation of two-dimensional regions so that all the relationships can be expressed in homogeneous form.

21.8   A SHORT NOTE ON FINITE-DIFFERENCE TIME-DOMAIN METHOD (F-D T-D)

21.8.1   Introduction

The interaction of electromagnetic waves with arbitrarily shaped objects cannot be modelled so easily nor accurately. Antenna apertures, cavity resonators, material inhomogeneities, etc. are some of the examples of engineering interest. The modal transmission in such structures cannot be modelled numerically so easily as to obtain correct information regarding magnitude and phase. The methods for modelling such structures have been based on frequency domain integral equation approach. The method of moments (MOM) and the finite element method (FEM) are of this category. But these methods may require large matrices to be inverted. Hence for such structures the F-D T-D method has certain advantages.

The F-D T-D method gives a direct solution of Maxwell's time-dependent curl equations (i.e. Faraday's law and modified Ampere's law equations). It employs simple second-order central difference approximation for space and time derivatives of the electric and the magnetic fields (Though for time-derivatives, sometimes forward-difference approximation is preferred.) The F-D-T-D is a time marching process which simulates the continuous actual waves by sampled-data numerical analogues stored in the computer.

To illustrate the technique of the FD-TD method, a simple problem has been considered here. As an example, a simple first order partial differential equation is solved. The equation has one space variable and a time variable, i.e.

The potential function ϕ is assumed to be a function of z-coordinate (space) and time t.

$$\therefore \qquad\qquad \phi = \phi(z, t) \qquad\qquad (21.84)$$

The equation under consideration is

$$\frac{\partial \phi}{\partial z} + \frac{1}{c} \frac{\partial \phi}{\partial t} = 0 \qquad\qquad (21.85)$$

with the initial condition

$$\phi(z, t = 0) = F(z) \qquad \text{(say)} \qquad\qquad (21.86)$$

(This equation is sometimes called the advection equation.)

It should be noted that the analytical solution of this equation is

$$\phi(z, t) = F(z - ct) \qquad\qquad (21.87)$$

which is a wave travelling in the $+z$-direction.

A point of further interest is that Eq. (21.87) is also a solution of the one-dimensional wave equation where equation is of the form

$$\frac{\partial^2 \phi}{\partial z^2} - \frac{1}{c^2} \frac{\partial^2 \phi}{\partial t^2} = 0 \qquad\qquad (21.88)$$

Both the wave equation (i.e. Eq. (21.88) and the advection equation (i.e. Eq. (21.85), belong to the family of differential equations known as 'hyperbolic equations'. The scalar diffusion equation (or heat conduction equation) is a 'parabolic equation' and Laplace's and Poisson's equations are called 'elliptic equations'. The vector eddy current equation, with harmonic time variation (i.e. $e^{j\omega t}$) can be reduced to 'elliptic equation with complex variables'.

A three-dimensional view of ϕ variation can be obtained pictorially with z and t as two coordinate axes and ϕ along the third axis orthogonal to z and t as shown in Figure 21.22.

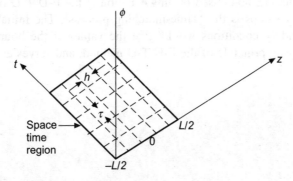

Figure 21.22 Grid system used for evaluation of ϕ of Eq. (21.85).

Since the problem is to be solved numerically, the space dimension (say L) in which the wave is propagating, has been sub-divided into N sections, so that

$$h = \frac{L}{N} \qquad (21.89)$$

It the velocity of propagation is c, then let τ be the time-period required to transverse the length h of the grid, so that

$$h = c\tau \qquad (21.90)$$

At this stage, the numerical stability is not be discussed; and assuming 'periodic boundary condition', i.e. when the wave reaches the boundary $z = L/2$, it reappears at the same time at $z = -L/2$, and thus continues to propagate in the region $-L/2 \leq z \leq +L/2$.

Next, Eq. (21.85) is converted to F.D. form. This can be done by Taylor series expansion or by line integration, as shown in Chapter 5, Section 5.5.2). Hence without going through the intermediate steps again, the final result is written down directly here.

The time derivative term is approximated by using forward difference,

$$\frac{\partial \phi}{\partial t} = \frac{f(z_i, t_n + \tau) - f(z_i, t_n)}{\tau} \qquad (21.91)$$

where

$$z_i = \left(i - \frac{1}{2} \right) h - \frac{L}{2}, \qquad t_n = (n-1)\tau \qquad (21.91a)$$

referring to Figure 21.22.

The space derivative is approximated by using central differences,

$$\frac{\partial \phi}{\partial z} = \frac{\phi(z_i + h, t_n) - \phi(z_i - h, t_n)}{2h} \qquad (21.92)$$

Substituting from Eq. (21.91) and (21.92), Eq. (21.85) reduces to:

$$\frac{\phi(z_i + h, t_n) - \phi(z_i - h, t_n)}{2h} + \frac{1}{c} \frac{\phi(z_i, t_n + \tau) - \phi(z_i, t_n)}{\tau} = 0 \qquad (21.93)$$

Of the four terms in the above equation, three terms are at the time instant t_n and one term is at the instant $t_n + t$. Hence rewriting the equation,

$$\phi(z_i, t_n + \tau) = \phi(z_i, t_n) - \frac{c\tau}{2h} \left[\phi(z_i + h, t_n) - \phi(z_i - h, t_n) \right] \qquad (21.94)$$

The finite difference method based on this equation is the F-D T-D method. The evaluation of these terms in the time-steps is the 'Time-marching process'. The initial values are all known at $t_0 = 0$, and the boundary conditions would give the values at the boundaries.

This is the underlying principle of the F-D T-D method, and serves as an introduction to this method.

22

Modern Topics and Applications

22.1 INTRODUCTION

In our study of electromagnetism, we have so far discussed both the magnetic diffusion (i.e. eddy currents) and most of the aspects of electromagnetic waves (i.e. propagation, guidance and radiation). Apart from the applications discussed till now, there are other areas of applications of electromagnetism. Some of these applications are microwaves used in diverse areas ranging from satellite communication, EM interference and compatibility, remote seusing, heating, radar, radio astronomy and so on, lasers, fibre optics, etc. on the high frequency side, and electrical machines and allied power generating equipment on the low frequency side. We shall now briefly describe and discuss some of the new applications since the old applications have been comprehensively discussed in specialized textbooks elsewhere.

We shall start with some of the important high frequency applications first and then go on to describe briefly the new power frequency applications as well.

22.2 MICROWAVES

Microwaves are electromagnetic waves within the frequency range of approximately 300 MHz to 1000 GHz.

In the field of communication, the main means for carrying thousands of channels over long distances are:

(1) Microwave links (2) Co-axial cables, and (3) Optical fibres (this being a new device, it will be discussed briefly later.

Microwaves are highly attractive for communications because of the following properties:

(a) Wide available bandwidth
(b) Directive properties of short wavelengths.

Because of these properties, microwave communication has now become more common than the radio and TV. A microwave system usually consists of a transmitter which includes microwave oscillator, waveguides and a transmitting antenna and receiver sub-system made up of receiving antenna, transmission line or waveguide, microwave amplifier and a receiver. The use of microwaves has very significantly increased. Some of the examples are telecommunications, radio astronomy, land surveying (by remote sensing). Radar, terrestrial microwave links, heating, medicines and so on. We shall briefly describe qualitatively the salient aspects of some of these applications. We shall also describe some of the important low-frequency applications.

22.2.1 Microwave Heating

Microwaves are preferred over the low frequency electromagnetic waves because the microwave energy can be more easily directed, controlled and concentrated. Also various atomic and molecular resonances occur at the microwave frequencies. So this energy can be used for heating purposes (another being remote sensing). The heating property of microwave power is used in a wide variety of domestic, commercial and industrial applications. The microwave oven is one such typical example (Figure 22.1).

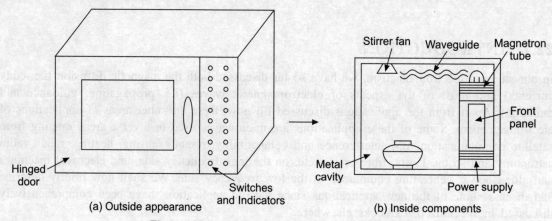

Figure 22.1 Microwave oven (a typical one).

The oven gets the microwave energy for cooking from a magnetron which is a thermionic valve capable of producing high power oscillations in the microwave region. The magnetron consists of a heater, central cathode and a concentric, radially segmented anode, all enclosed in an evacuated container, located in the gap of an external magnet. The movement of electrons is controlled by a combination of crossed electric and magnetic fields. It is also used extensively in radars. The energy from the magnetron is carried through a waveguide into the oven which is basically a resonant cavity in which the food for cooking is located. The reflections from the stationary walls and the motion of the stirring fan ensure the microwave energy to be well distributed in the cavity. The shape of the oven cavity is usually a rectangular parallelepiped, though there are some ovens with cylindrical cavity having a hemispherical top for more uniform cooking. Thus the microwave makes the cooking to be fast and evenly distributed. In modern microwave ovens, facilities are provided for grilling, convective cooking as well, in addition to the microwave cooking. These two additional facillities are done at normal frequency and so these sources (i.e. heater and fan) get their electricity at power frequency, thus bypassing the magnetron. The microwave oven operates at 2.4 GHz. Apart from this type of domestic cooking, the microwave heating capability is used in physical diathermy (in medical treatment) and in drying potato crisps, paper, cloth, etc.

22.2.2 Radar Systems

The word radar is an acronym for **RA**dio **D**etection **A**nd **R**anging. It includes any system that employs microwaves for the purpose of locating, identifying, navigating or guiding such moving objects as ships, aircraft, missiles, or artificial satellites. It is now also used for burgler alarms, garage-door openers, and police speed detectors.

The system essentially consists of a generator of electromagnetic radiation of centimetre wavelengths, the output of which is pulse-modulated at a radio frequency and fed to a movable antenna from where it is radiated as a beam. Distant objects crossing the path of the beam reflect the pulses back to the transmitter which also acts as a receiver. A cathode-ray tube (CRT) indicator displays the received signal in the correct time sequence so that the time required for a pulse to travel to the object and back can be measured. Thus the distance of the object from the transmitter can be calculated and its direction can be found from a knowledge of the direction of the antenna. This fundamental technique has now been extrapolated so that automatic guidance and navigation can also be made by computers without requiring a display system.

The radio transmitter should be of high power and the receiver has to be extremely sensitive. The receiving antenna is also highly directional. The amplitude and delay of the receiving signal are the two important parameters required for estimating the size and the distance of the observed object from the radar. The size of the object is characterized by a parameter called the "radar cross-section". This is a complex function of the reflectivity of the object and its physical shape and size. For example, metallic objects have higher radar cross-section compared with dielectric objects.

Power reflected by an object

= Power density of the incident wave × Radar cross-section (= σ)

Let

P_t = Transmitting power of the antenna

G = Directive gain of the antenna

A_e = Effective aperture of the antenna in the receiving mode $= \dfrac{G\lambda^2}{4\pi}$ (since the same antenna

is used for transmission and reception)

$\therefore$ Power density of the transmitted signal (at the object),

$$W = \frac{P_t G}{4\pi r^2} \tag{22.1}$$

where r is the distance of the object from the radar.

$\therefore$ Power reflected by the object,

$$P_{\text{ref}} = P_\sigma = \frac{P_t G \sigma}{4\pi r^2} \tag{22.2}$$

$\therefore$ Power density of the reflected power at the radar,

$$W_r = \frac{P_{\text{ref}}}{4\pi r^2} = \frac{P_t G \sigma}{(4\pi r^2)^2} \tag{22.3}$$

(This assumes that the reflected power is uniformly distributed in all directions.)

∴ Power received by the radar antenna,

$$P_{\text{rec}} = W_r A_e = \frac{P_t G \sigma}{(4\pi r^2)^2} \frac{G\lambda^2}{4\pi} = \frac{P_t \sigma}{4\pi} \left(\frac{G\lambda}{4\pi r^2} \right)^2 \tag{22.4}$$

Thus P_{rec} must be greater than the minimum detectable power of the receiver, for detection of objects.

Since $r \gg \lambda$, G must be quite large so as to maintain P_t within acceptable limits.

Hence radars use highly directional antennae like parabolic dishes.

The energy transporting medium from the transmitter to the antenna is usually a metal wave-guide (rectangular or circular) since the radar needs high power to be transmitted.

The radars, though originally developed for military purposes, now have many civilian applications, like weather monitoring, geological survey, air-traffic control, remote sensing and planetary explorations. In defence applications, when they talk of invisible bombers, it is meant that these planes are not visible on the radar.

In a sense, the defence requirements on radars are contradictory, because on one side the radar research aims at detecting targets with highest resolution and sensitivity whilst on the other side aircraft and ships are being developed with extremely low radar cross-section so as to make them as invisible to radar detection as possible. (Invisible planes are used for spying purposes).

22.2.3   Remote Sensing

In radio remote sensing, the microwave frequencies are used for geological survey (i.e. to probe the terrain). A radar is mounted on a moving platform which can be an aircraft or a satellite above the surface of the earth. Proper frequencies have to be selected for effective imaging of a region since the reflectivity of earth's surface is a function of both location as well as frequency.

Two types of radars are used for getting high quality radio images of the earth's surface, i.e.

1. Side looking radar (SLR)
2. Synthetic aperture radar (SAR).

In a SLR, the reflection from a region illuminated by the beam of the radar gives the average reflectivity of that region. As the radar carrier moves, the beam spot on the region also moves and thereby the reflectivity profile of the region along a strip is produced. Multiple scanning of adjacent strips is done to build an image of the complete region. To obtain high resolution, large antennae have to be used, and the radar vehicle should be at low attitude for better linear resolution in the images.

In the SAR, the reflected signals for the entire flight of the radar are stored and then coherently processed to form a synthesized antenna beam which is much narrower compared to the beam of the radar antenna. The linear resolution of the SAR is proportional to the size of the antenna, i.e. the resolution of the image improves as the size of the antenna is made smaller. Also the resolution is independent of the height of the vehicle.

Numerical electromagnetic techniques are used to obtain accurate models of the earth's surface.

22.2.4   Radio Astronomy

This is the study of heavenly bodies by the reception and analysis of the 'radio frequency electromagnetic radiaton' which they emit or reflect. In general the electromagnetic radiations from the extra-terrestrial sources are either absorbed by the earth's atmosphere or reflected away from the earth by the ionosphere. The two exceptions are: (i) the optical wavelengths which are able to penetrate the atmosphere, and (ii) the radio wavelengths in the band 1 cm to 10 metres which are too long to be absorbed by the atmosphere and too short to be absorbed by the ionosphere. These radiations which pass through the 'radio window' come from a variety of sources ranging from objects within the solar system to galaxies which are too far to be observed by optical telescopes. The origin of these radio frequency emissions can be thermal or non-thermal. Information is extracted from the apparently incoherent radio noise from the universe, by constructing maps of the sky in terms of radio emission at several different frequencies which are then compared with optical observations. Thus the radio sources and radio galaxies have been identified.

Radio telescopes are the instruments used in radio astronomy to pick up and analyse the radio frequency electromagnetic. radiations of extraterrestrial sources. The two main types of radio telescopes are:

(i) *Parabolic reflectors* (paraboloid reflector—a concave reflector, the section of which is a parabola—also called a dish antenna). These are usually steerable so that they can be pointed to any part of the sky and they reflect the incoming radiation to a small antenna at the focus of the paraboloid.

(ii) *Fixed radio interferometers*. These consist of two or more separate antennae (an array), each receiving electromagnetic radiation of radio frequencies from the same source and each joined to the same receiver.

This type of telescope has greater position finding accuracy and can distinguish a small source against an intense background better than the parabolic type. On the other hand the parabolic type is more verslatile because of its mobility.

To achieve the same or similar resolution of optical telescopes, the radio telescope, operating at radio frequencies would need to have a size a few hundred metres to few kilometres. Since building a continuous aperture type of telescope of such sizes is not a viable proposition, the radio astronomers have developed a technique known as the 'aperture synthesis technique' by using which a large aperture can be synthesized without actually building one of that magnitude. The method is based on the measurment of the spatial Fourier spectrum of the brightness distribution (and not measuring this distribution directly). This spectrum is the auto-correlation function (also called visibility function) of the incoming radiation from the sky. The Fourier inversion of the visibility function then provides the brightness distribution of the sky.

22.2.5 Satellite Communication

This has been one of the important modes of long distance communication. There are many advantages of this technique, e.g. large bandwidth, mobility, dynamic assigment of resources and so on. Communication satellites are artificial earth satellites used for relaying radio, television and telephone signals around the curved surface of the earth. 'Passive' satellites merely reflect the transmissions from their surfaces whereas the 'active' satellites are equipped to receive and retransmit signals.

The orbit of an artificial earth satellite which has a period of 24 hours is called synchronous orbit (or stationary orbit). The altitude corresponding to such an orbit is about 35,700 km, and a satellite in a circular orbit parallel to the equator at this altitude would appear to be stationary in the sky (it is called a geostationary satellite). Communication satellites in synchronous orbits are used for relaying radio signals between widely separated points on the earth.

In satellite communication, radio signals are transmitted from a transmitter on the earth (this is called the 'earth station') towards the satellite. The satellite on receiving the signal, changes its frequency and retransmits it towards the earth. The satellite generally offers point to multipoint transmission (i.e. broadcasting). Generally microwave frequencies are used for satellite communication, since microwaves propagate along straight lines like a light ray and are not bent by ionosphere as are lower frequency signals. The design of a satellite communication link takes into consideration all the facts of the electromagnetic waves which have been discussed so far. The satellite link design gives an estimate of both, i.e. (a) the power which the satellite would receive from an earth station, and (b) the power which a receiving station on the ground would get from the satellite. This design would have to take into account aspects such as (i) energy absorption by the space between the satellite and the earth, (ii) changes in wave characteristics during propagation, and (iii) design of antenna system. Since the power at the satellite is limited, the antenna must be designed for high directivity as well as high efficiency. The antenna is a crucial component of this link system.

The energy loss in the path (i.e. the path-loss) is independent of the transmitting and the receiving systems. The path-loss is inversely proportional to the square of the wavelength and hence the shorter wavelengths (i.e. higher frequencies) suffer greater path-loss. A geostationary satellite operating (say) at 6 GHz would have a path-loss of about 200 dB.

22.2.6 Electromagnetic Interference and Compatibility (EMI and EMC)

Electromagnetic Interference (EMI): It is the degradation of performance and consequent malfunctioning of electronic devices and systems due to environmental electromagnetic fields.

There are various sources of electromagnetic emission, like spark plugs, relays, electric motors and generators. The disturbing fields due to such devices are comparatively localized, though there are electronic devices whose disturbing fields are more distributed. (*Note:* By disturbing fields it is meant that these fields are more of accidental by-products of the design of the device or the system. These are called 'radiated emissions'). So it can be said that the electromagnetic environment consists of apparatuses like radio and TV broadcast stations, radar systems (both air-port as well as traffic ones), flourescent lights, car ignition systems, mobile radios, navigational aids and so on, which radiate electromagnetic energy as they operate. The results of such interference are obvious in every day life, such as 'ghosting' in television reception, high voltage power lines causing interference with personal computer operation, taxicab radio interference with police radio system. Hence electromagnetic compatiblity can be defined as follows:

Electromagnetic Compatibility (EMC): An electronic system is said to 'electromagnetically compatible' with its environment when the system is able to perform compatibly with other electronic systems and neither produces nor be susceptible to the environmental electromagnetic disturbances.

To achieve EMC, all electronic devices should be able to co-exist and operate in harmony, i.e. the device should be able to function as per the designed purpose in presence of and in spite of the others. In fact EMI is the problems caused by the unwanted voltages, currents and fields on the devices and EMC is the solution to the problem. The goal of EMC is to achieve the system compatibility which is achieved by freeing the system of EMI problems.

22.2.7 Sources and Characteristics of EMI

EMI can be classified in terms of its causes and sources, so that it will be easier to control this type of disturbance. As stated earlier, any electronic device can be the source of EMI even though the designer may not have intended so. The cause of EMI can be within the system (i.e. an intrasystem problem) or can be from outside (i.e. an intersystem problem). Some examples of both the types are listed below. Here the sources have been termed emitters and the victims susceptors.

A. Intrasystem Causes		B. Intersystem Causes	
Emitters	*Susceptors*	*Emitters*	*Susceptors*
Power supplies	Relay	Lightening stroke	Radio receivers
Radar transmitters	Radar relays	Computers	TV sets
Mobile radio transmitters	Mobile radio receivers	Power lines	Heart pacers
Flourescent lights	Ordnance	Radar transmitters	Aircraft navigation systems
Car ignition systems	Car radio receivers		

The sources of EMI can be natural or man-made (artifical).

22.2.8 Control of EMI

There are three ways of preventing EMI and making systems compatible.

   (i)   Supressing the emission at the source
   (ii) Making the transmission path inefficient
   (iii) Making the receiver less susceptible to emission.

The first line of defence would be to avoid fast switching of the signals. This should be done even in digital systems by switching smoothly so as to reduce the high frequency content of EMI, thus reducing the coupling of the interference. Grounding establishes an electrically conducting path between two points to connect electrical and electronic elements of a system to one another or to some reference point (designated as the ground). An ideal ground plane is a zero-potential, zero-impedance body used as reference for all signals in associated circuitry. All undesired currents can be transferred to it for elimination of their effects. 'Floating point ground' is for electrical isolation from a common ground plane. But this can cause a hazard. The single-point grounding is used for minimizing the effects of gound currents and eliminating the effects of loop currents in multiple-earthing.

Shielding is done to prevent radiated energy from entering a specific region or to confine the radiated energy in a specified region (Figure 22.2). The term 'shield' usually refers to a metallic enclosure that completely encloses a particular electronic device or sub-system through non-solid and braid, as is used on cables. The shielding effectiveness is defined by:

$$SE = 10 \log_{10} \frac{\text{incident power density}}{\text{transmitted power density}} \tag{22.5}$$

where the incident power density is the power density measured at a point before the shield has been installed, and the transmitted power density is the power density at the same point after the shield has been installed. SE can also be defined in terms of electric or magnetic field strengths, i.e.

$$\text{SE} = 20 \log_{10} \frac{E_i}{E_t} \qquad \text{for electric fields}$$

and
$$\text{SE} = 20 \log_{10} \frac{H_i}{H_t} \qquad \text{for magnetic fields}$$

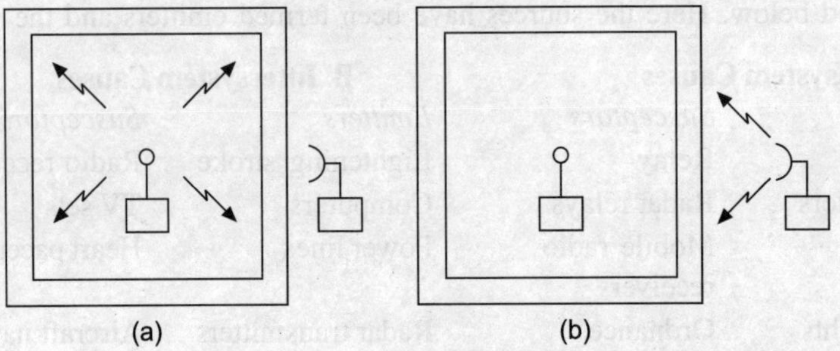

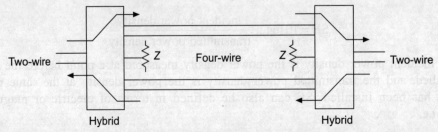

(a)   (b)

Figure 22.2   Electromagnetic shielding.

Filtering: An electrical filter is a network (either lumped or distributed) of resistors, inductors and capacitors that allows certain frequencies to pass through while blocking the other frequencies. Filters usually reduce the levels of conducted interference substantially. The most important characteristic of a filter is its insertion loss (IL) which is a function of frequency.

$$\text{IL} = 20 \log_{10}(V_1/V_2)$$

where

V_1 = output voltage of a signal source, with the filter in the circuit

V_2 = output voltage of the signal source, without the filter in the circuit.

22.3 TELEPHONE NETWORKS

In telephone networks, all transmission is through a pair of wires. All subscriber loops in the telephone networks are made with a single pair of wires, using bidirectional transmission (i.e. the users at both ends of the line talk simultaneously, thereby superimposing their signals on the wire pair).

For long distance transmission (i.e. between two switching offices) it is better to use two unidirectional transmissions on different pairs of wires. The reason for this requirement is that the long distance transmission requires amplifiers and these are unidirectional. Hence the long distance transmission becomes a four-wire system (Figure 22.3). So for long distance connection, at some point there has to be a conversion from two-wire to four-wire system and vice-versa. This conversion device is called a 'hybrid'.

Figure 22.3   Two-wire to four-wire connections in telephone lines using hybrids.

In earlier days, the hybrid circuits were connected through interconnected transformers. But nowadays, the electronic hybrids need only the impedance matching for perfect isolation between oppositely travelling signals. When there is an impedance mismatch on the lines (due to the variable impedance of the two-wire line in switching environment), there would be reflections on the line causing an echo. The echoes are minimized by adaptive signal processing techniques.

22.4 LASERS

Laser is an abbreviation of the words **L**ight **A**mplification by **S**timulated **E**mission of **R**adiation. It is essentially an optical maser (see below for maser). The laser produces a powerful, highly directional, monochromatic, and coherent beam of light. Its working principle is essentially same as that of a maser, except that the 'active medium', in the case, consists of or is contained in an optically transparent cylinder with a reflecting surface at one end and a partially refltecting surface at the other. The stimulated waves pass up and down the cylinder repeatedly, some of them emerging as light through the partially reflecting end.

In a 'ruby laser', the chromium atoms of a cylindrical shaped ruby crystal are optically pumped to an excited state by a flash lamp and then it emits pulses of highly coherent light (population inversion). There are lasers which have been constructed by using a mixture of inert gases (e.g. helium and neon) to produce a continuous beam. These is also another type of laser consisting of a cube of specially treated gallium arseuide which can emit infra-red radiation when a current is passed through it. Lasers have been used in eye surgery, holography and metal cutting, etc.

Maser: This word is an acronym of **M**icrowave **A**mplification by **S**timulated **E**mission of **R**adiation. This is a class of amplifiers and oscillators which make use of the internal energy of atoms and molecules in order to obtain low-noise level amplification and microwave oscillations of precisely determined frequencies. The basic principle of operation of these devices is the stimulated emission which is the emission by an atom in an excited quantam state of a photon, as the result of the impact of a photon from outside of exactly equal energy. Then the stimulated photon or wave is augmented by the one emitted by the excited atom.

A maser consists of an active medium which can be either in the gaseous or solid state, in which most of the atoms can be optically pumped to an excited state which is done by subjecting the system to electromagnetic radiation of different frequencies to that of the stimulating frequency.

The active medium is enclosed in a resonant cavity so that a wave is built up modally (i.e. with only one mode of oscillation) thereby giving a single output frequency. Masers when made to operate at optical frequencies, are referred to as lasers. (*Note:* 'Population inversion': In a laser, when a large proportion of the emitting ions have been raised to an excited energy level by the process of optical pumping which means that the energy has been introduced in the system by an external light source, then the state of population inversion exists in it (the laser). This is an essential step in the process of stimulated emission.

It should be noted that the laser is essentially an amplifier and not a light generating device. But, since any amplifier can be converted into an oscillator by feedback with a properly selected frequency, a laser can also be converted into a source of coherent light. The crucial component of the laser is a frequency feedback device. This feedback is done by creating a resonant cavity around the active (i.e. the amplifying) medium. Figure 22.4 shows the basic elements of a laser.

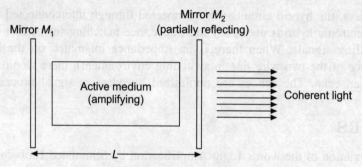

Figure 22.4 Basic elements of a laser.

Only certain frequencies of the light would get sustained amplification as a result of repeated reflection between the two mirrors M_1 and M_2. For a sustained oscillation of that frequency (= ω), the gain (= G) due to the round trip between the two mirrors should be unity and the phase difference due to this trip would be a multiple of 2π. Hence if the reflection coefficients of the two mirrors are denoted by R_1 and R_2 respectively, then

$$R_1 R_2 \exp(2GL) = 1 \tag{22.6}$$

and

$$2\beta L = 2m\pi, \quad m \text{ being an integer} \tag{22.6a}$$

where

β = phase constant of the light wave of frequency ω

$= \dfrac{\omega n}{c}$, where n = refractive index of the active medium.

$\therefore$

$$\omega = \frac{m\pi c}{nL} \tag{22.7}$$

The light coming out of a laser has random polarization to achieve normal polarization, the light from the laser has to be reflected from a dielectric slab at the 'Brewster angle' as mentioned in Chapter 17. Section 17.15.

22.5 OPTICAL FIBRE

Through the last century (20th), the basic media for transmitting radio frequency (RF) energy have been wire-pairs (i.e. conductors), co-axial cable, waveguides and atmosphere. Radio frequency range has been 10 kHz to 300 GHz. With increasing demands for more communication channels, a new technology has been developing and the upper limit of the radio frequency is being pushed to and beyond the infra-red and visible portion of the spectrum. This is the development and use of optical fibres which are small diameter cylindrical glass filaments which transmit EM waves at frequencies near the visible part of the spectrum. Light differs from radio in that it has both the properties of particles called photons and the properties of EM waves. 'Photonics' is the term commonly applied to optical fibres. Both particle physics and EM wave theory are necessary to understand completely the working of optical fibre systems. Particles are characterized by their energy, momentum, and they can be individually physically identified. EM waves, on the other hand are characterized by frequency, wavelength, polarization, and velocity. Basically optical fibre is a cylindrical dielectric waveguide operating at optical frequency.

Optical fibres are specially constructed glass, plastic or ceramic cylindrical waveguides to contain the propagating electromagnetic fields. The fibres operate at very high range of the frequency scale, so that it has been customary to express optical energy in terms of wavelengths (= λ). The visible spectrum ranges from 0.4×10^{-6} metres (blue) to 0.6×10^{-6} metres (red). In terms of frequency, it will be in tera hertz [= THz (10^{12})]. The most commonly used optical fibres are constructed from silica (SiO_2) which has been purified and doped in order to reduce the energy loss. The optimum performace wavelength range for SiO_2 is from 0.8×10^{-6} metres to 1.6×10^{-6} metres. An obvious advantage of operating at high frequencies is the increase in bandwidth available for transmitting information. Modulated laser bandwiths for optical fibre transmission are about 100 GHz wide, i.e. about 0.1% of the carrier frequency.

Communication systems have a wide range of power values. A laser transmitter array might be radiating 100 mW into a fibre whilst the detector at the end of the fibre might be receiving one-ten thousandth of a mW—a difference of 10^6. So the relative powers are expressed in terms of decibels.

The velocity of light (i.e. EM waves) in free space or vacuum is v = c = 3×10^8 m/s The velocity of light in water, glass or any media other than free space is lower and is given by v = c/n, where n = index of refraction in the particular medium.

In every medium other than a vacuum, the velocity exhibits some degree of frequency dependence. Most RF signals have multiple frequency components usually because of modulation sidebands on a carrier. This dependence of velocity on frequency (or wavelength λ) can present significant problems. This phenomenon is called dispersion.

The indices of refraction of most materials used for different components of any optical fibre system are greater than unity (this being the refractive index of free space). In circular section optical fibres, the central section (or core) has a higher refractive index than the outer annulus (called the cladding). Usually the core index is about 1.5 and that of the cladding is slightly lower.

The velocity of the EM optical waves is less in a medium with refractive index >1 (this being the refractive index of free space). Hence, when two media of differing refractive indices meet, the optical wave is refracted or bent on the interface. Thus the wave in the second medium either speeds up or slows down depending whether its (second medium) refractive index is less than or greater than that of the first medium. The bending (or the refraction) is either towards the normal to the interface ($n_1 < n_2$) or away from the normal to the interface ($n_1 > n_2$). In an optical fibre, since the central core has higher refractive index than the outer cladding, the light which impinges on the core-cladding interface is bent back to the centre and guided along the fibre, due to total internal reflection.

The EM wave theory is used to analyse the propagation of light in the optical fibre medium. The particle theory is used for calculating the energy of the system by considering the energy of the photons. The behaviour of photons is needed for describing the laser and light-detector performances. The energy of a single photon of frequency f is

$$W \text{ (joules)} = h \times f = h \times c/\lambda$$

where $\left. \begin{array}{c} \\ h = \text{Planck's constant} = 6.626 \times 10^{-34} \text{ J-s} \end{array} \right\}$ (22.8)

22.5.1 An Optical System

For most of the applications the system has three components (Figure 22.5):

1. *An optical source:* There are two types of sources: (a) lasers, and (b) LEDs (Light

Emitting Diodes). Both these are electrical to optical energy converter (E/O). Lasers, at high electrical drive levels, increase their outputs through an internal oscillation. This permits high output powers and narrow source bandwidth. LEDs are semi-conductors, small in size and consume little power, easier to couple to fibres and integrate, and are of low cost. Both LEDs and lasers at low drive levels emit light through spontaneous emission, which is a random process and broadband.

2. *Optical detectors:* These convert optical signals to electrical signals (O/E), so that the original signals can be recovered. These are made of semiconductor materials like Si, Ge or InGeAs. Their choice is a function of the required wavelength λ. In some detectors ·like avlanche photo-detector, internal gain can be achieved by using high voltages.

3. *Optical fibres* (or the media) to carry the optical signals from the source to the detector. An optical fibre is basically a cylindrical dielectric rod called core, surrounded by a dielectric annulus called cladding. The cladding has an outer jacket (i.e. buffer or coating). The electrical signals which modulate the carrier can be either analogue or digital, and are referred to as baseband input signals. The digital signals, using pulses of same level and shape (to represent the original signal) require more complicated coding, modulation/demodulation but have better noise and cost advantages. This is because of the tremendous progress in the integrated electronics uses for digital signal processing (DSP) and transmission. The electrical signals will also be part of a time-division multiplexed (TDM) bit stream, and the source might be internally or externally modulated. The source has to be carefully coupled to the fibre and might be combined with other optical signals using wavelength division multiplexing (WDM). The fibre would be probably part of a cable that contains other fibres. The fibres can be either large core multimode or small core single-mode. A long fibre would need splices at intermediate points. At the receiver end, the components are required in the reverse order to restore the electrical signal.

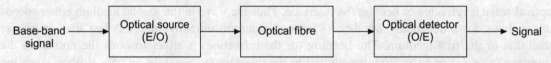

Figure 22.5   Optical fibre system.

22.5.2   Optical Fibre Characteristics

An optical fibre is made up of three concentric cylindrical sections, the core, the cladding and the buffer. The core consists of one or more thin strands of glass or plastic. The cladding is plastic or glass coating surrounding the core which may be step-index or gradient index. In the step-index core, the refreactive index is uniform but undergoes an abrupt change at the interface of the core and the cladding. The graded-index core is of the type in which the refractive index of the core varies as a function of the radial distance from the central axis of the core. The jacket or the buffer usually surrounds one or more of the cladded fibres and acts as a protection against environmental moisture or sunshine and so on (Figures 22.6 to 22.8).

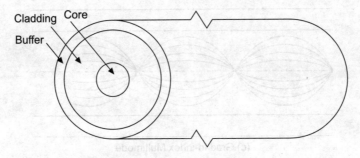

Figure 22.6 Optical fibre structure.

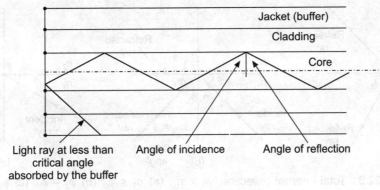

Figure 22.7 Behaviour of light ray in a fibre.

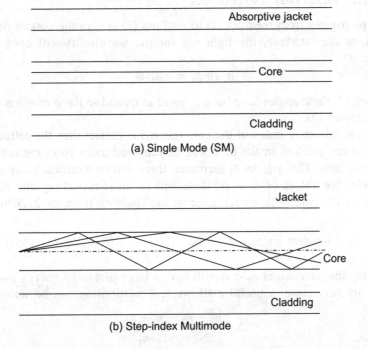

(a) Single Mode (SM)

(b) Step-index Multimode

Figure 22.8 Contd.

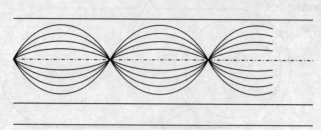

(c) Graded-index Multimode

Figure 22.8 Optical fibres transmission modes.

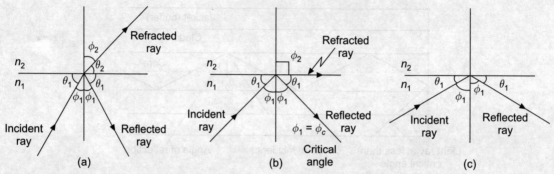

(a) (b) (c)

Figure 22.9 Total internal reflection, $n_1 > n_2$: (a) $\phi_1 < \phi_c$; (b) $\phi_1 = \phi_c$; (c) $\phi_1 > \phi_c$

22.5.2.1 Total internal reflection

As the light ray propagates from medium (1) to medium (2) (i.e. in the optical fibre from the core to the cladding), at the interface, the light ray (or the wavefront) will obey the Snell's law, (Figure 22.9), i.e.

$$n_1 \sin\phi_1 = n_2\sin\phi_2 \qquad (22.9)$$

(*Note:* In Chapter 17, these angles have been denoted as θs and so the ϕ mentioned here is complement of the θ in Chapter 17).

Also, since the refractive index of the core (i.e. n_1) is greater than the refractive index of the cladding (i.e. n_2) a ray incident in the core will be refracted away from the normal to the core–cladding interface [Figure 22.9(a)]. As ϕ_1 increases, there will be a critical value of ϕ_1, i.e. $\phi_1 = \phi_c$, for which $\phi_2 = 90°$. For values of $\phi_1 > \phi_c$, there will be no refracted ray and all the energy will be reflected back in the core with no leakeage in the cladding [Figures 22.9(b) and (c)].

i.e.

$$\phi_1 = \text{incident angle} = \phi_c = \sin^{-1}\left(\frac{n_2}{n_1}\right) \qquad \text{[Ref. Eq. (17.155)]} \qquad (22.10)$$

A ray striking the interface at $\phi_1 < \phi_c$ will have a large part of its energy lost in the cladding. Since n_1 and n_2 are very close, a useful mathematical relationship can be written down as

$$\Delta = \frac{n_1^2 - n_2^2}{2n_1^2} \simeq \frac{n_1 - n_2}{n_1} \qquad (22.11)$$

or

$$n_2 \simeq n_1(1 - \Delta) \qquad (22.11a)$$

It follows from the above that a very small Δ means that the critical angle ϕ_c is close to 90°. This is typical of silica fibres. In all plastic fibre with a large core diameter, Δ is much greater and ϕ_c is much smaller. Both these types have important applications.

For the present discussion, the 'plane of incidence' of the incident ray is as defined in Chapter 17, Section 17.13. Any linearly polarized wave of arbitrary polarization can be resolved into parallel and perpendicular (normal) components with reference to the plane of incidence. Hence the coefficients of energy reflection can be easily written down from the Fresnel's laws of reflection [Ref. Eqs. (17.153a–d)].

$$R_P \text{ (Parallel polarization)} = R_P = \left| \frac{-n_2^2 \cos\phi_1 + n_1\sqrt{(n_2^2 - n_1^2 \sin^2\phi_1)}}{n_2^2 \cos\phi_1 + n_1\sqrt{(n_2^2 - n_1^2 \sin^2\phi_1)}} \right|^2 \quad (22.12a)$$

$$R_N \text{ (Normal polarization)} = R_N = \left| \frac{n_1 \cos\phi_1 - \sqrt{(n_2^2 - n_1^2 \sin^2\phi_1)}}{n_1 \cos\phi_1 + \sqrt{(n_2^2 - n_1^2 \sin^2\phi_1)}} \right|^2$$

It should be noted that the glass-to-air interface has a critical angle of 41.8° and the air-to-glass interface has no critical angle.

With parallel polarization for both of them, there is Brewster angle for which there is ZERO reflection, a condition obtained by making the numerator of R_P equal to zero, so that

$$\phi_{iB} = \text{Brewster angle} = \tan^{-1}\frac{n_2}{n_1} \quad (22.13)$$

22.5.2.2 Numerical aperture

This is one of the most important parameters of an optical fibre (or any optical device which accepts and uses light energy). The numerical aperture is "the proportion of the impinging light that can be accepted and used." Figure 22.10 shows a fibre accepting light from a source. It should

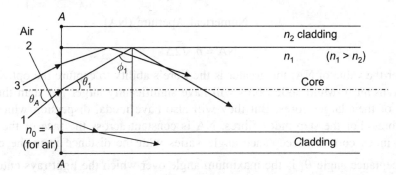

Figure 22.10 Numerical aperture and acceptance angle (longitudinal section of the fibre).

be noted that some rays from the source will not be guided because they enter the fibre at too great an incident angle. (The incident angle is the angle made by the entering ray with the axis of the core.) Their incident angle is refracted in the core and hit the core/cladding interface at an angle less than the fibre's critical angle. The interface between the outside air and the fibre glass core and cladding does not have critical angle (Section AA) because in this case $n_1 < n_2$. There are two types of rays which will propagate in the fibre i.e. meridian and skew. Meridional rays are confined to meridian planes which are longitudinal sections of the fibre, each containing the central axis (the section shown in Figure 22.10 being one such plane). Skew rays are not restricted to one such plane and follow a helical path along the guide. Skew rays probabley make up the larger proportion of the total number of rays, but meridian rays are responsible for longer distance transmission in the fibre.

In Figure 22.10, the ray (1) whose angle of incidence on the air/core interface is θ_A is a meridian ray lying in the meridian plane coinciding with the plane of the paper. The ray (2) is refracted out of the core into the cladding. The ray (3) is a skew ray whose point of incidence is not on the line AA' (as seems to be in the figure) but lies in the plane through AA normal to the plane of the paper and its projection on the line AA is as shown in the figure. Its plane is NOT a meridian plane and the ray is skew relative to the central axis of the core.

For the critical angle ϕ_c of the core

$$\sin\phi_c = \frac{n_2}{n_1} \tag{22.14}$$

and

$$\cos^2\phi_c = 1 - \frac{n_2^2}{n_1^2} = \frac{n_1^2 - n_2^2}{n_1^2} \tag{22.15}$$

By Snell's law $n_0 \sin\theta_A = n_1 \sin\theta_1$

where ϕ_A = acceptance angle   and $\theta_1 = \pi/2 - \phi_1$ \hfill (22.16)

Since $n_0 = 1$ for air outside the core,

and $\sin\theta_1 = \cos\phi_1 = \cos\phi_c$

$$\left.\begin{array}{l} \therefore\qquad \sin\theta_A = n_1\cos\theta_c = n_1\sqrt{\dfrac{n_1^2 - n_2^2}{n_1^2}} \\[4mm] = \sqrt{(n_1^2 - n_2^2)} = \sqrt{\{(n_1 - n_2)(n_1 + n_2)\}} \end{array}\right\} \tag{22.17}$$

= Numerical Aperture (NA)

Also $$\text{NA} \simeq n_1\sqrt{2\Delta} \tag{22.17a}$$

The larger the value of NA, the greater is the fibre's ability to capture the optical power from a source and transmit it. Multimode fibres will have significantly larger NA than the single-mode fibres because of their larger cores. But they will also have modal dispersion which is absent in single-mode fibres. For the step-index fibres, NA is constant across the face of the core whereas for the graded-index core the acceptance angle varies with the distance from the core axis.

Note: The acceptance angle θ_A is the maximum angle over which the light rays entering the fibre core will be trapped in the core. It has been seen that the maximum angle occurs when ϕ_c is the critical angle satisfying the condition for total internal reflection.

22.5.2.3 Modes

Since the fibre is basically a circular waveguide, the propagation of light, which is an electromagnetic wave will be in the form of modes, as seen in Chapter 18. Also from the previous discussion in that chapter, three types of modes can exist in the fibre, i.e. the transverse electric modes (with $E_z = 0$, $H_z \neq 0$, z being the direction of propagation — TE), the transverse magnetic modes (with $H_z = 0$ and $E_z \neq 0$ — TM), and the hybrid modes (with $E_z \neq 0$, $H_z \neq 0$—HE). It should also be remembered that the fields have circular symmetry when $E_z = 0$ or $H_z = 0$. When both E_z and H_z are non-zero, there is no circular symmetry. Another point to be noted is that all the modes excluding HE_{11} have finite cut-off frequencies. The HE_{11} mode does not have a cut-off frequency and hence the light of any wavelength can propagate inside an optical fibre in this mode.

This phenomenon gives a basis for defining the type of fibre, i.e. if only the HE_{11} mode propagates inside the fibre, then the fibre is called the single-mode fibre (SM). If other modes also propagate the fibre is called mutlimode fibre (MM). Givien below in Figure 22.11 is the E-field pattern in some of the lower modes of a step-index cylindrical guide. Some modes are linearly polarized and they are labelled as LP modes.

Fundamental (lowest order) mode

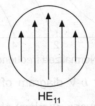

HE_{11}

First set of higher order modes—LP_{11}

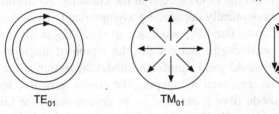

TE_{01} TM_{01} HE_{21}

Figure 22.11 E field vectors in step-index waveguide lowest order modes.

The modal performance in the core of a cylindrical, step-index, optical fibre depends on a number of parameters, i.e.

(a) Radius of the core = a
(b) Free space wavelength = λ
(c) Refractive index of the core = n_1
(d) Refractive index of the cladding = n_2.

A parameter called the 'normalized frequency ($=V$)' is a function of all these variables and is used for a simplified analysis of fibre design. V is defined as:

$$\left. \begin{array}{l} V = \dfrac{2\pi a}{\lambda} (n_1^2 - n_2^2)^{1/2} = \dfrac{2\pi a n_1}{\lambda} \sqrt{2\Delta} \\[4mm] \qquad = \text{normalized frequency} \\[4mm] \qquad = \dfrac{\omega a}{c} (n_1^2 - n_2^2)^{1/2} \end{array} \right\} \qquad (22.18)$$

A mode chart (or a *b–V* diagram) plots the relationship between these modes as a function of *V* and the refractive index *n* (or β the modal phase constant where $\beta = \omega n/c$) between the limits n_1 and n_2 (the indices of core and cladding respectively, i.e. $\beta_1 = \omega n_1/c$ to $\beta_2 = \omega n_2/c$).

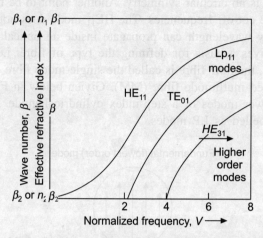

Figure 22.12   Mode chart or *b-V* diagram of an optical fibre (step-index).

The modal phase constant (i.e. the wave number) always lies between β_2 and β_1. As $\beta \to \beta_2$ the mode approaches the cut-off and the fields spread in the cladding. As the normalized frequency *V* increases, β also increases monotonically approacing asymptotically to β_1, i.e. as *V* increases the fields get more confined to the core. The LP$_{11}$ mode group (i.e. TE$_{01}$ mode) will not propagate if $V < 2.40$, which is the cut-off wavelength, and decides the region of single-mode propagation. A large difference in modal speeds would yield significant modal dispersion at the detector. The step-index modal performance can be improved by shaping the core's refractive index in the form of a parabola. This type of multimode fibre is referred to as graded index (or GRIN) fibre.

A mathematical model for a parabolic core profile of the graded index multimode fibre is given by

$$\left. \begin{aligned} n(r) &= n_1 \sqrt{\left\{ 1 - 2\left(\frac{r}{a}\right)^2 \Delta \right\}} \qquad &\text{for } r < a \text{ and}\\ &= n_2 \qquad &\text{for } r \geq a \end{aligned} \right\} \tag{22.19}$$

where

    a = radius of the core

    r = radial distance from the core-axis.

An equation for the variation of NA for this fibre, as function of the radius is

$$\text{NA} = n_1 \sqrt{2\Delta} \sqrt{\left\{ 1 - \left(\frac{r}{a}\right)^2 \right\}} \tag{22.20}$$

When
$$r = 0, \quad \text{NA} = n_1 \sqrt{2\Delta} \tag{22.20a}$$
which is same as for the step-index type core.

The normalized frequency parameter V for a GRIN fibre is obtained using the same equation as the step-index fibre. The number of modes in a multimode GRIN fibre is reduced and approximated by

$$N = \frac{V^2}{4} \quad \text{for } V > 10 \tag{22.21}$$

which is half the number obtained in a step-index fibre with same V.

22.5.3 Optical Fibre Performance

Though it is commonly thought that optical fibres do not have any degradation of transmission, there are three basic phenomena governing the performance of the fibres. They are:

1. Attennation losses: diminished levels of light at the optical detector due to loss of signal energy.
2. Dispersion: time of arrival differences between different wavelength components of the signal (i.e. delay distortion or dispersion).
3. Inability of conventional silica fibres to maintain polarization.

22.5.3.1 *Attenuation*

There are three sources of losses causing the attenuation of signals. They are:

(a) *Material absorption:* Small amounts of light get absorbed in an optical fibre due to the chemical composition of glass. The energy gets converted to heat. The basic mechanism which causes this is the excitation of molecular modes of vibration called resonance. Some of the other sources are the metal impurities, which have now been controlled much better, and the water vapour in the form of OH ions. Modern manufacturing techniques have been able to control this component as well.

(b) *Scattering losses:* Light propagating in a fibre can be converted into unbound and back-scattered light due to molecular level irregularities within or on the surface of the glass. This type of attenuation is called Rayleigh scattering. The energy of this scattered light is proportional to $1/\lambda^4$.

(c) *Bending losses:* Bending in a fibre can lead to increased losses.

Large scale bends having radii greater than the fibre diameter are called macrobends and are caused by pulling, sequeezing, bending of the cable during installation. Microbends are a continuous succession of very small bends due to non-uniformity at the cladding/coating interface, non-uniform lateral pressure from cabling process, microscopic variations in the location of the core-axis.

These losses can be minimized during fibre/cable manufacturing.

22.5.3.2 *Dispersion (Arrival time distortion)*

Dispersion is defined as "a spreading in time of arrival of a received signal beyond its original time spread."

Each of the components in a fibre system contributes to dispersing or spreading out the signal energy over time as it (the signal) travels. A system which has been designed according to time of arrival distortion caused by dispersion is called bandwidth or rise-time limited. The fibre itself is generally the greatest contributor to the total system dispersion.

In the present generation of optical systems where only intensity (power) is modulated and detected, phase distortions cause non-constant group velocity (= v_{gr}) resulting in arrival time distortions. Pulse spreading with time and distance causes interference with each other and wavelengths also get modulated.

In multimode fibres there are many modes (hundreds of modes) present during the signal propagation in the steady state. The dominant cause of arrival time distortion in those fibres is the modal dispersion (also called inter-modal dispersion) which is the spread in arrival times of these modes. Single-mode fibres, propagating only the fundamental mode, do not have modal dispersion, i.e. material and waveguide dispersion. When combined they are called chromatic dispersion or intramodal dispersion. These effects are also present in multimode fibres but are minor relative to the modal dispesion. The effects of chromatic dispersion on the signals are proportional to the source line-width. Modal dispersion effects are not dependent on the source line-width. The intermodal dispersion is defined as the pulse broadening per unit length of the fibre and is expressed as

$$D_{inter} = \frac{n_1(n_1 - n_2)}{n_2 c} \tag{22.22a}$$

D_{inter} has unit ps/km.

The intramodal dispersion is defined as the pulse broadening per unit length of the fibre per unit spectral width of the signal and is expressed as

$$D_{intra} = \frac{\lambda V}{2\pi c} \frac{\partial^2 \beta}{\partial V^2} \tag{22.22b}$$

where D_{intra} has unit ps/km/nm.

The pulse broadening,

$$\tau = D_{intra} \, \sigma_\lambda L \tag{22.23}$$

where

σ_λ = the spectral width of the signal
L = length of the fibre.

The maximum data rate which the fibre can support is $= \dfrac{1}{\tau}$

∴ For higher data rates, τ and the dispersion must be as small as possible.

∴ The SM fibre has much larger bandwidth ($\because D_{inter} \gg D_{intra}$).

But to make a fibre single-mode, the normalized frequency of the fibre, i.e. V must be ≤ 2.4. This numerical value is a consequence of the root of the J_0 Bessel function which comes in the mathematical expressions of the cylindrical waveguide (Ref. Chapter 18, Section 18.3.6.2).

(*Note:* Refering to Figure 22.12 the slope of the b-V curve is proportional to $\dfrac{\partial \beta}{\partial \omega}$ (since $V \propto \omega$).

Since $\dfrac{\partial \beta}{\partial \omega} = \left(\dfrac{\partial \omega}{\partial \beta}\right)^{-1} = \dfrac{1}{v_{gr}}$. Refer to Section 18.3.4, Eq. (18.100), the slope of the b-V curve is a measure of the group-delay time.)

22.6 LOW FREQUENCY (POWER FREQUENCY) APPLICATIONS

22.6.1 Introduction

The applications of the electromagnetic phenomena to the development of low frequency (i.e. mostly power frequency) devices started with the discovery of Faraday's law of electromagnetic induction, even before Maxwell had completed the unification of the laws of electromagnetism. The rotating energy converting devices (i.e. rotary electric motors and generators) and the subsequent allied generating equipment like trnasformers, switchgears, etc. are some of the earlier examples of applications of the electromagnetic phenomena in the power frequency range. These devices have been in use for quite some time now in different areas of applications and are quite familiar to most of us. But there are new and not so new areas of applications which are coming up with the developments in other fields such that what was not viable earlier, are becoming now possible and useful. We shall briefly outline some of these new areas here. The basic elements of the underlying theory have already been discussed in various chapters earlier (i.e. Chapters 6–15) and hence will be referred to at relevant places.

We will now list some of the important areas of application. Though major areas have been covered, it is not a fully comprehensive list and there may be areas which may not appear important at present, but can be important in the future due to discoveries in other allied areas:

1. Linear transportation—both high speed long distance as well as low speed short distance.
2. Linear pumping—linear flat as well as circular linear pumping.
3. Induction heating
4. Induction melting
5. Induction stirring
6. Controlling the flow of molten metal (i.e. steel in continuous casting of iron).
7. Transportation of metal sheets by levitation.
8. Sliding door openers.
9. Curtain openers
10. Magnetic gears
12. Electromagnetic launchers
    - MHD power generation
    - Superconducting motors and generators
    - Superconductivity in linear transportation
    - Electromagnetic flowmeters
    - Electromagnetic separator
    - Magnetic cranes

22.6.2 Linear Transportation

Though human mode of travel has been linear, most of the mechanical devices to aid and accelerate motion have been rotary, i.e. due to faster rotation of wheels. All mechanical devices like motor cars, trains, etc. and electrical devices like electric motors have achieved higher speeds by rotating wheels faster. The rotary motion is converted into linear motion by bringing into contact the edge of the wheel with the linear path. This process involves the use of friction between the two surfaces because if there was no adhesion between the two surfaces (i.e. the track and wheel-edge) there would be no smooth rotation and instead the wheel would slip on the track. In the case of electrically driven wheels of the electric train, the drive motor (mostly either dc or ac induction-type), the axle is rotated by the rotating shaft of the motor. The shaft rotation is produced by the motor electromagnetically.

The electric motor (or the generator) is basically a double cylindrical structure (Figure 22.13) consisting of an inner shaft-mounted cylinder and an outer cylindrical annulus mounted co-axially with the inner cylinder such that there is an air-gap between the two which is also of cylindrical

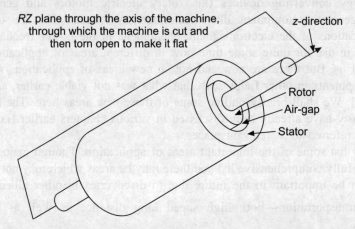

Figure 22.13   Schematic of the basic structure of a rotating machine (not to scale). Slots and windings are not shown. Also the end-structure has been omitted. The magnetic field in the air-gap is radial, the current flow in the conductors located in the slots is axial. The effective current sheet has axially flowing currents. The magnetic field in the air gap is rotating circumferentially. The air gap magnetic field and the rotor currents interact to produce a force on the rotor such that it also rotates in the same direction as the magnetic field.

annular shape. Both are magnetic in nature (i.e. made of Si-Fe sheets stacked together) and they carry windings for carrying currents, the windings being located near the annular air-gap between the two members. The inner cylinder called the rotor is the rotating member and the outer member which is stationary is called the stator. When the device is used for converting mechanical energy to electrical energy, it is called a generator and when it converts electrical energy to mechanical energy it is called the electric motor. The energy conversion takes place by the interaction of the travelling (or rotating) magnetic fields, produced by the currents (or effective current-sheets) in the two sets of windings, across the air-gap between the two members. "When the device is acting as an electrical generater, a 3-phase current is induced in the stator winding by the rotating magnetic field in the air-gap produced by the currents in the rotor winding." The direction of the magnetic field is radial and its direction of travel is circumferential. The winding on the rotor cylinder is mechanically made to rotate so that there is a relative motion between the magnetic field in the air-gap and the stator winding, whereby an emf is induced in the winding which feeds a current into any electrical load connected to the winding (ref: Section 10.7.6 of Chapter 10, Sections 11.6 to 11.16.1, Chapter 11). When the device is operating as a motor, the rotor winding is fed with a current (direct or alternating, depending on the type of motor) and this current in the winding interacts with the air-gap magnetic field produced by the stator currents whereby a force is generated on the rotor winding, which then makes the rotor to rotate in the same direction as the travelling magnetic field. This in brief is a qualitative description of the basic principle of operation of an electric generator or motor. The motor is connected with the shaft of the wheels which then rotate and the train thus runs on its iron tracks. Thus the rotational motion of the motor is converted into the linear motion of the train on its iron tracks.

However it is possible to convert the rotary motion of the electric motor to linear motion directly without using the intermediate device of wheels. This can be better explained by looking at Figures 22.14 and 22.15. Such devices which produce a linear force directly, are called linear motors, and as in the case of rotary motors, there are different types of linear motors, i.e. linear direct current motor, linear induction motor, linear synchronous motor and so on. The most commonly used types for linear transportation are the linear induction motor and the linear synchronous motor. Since, in these types of motors, both the stator and the rotor are flat and parallel (and not co-axially rotating), to get the advantage of direct generation of linear force and its utilization, it is essential that the moving object (which would be the 'train' in this case) is made to levitate* to eliminate the loss due to friction. It should be noted that absolutely no friction is required in such a device, since wheels are now not required for the linear motion. So now the vehicles have to be both propelled as well as levitated.

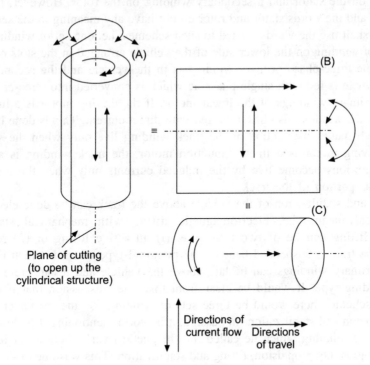

Figure 22.14   Topological manipulations to convert a cylindrical machine (A) to a flat linear machine (B), and then to a tubular linear machine (C). The direction of magnetic flux is radial in (A), normal to the plane of paper in (B), and again radial in (C).

Note: Levitate means that the object is lifted and floats in stable condition.

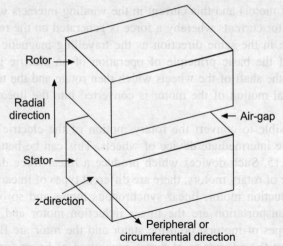

Rotor

Radial direction

Air-gap

Stator

z-direction

Peripheral or circumferential direction

Figure 22.15 Topologically opened form of the rotating machine, converting it into flat linear machine (the dimensions are not to scale). The windings and slots have not been shown. (Basis for a single-sided flat linear machine).

The propulsion is done by the linear motor which has at least two sets of windings, i.e. a primary winding on the stator and a secondary winding on the rotor. However, this arrangement is interchangable and the words stator and rotor do not have any meaning in the sense of the rotary machines, so we shall use the words related to such schemes, i.e. one set of winding on the 'track' and another set of winding on the lower side of the vehicle arranged in the slots of laminated iron sheets. Usually the three-phase primary winding is in the vehicle and the secondary winding on the track. The vehicle is fed with single-phase ac which is converted into three-phase currents and then fed to the primary windings of the linear motor. If the driving motor is a linear synhronous motor, then the track winding also has to be fed with direct current. This is done by sectionalizing the winding which makes the section of the track winding live only when the vehicle is above it. When the driving motor is a linear induction motor, the track winding is a short-circuited winding whose portions become live by the induced currents only when the moving vehicle is above a particular portion of the track.

The lifting and stabilization of the vehicle above the track can be done electromagnetically or by mechanical means, i.e. electromagnetic lifting with mechanical stabilization. The electromagnetic lifting can be of two types, i.e. (i) attractive lifting or (2) repulsive lifting. Furthermore if the train is suspended beneath the monorail type of track which is on an elevated level, then the primary windings can be laid above the vehicle and it can preferably be double-sided motor winding type. It would be clear from this brief discussion that if it is a complete electromagnetic scheme, there would be three sets of windings on the (or under the) vehicle for propulsion, supension and stabilization. In passing, it is worth mentioning that Prof. Laithwaite has suggested a type of winding which he called the 'magnetic river' where a single set of winding does all the three jobs, i.e. propulsion, lifting and stabilization. This was one of the late discoveries of Late Prof. Laithwaite, and still significant work remains to be done on this scheme before it becomes commercially viable.

At present these are linear motor driven levitated trains operating in various countries all over the world, the oldest being in the UK and then in Germany, Japan, USA, Canada, Australia and China. These are of both the types, i.e. high speed long distance as well as low speed short distance (with frequent stops). Japan has made significant progress with a high speed levitated train using superconducting coils. The latest among the levitated trains is the one in China operating between Shanghai airport to city centre. This runs on the 'maglev principle' developed in Germany using linear synchronous motor.

22.6.3 Linear Pumps

Linear pumps are the earliest application of linear motors and were used very successfully even before the linear motors were used for transportation purposes. Though the linear pumps can be either dc or ac, the first successful pumping was done by using the principle of linear induction motor. This was done in a fast breeder reactor to transport the liquid sodium-pottassium alloy at the rate of 400 gallons per minute. The pumps were flat linear induction type (FLIP) which had two stator windings on two sides of a rectangular pipe [see Figures 22.16 and 22.17(a)] which replaced the rotor (or the secondary). Each stator had three-phase windings which produced travelling magnetic fields in the direction across the width of the pipe and travelled along the axis of the pipe (for analysis, see Problem: 11.14 of *Electromagnetism: Problems with Solutions*, 2nd Edition, 2008, in which a simplified problem neglecting the end effects and the transverse edge effects has been considered). These pumps were designed and used more because of safety considerations than their efficiency. In fact the efficiency of these pumps was only 4% but with this type of design it was possible to isolate either the hydraulic or the electrical circuit separately without breaking the other circuit.

It should be noted that as with the linear motors, the linear pump has lower efficiency compared with cylindrical devices, and the end effects are most significant compared with cylindrical devices. The reason for this is that in the cylindrical devices, there are only two ends in the axial direction. But in the flat linear devices, there are not only two axial ends, but also there are two transverse edges. Also the armature reaction is higher in flat linear devices compared to that in the cylindrical machine.

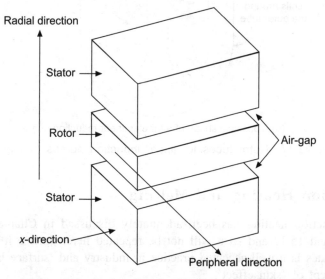

Figure 22.16 Schematic of a double-sided flat linear machine.

There was also a proposal for a tubular linear pump for larger capacity pumping of the alloy. The conceptual design of such a device can be better understood from Figure 22.14(C). A possible design of the 'rotor' of the pump is shown in Figure 22.17(b), which shows how and where the secondary coils would be located. In such a structure, both the primary and the secondary windings would be made up of circular coils which would then be arranged in a manner to produce a three-phase coil arrangement located around the outer periphery of the pump and a short-circuited secondary to be positioned in the inner annular space of the pump as shown in Figure 22.17(b). However, such a pump was not constructed ultimately.

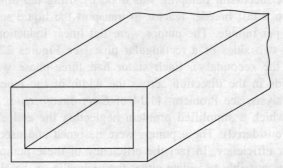

(a) Section of rectangular tube of flat linear induction pump

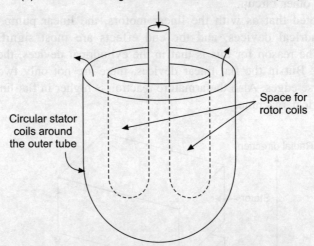

Space for
rotor coils

Circular stator
coils around
the outer tube

(b) A possible shape of a tubular linear induction pump

Figure 22.17 Rotor tubes for linear induction pumps (not to scale).

22.6.4 Induction Heating and Melting

The theory of induction heating has been adequately discussed in Chapter 15, Sections 15.2, 15.2.1, 15.3, 15.5 and 15.17 and so it will not be repeated here. Suffice it to say that induction heating of metal plates is a well-accepted practice in industry and 'surface hardening' is done by exploiting the concept of 'skin effect'.

Induction melting is merely a further extrapolation of induction heating. An arrangement for a suspended metal ball melting is shown in Figure 22.18. If this is done in vacuo or an atmosphere of inert gas, then highly purified liquid metal (without any oxidized surface coating, uncontaminated by any impurities in a crucible) can be obtained. The melted metal would also be suspended within the melting-cum-levitating coil arrangement, though the shape of the molten metal changes to some extent as shown in Figure 22.18(b). For stable suspension, a short-circuited flat coil is needed to be placed at a suitable height above the crucible arrangement.

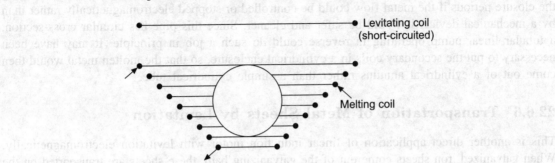

Levitating coil
(short-circuited)

Melting coil

Figure 22.18(a)   Induction melting of a spherical metal ball with levitation.

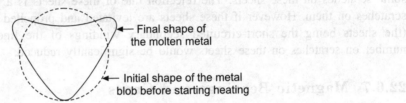

Final shape of
the molten metal

Initial shape of the metal
blob before starting heating

Figure 22.18(b)   Change of shape of the metal blob. (The crucible coil is not shown here.)

22.6.5   Induction Stirring and Valves

Induction stirring has been widely used in steel industry and induction stirrers are commercially available. There are two types of stirrers possible, i.e. single-phase and three-phase. The three-phase stirrers which produce a travelling magnetic field are preferable as the stirring is then more uniform and evenly distributed as shown in the Figure 22.19.

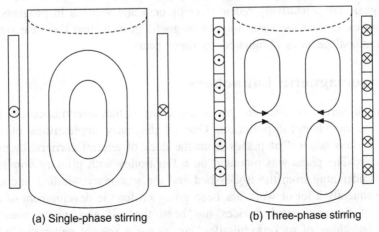

(a) Single-phase stirring   (b) Three-phase stirring

Figure 22.19   Induction stirring action in molten metal.

The use of an induction valve was suggested in the process of continuous casting of steel. When the molten alloy comes out of the bottom outlet of the tundish from where the process of continuous casting starts, it is necessary to control and stop the outflow of liquid metal at regular intervals. This is because at the tundish outlet there is ceramic pipe ot short axial length, which needs to be replaced at regular time intervals since the pipe has finite life. It was felt that during the closure periods if the metal flow could be controlled or stopped electromagnetically rather than by a mechanical device, it would be safer and cleaner. Since this pipe has circular cross-section, a tubular linear pump operating in reverse could do such a job in principle. It may have been necessary to put the secondary coils in a cylindrical enclosure, so that the molten metal would then come out of a cylindrical annulus rather than a simple cylindrical tube.

22.6.6 Transportation of Metal Sheets by Levitation

This is another direct application of linear induction motor with levitation electromagnetically. When galvanized iron sheets come out of the galvanizing bath, these sheets are transported on the rolling roller beds to the storage area. Since the sheets rub with the roller surface, there would be some scratches on these sheets. The rejection rate of these sheets is a function of the number of scratches on them. However if these sheets are levitated and propelled by linear induction motor (the sheets being the short-circuited secondary windings of the linear induction motor), the number on scratches on these sheets would be significantly reduced.

22.6.7 Magnetic Bearings and Gears

Magnetic bearings have been in use for quite some time now. Magnetic bearings come in a very wide size range, i.e. from very large ones to small ones like the suspended disc of energy meters. The bearings can be classified into two types, i.e. (a) active bearings in which balancing and positioning of the shaft is achieved by negative feedback of amplified error signals of positions of various points of the shaft and (b) passive bearings in which there is no negative feedback signal, an example being the energy meter disc.

A point to note in this matter is 'Earnshaw's theorem' according to which static equilibrium is not achievable by protential energy alone. For further information on this subject, the interested reader is recommended P.J. Geary's "Magnetic Suspension".

Magnetic gears are a relatively recent development and work is in progress on this subject in different countries. One of the attractions of magnetic gears is that the wear out of the toothed wheels in conventional gears is eliminated by these gears.

22.6.8 Electromagnetic Launchers

One of the great attractions of electromagnetic launching is that environmentally it is completely clean and there is no chemical pollution. One of the early applications of electromagnetic launchers was for short take-off of planes from the deck of aircraft carriers, though it was not a commercial success. The plane was mounted on a flat trolley with primary winding of the linear induction motor underslung from the trolley-bed and the secondary winding laid out on the take-off surface. Subsequently a lot of work has been going on for the development of electromagnetic launchers. One of the successful devices has been the rail gun which uses direct current. Electromagnetic launching of rockets, missiles, etc. requires special generators with high energy output for short durations.

22.6.9 Electromagnetic Flowmeters

A typical electromagnetic flowmeter for measuring the velocity of fluid has been discussed in Problem 6.36 of *Electromagnetism: Problems with Solutions*, 2nd Edition, 2008.

22.6.10 Electromagnetic Separator

A magnetic separator for concentrating the ore of rare earth elements was developed and successfully tested. There are different types of separators under development and in operation in a number of organizations.

22.6.11 General Comments

Other applications, mentioned in the list of Section 22.6.1, e.g. sliding door openers, curtain openers, etc. are one-off devices using small linear motors, which would use even linear dc motor or reluctance type linear motor. Another application where linear motors of small sizes have been successfully used is the 'pen drive' in X-Y plotters where the pen has to move in the X-direction as well as in the Y-direction. Magnetic cranes have been in use for quite some time now. Super-conducting motors and generators, in spite of their early promise, have not been accepted for general use as yet. Japan has successfully experimented with high speed levitated train with superconducting windings for the linear motor and levitation. It may be commercially viable in the near future.

Rotating motors and generators have been with us for quite sometime (this application uses Faraday's law of induction) and have to be analysed for eddy current effects. There are excellent textbooks for the study and analysis of rotating machines and hence this application has not been discussed in detail here. The induction devices discussed here are mostly the devices in which 'the eddy currents' are 'usefully' used and not like rotating machines where the eddy currents are unwanted side-effects.

We have given mostly introductory comments on all these applications. Most of these devices are now being analysed in great depth by using the numerical methods like, FEM, FDM, FDTD, moment method, Green's function and so on, since the availability of modern high-speed computers. Discussion of these methods as applied to these problems would be a subject of more advanced and specalized texts beyond the scope of this book. What we have mostly discussed here, are the basics of electromagnetism from the point of view of applications.

22.7 MICROSTRIP TRANSMISSION LINES AND ANTENNAE

22.7.1 Microstrip Transmission Lines

These transmission lines belong to a group known as parallel plate transmission line and are very widely used in present-day electronics, i.e. for microwave integrated circuits, and in components like filters, couplers resonators, antennae and so on. These lines are much more flexible in comparison to co-axial cables and aslo more compact.

It consists of an infinitely large conducting plane with a metal strip placed at a distance from it (Figure 22.20) separated by a dielectric substrate. It is constructed by the photographic processes used for integrated circuits. A rigorous analytical derivation of the characteristic properties of the line is rather tedious and cumbersome. Because of its open structure, the EM field leaks out of the dielectric substrate [Figure 22.20(b)]. An approximate formula for its characteristic impedance is

$$Z_0 = \frac{60}{\sqrt{\varepsilon_{\text{eff}}}} \ln\left(\frac{8h}{W} + \frac{W}{h}\right) \qquad \text{for} \quad \frac{W}{h} \le 1$$

and

$$\frac{1}{\sqrt{\varepsilon_{\text{eff}}}} \frac{120\pi}{\left(\dfrac{W}{h} + 1.393 + 0.667 \ln\left(\dfrac{W}{h} + 1.444\right)\right)} \qquad \text{for} \quad \frac{W}{h} \ge 1$$

where

$$\varepsilon_{\text{eff}} = \frac{\varepsilon_{\text{r}} + 1}{2} + \frac{\varepsilon_{\text{r}} - 1}{2\sqrt{\left\{1 + \dfrac{12h}{W}\right\}}}$$

taking account of the leakage field in air.

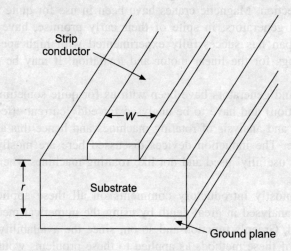

Figure 22.20(a) Microstrip transmission line.

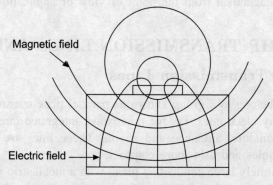

Figure 22.20(b) Pattern of electromagnetic field of a microstrip line (at any section normal to the direction of transmission).

22.7.2 Microstrip Antenna

The derivation of microstrip antenna from the transmission line came up with the aerospace applications, such as spacecraft and missiles. The basic rectangular microstrip antenna was first designed in 1972. Such a device is shown in Figure 22.21. The conducting patch shown in the figure is rectangular though it can be circular as well, or more generally it can be of any shape.

The advantages of microstrip antennae are:

(i)   Low cost fabrication
(ii)   Can conform to curved surface of a vehicle or product
(iii) Resistant to shock and vibration
(iv)   The range of gain is considerable
(v)   Antenna profile is small.

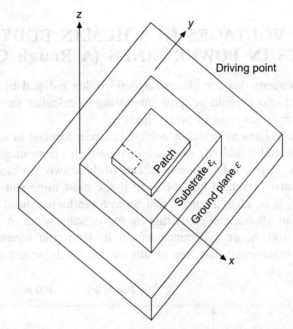

Figure 22.21   Rectangular microstrip antenna. Patch geometry is shown to be rectangular here, though it can be of any shape. The feed point is located at a point which is chosen to match the antenna with a desired impedance.

Some of the disadvantages of microstrip antennae are:
(i)   Narrow bandwidth
(ii)   Low efficiency due to large dielectric and conductor losses
(iii) Sensitive to environmental factors like temperature and humidity.

22.7.3   Printed Antenna

Due to bandwidth requirements, in some case the antenna is designed as a 'planar antenna'. Such antennae are referred to as 'printed' antennae. Figure 22.22 shows such a 'seven-/section omni-directional antenna', which is a printed antenna.

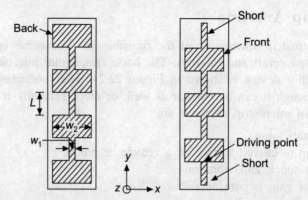

Figure 22.22 A printed antenna: seven-section omnidirectional microstrip antenna.

22.8 INDUCED VOLTAGES IN A HUMAN BODY DUE TO CURRENTS IN POWER LINES (A Rough Calculation)

There has often been concern that the electromagnetic fields radiated by power lines might be injurious to human health. So it could be quite interesting to calculate the induced voltage in the human body that result from currents in power lines.

There are two mechanisms by which a voltage can be produced in such a situation. (i) that produced by the electric field, and (ii) that induced through electromagnetic induction due to magnetic field variations. Here a calculation of effects of these two mechanisms on a human head is presented. It is, of course, assumed that the head is the most important and the most sensitive part of the human body. It is, also, assumed that an average human head can be represented by a 'sphere' with a radius of 10 cm, and consisting mostly of salty water. A power line carrying an unbalanced current of 100 A, at a distance of 20 m from the human head is considered (Figure 22.23). For any other input data, the results can be easily scaled up or down.

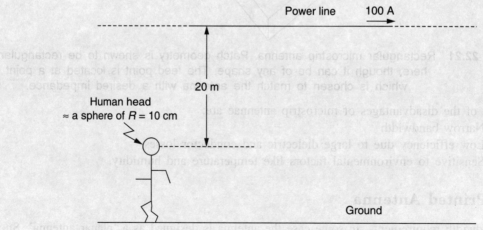

Figure 22.23 A human in the vicinity of a power line (not to scale).

The magnetic flux density 20 m from a wire with 100 A of current is

$$B = \frac{\mu_0 I}{2\pi r} \approx 1 \ \mu T \tag{22.24}$$

(An idea of how large this value is, can be easily appreciated if it is remembered that the earth's dc magnetic field is on the average 50 μT on the surface, and as person moves in this field some voltage would be induced, but human being are presumably adapted to this effect). Using Faraday's law to calculate the induced emf around the head, using the calculated value of B,

$$\oint_{\substack{\text{around}\\\text{head}}} \mathbf{E} \cdot \mathbf{d}l = -\frac{\partial}{\partial t} \iint_{\substack{\text{head}\\\text{cross-section}}} \mathbf{B} \cdot \mathbf{dS} \tag{22.25}$$

Using complex notation, the above equation results in

$$2\pi\delta_{\text{induced}} = -j\omega \ B\pi a^2 \tag{22.26}$$

where a is the radius of the head.

From here, the value of the voltage due to the induced field across a single 10 μm cell in our head is calculated to be about 29.7 {≈30} pV for a power line frequency of 50 Hz.

This is due to only one component of the effect of the power lines on the human. The other is due to the electric field, which depends on the voltage of the power line. A reasonable value for the electric field close to the power line is around kV/m. Salt water has a resistivity (= ρ_{sw}) of about 1 Ω-m; and to find the voltage across a single cell that can be added to the previously calculated induced voltage, the following reasoning can be justifiably made. The charge density {= σ} produced on the head due to the high field is evaluated and then the total charge Q is obtained by integration. The power line frequency being 50 Hz, this changing charge would produce a current I, and a corresponding current density J. This current density in the non-perfect conductor produces an ohmic voltage drop across a cell. The following equation describes the sequence of above arguments, assuming that the head is perfectly spherical.

$$\sigma(\theta) = 3\varepsilon_o E \cos \theta$$

Refer to Problem 3.1 from *Electromagnetism-Problems with Solution,* Third Edition, PHI Learning in which a problem of this type has been rigorously solve. Then

$$Q = \iint_{\text{head}} \sigma(\theta)ds = \int_0^{\pi/2} \sigma(\theta)2\pi a \cdot a d\theta = 3\pi\varepsilon_0 \ Ea^2$$

$$\therefore \qquad I = 2\pi f Q = 0.268 \ \mu A \text{ and } J = \frac{I}{\pi a^2}$$

$$\therefore \qquad V = \varepsilon \times 10 \ \mu m = \rho_{sm}J \times 10 \ \mu m = 97 \text{ pV} \tag{22.27}$$

Thus the total voltage across a cell in the human head due to a high-voltage line nearby is calculated to be about 127 pV. For comparison, the normal neural impulses are much larger: they are spikes with around 100 mV amplitudes, frequency being between 1 Hz and 100 Hz, and of duration of about a millisecond.

Appendix 18

Wave Polarization

A.18.1 INTRODUCTION

An important property of an electromagnetic wave is polarization which describes the orientation of the electric field **E**. In this regard, the IEEE standard definition for the polarization of a radiated electromagnetic wave is:

*That property of a radiated electromagnetic wave describing the time-varying direction and relative magnitude of the electric field vector; specifically, the figure traced as a function of time by the extremity of the vector at a fixed location in space, and the sense in which it is traced, as observed along the direction of propagation, i.e. polarization is the curve traced out by the end-point of the arrows representing the instantaneous electric field. The field must be observed **along** and **towards** the direction of propagation.*

Note: The same term 'polarization' is used in electromagnetic for both the purpose of the unrelated concept of contributions of atoms and molecules to the dielectric properties described in Sections 2.4 and 2.5 and for the above phenomenon. Usually the usage of this word would be clear from the context of the discussion.

For the simplicity of understanding we consider the simplest case of a uniform plane wave, transverse in nature, propagating along the z-axis of the referred co-ordinate system, travelling in the +ve z-direction. In this case, **E** and **H** vectors have to lie in a plane orthogonal to z-axis, but there is no constraint that **E** and **H** vectors have to be constant as function of space and/or time. The only requirements are that **E** and **H** should be perpendicular to each other, and the ratio of their magnitudes should be equal to η (= intrinsic impedance of the medium). Hence both the vectors can rotate in the transverse plane by the same angle and scale in the same proportion, without affecting the nature of the wave. Thus a knowledge of the **E** wave is sufficient to specify the **H** field unambiguously. Hence for complete understanding, it would be sufficient to discuss the behaviour of **E** field only (see Figure A.18.1).

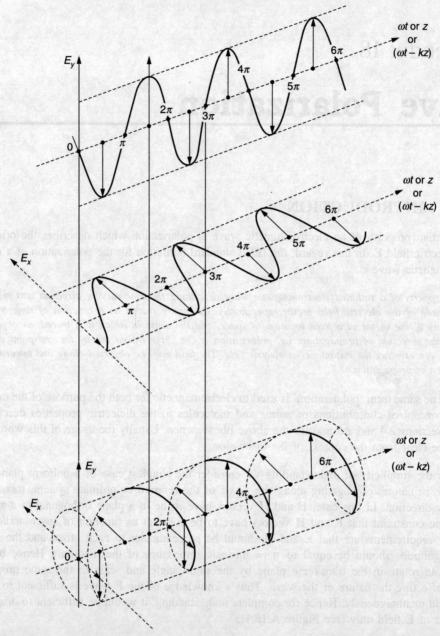

Figure A.18.1 Rotation of a plane electromagnetic wave, at a fixed space point (say z = 0) as a function of time. The figure shows the two orthogonal components (x- and y-)—of space phase displacement of $\pi/2$ and also the time phase difference of these two components. If the ωt axis is replaced by z-axis, then the above 3 diagrams would show the space rotation of the wave at a given instant of time $t = t_0$. Furthermore, if the ωt is replaced by ($\omega t = kz$), then the diagrams show the behaviour of a travelling wave propagating in z-direction, showing both time and space phase variations of the orthogonal components.

A.18.2 TYPES OF POLARIZATION

Polarization can be classified into three categories: linear, circular and elliptic. If the vector which describes the electric field at a point in space as a function of time is always directed along a straight line which is normal to the direction of propagation of the wave, then the field is said to be linearly polarized. In general, if the figure that the tip of the electric field vector traces is an ellipse, then the field is said to be elliptically polarized. Linear and circular polarizations are special causes of the elliptic polarization, and they can be obtained when the ellipse degenerates to a straight line or a circle.

The figure of the electric field (i.e. the closed loop) would be traced either in clockwise (CW) or counterclockwise (CCW) sense, looking at it along the direction of propagation as specified earlier. It is to be noted that the clockwise polarization is also known as right-handed (i.e. CW = RH) polarization and the counterclockwise polarization is known as left-handed (CCW = LH) polarization for all three-types of polarizations. It is being **reminded** that this sense of rotation (right-handed or left-handed) is obtained by viewing the progressive wave from its 'rear' in the direction of propagation. In the present example, the wave is travelling in the +ve z-direction (which has been taken as into the page), so that the rotation is being examined from an observation point looking into the page and perpendicular to it. (Figure A.18.2).

To study and analyse the different states of polarization of a wave, we consider two waves of same frequency propagating along the z-axis in the +ve z-direction and having electric fields oriented along the x- and the y-directions respectively. To maintain the generality, let the amplitudes of these two waves be unequal and an arbitrary phase difference between them. We assume the time-variations of both the waves to be of time-harmonic type and hence we can express the two-fields as

$$E_{xc} = E_1 = \text{Re}\{E_x e^{j(\omega t - \beta z)}\} = E_{xo} \cos(\omega t - \beta z + \phi_x) \qquad \text{(A.18.1a)}$$

$$E_{yc} = E_2 = \text{Re}\{E_y e^{j(\omega t - \beta z)}\} = E_{yo} \cos(\omega t - \beta z + \phi_y) \qquad \text{(A.18.1b)}$$

where ω is the angular frequency of the waves and β their propagation constant. To keep the analysis completely general, E_{xc}, E_{yc}, E_x, E_y are all complex with E_{xo}, E_{yo} being real and $\phi_y - \phi_x \neq 0$ (at this stage).

Next, in the above expression, if $\phi_y - \phi_x$ is +ve, E_y leads E_x, and if $\phi_y - \phi_x$ is –ve, E_y lags E_x. Since at present, the investigation is of the behaviour of the two fields as a function of time at any specified point in space, we can assume that point to be located at $z = 0$ (for principality of analysis) without any loss of generality. Thus the equations for the two fields become:

$$E_1 = E_x = E_{xo} \cos(\omega t + \phi_x) \qquad \text{(A18.2a)}$$

$$E_2 = E_y = E_{yo} \cos(\omega t + \phi_y) = E_{yo} \cos\{(\cot + \phi_x) + (\phi_y - \phi_x)\} \qquad \text{(A.18.2b)}$$

At any instant of time, the resultant **E** field would be the vector sum of these two instantaneous fields.

∴   At some instant of time t, the resultant field is:

$$\mathbf{E} = \mathbf{i}_x E_{xo} \cos(\omega t + \phi_x) + \mathbf{i}_y E_{yo} \cos(\omega t + \phi_y)$$

$$= \mathbf{i}_{\phi yx} \sqrt{\{E_{xo}^2 \cos^2(\omega t + \phi_x) + E_{yo}^2 \cos^2\{(\omega t + \phi_x) + (\phi_y - \phi_x)\}}$$

$$\angle \tan^{-1}\left\{\frac{E_{yo} \cos\{(\omega t + \phi_x) + (\phi_y - \phi_x)\}}{E_{xo} \cos\{\omega t + \phi_x\}}\right\} \qquad \text{(A.18.3)}$$

where $\mathbf{i}_{\phi yx}$ is the unit vector in the direction of **E** (see Fig. A.18.2).

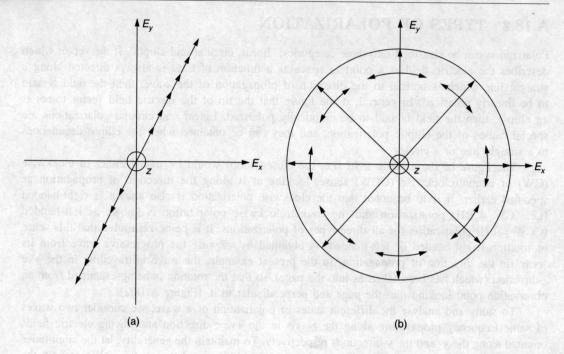

(a)

(b)

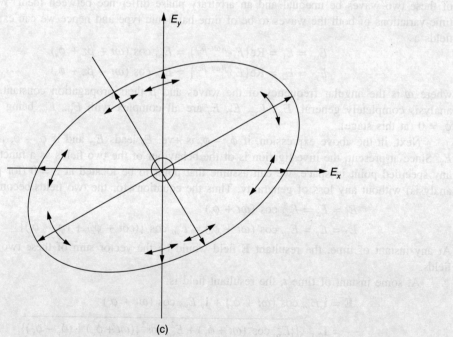

(c)

Figure A.18.2 Polarization figure traces of an electric fields vector tip as a function of time for a given space position: (a) linear, (b) circular, (c) elliptical (Possibilities of both handedness, i.e. LH as well as RH, are indicated by double-ended arrows).

It is obvious from the above equation that both the magnitude and the direction of the resultant **E**-field are functions of time and hence change with time. To obtain the locus of the tip of the **E** vector (by eliminating from these equations):

$$\cos(\omega t + \phi_x) = \frac{E_x}{E_{xo}} \quad \text{and} \quad \sin(\omega t + \phi_x) = \sqrt{\left\{1 - \frac{E_x^2}{E_{xo}^2}\right\}} \qquad \text{(A.18.4)}$$

Substituting in the expression for E_y,

$$\frac{E_y}{E_{yo}} = \cos(\omega t + \phi_y) = \cos\{(\omega t + \phi_x) + (\phi_y - \phi_x)\}$$

$$= \cos(\omega t + \phi_x) \cos(\phi_y - \phi_x) - \sin(\omega t + \phi_x) \cdot \sin(\phi_y - \phi_x)$$

$$= \frac{E_x}{E_{xo}} \cos(\phi_y - \phi_x) - \sqrt{\left\{1 - \frac{E_x^2}{E_{xo}^2}\right\}} \sin(\phi_y - \phi_x) \qquad \text{(A.18.5)}$$

Rearranging and squaring both sides,

$$\left\{\frac{E_x}{E_{xo}} \cos(\phi_y - \phi_x) - \frac{E_y}{E_{yo}}\right\}^2 = \left\{1 - \frac{E_x^2}{E_{xo}^2}\right\} \sin^{-2}(\phi_y - \phi_x)$$

Further rearranging,

$$\frac{E_x^2}{E_{xo}^2} - \frac{2E_x E_y \cos(\phi_y - \phi_x)}{E_{xo} E_{yo}} + \frac{E_y^2}{E_{yo}^2} = \sin^2(\phi_y - \phi_x) \qquad \text{(A.18.6)}$$

This is an equation of an ellipse. Hence the tip of the **E**-vector, in general, for a time-harmonic plane wave, traces an ellipse, as a function of time, once in every time-period. So this ellipse will be traced $\omega/2\pi$ times every second. Thus this wave is called an 'elliptically polarized wave'.

The equation of the ellipse and hence its orientation {i.e. its tilt to the x- or y-axis} would change with any change in E_{xo}, E_{yo} and/or $(\phi_y - \phi_x)$. Thus it is the phase of the ellipse, and not its absolute size, which is of interest in the study of the polarization of waves. The shape of the ellipse can be characterized by two sets of parameters, each set consisting of two parameters or their equivalent angles.

The first set of parameters consists of (i) the axial ratio (AR), i.e. the ratio of the major to the minor axes of the ellipse (which can also be expressed as angle ε as we shall see later) and the tilt angle (= τ), i.e. the orientation of the major axis of the ellipse with respect to the x-direction. The second set of parameters, denoted by (τ, δ) are also related to AR and the phase difference $\phi_y - \phi_x$. The inter-relationship between these two sets will be discussed while explaining the 'Poincare sphere' used for graphical representation of the state of polarization.

A.18.3 LINEAR POLARIZATION (Figure A.18.3)

The two components of the wave E_x and E_y may or may not have the same magnitude, but let their phase difference, i.e. $(\phi_y - \phi_x)$ be zero. Then Eq. (A.18.6) becomes:

$$\left\{\frac{E_x}{E_{xo}} - \frac{E_y}{E_{yo}}\right\}^2 = 0 \qquad \text{(A.18.7)}$$

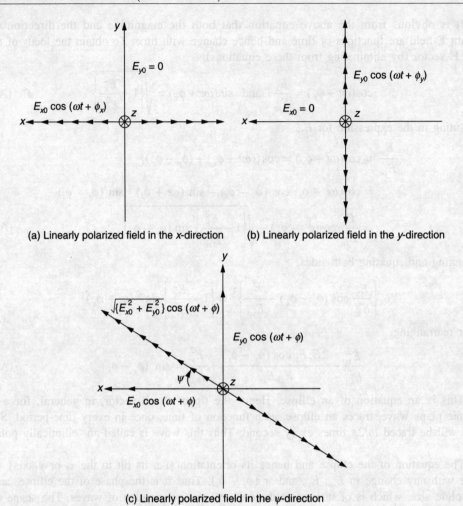

(a) Linearly polarized field in the x-direction   (b) Linearly polarized field in the y-direction

(c) Linearly polarized field in the ψ-direction

Figure A.18.3 Linearly polarized wave (the co-ordinate system is right-handed with the +ve z-direction into the plane of the paper and normal to the paper plane).

This gives

$$E_y = \left\{ \frac{E_{yo}}{E_{xo}} \right\} E_x \qquad (A.18.8)$$

This is the equation of a straight line whose slope is $\{E_{yo}/E_{xo}\}$, and so the tip of the electric field vector draws a straight line when $\phi_y - \phi_x = 0$ (i.e. $\phi_y = \phi_x = \phi$), independent of the relative amplitudes of E_x and E_y. This polarization is known as 'linear polarization', and the wave is said to be linearly polarized.

The instantaneous value of the resultant **E** vector will vary from zero to $\sqrt{\{E_{xo}^2 + E_{yo}^2\}} \cos(\omega t + \phi)$ when the two components are $E_{xo} \cos(\omega t + \phi)$ and $E_{yo} \cos(\omega t + \phi)$ in the first half-cycle and then to −ve maximum and back to zero in the next half-cycle, and this pattern along the straight line given by Eq. (A.18.8) will keep on repeating itself. The slope of this line would depend on the relative magnitudes of E_{xo} and E_{yo}.

Hence summarizing:

1. If $E_{xo} = 0$, this line becomes vertical and the wave is called 'vertically polarized wave'.
2. if $E_{yo} = 0$, the line becomes horizontal giving rise to a 'horizontally polarized wave'.
3. If $E_{xo} = E_{yo}$, the wave is said to be linearly polarized with 45° polarization angle.
4. In general, when both components E_x and E_y are at the same phase ϕ, the wave is said to be linearly polarized along a line that makes an angle ψ with the x-axis where

$$\psi = \tan^{-1}\left\{\frac{E_y}{E_x}\right\} = \tan^{-1}\left\{\frac{E_{yo}}{E_{xo}}\right\} \tag{A.18.9}$$

Hence, a time-harmonic field is linearly polarized at a given point in space if the electric field (or the magnetic field) vector at that point is always oriented along the same straight line at all instants of time.

This happens if the field vector possesses:

(a) only one component
(b) two orthogonal linearly polarized components which are in time-phase or 180° out of phase.

A.18.4   CIRCULAR POLARIZATION (Figure A.18.4)

A wave is said to be circularly polarized if the tip of the electric field vector traces out a circular locus in space. The electric field intensity of such a wave has the same amplitude (i.e. constant magnitude) at all instants of time, and also its (i.e. the vector's) orientation in space changes continually as a function of time, so as to describe a circular locus. Hence by studying the locus of the instantaneous electric field vector (= **E**) at the $z = 0$ plane at all times, we have

$$E_{xo} = E_{yo} = E_o \ (\sigma = E_R)$$

and

$$\phi_y - \phi_x = -\frac{\pi}{2} \tag{A.18.10}$$

This phase difference can be achieved either by taking (a) $\phi_x = 0$, $\phi_y = -\pi/2$ or (b) $\phi_y = 0$, $\phi_x = +\pi/2$, which in words means

(a) E_x is the reference vector and E_y lags E_x by 90° or $\pi/2$
(b) E_y is the reference vector and E_x leads E_y by 90° or $\pi/2$

In should be noted that these are only two different ways of expressing the same fact. Thus, mathematically,

(a) $\phi_x = 0$, $\phi_y = -\pi/2$ gives

$$\left. \begin{array}{l} E_x = E_R \cos \omega t \\ E_y = E_R \cos (\omega t - \pi/2) = E_R \sin \omega t \end{array} \right\} \tag{A.18.11}$$

The locus of the **E** field vector is given by

$$E = \sqrt{\{E_x^2 + E_y^2\}} = \sqrt{\{E_R^2(\cos^2 \omega t + \sin^2 \omega t)\}} = E_R \tag{A.18.12}$$

and it is directed along a line which makes an angle ψ with the x-axis such that

$$\psi = \tan^{-1}\left\{\frac{E_y}{E_x}\right\} = \tan^{-1}\left\{\frac{E_R \sin \omega t}{E_R \cos \omega t}\right\} = \tan^{-1}(\tan \omega t) = \omega t \tag{A.18.13}$$

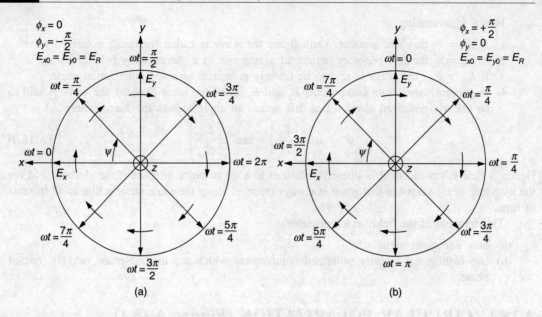

Right hand circularly polarized wave

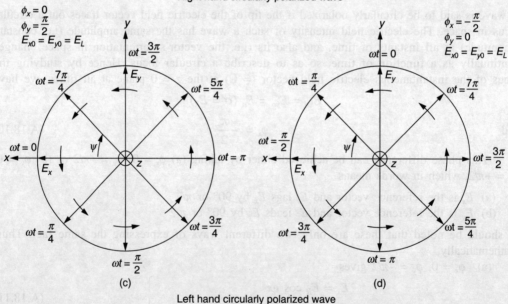

Left hand circularly polarized wave

Figure A.18.4 RH and LH circularly-polarized waves. (The co-ordinate system used is right-handed with the +ve z-direction into the plane of the paper and is normal to the paper plane).

If now, the locus of the **E** vector on the plane $z = 0$ is plotted as a function of time, then this locus is a circle of radius E_R $(= E_o)$ and it rotates in the clockwise sense as shown in Figure A.18.4(a). Thus the wave is said to have right-hand circular polarization.

It should be further noted that the instant $t = 0$ (i.e. $\omega t = 0$, the starting instant) is along the x-axis when $E = E_x$, and the sense of rotation is from the phase-leading component E_x to the phase-lagging component E_y which in this case is in the clockwise (CW or RH) direction.

(b) $\phi_x = +\pi/2$, $\phi_y = 0$ gives

$$\left.\begin{array}{l} E_x = E_{xo} \cos (\omega t + \pi/2) = -E_R \sin \omega t \\ E_y = E_R \cos \omega t \end{array}\right\} \tag{A.18.14}$$

and the locus of the amplitude of the **E** vector is given by

$$E = \sqrt{\{E_x^2 + E_y^2\}} = \sqrt{E_R^2 \{\cos^2 \cot + (-)^2 \sin^2 \omega t\}} = E_R \tag{A.18.15}$$

The angle ψ along which this E field is directed is given by (ψ being the angle that E makes with x-axis or E_x line),

$$\psi = \tan^{-1}\left\{\frac{E_y}{E_x}\right\} = \tan^{-1}\left\{\frac{E_R \cos \omega t}{-E_r \sin \omega t}\right\} = \tan^{-1}(-\cot \omega t) = \omega t + \frac{\pi}{2} \tag{A.18.16}$$

Thus, in this case also, the locus of **E** is a circle of radius E_R, E vector rotating in the clock-wise sense with an angular velocity ω as shown in Figure A.18.4(b), so that the polarization is right-handed circular. Now, the instant $t = 0$ is along the y-axis and the sense of rotation is from the phase-leading component E_x to phase-lagging component E_y.

Summarizing these two cases, it can be said that 'a right-handed circular polarization' can be obtained if and only it the two orthogonal linearly polarized components have equal magnitudes (or amplitudes) and a relative phase-difference of $\pi/2$ between the two. The sense of rotation {CW or RH here) is determined by rotating the phase-leading component towards the phase-lagging component. The observer is looking at the wave in the direction of its propagation as the wave travels away from the observer.

Next we consider the case of left-hand {or counterclockwise, i.e. LH or CCW} circular polarization. In this case, again

$$\left.\begin{array}{l} E_{xo} = E_{yo} = E_o \text{ (or } = E_L) \\ \phi_y - \phi_x = +\pi/2 \end{array}\right\} \tag{A.18.17}$$

and

It should be noted that for circular polarization, $E_R = E_L = E_{xo} = E_{yo}$ which is not the case in the general elliptic polarization.

As in the case of RH circular polarization, in the present type under discussion, the above-mentioned phase difference can be achieved either by taking (c) $\phi_x = 0$, $\phi_y = +\pi/2$ or by (d) $\phi_x = -\pi/2$, $\phi_y = 0$, which in words would mean:

(c) E_x is the reference vector and E_y leads E_x by $\pi/2$

(d) E_y is the reference vector and E_x lags E_y by $\pi/2$

Again, these are two different ways of stating the same fact, and mathematically, we get

(c) $\phi_x = 0$, $\phi_y = +\pi/2$, giving (on the plane $z = 0$)

$$\left.\begin{array}{l} E_x = E_L \cos \omega t \\ E_y = E_L \cos (\omega t + \pi/2) = -E_L \sin \omega t \end{array}\right\} \tag{A.18.18}$$

and the locus of the amplitude of E comes out to be

$$E = \sqrt{(E_x^2 + E_y^2)} = \sqrt{E_L^2 \{\cos^2 \omega t + (-)^2 \sin^2 \cot\}} = E_L \tag{A.18.19}$$

and the direction of E makes an angle ψ with the +ve x-axis, which is

$$\psi = \tan^{-1}\left\{\frac{E_y}{E_x}\right\} = \tan^{-1}\left\{\frac{-E_L \sin \cot}{E_L \cos \cot}\right\} = -\omega t \qquad \text{(A.18.20)}$$

Thus the locus of the **E** vector is a circle of radius E_L, rotating counter-clockwise with an angular velocity ω as shown in Figure A.18.4(c), and hence the wave has a left-hand circular polarization. The instant $t = 0$ (or $\omega t = 0$) is along the x-axis {or E_x axis}, and now E_y leads E_x by 90° (or $\pi/2$).

Next considering

(d) $\phi_x = -\pi/2$, $\phi_y = 0$ gives

$$\left.\begin{array}{c} E_x = E_L \cos (\omega t - \pi/2) = E_L \sin \omega t \\[2mm] E_y = E_L \cos \cot \end{array}\right\} \qquad \text{(A.18.21)}$$

$\therefore$ the locus of the amplitude of E is

$$E = \sqrt{\{E_x^2 + E_y^2\}} = \sqrt{E_L^2\{\sin^2 \omega t + \cos^2 \omega t\}} = E_L \qquad \text{(A.18.22)}$$

and ψ the angle defining the position of E relative to E_x is

$$\psi = \tan^{-1}\left\{\frac{E_y}{E_x}\right\} = \tan^{-1}\left\{\frac{E_L \cos \omega t}{E_L \sin \omega t}\right\} = \tan^{-1}(\cot \omega t) = \frac{\pi}{2} - \omega t \qquad \text{(A.18.23)}$$

Hence the locus of the **E** vector is a circle of radius E_L, rotating counter-clockwise with angular velocity ω as shown in Figure A.18.4(d), and thus the wave again has a left-hand circular polarization. The instant $t = 0$ is along the y-(or E_y) axis with E_x lagging E_y by 90°.

So summarizing for left-hand circular polarization, it can be said that this type can be achieved if and only if the two orthogonal components of the wave have equal amplitudes, and there is a relative phase difference of 90° between the two components. The direction of rotation (CCW or LH) is fixed by rotating the phase leading component (E in the present situation) toward the phase lagging component ($= E_x$). The observer is as usual looking at the wave as it travels away from him.

Combining the two types of circular polarization, the necessary and sufficient conditions can be stated as

1. The field must have two linearly polarized orthogonal components.
2. The two components must have equal magnitude.
3. The two components must have a relative phase difference of odd multiple of $\pi/2$.

The sense of rotation is always determined by rotating the phase-leading component toward the phase-lagging component, as the wave travels away from the observer. The rotation of the phase-leading component towards the phase-lagging component should be done through that angular separation (between the two components) which is less than π. Phases in the range $0 \le \phi \le 180°$ are leading and those in the range $180 \le \phi \le 360°$ are to be taken as lagging.

A.18.5   ELLIPTICAL POLARIZATION (Figure A.18.5)

A wave, whose **E** vector tip traces an elliptical locus in space, is said to be elliptically polarized. The electric field vector, being a function of time, changes continuously with time so as to describe

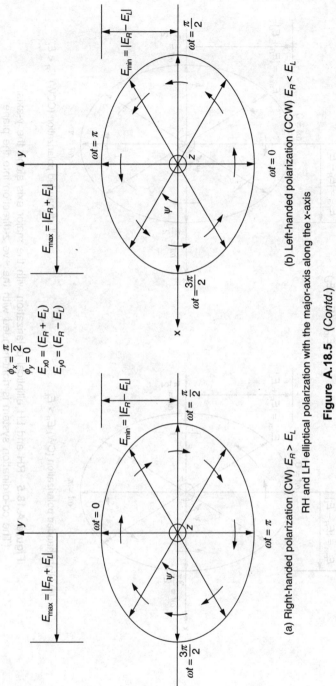

$$\phi_x = \frac{\pi}{2}$$
$$\phi_y = 0$$
$$E_{xo} = (E_R + E_L)$$
$$E_{yo} = (E_R - E_L)$$

(a) Right-handed polarization (CW) $E_R > E_L$

(b) Left-handed polarization (CCW) $E_R < E_L$

RH and LH elliptical polarization with the major-axis along the x-axis

Figure A.18.5 (*Contd.*)

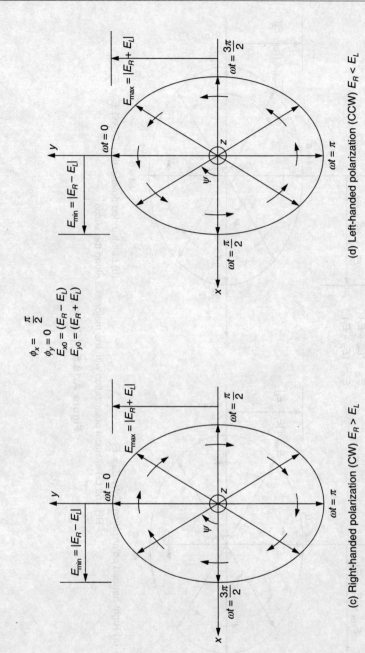

$\phi_x = \dfrac{\pi}{2}$
$\phi_y = 0$
$E_{x0} = (E_R - E_L)$
$E_{y0} = (E_R + E_L)$

(c) Right-handed polarization (CW) $E_R > E_L$

(d) Left-handed polarization (CCW) $E_R < E_L$

Figure A.18.5 RH and LH elliptical polarization with the major axis along the y-axis. (The co-ordination system is right-handed with the +ve z-direction into the plane of the paper and normal to the paper plane).

as ellipse as its locus. If this ellipse is described by clockwise rotation of the **E** vector, then it is said to be right-hand elliptically polarized, and if the sense of rotation is counter-clockwise, then the field is said to be left-hand elliptically polarized.

Hence starting with the **E** vector a harmonic transverse plane wave progressing in the +ve z direction, its equation in general terms is

$$\mathbf{E} = \mathbf{i}_x\, E_{xo} \cos\{\omega t - \beta z + \phi_x\} + \mathbf{i}_y\, E_{yo} \cos\{\omega t - \beta z + \phi_y\} = \mathbf{i}_x\, E_x + \mathbf{i}_y\, E_y$$

To study the locus of the instantaneous electric field vector **E** in the plane $z = 0$ at all times, let the fields have the following values:

$$\left.\begin{array}{l} \phi_x = \pi/2,\ \phi_y = 0;\ \text{and} \\[4pt] E_{xo} = E_R + E_L\ \text{and}\ E_{yo} = E_R - E_L,\ \text{where}\ E_R \neq E_L \end{array}\right\} \tag{A.18.24}$$

Then

$$\left.\begin{array}{l} E_x = (E_R + E_L) \cos\left(\omega t + \dfrac{\pi}{2}\right) = -(E_R + E_L) \sin \omega t \\[10pt] \end{array}\right.$$

and

$$\left.\begin{array}{l} E_y = (E_R - E_L) \cos \omega t \end{array}\right\} \tag{A.18.25}$$

Then the locus for the amplitude of the E vector is

$$E^2 = E_x^2 + E_y^2 = (E_R + E_L)^2 \sin^2 \omega t + (E_R - E_L)^2 \cos^2 \omega t$$

$$= (E_R^2 + E_L^2)(\sin^2 \omega t + \cos^2 \omega t) + 2E_R E_L (\sin^2 \omega t - \cos^2 \omega t)$$

$$\therefore \qquad E_x^2 + E_y^2 = E_R^2 + E_L^2 + 2E_R E_L (\sin^2 \omega t - \cos^2 \omega t) \tag{A.18.26}$$

But

$$\sin \omega t = \frac{-E_x}{E_R + E_L} \quad \text{and} \quad \cos \omega t = \frac{E_y}{E_R - E_L}$$

Substituting these values in Eq. (A.18.26) and rearranging,

$$E_x^2 \left\{1 - \frac{2E_R E_L}{(E_R + E_L)^2}\right\} + E_y^2 \left\{1 + \frac{2E_R E_L}{(E_R - E_L)^2}\right\} = E_R^2 + E_L^2$$

or

$$\left\{\frac{E_x}{E_R + E_L}\right\}^2 + \left\{\frac{E_y}{E_R - E_L}\right\}^2 = 1 \tag{A.18.27}$$

which is the equation for an ellipse with major axis as $E_{\max} = |E_R + E_L|$ and the minor axis as $E_{\min} = |E_R - E_L|$. The **E** vector rotates and since its length varies with time {Eqs. (A.18.25) and (A.18.26)}, it traces out an ellipse as shown in Figure A.18.5(a and b). The maximum and the minimum lengths of the vector are the major and the minor axes of the ellipse, given by

$$\left.\begin{array}{l} |E|_{\max} = |E_R + E_L|\ \text{when}\ \omega t = (2n + 1)\pi/2,\ n = 0, 1, 2, \dots \\[6pt] |E|_{\min} = |E_R - E_L|\ \text{when}\ \omega t = 2n\pi/2 = n\pi,\ n = 0, 1, 2, \dots \end{array}\right\} \tag{A.18.28}$$

and

The axial ratio {= AR} defined as the ratio of the major axis (with its sign) to the minor axis of polarization ellipse is

$$\text{AR} = -\frac{E_{\max}}{E_{\min}} = -\frac{E_R + E_L}{E_R - E_L} \tag{A.18.29}$$

where E_R and E_L are +ve real quantities. As per the above definition of AR, it can take +ve (for LH polarization) or –ve (for RH polarization) values over its range $1 \leq |\text{AR}| \leq \infty$. The instantaneous **E** vector can be written as

$$\mathbf{E} = \mathbf{i}_x(E_R + E_L) \cos (\omega t - \beta z + \pi/2) + \mathbf{i}_y(E_R - E_L) \cos (\omega t - \beta z)$$

$$= \text{Re}[\{\mathbf{i}_x j(E_R + E_L) + \mathbf{i}_y(E_R - E_L)\} e^{j(\omega t - \beta z)}]$$

$$= \text{Re}[\{E_R(j\mathbf{i}_x + \mathbf{i}_y) + E_L(j\mathbf{i}_x - \mathbf{i}_y)\} \ e^{j(\omega t - \beta z)}] \tag{A.18.30}$$

From this Eq. (A.18.30), we can deduce that an elliptically polarized wave can be considered as the sum of two circularly polarized waves, a right-handed one of amplitude E_R and left-handed one of amplitude E_L. If $E_R > E_L$, the AR will be –ve, and the amplitude of the RH circular component will be larger than that of the LH circular component, and so the resultant **E** vector would rotate in the RH manner producing a RH elliptically polarized wave as shown in Figure A.18.5(a). On the other hand, if $E_L > E_R$, then the LH circularly polarized component will predominate causing the resultant **E** vector to rotate in the same direction as the LH circularly polarized wave, and the situation is as shown in Figure A.18.5(b). Hence, the important point to be noted is that it is the sign of the axial ratio (AR) which determines the sense (or direction) of rotation of the **E** vector

Next, we change the **E** field parameters {as defined in Eq. (A.18.24)} to following and study the effects.

$$\left. \begin{array}{l} \phi_x = \pi/2, \ \phi_y = 0; \text{ and} \\[2mm] E_{xo} = E_R - E_L \text{ and } E_{yo} = E_R + E_L \text{ where } E_R \neq E_L \end{array} \right\} \tag{A.18.31}$$

Then

$$\left. \begin{array}{l} E_x = \{E_R - E_L\} \cos (\omega t + \pi/2) = -\{E_R - E_L\} \sin \omega t \\[2mm] E_y = \{E_R + E_L\} \cos \omega t \end{array} \right\} \tag{A.18.32}$$

and

In this case, the locus for the amplitude of the **E** vector becomes

$$E^2 = E_x^2 + E_y^2 = E_R^2 + E_L^2 + 2E_R E_L \{-\sin^2 \omega t + \cos^2 \omega t\} \tag{A.18.33}$$

whilst

$$\sin \omega t = \frac{-E_x}{E_R - E_L} \quad \text{and} \quad \cos \omega t = \frac{E_y}{E_R + E_L}$$

Hence the final equation comes out to be

$$\left\{ \frac{E_x}{E_R - E_L} \right\}^2 + \left\{ \frac{E_y}{E_R + E_L} \right\}^2 = 1 \tag{A.18.34}$$

which is again the equation for an ellipse whose major axis is $E_{\max} = |E_R + E_L|$ and the minor axis as $E_{\min} = |E_R - E_L|$. But now the major axis lies along the y-axis {E_y axis} and the minor axis along the x-axis, whereas in the previous two cases with the major axes were along the x-axis and the minor axes along the y-axis. Again

$$|E_{\max}| = |E_R + E_L| \text{ when } \omega t = 2n\pi/2 = n\pi, \ n = 0, 1, 2, \ldots \tag{A.18.35}$$

and

$$|E_{\min}| = |E_R - E_L| \text{ when } \omega t = (2n + 1)\pi/2, \ n = 0, 1, 2, \ldots \tag{A.18.36}$$

The polarization locii are shown in [Figure A.18.5(c) and (d)], for $E_R > E_L$ and $E_R < E_L$ respectively.

The equqtions (A.18.35) and (A.18.36) show that **E** measured along the major axis of the polarization ellipse is $\pi/2$ out of phase with the component of **E** measured along the minor axis. Also Eq. (A.18.33) can be used to show that the **E** vector rotates through 90° in **space phase** between the instants of time given by the Eqs. (A.18.35) and (A.18.36). Thus the major and the minor axes of the polarization ellipse are also orthogonal in **space** (as in time as well).

The linear polarization is a special degenerate case of the elliptic polarization and it can be represented as the sum of a right-hand (RH) and a left-hand (LH) circularly polarized waves (which is again a degenerate case of the elliptical polarization obtained by making $E_{xo} = E_{yo} = E_R$ or $E_{xo} = E_{yo} = E_L$), of equal amplitudes (which then means $E_R = E_L$). This condition, i.e. $E_R = E_L$ degenerates the elliptic polarization into linear polarization.

A completely generalized orientation of an elliptically polarized locus is that of the '**tilted ellipse**' as shown in Figure A.18.6. In this case,

$$\delta\phi = \phi_x - \phi_y \neq \frac{n\pi}{2}, \; n = 0, 1, 2, \ldots$$

$$\left.\begin{array}{l} \geq 0 \quad \text{for CW if } E_R > E_L \\ \qquad \text{for CCW if } E_R < E_L \end{array}\right\} \tag{A.18.37}$$

$$\left.\begin{array}{l} \leq 0 \quad \text{for CW if } E_R < E_L \\ \qquad \text{for CCW if } E_R > E_L \end{array}\right\} \tag{A.18.38}$$

and

$$\left.\begin{array}{l} E_{xo} = E_R \pm E_L \\ E_{yo} = E_R \mp E_L \end{array}\right\} \tag{A.18.39}$$

It should be noted that the major and the minor axes of the polarization ellipse are not coincident with the x- and y-axes (or E_x and E_y axes) of the co-ordinate system. They would coincide only if the phase difference between the two orthogonal components is equal to odd multiples of $\pm \pi/2$.

So now, we derive the locus of the tip of the **E** vector for this general case, i.e.

$$E_x = E_{xo} \cos (\omega t - \beta z + \phi_x)$$

and

$$\begin{aligned} E_y &= E_{yo} \cos (\omega t - \beta z + \phi_y) \\ &= E_{yo} \cos (\omega t - \beta z + \phi_x + \phi_y - \phi_x) \\ &= E_{yo} \cos (\omega t - \beta z + \phi_x + \delta) \end{aligned} \tag{A.18.40}$$

where

$$\delta = \phi_y - \phi_x \; (= -\delta\phi)$$

For the locus (of the tip of the **E** vector), the plane considered is $z = 0$. Hence the equations become:

$$\left.\begin{array}{l} E_x = E_{xo} \cos (\omega t + \phi_x) = (E_R \pm E_L) \cos (\omega t + \phi_x) \\ E_y = E_{yo} \cos (\omega t + \phi_x + \delta) = (E_R \mp E_L) \cos \omega t + \phi_x + \delta) \end{array}\right\} \tag{A.18.41}$$

$$\therefore \qquad \cos (\omega t + \phi_x) = \frac{E_x}{E_{xo}} = \frac{E_x}{E_R \pm E_L} \tag{A.18.42}$$

and

$$\frac{E_y}{E_{yo}} = \frac{E_y}{E_R \mp E_L} = \cos (\omega t + \phi_x + \delta) = \cos (\omega t + \phi_x) \cos \delta - \sin (\omega t + \phi_x) \sin \delta$$

$$= \frac{E_x}{E_{xo}} \cos \delta - \sin(\omega t + \phi_x) \sin \delta$$

$$\therefore \qquad \sin (\omega t + \phi_x) = \frac{E_x}{E_{xo}} \cot \delta - \frac{E_y}{E_{yo}} \operatorname{cosec} \delta = \frac{E_x}{E_R \pm E_L} \cot \delta - \frac{E_y}{E_R \mp E_L} \operatorname{cosec} \delta \tag{A.18.43}$$

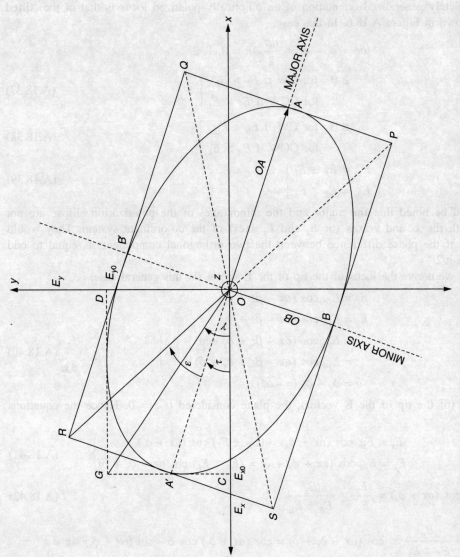

Figure A.18.6 Tilted ellipse of the 'elliptic polarization' (generalized situation) due to rotation of a plane electromagnetic wave at the point z = 0 looking along and in the direction of propagation (i.e. +ve z direction) of the wave, as a function of time.

Notes

1. The co-ordinate system is right-handed with the +ve z-direction being into the plane of the paper and intersecting this plane normally.
2. Characterization parametric angles are indicated with respect to the ellipse.

∴   The locus of the **E** vector tip is (obtained by eliminating t):

$$\cos^2 (\omega t + \phi_x) + \sin^2 (\omega t + \phi_x) = 1$$

or

$$\frac{E_x^2}{E_{xo}^2} + \left\{ \frac{E_x}{E_{xo}} \cot \delta - \frac{E_y}{E_{yo}} \csc \delta \right\}^2 = 1$$

or

$$\frac{E_x^2}{E_{xo}^2} + \frac{E_x^2}{E_{xo}^2} \cot^2 \delta - \frac{2E_x E_y}{E_{xo} E_{yo}} \cot \delta \csc \delta + \frac{E_y^2}{E_{yo}^2} \csc^2 \delta = 1$$

or

$$\frac{E_x^2}{E_{xo}^2} - \frac{2E_x E_y}{E_{xo} E_{yo}} \cos \delta + \frac{E_y^2}{E_{yo}^2} = \sin^2 \delta \qquad \text{(A.18.44a)}$$

which is same as the Eq. (A.18.34).

This can be rewritten as

$$\left\{ \frac{E_x}{E_{xo}} - \frac{E_y \cos \delta}{E_{yo}} \right\}^2 + \frac{E_y^2 \sin^2 \delta}{E_{yo}^2} = \sin^2 \delta \qquad \text{(A.18.44b)}$$

or

$$\left\{ \frac{E_x}{E_{xo} \sin \delta} - \frac{E_y}{E_{yo} \tan \delta} \right\}^2 + \frac{E_y^2}{E_{yo}^2} = 1 \qquad \text{(A.18.45a)}$$

or writing in terms of E_R and E_L, we obtain

$$\left[\frac{E_x}{(E_R \pm E_L) \sin \delta} - \frac{E_y}{(E_R \mp E_L) \tan \delta} \right]^2 + \frac{E_y^2}{(E_R \mp E_L)^2} = 1 \qquad \text{(A.18.45b)}$$

This tilted ellipse is shown in Figure A.18.6, with all the specifying angles marked on it, i.e.

$$\gamma = \tan^{-1} \left(\frac{E_{yo}}{E_{xo}} \right), \quad 0° \le \gamma \le \frac{\pi}{2} \qquad \text{(A.18.46)}$$

δ = the phase difference between E_y and E_x (which cannot be shown in figure) ...

$$-\pi \le \delta \le \pi \qquad \text{(A.18.47)}$$

$$\left. \begin{array}{l} \varepsilon = \cot^{-1}(\text{AR}), \qquad\qquad -\dfrac{\pi}{4} \le \varepsilon \le \dfrac{\pi}{4} \\[2mm] \text{AR} = \pm \dfrac{\text{Major axis}}{\text{Minor axis}} = \pm \dfrac{\text{OA}}{\text{OB}}, \qquad 1 \le |\text{AR}| \le \infty \end{array} \right\} \qquad \text{(A.18.48)}$$

and τ = tilt angle of the ellipse, relative to the x-axis, $0 \le \tau \le \pi$ and its magnitude is given by

$$\left. \begin{array}{l} \tau = \dfrac{\pi}{2} - \dfrac{1}{2} \tan^{-1} \left\{ \dfrac{2E_{xo} E_{yo}}{E_{xo}^2 - E_{yo}^2} \cos \delta \right\} \\[4mm] \quad = \dfrac{\pi}{2} - \dfrac{1}{2} \tan^{-1} \left\{ \dfrac{2(E_R \pm E_L)(E_R \mp E_L)}{(E_R \pm E_L)^2 - (E_R \mp E_L)^2} \cos \delta \right\} \end{array} \right\} \qquad \text{(A.18.49)}$$

and

$$\text{OA} = \left[\frac{1}{2} \left\{ E_{xo}^2 + E_{yo}^2 + (E_{xo}^4 + E_{yo}^4 + 2E_{xo}^2 E_{yo}^2 \cos 2\delta)^{1/2} \right\} \right]^{1/2} \qquad \text{(A.18.50a)}$$

$$\text{OB} = \left[\frac{1}{2} \left\{ E_{xo}^2 + E_{yo}^2 - (E_{xo}^4 + E_{yo}^4 + 2E_{xo}^2 E_{yo}^2 \cos 2\delta)^{1/2} \right\} \right]^{1/2} \qquad \text{(A.18.50b)}$$

The +ve sign in Eq. (A.18.48) is for left-hand and the –ve sign is for right-hand polarization respectively.

When $\delta = \dfrac{n\pi}{2}$, the major axis of the polarization ellipse coincides with the either of the co-ordinate axes, depending on the value of n.

A.18.6 POINCARÉ SPHERE: A GRAPHICAL REPRESENTATION OF POLARIZATION STATES

From the discussions so far, it is obvious that the state of polarization of a wave is defined by the shape, the orientation and the sense of rotation of the polarization ellipse. Using these parameters, the state of polarization can be defined unambiguously as follows:

(i) the shape of the ellipse which is defined by its axial ratio (AR), i.e. the ratio of the major axis to the minor axis of the ellipse which can also be expressed as an angle, i.e.

$$\varepsilon = \cot^{-1} (\pm \text{ AR}) \tag{A.18.51}$$

(ii) the orientation of the ellipse is measured by the tilt angle $(= \tau)$ which is the angle made by the major axis of the ellipse with the +ve x-axis of the co-ordinate system.

(iii) the sense of rotation of the polarization ellipse can be defined by adopting a definite convention for signs and adding to the axial ratio (= AR) which by definition is a +ve quantity. Thus the used convention is that the +ve AR represents left-handed rotation (= LH) and –ve AR is representing the right-handed rotation (= RH), always looking from behind the wave which is progressing in the +ve z-direction.

This complete definition of the state of polarization is now obtained by the two geometrical parameters, i.e. $\pm$ AR and τ (or ε and τ) of the polarization ellipse. Such a representation can also be obtained in terms of the electrical quantities, i.e. the ratio E_{yo}/E_{xo} and the corresponding phase difference between the two component waves which is $\delta = \phi_y - \phi_x$. This is possible because there is a one-to-one correspondence between the geometrical (i.e ellipse) parameters (ε and τ) and the electrical parameters [$= E_{yo}/E_{xo} = \tan \gamma$ or $\tau = \tan^{-1}(E_{yo}/E_{xo})$ and $\delta = \phi_y - \phi_x$]. This implies that knowing the amplitudes and phases of the two electric fields E_x and E_y, it should be possible to obtain the polarization ellipse generated by these two component waves, or vice versa starting from the complete knowledge of the polarization ellipse, we should be able to find the two **E** waves which generate the specified ellipse.

The correspondence between these two representations of the polarization and a compact graphical representation of this state was first given by the Franch scientist Poincare'. It can be shown that all the states of polarization can be contained on the surface of a sphere which is called '**Poincaré sphere**'. For this purpose we now define the limits of these four parametric angles ε, τ, and γ, δ, where

$$\varepsilon = \cot^{-1} (\pm \text{ AR}) \text{ and } \gamma = \tan^{-1} \{E_{yo}/E_{xo}) \tag{A.18.52}$$

Since AR can vary from 1 to ∞ (where 1 is for a circle and ∞ for a straight line), the range of ε would be from $-\pi/4$ to $+ \pi/4$. The tilt angle τ of the ellipse would lie between the range 0 to π.

For the electrical parameters, the range of γ from 0 to π would permit E_{xo} and E_{yo} to be both +ve and –ve as required, and the phase difference δ would vary between $-\pi/2$ to $+\pi/2$.

Next we consider a sphere (or even a spherical shell) similar to a globe with the circles of latitudes and longitudes marked on it. If now a point P on the surface of this sphere has the latitude $= 2\varepsilon$ and longitude $= 2\tau$, then this spherical surface would cover **all** the states of polarization uniquely.

On the equator of the sphere, for all such points $\varepsilon = 0°$, i.e. AR $\to \infty$, and hence the state of polarization is linear. The point where the $0°$ longitude crosses the equator (i.e. the point of intersection of x-axis with the equator), $\tau = 0$ and thus the linear polarization is horizontal. As the longitudinal angle increases, the polarization angle also increases. At $180°$ longitude, the tilt angle $\tau = 90°$ and hence the linear polarization becomes vertical.

At the two poles of the sphere (i.e. the north pole and the south pole), the angle defining the AR $= \varepsilon\{= \cot^{-1} (\pm \text{ AR})\}$ has the values $\pm 45°$ (or $\pm \pi/4$) so that AR $= \pm 1$ respectively. With the sign convention already defined earlier, thus the north pole represents left-handed circular polarization and the south pole represents the right-handed circular polarization. It follows from these points discussed so far, the remaining points on the sphere (which exclude the two poles and the equator) would represent elliptical polarization in general. Since the AR is +ve in the northern hemisphere, all the points in this region would represent left-handed polarization; and since AR is −ve in the southern hemisphere, the points here would represent right-handed polarization.

All the polarization states, their locations and the characterization angles are shown pictorially on the Poincare' sphere in the Figures A.18.7 and A.18.8 (the angles have been explained in the Figure A.18.8a). The geometrical relationships between the two sets of angles can be derived by using spherical trigonometry, which gives us

$$\left. \begin{array}{l} \cos(2\gamma) = \cos(2\varepsilon)\cos(2\tau) \\ \tan(\delta) = \dfrac{\tan(2\varepsilon)}{\sin(2\tau)} \end{array} \right\} \tag{A.18.53}$$

or

$$\left. \begin{array}{l} \sin(2\varepsilon) = \sin(2\gamma)\sin(\delta) \\ \tan(2\tau) = \tan(2\gamma)\cos(\delta) \end{array} \right\} \tag{A.18.54}$$

Thus the Poincare' sphere is a very elegant and compact way of representing the states of polarization. The practical use of such a representation is that it enables us to find out the closeness between any two polarization states, which is a measure of the interaction between the two states—an important aspect of a communication system. When two states of polarization are the same, there is full interaction between them, and they are called the 'matched states' of polarization. On the other hand when the two states are completely non-interacting, then they are called the 'orthogonal states' of polarization.

As every antenna system has a state of polarization, its response would be maximum for a particular state of polarization. When an e.m. wave with some different state of polarization is incident on an antenna system, the power transfer efficiency from the wave to the antenna would depend on the closeness of their states of polarization. This efficiency ($= \eta_{\text{pol}}$) increases with the increasing closeness of the polarization states. If the two states are orthogonal (i.e. completely non-interacting), then there is no power transfer between the wave and the antenna (i.e. they are transparent to each other).

On the other hand, when the signal transmission capacity of a communication channel has to be doubled, we use two orthogonal states of polarization because there is no power transfer between any two orthogonal states.

The power transfer efficiency between any two states is given by

$$\eta_{\text{pol}} = \cos^2\left\{ \frac{\angle MOM'}{2} \right\} \tag{A.18.55}$$

where $\angle MOM'$ = angle subtended by the are MM' on the Poincare' sphere, at its centre O (Figure A.18.7(a)). When M and M' are same, $\angle MOM' = 0$ and the efficiency = 1. When

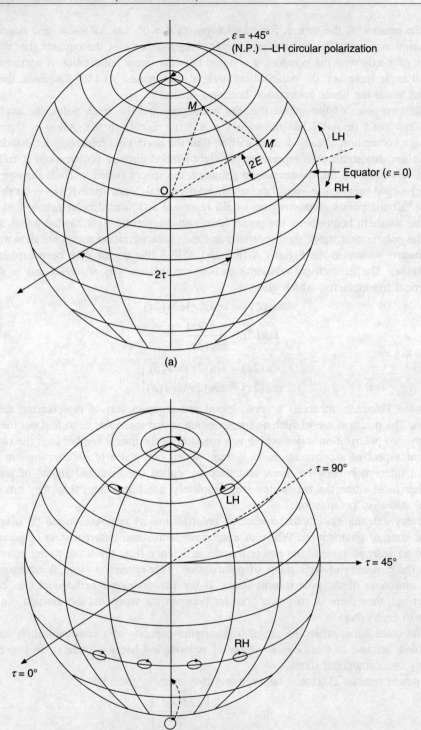

Figure A.18.7 Poincare' sphere (a) characterization angles, (b) polarization.

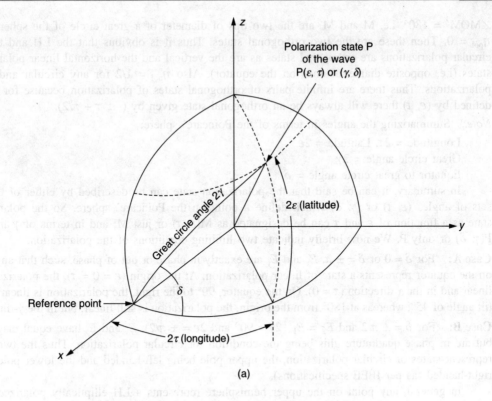

(a)

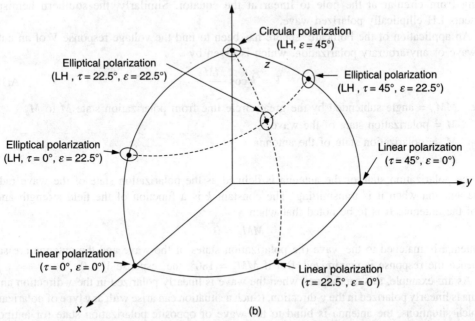

(b)

Figure A.18.8 Octant of the Poincare' sphere (for values of the co-ordinate axes) for the polarization state of an electromagnetic wave: (a) Poincare' sphere, (b) polarization states.

$\angle MOM' = 180°$, i.e. M and M' are the two tips of diameter of a great circle of the sphere, then $\eta_{pol} = 0$. Then these are the two orthogonal states. Thus it is obvious that the LH and the RH circular polarizations are orthogonal states as are the vertical and the horizontal linear polarization states (i.e. opposite diametral ends on the equator). Also $\eta_{pol} = 1/2$ for any circular and linear polarizations. Thus there are infinite pairs of orthogonal states of polarization because for a state defined by (ε, τ) there will always be an orthogonal state given by $(-\varepsilon, \tau + \pi/2)$.

Note: Summarizing the angles in terms of the Poincare' sphere:

Longitude $= 2\tau$, Latitude $= 2\varepsilon$

Great circle angle $= 2\gamma$

Equator to great circle angle $= \delta$

In summary, it can be said that the polarization state can be described by either of the two sets of angles (ε, τ) or (γ, δ) which define a point on the Poincare' sphere. So the polarization state as a function of ε and τ can be designated as $M(\varepsilon, \tau)$ or just M; and in terms of γ and δ as $P(\gamma, \delta)$ or only P. We now briefly indicate two limiting conditions of the polarization.

Case A: For $\delta = 0$ or $\delta = \pm \pi$, E_x and E_y are exactly in phase or out of phase, such that any point on the equator represents a state of linear polarization. At the origin $(\varepsilon = 0 = \tau)$, the polarization is linear and in the x-direction $(\tau = 0)$. On the equator, 90° to the right, the polarization is linear with a tilt angle of 45°, whereas at 180° from the origin, the polarization is still linear, but in the y-direction.

Case B: For $\delta = \pm \pi/2$ and $E_2 = E_1$ {$2\gamma = 90°$ and $2\varepsilon = \pm \pi/2$), E_x and E_y have equal magnitude but are in phase quadrature, this being the condition for circular polarization. Thus the two poles represent states of circular polarization, the upper pole being left-handed and the lower pole being right-handed (as per IEEE specifications).

In general, any point on the upper hemisphere represents a LH elliptically polarized wave starting from circular at the pole to linear at the equator. Similarly, the southern hemisphere represents LH elliptically polarized wave.

An application of the Poincare' sphere has been to find the voltage response V of an antenna to a wave of any arbitrary polarization, which is given by

$$V = k \cos \frac{MM_a}{2} \qquad\qquad (A.18.56)$$

where MM_a = angle subtended by the great circle line from polarization state M to M_a.

M = polarization state of the wave

M_a = polarization state of the antenna

k = constant

Here the polarization state of the antenna is defined as the polarization state of the wave radiated by the antenna when it is transmitting. The constant k is a function of the field strength and the size of the antenna. It is to be noted that when

$$MM_a = 0$$

the antenna is matched to the wave (i.e polarization states of the wave and the antenna are same), and hence the response is maximized. But if $MM_a = 180°$, the response $V = 0$.

As an example, this can happen when the wave is linearly polarized in the x-direction and the antenna is linearly polarized in the y-direction. (Such a situation can arise with any type of polarization). For such situations, the antenna is blind to the wave of opposite polarization state (or antipodal).

Note: Thus it is obvious that the 'state of polarization' is defined by a point on the Poincare' sphere. (*Note:* Some authors use the notation P instead of M to specify the state).

A.18.7 COROLLARY: DERIVATION OF THE EQUATIONS (A.18.49) AND (A.18.50)

(a) TILT ANGLE τ IN TERMS OF THE AMPLITUDES OF THE COMPONENT **E** FIELDS AND THE RELATIVE PHASE DIFFERENCE δ.

The general equations for the instantaneous values of the two components of the **E** field have been

$$\left.\begin{array}{l} E_x = E_{xo} \cos(\omega t - \beta z + \phi_x) \\ E_y = E_{yo} \cos(\omega t - \beta z + \phi_y) \end{array}\right\} \tag{A.18.57}$$

so that on the plane $z = 0$, these components are:

$$\left.\begin{array}{l} E_x = E_{xo} \cos(\omega t + \phi_x) \\ E_y = E_{yo} \cos(\omega t + \phi_y) \\ \quad = E_{yo} \cos(\omega t + \phi_x + \delta) \end{array}\right\} \tag{A.18.58}$$

where the phase difference between the two components is $\delta = \phi_y - \phi_x$, from which the locus of the tip of the **E** vector has been obtained as {Eqs. (A.18.44a) and (A.18.45c)}.

$$\frac{E_x^2}{E_{xo}^2} - \frac{2E_x E_y}{E_{xo} E_{yo}} \cos\delta + \frac{E_y^2}{E_{yo}^2} = \sin^2\delta \tag{A.18.59}$$

which is the equation to an ellipse whose major and minor axes are tilted from the co-ordinate directions as shown in Figure A.14.6, on which various angles of relevance, dimensions of the major and the minor axes of the ellipse, E_{xo}, E_{yo}, etc. have all been marked. These angles have also been shown on the spherical surface of the Poincare' sphere in Figure A.18.8(a). Now,

τ = tilt angle of the ellipse, is the angle that the major axis of the ellipse (AOA') makes with the x-axis of the co-ordinate system (i.e. the direction of E_x or E_{xo}).

Also, $\dfrac{E_{yo}}{E_{xo}} = \tan\gamma$, and the axial ratio of the ellipse is

$$= \frac{\text{Major axis}}{\text{Minor axis}} = \frac{\text{OA}}{\text{OB}} = \cot\varepsilon \tag{A.18.60}$$

Hence to evaluate the tilt angle τ in terms of the amplitudes E_{xo}, E_{yo} and the phase difference angle δ, we use the relations from the spherical trigonometry (the basis of which is given by the relationships shown on the Poincare' sphere),

$$\tan 2\tau = (\tan 2\gamma)(\cos\delta)$$

$$= \left(\frac{2\tan\gamma}{1 - \tan^2\gamma}\right)\cos\delta$$

$$= \frac{2\left(\dfrac{E_{yo}}{E_{xo}}\right)}{1 - \left(\dfrac{E_{yo}}{E_{xo}}\right)^2} \cdot \cos\delta = \frac{2E_{xo}E_{yo}\cos\delta}{E_{xo}^2 - E_{yo}^2}$$

$$\therefore \qquad \tau = \frac{1}{2}\tan^{-1}\left(\frac{2E_{xo}E_{yo}}{E_{xo}^2 - E_{yo}^2}\cos\delta\right) \qquad\qquad \text{(A.18.61)}$$

But since $\dfrac{OA}{OB}$ is in the −ve quadrant, making the sign correction, we have

$$\tau = \frac{\pi}{2} - \frac{1}{2}\tan^{-1}\left\{\frac{2E_{xo}E_{yo}}{E_{xo}^2 - E_{yo}^2}\cos\delta\right\} \qquad\qquad \text{(A.18.62)}$$

(b) LENGTHS OF THE SEMI-MAJOR AND THE SEMI-MINOR AXES OF THE POLARIZATION ELLIPSE

The spherical trigonometrical relationship to be used is

$$\sin 2\varepsilon = \{\sin 2\gamma\}\sin\delta$$

Now, $\tan\gamma = \dfrac{E_{yo}}{E_{xo}}$, and hence $\sin\gamma = \dfrac{E_{yo}}{\sqrt{\{E_{xo}^2 + E_{yo}^2\}}}$ and $\cos\gamma = \dfrac{E_{xo}}{\sqrt{\{E_{xo}^2 + E_{yo}^2\}}}$

$$\therefore \qquad \sin 2\varepsilon = \frac{2E_{xo}E_{yo}}{E_{xo}^2 + E_{yo}^2}\sin\delta \qquad\qquad \text{(A.18.63)}$$

$$\therefore \qquad \cos 2\varepsilon = \frac{\sqrt{[(E_{xo}^2 + E_{yo}^2)^2 - 4E_{xo}^2 E_{yo}^2 \sin^2\delta]}}{E_{xo}^2 + E_{yo}^2}$$

$$= \frac{\sqrt{[E_{xo}^4 + E_{yo}^4 + 2E_{xo}^2 E_{yo}^2 \cos 2\delta]}}{E_{xo}^2 + E_{yo}^2} \qquad\qquad \text{(A.18.64)}$$

$$\therefore \qquad \tan 2\varepsilon = \left\{\frac{2\tan\varepsilon}{1 - \tan^2\varepsilon}\right\} = \frac{2E_{xo}E_{yo}\sin\delta}{\sqrt{\{E_{xo}^4 + E_{yo}^4 + 2E_{xo}^2 E_{yo}^2 \cos 2\delta]}} \qquad\qquad \text{(A.18.65)}$$

or $\quad \{2E_{xo}E_{yo}\sin\delta\}\tan^2\varepsilon + \left[2\sqrt{\{E_{xo}^4 + E_{yo}^4 + 2E_{xo}^2 E_{yo}^2 \cos 2\delta\}}\right]\tan\varepsilon - 2E_{xo}E_{yo}\sin\delta = 0$

$$\therefore \qquad \tan\varepsilon = \frac{-\sqrt{\{E_{xo}^4 E_{yo}^4 + 2E_{xo}^2 E_{yo}^2 \cos 2\delta\}} \pm \sqrt{\{E_{xo}^4 + E_{yo}^4 + 2E_{xo}^2 E_{yo}^2 \cos 2\delta + 4E_{xo}^2 E_{yo}^2 \sin^2\delta\}}}{2E_{xo}E_{yo}\sin\delta}$$

$$= \frac{-\sqrt{\{E_{xo}^4 + E_{yo}^4 + 2E_{xo}^2 E_{yo}^2 \cos 2\delta\}} \pm \sqrt{\{E_{xo}^4 + E_{yo}^4 + 2E_{xo}^2 E_{yo}^2\}}}{2E_{xo}E_{yo}\sin\delta}$$

$$= \frac{[E_{xo}^2 + E_{yo}^2 \pm \sqrt{\{E_{xo}^4 + E_{yo}^4 + 2E_{xo}^2 E_{yo}^2 \cos 2\delta\}}]}{2E_{xo}E_{yo}\sin\delta} \qquad\qquad \text{(A.18.66)}$$

Next consider the (denominator)^2, i.e.

$$4E_{xo}^2 E_{yo}^2 \sin^2 \delta = 4E_{xo}^2 E_{yo}^2 \left\{\frac{1 - \cos 2\delta}{2}\right\} = 2E_{xo}^2 E_{yo}^2 \{1 - \cos 2\delta\}$$

$$= \{E_{xo}^4 + E_{yo}^4 + 2E_{xo}^2 E_{yo}^2\} - \{E_{xo}^4 + E_{yo}^4 + 2E_{xo}^2 E_{yo}^2 \cos 2\delta\}$$

$$= \{E_{xo}^2 + E_{yo}^2\}^2 - [\sqrt{\{E_{xo}^4 + E_{yo}^4 + 2E_{xo}^2 E_{yo}^2 \cos 2\delta\}}]^2$$

$$= [E_{xo}^2 + E_{yo}^2 + \sqrt{\{E_{xo}^4 + E_{yo}^4 + 2E_{xo}^2 E_{yo}^2 \cos 2\delta\}}] [E_{xo}^2 + E_{yo}^2 - \sqrt{\{E_{xo}^4 + E_{yo}^4 + 2E_{xo}^2 E_{yo}^2 \cos 2\delta\}}]$$

$\therefore \qquad \tan \varepsilon = \dfrac{1}{\text{AR}} = \dfrac{\text{Minor axis}}{\text{Major axis}}$

$$= \frac{\sqrt{[E_{xo}^2 + E_{yo}^2 - \sqrt{(E_{xo}^4 + E_{yo}^4 + 2E_{xo}^2 E_{yo}^2 \cos 2\delta)}]}}{\sqrt{[E_{xo}^2 + E_{yo}^2 + \sqrt{(E_{xo}^4 + E_{yo}^4 + 2E_{xo}^2 E_{yo}^2 \cos 2\delta)}]}} = \frac{\text{OB}}{\text{OA}}$$

$\therefore \qquad \qquad AB^2 = OA^2 + OB^2 = 2(E_{xo}^2 + E_{yo}^2)$

But AB^2 should be equal to $= E_{xo}^2 + E_{yo}^2$ (Figure A.18.6) $\hfill$ (A.18.67)

$\therefore$ In the above ratio, both the numerator and the denominator should be multiplied by $\dfrac{1}{\sqrt{2}}$ so

that OA and OB are as given in the Eqs. (A.18.50).

A.18.8   WAVE POLARIZATION AND POYNTING VECTOR

In complex notation, the Poynting vector is:

$$\mathbf{S} = \frac{1}{2}\mathbf{E} \times \mathbf{H}^*$$

The average Poynting vector is the real part of the above expression, i.e.

$$\mathbf{S}_{av} = \text{Re}\,\mathbf{S} = \frac{1}{2}\text{Re}[\mathbf{E} \times \mathbf{H}^*)$$

Considering the general elliptically polarized wave, the x- and the y- components of the wave can be expressed as

$$E_x = E_1 \exp\{j(\omega t - \beta z)\} \qquad \qquad \text{(A.18.68a)}$$

$$E_y = E_2 \exp\{j(\omega t - \beta z + \delta)\} \qquad \qquad \text{A.18.68b)}$$

where $\delta = \delta_y - \delta_x$ and taking E_x as the reference vector, i.e. $\delta_x = 0$.

On the plane $z = 0$, the $\mathbf{E}$ vector can be expressed as

$$\mathbf{E} = \mathbf{i}_x E_x + \mathbf{i}_y E_y = \mathbf{i}_x E_1 \exp\{j\omega t\} + \mathbf{i}_y E_2 \exp\{j(\omega t + \delta)\} \qquad \text{(A.18.69)}$$

Thus $\mathbf{E}$ has two components, each with a space vector and a time-phase factor.

The $\mathbf{H}$ field component associated with E_x is

$$H_y = H_1 \exp\{j(\omega t - \beta z - \zeta)\} \qquad \qquad \text{(A.18.70a)}$$

where ζ is the phase lag of H_y w.r.t. E_x.

The **H** field component associated with F_y is:

$$H_x = -H_2 \exp \{j(\omega t - \beta z + \delta - \zeta)\} \qquad \text{(A.18.70b)}$$

The total **H** field vector on the plane $z = 0$, for a wave travelling in the $+z$ direction is

$$\mathbf{H} = \mathbf{i}_y H_y - \mathbf{i}_x H_x = \mathbf{i}_y H_1 \exp \{j(\omega t - \zeta)\} - \mathbf{i}_x H_2 \exp \{j(\omega t + \delta - \zeta)\} \qquad \text{(A.18.71)}$$

Its complex conjugate is

$$\mathbf{H}^* = \mathbf{i}_y H_1 \exp\{-j(\omega t - \zeta)\} - \mathbf{i}_x H_z \exp\{-j(\omega t + \delta - \zeta)\} \qquad \text{(A.18.72)}$$

Hence, the average Poynting vector on the plane $z = 0$ is

$$\mathbf{S}_{av} = \frac{1}{2} \text{Re} \left[(\mathbf{i}_x \times \mathbf{i}_y) E_x H_y^* - (\mathbf{i}_y \times \mathbf{i}_x) E_y H_x^* \right]$$

$$= \frac{1}{2} \mathbf{i}_z \, \text{Re} \, \{E_x H_y^* + E_y H_x^*\}$$

Hence, the average power of the wave per unit area is

$$\mathbf{S}_{av} = \frac{1}{2} \mathbf{i}_z [E_1 H_1 \exp (j\zeta) + E_2 H_2 \exp (j\zeta)]$$

$$= \frac{1}{2} \mathbf{i}_z \{E_1 H_1 + E_2 H_2\} \cos \zeta \; \frac{\text{W}}{\text{m}^2} \qquad \text{(A.18.73)}$$

It should be noted that $\mathbf{S}_{av}$ is independent of $\delta (= \delta_y - \delta_x)$.

In a loss-less medium,

$\zeta = 0$ — the electric and the magnetic fields are in time-phase

and $\dfrac{E_1}{H_1} = \dfrac{E_2}{H_2} = Z_0$ = intrinsic impedance of the medium

$$\therefore \qquad \mathbf{S}_{av} = \frac{1}{2} \mathbf{i}_z \{E_1 H_1 + E_2 H_2\}$$

$$= \frac{1}{2} \mathbf{i}_z \{H_1^2 + H_2^2\} Z_0 = \frac{1}{2} \mathbf{i}_z H^2 Z_0 \; \text{W/m}^2$$

$$= \frac{1}{2} \mathbf{i}_z \frac{\{E_1^2 + E_2^2\}}{Z_0} = \frac{1}{2} \mathbf{i}_z \frac{E^2}{Z_0} \; \text{W/m}^2 \qquad \text{(A.18.74)}$$

where $H = \sqrt{\{H_1^2 + H_2^2\}}$ = amplitude of the total **H** field

and $E = \sqrt{\{E_1^2 + E_2^2\}}$ = amplitude of the total **E** field.

A.18.9 PARTIAL POLARIZATION AND THE STOKES PARAMETERS

So far the discussions have been about **completely** polarized wave, i.e. for waves for which E_1, E_2 and δ are constants (or very slowly varying functions of time). Such situations exist with a single frequency (or monochromatic) radio transmitters. But radiations from many celestial radio sources extend over a wide frequency range, and within any band width Δf consisting of the superposition of a large number of statistically independent waves of different polarizations. The resultant wave is then said to be **incoherent** or **unpolarized** (the polarized wave being coherent). Such a wave can be expressed as

$$E_x = E_1(t) \sin \omega t \tag{A.18.75a}$$

$$E_y = E_2(t) \sin (\omega t + \delta(t)) \tag{A.18.75b}$$

where all the time functions are independent. However, the time variations of the function, i.e. $E_1(t)$, $E_2(t)$ and $\delta(t)$, are much slower compared with the mean frequency f, where $f = 2\pi/\omega$, and their bandwidth is of the order of Δf. It is possible to generate a wave of this type by connecting a noise generator to a linearly polarized antenna which is polarized in the y-direction and a second noise generator connected to another linearly polarized antenna which is polarized in the x-direction. If, now at an observers point, the waves from both antennae have the some average power, then the observer would notice a **completely unpolarized** wave.

A partially polarized wave, which is the most general situation, can be considered to be made up of two parts, i.e. one completely polarized and the other completely, unpolarized.

This phenomenon can be dealt most conveniently by using the 'Stokes parameters' which were introduced by Sir George Stokes in 1852. The four stokes parameters I, Q, U, V are defined below:

$$I = S = S_x + S_y = \frac{\langle E_1^2 \rangle}{Z} + \frac{\langle E_2^2 \rangle}{Z} \tag{A.18.76a}$$

$$Q = S_x - S_y = \frac{\langle E_1^2 \rangle}{Z} - \frac{\langle E_2^2 \rangle}{Z} \tag{A.18.76b}$$

$$U = \frac{2}{Z} \langle E_1 E_2 \cos \delta \rangle = S \langle \cos 2\varepsilon \sin 2\tau \rangle \tag{A.18.76c}$$

$$V = \frac{2}{Z} \langle E_1 E_2 \sin \delta \rangle = S \langle \sin 2\varepsilon \rangle \tag{A.18.76d}$$

where

S = total Poynting vector magnitude for the wave

S_x = Poynting vector component of the wave polarized in the x-direction

S_y = Poynting vector component of the wave polarized in the y-direction

E_1 = amplitude of the electric field component of the wave polarized in the x-direction

E_2 = amplitude of the electric field component of the wave polarized in the y-direction

Z = intrinsic impedance of the medium under consideration

The angles δ, γ are same as defined earlier in the sections dealing with 'Wave Polarization' and 'Poincare' sphere', and restated as:

δ = relative phase difference between E_x and E_y or E_1 and $E_2 \{= \delta_y - \delta_x\}$, and is also the 'equator to the great circle angle'

$2y$ = great circle angle

where the angles are measured on the "Poincare' sphere from R reference point on the equator (at the x-axis) and the great circle on the sphere through the reference point and the point under consideration (i.e. observer's point).

τ = tilt angle of the polarization ellipse

$\varepsilon = \cot^{-1} (\pm AR)$ and hence is half the latitude angle between the equator and the latitude through the point under consideration (Figures A.18.7 and A.18.8}.

The time averaging has been indicated by angled brackets (It should be noted that earlier the time-averaged quantities have been represented by a straight bar on the top, but now as long expressions are involved, this is a more convenient notation to use for such expressions}, i.e.

$$\langle E_1^2 \rangle = \frac{1}{T} \int_0^T [E_1(t)]^2 \, dt \tag{A.18.77}$$

For a **completely unpolarized wave**, $S_x = S_y$ and E_1 and E_2 are uncorrelated. Under such conditions, it can be shown that

$$\langle E_1 E_2 \cos \delta \rangle = \langle E_1 E_2 \sin \delta \rangle = 0$$

and hence $I = S$, $Q = 0$, $U = 0$, $V = 0$, where S is the total Poynting vector of the wave. Thus for a completely unpolarized wave, the required condition is $Q = U = V = 0$.

Next, for **completely polarized wave**, E_1, E_2, δ, ε and τ could be considered as constants so that the Stokes parameters would not require time-averages and hence $\langle E_1^2 \rangle = E_1^2$ and so on.

Hence, for a **linearly (completely) polarized wave** with **E** in the x-direction {$E_2 = 0$, $\tau = \varepsilon = 0$}, the Stokes parameters are:

$$I = S, \ Q = S, \ U = 0, \ V = 0 \tag{A.18.78}$$

Similarly, for a **linearly (completely) polarized wave** with **E** in the y-direction {$E_1 = 0$, $\tau = 90°$, $\varepsilon = 0$}, the Stokes parameters are:

$$I = S, \ Q = -S, \ U = 0, \ V = 0 \tag{A.18.79}$$

Next, for a **LH circularly (completely) polarized wave** ($E_1 = E_2$, $\delta = 90°$), the Stokes parameters become

$$I = S, \ Q = 0, \ U = 0, \ V = S \tag{A.18.80}$$

And similarly for a **RH circularly (completely) polarized wave** {$E_1 = E_2$, $\delta = 270°$}, the Stokes parameters are

$$I = S, \ Q = 0, \ U = 0, \ V = -S \tag{A.18.81}$$

By considering other polarization states, the physical interpretation of the Stokes parameters can be deduced as

I = total power (density) of the wave (= S)

Q = the power in the linearly polarized components (in either x or y-directions)

U = the power in the linearly polarized components at the tilt angles of 45° or 135°

V = the power in the circularly polarized component (LH or RH)

The handling of the Stokes parameters becomes more convenient if they are normalized by using S as the base value. The normalized stokes parameters are denoted by s_0, s_1, s_2, s_3 where

$$s_o = \frac{I}{S} = 1, \ s_1 = \frac{Q}{S}, \ s_2 = \frac{U}{S}, \ s_3 = \frac{V}{S} \tag{A.18.82}$$

{Results tabulated in Table A.18.1}

Table A.18.1   Normalized Stokes Parameters for Some Polarization States

Normalized Stokes parameters	Completely unpolarized wave	Completely polarized waves					
		Linearly polarized				Circularly polarized	
		$\tau = 0$	$\tau = 90°$	$\tau = 45°$	$\tau = 135°$	LH	RH
s_0	1	1	1	1	1	1	1
s_1	0	1	-1	0	0	0	0
s_2	0	0	0	1	-1	0	0
s_3	0	0	0	0	0	1	-1

If any of the parameters, i.e. Q, U or V (or s_1, s_2, s_3) has a non-zero value, it indicates the presence of a polarized component in the wave. The degree of polarization $\{= d\}$ is defined as

$$d = \frac{\text{Completely polarized power}}{\text{Total power}}, 0 \le d \le 1$$

or

$$d = \frac{\sqrt{Q^2 + U^2 + V^2}}{I} = \frac{\sqrt{s_1^2 + s_2^2 + s_3^2}}{I} \qquad (A.18.83)$$

Hence a completely polarized wave is one for which $Q^2 + U^2 + V^2 = I^2$ or $s_1^2 + s_2^2 + s_3^2 = 1$. Thus a partially polarized wave can be considered as the sum of a completely unpolarized wave and a completely polarized wave. This can be expressed in a compact matrix form as

$$\begin{bmatrix} s_0 \\ s_1 \\ s_2 \\ s_3 \end{bmatrix} = \underbrace{\begin{bmatrix} 1-d \\ 0 \\ 0 \\ 0 \end{bmatrix}}_{\text{Unpolarized part}} + \underbrace{\begin{bmatrix} d \\ d\cos 2\varepsilon \cos 2\tau \\ d\cos 2\varepsilon \sin 2\tau \\ d\sin 2\varepsilon \end{bmatrix}}_{\text{Polarized part}} \qquad (A.18.84)$$

Now, let a wave with Stokes parameters s_0, s_1, s_2, s_3 be incident on an antenna whose Stokes parameters are s_{a0}, s_{a1}, s_{a2}, s_{a3}. It is to be noted that would be the parameters for the antenna when it is in the transmitting mode, and when the incident wave is hitting the antenna, it is in the receiving mode. Therefore, the power available from the antenna to a receiver, produced by the above incident wave is

$$P = \frac{1}{2} A_e S \begin{bmatrix} s_{ao} & s_{a1} & s_{a2} & s_{a3} \end{bmatrix} \begin{bmatrix} s_o \\ s_1 \\ s_2 \\ s_3 \end{bmatrix}$$

$$= \frac{1}{2} A_e S \{s_{a0} s_0 + s_{a1} s_1 + s_{a2} s_2 + s a_3 s_3\} \text{ W} \qquad (A.18.85)$$

where A_e = effective aperture of the antenna

S = Poynting vector of the incident wave in W/m^2

This value can also be expressed as

$$P = \frac{1}{2} A_e S \{1 + d \cos MM_a\}$$

$$= \frac{1}{2} A_e S (1 - d) + S A_e (d) \cos^2 \frac{MM_a}{2} \qquad (A.18.86)$$

where MM_a = the angle subtended by the great-circle line between the wave and the antenna polarization states on the Poincare' sphere.

∴ In the above

$$SA_e \cos^2 \frac{MM_a}{2} = \text{Polarized power available} = \text{Incident polarized power}$$

$$\frac{1}{2} A_e S (1 - d) = \text{Unpolarized power available} = \frac{1}{2} \times \text{Incident unpolarized power}$$

Rearranging the equation,

$$P = \left\{ \frac{1 - d}{2} + d \cos^2 \frac{MM_a}{2} \right\} A_e S = F A_e S \qquad (A.18.87)$$

where F = wave-antenna coupling factor, and is a function of the (i) degree of polarization and (ii) the angle MM_a.

F = Fraction of the power $A_e S$ which is received. It is dimensionless and $0 < F < 1$

Its range as a function of $d\{= \text{the degree of polarization}\}$ is shown in Figure A.18.9.

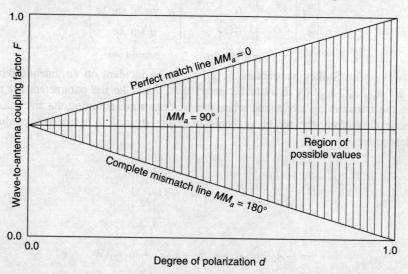

Figure A.18.9 Power received as a function of the degree of polarization.

∴ For perfect match $\{MM^a = 0°\}$, F varies from 1/2 to 1 as d increases from 0 to 1; and for a complete mismatch $\{MM_a = 180°\}$, F varies from 1/2 to 0 as d changes from 0 to 1. Between these two bounds $\{MM^a = 0° \text{ and } MM_a = 180°\}$, there exists the region of partial mismatch between the antenna and the wave, e.g. $MM_a = 90°$.

Equation (A.18.87) signifies the response P of the system, given by the product of maximum available power $\{=A_eS\}$ multiplied by the factor F—characteristic of the receiving antenna. Thus this relationship $\{=FA_eS\}$ is an indication that any measuring system can be optimized for a specific system. This can be better illustrated by defining some new parameters both for the incident wave as well as the receiving antenna as follows:

$$\left. \begin{array}{ll} s_{11} = \dfrac{(s_0 + s_1)}{2}, & s_{12} = \dfrac{(s_2 + js_3)}{2} \\[3mm] s_{21} = \dfrac{(s_2 - js_3)}{2}, & s_{22} = \dfrac{(s_0 - s_1)}{2} \end{array} \right\} \tag{A.18.88}$$

and

$$\left. \begin{array}{ll} s_{a11} = \dfrac{(s_{a0} + s_{a1})}{2}, & s_{a12} = \dfrac{(s_{a2} + js_{a3})}{2} \\[3mm] s_{a21} = \dfrac{(s_{a2} - js_{a3})}{2}, & s_{a22} = \dfrac{(s_{a0} - s_{a1})}{2} \end{array} \right\} \tag{A.18.89}$$

so that the available power can now be expressed by the following 2×2 matrix as:

$$P = A_e S\, T_r \left\{ \begin{bmatrix} s_{a11} & s_{a12} \\ s_{a21} & sa_{22} \end{bmatrix} \begin{bmatrix} s_{11} & s_{12} \\ s_{21} & s_{22} \end{bmatrix} \right\} \tag{A.18.90}$$

where T_r = the trace, i.e.

$$P = A_e S \left\{ sa_{11}\, s_{11} + sa_{12}\, s_{21} + sa_{21}\, s_{12} + sa_{22}\, s_{22} \right\}$$

or

$$P = A_e S\, T_r\{[s_{aij}]\,[s_{ij}]\} = A_e SF \tag{A.18.91}$$

where F = wave-to-antenna coupling factor, as before.

These matrix relation are similar to ones used in optics. In optics the matrices are called 'coherency matrices'.

A.18.10   CROSS-FIELD

So far the study of polarization of waves has considered the situation where the **E** vectors at a given point have always been orthogonal to the direction of propagation.

There is, however, another situation where the **E** vector rotates in a plane parallel to the direction of propagation. This condition, which is called 'cross field', does not exist for a single plane wave in free space because such a wave has no field component in the direction of propagation. But in the 'near field of an antenna' {Fresnel zone}, there are **E** field components in both the directions of propagation and normal to this direction, so that cross field is present. The cross field may also be present near the surface of a conducting medium when a plane wave is travelling parallel to the surface. If the medium is not perfectly conducting {i.e. of finite conductivity}, the direction of **E** is tilted forward near the surface so that then **E** has a component E_x normal to the surface and a component E_y tangential to the surface directed in the direction of propagation. In general cross-field can be present whenever two waves of the same frequency travelling in different directions cross, an example being a reflection from a conducting surface to which the incident wave has hit obliquely.

A.18.11   COHERENCE

Coherence has been explained in the context of wave polarization, i.e. if the two components of the **E** wave are expressed as

$$E_x = E_1(t) \sin \omega t$$

$$E_y = E_2(t) \sin (\omega t + \delta(t))$$

where all the three time functions are independent, then the resultant wave is said to be completely **unpolarized** or **incoherent** {which implies that a completely **polarized wave** is a **coherent wave**}, it being assumed that $\langle E_1^2(t) \rangle = \langle E_2^2(t) \rangle$.

Coherence will now be discussed in a different sense. Let us consider a plane **E** wave travelling to the right as shown in Figure A.18.10. As the wave travels from point 1 to point 2, the phase at point 2 will be retarded from that at point 1 by an amount equal to βd. However, on the wave-front, points 1 and 3 will be in phase {i.e. zero phase difference}. Similarly, the phase difference between points 2 and 4 {both on the moved position of the wave-front} will also be zero. The condition described here characterize the providing of **wave-front coherence** as distinct from the situation regarding polarization. In homogeneous media, wave-front coherence exists, but the waves need not necessarily be polarization coherent.

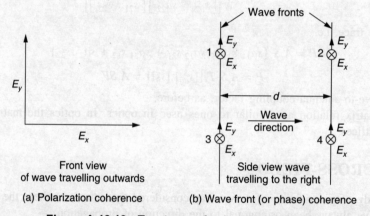

(a) Polarization coherence   (b) Wave front (or phase) coherence

Figure A.18.10   Two types of coherence is waves.

In non-homogeneous media there can exist wave-front incoherence, in which case it is not possible to define a wave-front, i.e. an equiphase surface. In such a medium, referring to Figure A.18.10, the E_x component of the field at points 1 and 3 will not necessarily be in phase and be time-independent.

Wave-front incoherence can exist for wavelengths of 10–20 m for waves coming through earth's ionosphere from celestial radio source.

Appendix 19

Mechanism of Radiation

A.19.1 INTRODUCTION

The question to which the answer is being attempted now is how does radiation take place. That is to say, how are the electromagnetic fields generated by the source, then contained and guided within the transmission line and the antenna and ultimately get detached from the antenna (the source) to form free-space wave. This can be best explained by some examples. So we start our study by examining some basic sources of radiation.

A.19.2 SINGLE WIRE

Conducting wires are the main devices in which the motion of electric charges takes place and thus create the electric current flow.

Let there be an electric volume charge-density (q_v C/m^3), distributed uniformly in a cylindrical wire of circular cross-section of area A and volume V. The total charge in this specified volume V is Q which is moving in the z-direction with an average uniform velocity v_z m/s. Hence the current density **J** A/m^2 over the cross-sectional area of the wire is:

$$J_z = q_v v_z \tag{A.19.1}$$

If the conductor was made up of ideal material of infinite conductivity, this current would become a surface current of density J_s A/m and this would be

$$J_s = q_s v_z \tag{A.19.2}$$

where q_s C/m^2 is the surface charge density.

If on the other hand, the wire is very thin (ideally of zero radius), the current would be a line current, given by

$$I_z = q_l v_z \tag{A.19.3}$$

where q_l C/m is the charge per unit length of the wire.

Next, we consider the very thin wire (although the conclusions arrived at would apply to all the three types considered so far). The current in the wire is of time-varying type. Hence,

$$\frac{dI_z}{dt} = q_l \frac{dv_z}{dt} = q_l a_z \tag{A.19.4}$$

where $\frac{dv_z}{dt}$ a_z metres/s^2 is the acceleration. If now the wire is of length l, the above equation can be rewritten as:

$$l \frac{dI_z}{dt} = lq_l \frac{dv_z}{dt} = lq_l a_z \qquad \text{(A.19.5)}$$

which is the basic relation between the current and charge, and is also the fundamental relation for electromagnetic radiation. Expressing in words, it says that:

to create electromagnetic radiation, there must be a time-varying current or an acceleration (+ve or −ve, i.e. acceleration or deceleration) of charge.

In applications where the time is changing harmonically, current is used and in transient problems charges are used. To produce changes in charge velocity (i.e. +ve or −ve), the wire must be curved, bent, discontinuous or terminated. Time-varying currents are also produced when charges are oscillating in a time-harmonic motion. All these aspects can be summarized as follows:

1. If a charge is stationary, no current is created and hence there is no radiation.
2. If charge is moving with uniform velocity (i.e. zero acceleration)
   (a) there is no radiation if the wire is straight and infinite in length.
   (b) if the wire is curved, bent, discontinuous, terminated or truncated, then there would be radiation.
3. If the charge is oscillating time-harmonically, the wire would radiate even if it is straight.

We can now explain the radiation process qualitatively by considering a pulse source connected to an open-ended conducting wire which has a grounded discrete load connected at the open end. Initially as the wire is energized, the free electrons (i.e. the charges) in the wire are set in motion by the electrical lines of force which are due to the source. These charges get accelerated in the source-end of the wire and decelerated during the reflection from the other end, and during this process, radiated fields are produced at the ends as well as along the remaining length of the wire. If the pulses are of shorter duration, the radiation is stronger with a broad frequency spectrum, whereas continuous time-harmonic oscillating charge produces radiation of single frequency which depends on the frequency of oscillation (of the charges). The forces of the external sources set the charges in motion and thus accelerate the charges, thus producing the associated radiated field. The internal (self) forces, associated with the induced field caused by the increasing charge concentration at the ends of the wire, produce the deceleration of the charges at the end of the wire. The energy for the internal forces comes from the charge build-up at the ends of the wire where the velocity of the charges reduce to zero.

Thus the mechanisms responsible for the electromagnetic radiation are: (a) charge acceleration due to an exciting electric field; (b) deceleration due to impedance discontinuities; and (c) smooth curves of the wire.

It is to be noted that whilst the current density $\mathbf{J}_c$ and the charge density q_v are both source terms in Maxwell's equation, it is usual to consider the charge as the more fundamental quantity.

A.19.3   TWO WIRES

The starting point this time is a two-conductor transmission line, connected to an antenna, has been connected to a voltage source. Thus an electric field is created between the conductors. This electric field has with it electric lines of force which are tangent to the $\mathbf{E}$ field at each point and their strength is proportional to the electric field intensity. These lines of force tend to act on the free electrons which are easily detachable from the atoms of the conductor, thus creating a current in it (i.e. the conductors) which in turn produces a magnetic field intensity with which there are magnetic lines of force tangential to the magnetic field.

Further it is accepted that the electric field lines start on +ve charges and end on –ve charges or at infinity. These lines can also start at infinity and end on –ve charges. Sometimes they can also form closed loops neither starting or ending on any charge. Magnetic field lines always form closed loops which enclose current-carrying conducting regions.

The electric field lines drawn between the two conductors indicate the distribution of charge on the conductors. For example, if the voltage from the source is varying sinusoidally with time, the electric field between the conductors would also have sinusoidally distribution with its periodicity same as that of the source. The relative magnitude of the **E** field would be indicated by the density of the lines of force and the direction by the arrows on these lines (+ve or –ve). The creation of the time-varying electric and the associated magnetic fields between the conductors produces the e.m. waves travelling along the transmission lines (Figure A.19.1). These waves enter the antenna

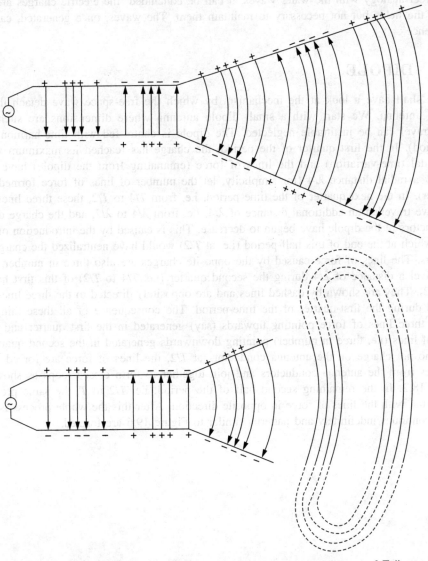

Figure A.19.1 Antenna, transmission line source and detachment of **E** lines.

and have associated with them the charges and the currents. If parts of the antenna structure were removed, free-space waves can be formed by 'connecting' the open ends of the electric lines of force as shown. The free space waves are also periodic and a constant phase point moves outwardly with the velocity of light, travelling a distance $\lambda/2$ in the time of half a period.

However, we have still not answered the question as to how the guided waves get detached from the antenna to form the waves in free space, as shown earlier in Figure 19.6. This we shall do for the basic antenna structure of a linear dipole. At this stage to clarify ideas, an analogy of water waves is used. Water waves in a calm water pool can be created by dropping a stone or pebble in it. Circular waves, starting from the point where the pebble was dropped, begin to travel outwards. Furthermore if the source pebble is removed, the waves do not extinguish themselves (or die out) but continue to travel outwards. The same is true for e.m. waves created by electric disturbance. So by direct analogy with the water waves, it can be concluded 'the electric charges are required to excite the fields but not necessary to maintain them. The waves, once generated, can exist in their absence'.

A.19.4 DIPOLE

Now, we shall have a look at the mechanism by which the free-space wave detach themselves from the antenna. We start with a small dipole antenna where dimensions are such that the time of travel can be justifiable neglected. The dipole is centre-fed with time-harmonic signals (T = period). In the first quarter of the period, the charge has reached its maximum value (for a sinusoidal time-variation) and the lines of force (emanating from the dipole) have travelled outwardly a radial distance $\lambda/4$ (for simplicity, let the number of lines of force formed be three in number). In the next quarter of the time period, i.e. from $T/4$ to $T/2$, these three lines of force would have travelled an additional distance of $\lambda/4$, i.e. from $\lambda/4$ to $\lambda/2$, and the charge density on the conductors of the dipole have begun to decrease. This is caused by the introduction of opposite charges which at the end of this half-period (i.e. at $T/2$) would have neutralized the charges on the conductors. The lines of force caused by the opposite charges are also three in number, and they would travel a distance of $\lambda/4$ during the second quarter (i.e. $T/4$ to $T/2$) of this first half period (up to $T/2$). They are shown by dashed lines and are oppositely directed to the three lines of force generated during the first-quarter of the time-period. The consequence of all these things is that there are three lines of force pointing upwards (say) generated in the first quarter and the same number of lines (i.e. three in number) pointing downwards generated in the second quarter. Since there is no net charge on the antenna conductors at $T/2$, the lines of force are forced to detach themselves from the antenna conductors and join together to form closed loops as shown in the Figure A.18.2. In the remaining second half of the period, i.e. $T/2$ to T, the same procedure is repeated, but with the lines of force in opposite direction. After this the whole process is repeated and this continues indefinitely and patterns similar to Figure 19.6 are formed.

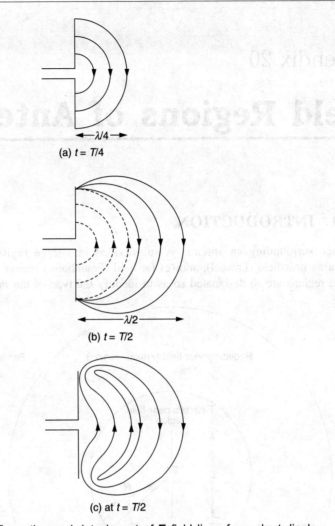

(a) $t = T/4$

(b) $t = T/2$

(c) at $t = T/2$

Figure A.19.2 Formation and detachment of **E** field lines for a short dipole.

Appendix 20

Field Regions of Antennae

A.20.1 INTRODUCTION

The space surrounding an antenna is sub-divided into three regions: (a) reactive near field, (b) radiating near field (Fresnel), and (c) far-field (Fraunhofer) regions as shown in Figure A.20.1. The field regions are so designated so as to identify the type of the field in each.

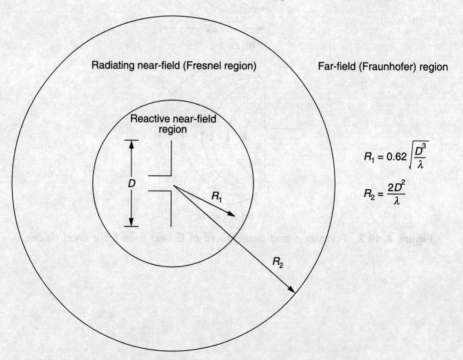

Figure A.20.1   Field regions of an antenna.

Even though there is no abrupt or step change in the field patterns across the specified boundaries, there are distinct differences amongst these regions. The boundaries separating these regions have not been uniquely defined, yet various criteria have been established and are being used to identify these regions.

A.20.2 REACTIVE NEAR-FIELD REGION

'It is that portion of the near-field region immediately surrounding the antenna itself where the reactive field predominates'. For most antennae, the outer boundary of this region is taken to exist at a radial distance R, such that $R < 0.62\sqrt{D^2/\lambda}$, starting from the antenna surface. In this expression λ is the wavelength and D is the largest dimension of the antenna. Hence for a very short dipole (e.g. Hertzian), the equivalent outer boundary is usually considered to exist at $R = \dfrac{\lambda}{2\pi}$, starting from the antenna surface.

A.20.3 RADIATING NEAR-FIELD (FRESNEL) REGION

'This is that part of field region of an antenna lying between the reactive near-field region and the far-field region, where the radiating field predominated and also the angular field distribution is dependent upon the distance from the antenna'. If for an antenna, the maximum dimension D is **not** large compared to the wavelength λ, this region may not exist. This region is referred to as Fresnel region for those antennae which are focussed to infinity. For this region, the inner boundary is at $0.62\sqrt{\dfrac{D^3}{\lambda}}$ and the outer boundary is at $R < 2D^2/L$, D being the largest dimension of the antenna. In this region, the field pattern is, in general, a function of the radial distance and the radial field component $(= B_r)$ can be appreciable.

A.20.4 FAR-FIELD (FRAUNHOFER) REGION

'It is that part of the region of the field of an antenna where the angular field distribution is essentially independent of the distance from the antenna'.

When the antenna has a maximum overall dimension D (for the validity of this limit, this value D must also be large compared with the wavelength λ of propagation, i.e. $D > \lambda$), the far-field region is usually taken to exist at distances greater than $2D^2/\lambda$ from the antenna. This limit may not be adequate for certain antennae like multi-beam reflection antennae which are sensitive to phase variation over their apertures. In physical media, when D the maximum overall dimension of the antenna is large compared to $\pi/|\gamma|$, the inner boundary of the far-field region can be equal to $|\gamma| D^2/\pi$ from the antenna, γ being the propagation constant in the medium under consideration. For an antenna focussed on infinity, the far-field region is denominated as 'Fraunhofer region'—the basis being optical analogy. In this region, the field components are essentially transverse and the angular distribution is independent of the radial distance. The inner boundary of the radial distance R is now taken as $R = 2D^2/\lambda$ and the outer boundary at infinity.

Appendix 21

The Concept of Aperture

A.21.1 INTRODUCTION

This parameter is special to the receiving antenna and deals with various facets of the power capturing ability of an antenna. Let a receiving antenna of any type (it could be a linear dipole or loop or a horn or any other type) be immersed in the field of uniform plane wave. Let the power density of the plane wave (or its Poynting vector) be S W/m^2, and the area of the inlet of the antenna be A m^2. If the particular antenna extracts all the power from the wave over its entire inlet area A, then the total power = P absorbed from the wave is given by

$$P = AS \text{ W} \tag{A.21.1}$$

So it is justified to look at this antenna as an 'aperture', and the total power which it extracts from a passing wave is proportional to the aperture or the area of its inlet.

There are different types of apertures, such as effective aperture, scattering aperture, loss aperture, collecting aperture and physical aperture which will now be defined as discussed in some depth.

A.21.2 EFFECTIVE APERTURE

Let a dipole receiving antenna (say $\lambda/2$) be located in the field of an e.m. wave passing the antenna. The antenna collects power from the wave and delivers to the load impedance(= Z_T) terminating its circuit. The power density of the wave is S W/m^2, which is also its Poynting vector. The antenna can be represented by its equivalent circuit which is a voltage source V and an internal impedance Z_A.

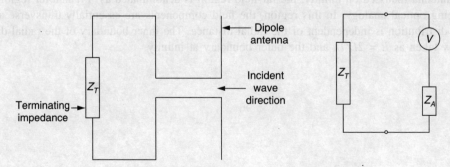

Figure A.21.1 Receiving antenna and its equivalent.

466

The travelling wave which is passing by the antenna induces a voltage V in it, and this voltage produces a current I in the terminating impedance Z_T (= load impedance) of the antenna which can be expressed as:

$$I = \frac{V}{Z_T + Z_A} \tag{A.21.2}$$

where V and I are R.M.S. values.

Both the above impedances are complex, and hence,

$$Z_T = R_T + jX_T \quad \text{and} \quad Z_A = R_A + jX_A \tag{A.21.3}$$

The antenna resistance R_A is made up of two parts, a radiation resistance R_R and a non-radiative (= loss) resistance R_L such that

$$R_A = R_R + R_L \tag{A.21.4}$$

Let P = Power delivered by the antenna to the terminating (load) resistance.

$\therefore$
$$P = I^2 R_T$$

The magnitude of this current is

$$I = \frac{V}{\sqrt{\{(R_R + R_L + R_T)^2 + (X_A + X_T)^2\}}} \tag{A.21.5}$$

$\therefore$
$$P = \frac{V^2 R_T}{\sqrt{\{(R_R + R_L + R_T)^2 + (X_A + X_T)^2\}}} \tag{A.21.6}$$

The ratio of the power P in the terminating resistance to the power density of the incident wave (= its Poynting vector) is an area A. So,

$$\frac{P}{S} = A$$

where P = power in termination, W
     S = power density of the incident wave, W/m^2
     A = area, m^2

If however, the power P is expressed in watts per square wavelength (W/λ^2), then A is in square wavelengths (λ^2)—a convenient unit for measurement of areas.

$\therefore$
$$A = \frac{V^2 R_T}{S\{(R_R + R_L + R_T)^2 + (X_A + X_T)^2\}} \tag{A.21.7}$$

It should be noted that unless otherwise stated, the induced voltage V is obtained by orienting the antenna for maximum response and that the polarization of the antenna is same as that of the incident wave. The value of A as obtained above, takes into account any antenna losses represented by R_L and any mismatch between the antenna and its terminating impedance (= load impedance).

Next, we consider the condition for maximum power transfer, i.e. when the terminating impedance is the complex conjugate of the antenna impedance. Thus,

$$X_T = -X_A \quad \text{and} \quad R_T = R_R + R_L \tag{A.21.8}$$

Then from the Eqs. (A.21.1) and (A.21.8), the 'effective aperture A_e' of the antenna is obtained as

$$A_e = \frac{V^2}{4S(R_R + R_L)} (m^2 \text{ or } \lambda^2) \tag{A.21.9}$$

When the antenna is loss-less, i.e. $R_L = 0$, the 'maximum effective aperture A_{em}' of the antenna is obtained as

$$A_{em} = \frac{V^2}{4SR_R} (m^2 \text{ or } \lambda^2) \tag{A.21.10}$$

$$= \text{Area over which power is extracted from the}$$
$$\text{incident wave and delivered to the load.}$$

There are times when R_T the terminating impedance is not located physically at the antenna terminals, as for example in a receiver connected to the antenna by a transmission line. In such cases, the power delivered to the receiver would be same as the power delivered to the equivalent Z_T only if the transmission line is loss-less. If the transmission line is lossy (i.e. it is attenuating), the power at the receiver would be reduced from the power at the equivalent terminating impedance by the amount lost in the transmission line.

A.21.3   SCATTERING APERTURE

While deriving the effective aperture of an antenna, it was seen that this was the area from which power is absorbed. At the terminal (or load) impedance Z_T, the power absorbed is square of the current through the load multiplied by the real part of the load impedance. The current is produced by the induced voltage in the antenna, and it (the current) passes through both the load impedance Z_T as well as the antenna impedance Z_A. Considering the power appearing at the antenna impedance Z_A, it should be remembered that the real part of Z_1 (i.e. R_A) is made up of two parts: (i) the radiation resistance R_R and (ii) the loss resistance R_L such that $R_A = R_R + R_L$. Hence it is seen that some part of the power received at the antenna would be dissipated as heat in the antenna, and this is given by

$$P' = I^2 R_L \tag{A.21.11}$$

The remainder of the received power is spent in the radiation resistance of the antenna, i.e. it is re-radiated from the antenna. This re-radiated power is

$$P'' = I^2 R_A \tag{A.21.12}$$

This is the **re-radiated or scattered power** from the antenna. An analogy to this scattering is the dissipated power of a generator which is supplying power to a load. Also to be noted is that the condition for maximum power transfer is that dissipated power should equal the power delivered to the load.

As in the previous section, re-radiated power can be related to a **scattering aperture** or scattering cross-section. This aperture denominated as A_s can be defined as a ratio, stated below:

$$\text{Scattering aperture} = A_s = \frac{\text{Re-radiated power}}{\text{Power density of the incident wave}} = \frac{P''}{S} \tag{A.21.13}$$

where

$$P'' = I^2 R_R = \frac{V^2 R_R}{(R_R + R_L + R_T)^2 + (X_A + X_T)^2} \tag{A.21.14}$$

The conditions for maximum power transfer (i.e. matched antenna) are $R_L = 0$, $R_T = R_L$ and $X_T = -X_A$ (i.e. $Z_T = Z_A{}^*$), then,

$$A_s = \frac{V^2}{4SR_R} \tag{A.21.15}$$

i.e. the scattering aperture $= A_{smpt} = A_{em}$ or when maximum power is delivered to the load ($= R_T$), an equal power is re-radiated (or scattered) from the receiving antenna.

Next, when the load resistance is zero ($R_T = 0$) and $X_T = -X_A$ resonant antenna, then the re-radiated power is:

$$P''_{RA} = \frac{V^2}{R_T} \tag{A.21.16}$$

This condition is referred to as resonant short-circuit (RSC). Now the corresponding scattering aperture becomes

$$A_s = \frac{V^2}{SR} = 4A_{em} \tag{A.21.17}$$

∴   For a given antenna for the RSC condition,

The scattering aperture $= 4 \times$ its maximum effective aperture.

We now define **scattering ratio** β as

$$\text{Scattering ratio } \beta = \frac{\text{Scattering aperture}}{\text{Effective aperture}} = \frac{A_s}{A_e} \quad \text{(dimensionless)} \tag{A.21.18}$$

This quantity β lies between zero and infinity, i.e. $0 \leq \beta \leq \infty$. For conditions of maximum power transfer and zero antenna losses, the scattering ratio $\beta = 1$.

If R_T is increased, both A_s and A_e decrease, but A_s decreases more rapidly then A_e, and hence β becomes smaller.

Hence as R_T is increased, the ratio (Scattered power/Power in the load) → smaller and smaller, but the load power also get reduced.

A point to note is that the scattered field of a receiving antenna can be considered to have interfered with the incident field and hence may cast a **shadow** behind the antenna.

A.21.4   LOSS APERTURE

When the loss resistance R_L is not zero, $R_L \neq 0$, some power would be dissipated as heat in the antenna. This can be represented by an equivalent aperture known as **loss aperture** ($= A_L$). This is expressed as:

$$A_L = \frac{I^2 R_L}{S} = \frac{V^2 R_L}{S[(R_R + R_L + R_T)^2 + (X_A + X_T)^2]} \tag{A.21.19}$$

A.21.5   COLLECTING APERTURE

The three types of apertures (i.e. effective, scattering and loss) described so far, are related to the three ways in which the collected power of the antenna can be divided: (i) power in the terminal resistance (effective aperture); (ii) dissipative heat in the antenna (loss aperture); (iii) reradiated power (scattering aperture). By the principle of conservation of energy, the total collected power by the antenna is the sum of these three components. Hence, these apertures added together would give the collecting aperture (= A_c), i.e.

$$A_c = \frac{V^2(R_R + R_L + R_T)}{S[(R_R + R_L + R_T)^2 + (X_A + X_T)^2]} = A_s + A_L + A_e \qquad (A.21.20)$$

(see Figure A.21.2)

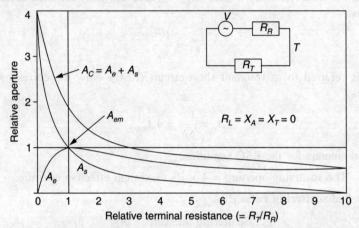

Figure A.21.2 Variations of apertures as function of (R_T/R_R).

A.21.6 PHYSICAL APERTURE

As a matter of convenience, another type of aperture (a fifth type) has been defined and it has been named as **physical aperture** (= A_p). This aperture is a measure of the physical size of the antenna; and its manner of definition is completely arbitrary; e.g. it may be defined as the physical cross-section (either in square metres or square wavelengths) perpendicular to the direction of propagation of the incident wave when the antenna has been oriented for maximum response.

For example,

  (i) physical aperture of an electromagnetic horn = area of its mouth
  (ii) physical aperture of a linear cylindrical dipole = cross-sectional area of the dipole

It should be noted that the physical aperture has a simple definite meaning only for some antennae, whilst the effective aperture has a definite, simply defined value for all antennae.

A.21.7 APERTURE EFFICIENCY (= $\mathscr{E}_{ap}$)

This is defined as:

$$\mathscr{E}_{ap} = \frac{\text{Effective aperture}}{\text{Physical apertue}} = \frac{A_a}{A_p} \qquad \text{(dimensionless)} \qquad (A.21.21)$$

$$0 < \mathscr{E}_{ap} < \infty,$$

but for large (in terms of λ) broad-side apertures,

$$\mathscr{E}_{ap} < 1$$

Appendix 22

Extension of Principle of Duality to Time-varying Problems: Maxwell's Equation and Babinet's Principle

A.22.1 INTRODUCTION

In Appendix 1 [Electromagnetism (Theory) Volume 1], the principle of duality has been explained by using examples from electrostatics and magnetostatices, and then used for solving problems dealing with statics fields as well as those of steady time-invariant current-flow problems. It should be clearly understood that this is not a constraint on this principle, and it can equally well be applied to solve problems dealing with time-varying fields. However, before we discuss any specific problems, we shall state a general formal definition of this principle.

"When two equations which describe the behaviour of two different variables are of identical mathematical form, their solutions will also be of the same form. The variable in such two equations occupying identical positions are known as dual quantities, and a solution of any one of these equations can be obtained by a systematic interchange of variables to the other."

This is the 'principle of duality' and is also known as the 'duality theorem'.

A.22.2 EXAMPLES OF THE PRINCIPLE OF DUALITY

An example of the two 'curl' equations of Maxwell's, in charge-free regions without conduction currents (or high frequency range where conduction current can be neglected in comparison with the displacement current is:

$$\left.\begin{array}{l} \nabla \times \mathbf{E} = -j\omega\mu\mathbf{H} \\ \nabla \times \mathbf{H} = j\omega\varepsilon\mathbf{E} \end{array}\right\} \tag{A.22.1}$$

and

assuming time-harmonic variation of signals.

It is obvious that if $\mathbf{E}$ is replaced by $\mathbf{H}$, $\mathbf{H}$ by $-\mathbf{E}$, μ by ε and ε by μ, the original equations are obtained again. Hence if one problem is solved, the solution of the second problem would also be obtained from the first one by merely interchanging the variables as indicated above. However, it might be difficult to specify appropriate boundary conditions because for the second solution magnetic equivalent of 'perfect' electrical conductor is not realizable at high frequencies.

One example where the use of this principle saves work in solving a practical problem is in the calculation of principal mode in transmission of waves in a wedge-shaped dielectric region between two inclined plane conductors (Figure A.22.1). This mode has electromagnetic field components E_ϕ and H_z. If the problem is further simplified by assuming no variation in ϕ- and z-directions, then the solutions are further simplified and are of the form stated below, i.e.

$$\left. \begin{aligned} H_z &= AH_0^{(1)}(kr) + BH_0^{(2)}(kr) \\ E_\phi &= -j\sqrt{\frac{\mu}{\varepsilon}} \left\{ AH_1^{(1)}(kr) + BH_1^{(2)}(kr) \right\} \end{aligned} \right\} \tag{A.22.2}$$

These expressions have been obtained by merely interchanging the parameters mentioned above from the expressions for E_z and H_ϕ of parallel-plane radial transmission lines, whose equation when solved gives the solution as

$$\left. \begin{aligned} E_z &= AH_0^{(1)}(kr) + BH_0^{(2)}(kr) \\ H_\phi &= \frac{j}{\eta} \left\{ AH_1^{(1)}(kr) + BH_1^{(2)}(kr), \qquad \eta = \sqrt{\frac{\mu}{\varepsilon}} \right. \end{aligned} \right\} \tag{A.22.3}$$

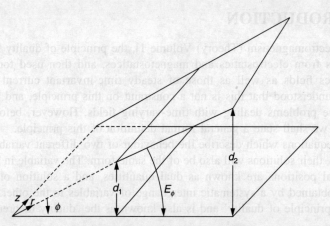

Figure A.22.1   Inclined plane guide.

The principle of duality has been very widely used for obtaining mathematical solutions of different types of fields as well as for experimental solutions of such problems by using analogue models. There are many examples of such models, i.e. Section 6.5 Analogy between electric current and electric flux, Sections 9.3.2 to 9.3.3.2 [electromagnetism (Theory) Volume 1], conducting paper analogue (for magnetic field studies), and so on.

So far we have been discussing the duality between different types of fields, both steady-state time-invariant and time-varying types (mostly time-harmonic type of variations), but it (duality concept) can be extended to combine field concepts with circuit approach as well. An example of this is in the study of antennae which can be treated either as a circuit device (looking at it from the terminals) or a space device (field-based approach) on the other-hand. This is illustrated schematically in Figure A.22.2.

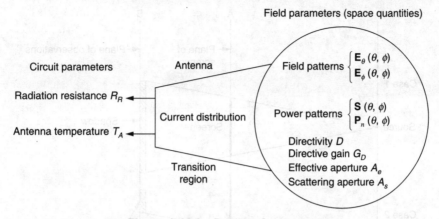

Figure A.22.2 Duality of antenna.

A.22.3 BABINET'S PRINCIPLE (WITH BOOKER'S EXTENSION)

The principle of duality has been further extended to study and analyse the field patterns of different types of antennae, for example wire and aperture types (linear dipoles and slot types) with the relationships between their fields. For this purpose, we now introduce Babinet's principle which was introduced first in the study of optics. In optics, this principle states that 'given a source producing a field, the field at any point behind a screen having an opening, if added to the field of a complementary structure, the resulting field is equal to the field when there is no screen'.

This principle can be best explained by using an example from optics, in which case there is a point source and two imaginary planes, one being a plane of screen A, and the next one of observation B arranged sequentially as shown in Figure A.22.3. First let a perfectly absorbing screen be placed, as shown, in plane A, which produces a region of shadow in plane B as indicated in the figure. Let this field behind the screen be some function f_1 of the co-ordinates x, y, z. Hence

$$F_s = F_1(x, y, z) \tag{A.22.4}$$

Next the screen in plane A is replaced by its complementary structure. (The complementary structure is such that when it is combined with the original structure, then there would be a single solid screen with no overlaps.) The field due to this complementary screen would now be

$$F_{cs} = f_2(x, y, z) \tag{A.22.5}$$

Finally when there is no screen present, the field is given by

$$F_0 = f_3(x, y, z) \tag{A.22.6}$$

Babinet's principle states that at the same point (x_1, y_1, z_1),

$$F_s + F_{cs} = F_0 \tag{A.22.7}$$

The source need not necessarily be a point source, and there can be a distribution of source; and the observation point is not restricted to a particular plane B. In fact it can be any plane behind the screen. Though this principle has been illustrated here by considering a case of simple shadow, it is equally applicable when there is diffraction.

Babinet's principle, originally enunciated for optics did not take account of the vector nature (i.e. polarization of waves) of electromagnetic waves. This extension and generalization, taking account of wave polarization was done by Booker, and he took into account the nature of more practical conducting screens. So if one screen is a perfect conductor of electricity (i.e. $\sigma \to \infty$),

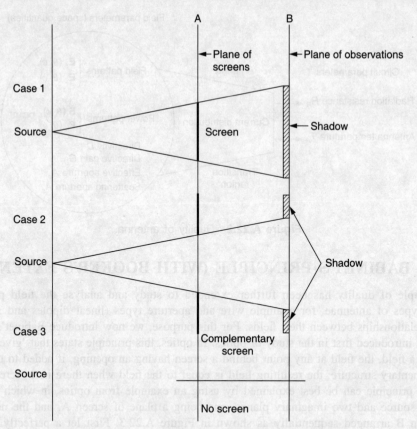

Figure A.22.3 Example of Babinet's principle in optics.

then the complementary structure is a perfect conductor of magnetization, i.e. it is infinitely permeable $\mu_r \to \infty$. It is to be noted that though in practice, neither infinitely permeable exists nor infinitely conducting ($\sigma \to \infty$), and at present the only perfect conductors are superconductors existing at extremely low temperatures, though it is expected that soon they may be available at ordinary temperatures. But metals like gold and silver have such high σ that the assumption of infinite conductivity is justifiable with negligible error in many applications. Hence the equivalent effect can be obtained by making both the original screen and its complementary structure to be made of perfectly conducting material, and then interchanging the electric and magnetic quantities every where.

Hence, Booker's extension gives the following equivalence. We start by assuming an electric source **J** radiating into an unbounded medium of intrinsic impedance $\eta = \sqrt{\mu/\varepsilon}$ and this produces the fields $\mathbf{E}_0$, $\mathbf{H}_0$ at a point P (Figure A.22.4(a)}.

The same fields can be obtained by superposing the fields generated by the same electric source in the medium of intrinsic impedance $\eta = \sqrt{\mu/\varepsilon}$ in the presence of:

1. an infinite, planar, very thin, perfect electric conductor with an opening S_a, producing at point P the fields $\mathbf{E}_e$, $\mathbf{H}_e$ {Figure A.22.4(b)}; and
2. a flat, very thin, perfect magnetic conductor S_a producing at the (same) point P, the fields $\mathbf{E}_m$, $\mathbf{H}_m$ {Figure A.22.4(c)}.

Then
$$\left. \begin{array}{c} \mathbf{E}_0 = \mathbf{E}_e + \mathbf{E}_m \\ \mathbf{H}_0 = \mathbf{H}_e + \mathbf{H}_m \end{array} \right\}$$ (A.22.8)

The original fields produced by the source, i.e. $\mathbf{E}_0$, $\mathbf{H}_0$ can also be obtained by additions of the fields of:

1. an electric source $\mathbf{J}$ in the medium of intrinsic impedance $\eta = \sqrt{\mu/\varepsilon}$ in the presence of an infinite, planar, very thin, perfect electric conductor S_a producing at the given point P the fields $\mathbf{E}_e$, $\mathbf{H}_e$ {Figure A.22.4(b)}; and the electric screen with the opening S_a in Figure A.22.4(b) and the screen in Figure A.22.4(d) are dual of each other, i.e. the complementary structures as defined earlier, as they form, when superimposed, a complete solid screen with no overlaps.

It can be shown (by using Booker's extension) that if a screen and its complement are immersed in a medium with intrinsic impedance η, then the terminal impedances of the two structures (i.e. Z_s and Z_{cs} respectively) are related as:

$$Z_s Z_{cs} = \frac{\eta^2}{4}$$ (A.22.9)

In a practical arrangement of a linear dipole, the far field components radiated by the opening of the screen (i.e. $\mathbf{E}_{\theta_s}$, $\mathbf{E}_{\phi_s}$, $\mathbf{H}_{\theta_s}$, $\mathbf{H}_{\phi_s}$) and the equivalent components of the complement structure ($\mathbf{E}_{\theta_{cs}}$, $\mathbf{E}_{\phi_{cs}}$, $\mathbf{H}_{\theta_{cs}}$, $\mathbf{H}_{\phi_{cs}}$) are related as follows:

$$\mathbf{E}_{\theta_s} = \mathbf{H}_{\theta_s}, \quad \mathbf{E}_{\phi_s} = \mathbf{H}_{\theta_{cs}}, \quad \mathbf{H}_{\theta_s} = -\frac{\mathbf{E}_{\theta_{cs}}}{\eta_0^2}, \quad \mathbf{H}_{\phi_s} = \frac{\mathbf{E}_{\phi_{cs}}}{\eta_0} \qquad \text{(in free space)} \quad \text{(A.22.10)}$$

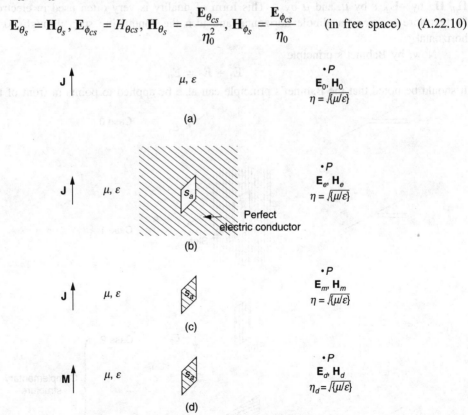

Figure A.22.4 Babinet's principle based equivalent of an electric source in an unbounded medium.

Pictorially this would be as shown below in Figure A.22.5, where now the current element **J** has been replaced by a short linear dipole (centre-fed). Initially the dipole is held horizontally and there is no screen between the dipole and the observation point P so that the field at P, E_0 is directed horizontally (Figure A.22.5 case 0). Then an infinite, perfectly conducting, plane, infinitesimally thin screen with a vertically cut slot (as indicated in Figure A.22.5 case 1) is introduced between the dipole and the point of observation so that the field is now E_1 at P. Then next in case 2, the original infinite screen is replaced by a complementary screen which consists only the size of the slot and has identical properties as before. Also the dipole source is now turned through 90° making it vertical so that **E** and **H** get interchanged. The field at P is now E_2. An alternative situation for the case would be

2. a magnetic source **M** radiating in the medium of intrinsic impedance given by $\eta_d = \sqrt{\varepsilon/\mu}$ in the presence of a flat, very thin, perfect electrical conductor S_a which produces at the point P the fields E_d, H_d {Figure A.22.4(d)}.

Thus

$$\left.\begin{array}{l} E_0 = E_e + E_d \\ H_0 = H_e + H_d \end{array}\right\} \qquad (A.22.11)$$

It should be noted that the dual shown in Figure {A.22.4(d)} can be realized more easily in practice as compared with that of Figure A.22.4(c).

To obtain situation (d) from situation (c) of Figure A.22.4, **J** is to be replaced by **M**, E_m by H_d, H_m by $-E_d$, ε by μ, and μ by ε. This form of duality is very often used in electromagnetics. Furthermore to keep the dipole horizontal and turn the conducting strip through 90° making it horizontal.

Now, by Babinet's principle

$$E_1 + E_2 = E_0 \qquad (A.22.12)$$

It should be noted that the Babinet's principle can also be applied to points in front of the screens.

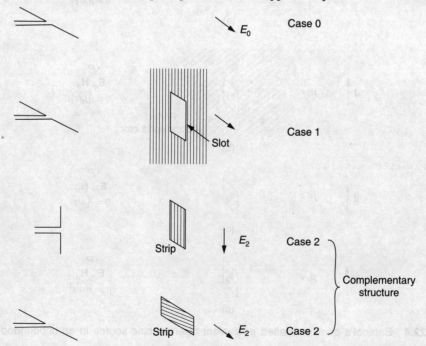

Figure A.22.5 A chart linear dipole and a conducting screen with slot to illustrate Babinet's principle.

Appendix 23

Integral Solutions of Maxwell's Equations in Terms of Source
Stratton–Chu Formulation

A.23.1 INTRODUCTION

A rigorous solution of Maxwell's equations in integral form is presented here. It gives the values of the field at any point within a volume V in terms of the sources within V and the field values on the surface S which encloses volume V. Apart from the rigour of the solution, the results are directly applicable to two types of antennae (dipoles and helices). Also the retarded potential function come out an exact consequence of the solution expressions.

A.23.2 THE STRATTON-CHU SOLUTION

Maxwell's equation are considered in free space and hence the time variations can be taken as harmonic, i.e. $e^{j\omega t}$ without any loss of generality as ω can be taken as a component of a Fourier series or integral, any arbitrary time variation can be considered from this analysis. Also the presence of any dielectric media and/or magnetic media can also be taken into account since the **P** (Polarization vector) and the **M** (Magnetization vector) can be taken as pertinent dipoles in vacuo to represent these media. Even the conducting media could be taken into account by considering the oscillatory motion of the electron cloud. So the presence of all these materials in the regions would satisfy the requirements for constructing the antenna and so this analysis has wide applicability.

The Maxwell's equation for time-harmonic sources in the free space (region containing these sources) are:

$$\nabla \times \mathbf{E} = -j\omega \mathbf{B}$$

$$\nabla \times \mathbf{B} = \frac{J}{\mu_0^{-1}} + \frac{j\omega}{c^2}\mathbf{E} \qquad (A.23.1)$$

$$\nabla \cdot \mathbf{E} = \frac{\rho}{\varepsilon_0}$$

477

$$\nabla \cdot \mathbf{B} = 0$$

where $c^2\mu_0\varepsilon_0 = 1$, and the equation of continuity

$$\nabla \cdot \mathbf{J} = -j\omega\rho \tag{A.23.2}$$

The time factor $e^{j\omega t}$ is implicit in all these equations, and the fields are all complex vector functions including the current density. The charge density is a complex scalar function.

These equations reduce to the vector wave equations:

$$\nabla \times \nabla \times \mathbf{E} - k^2\mathbf{E} = -j\omega\left(\frac{\mathbf{J}}{\mu_0^{-1}}\right) \tag{A.23.3}$$

$$\nabla \times \nabla \times \mathbf{B} - k^2\mathbf{B} = \nabla \times \left(\frac{\mathbf{J}}{\mu_0^{-1}}\right) \tag{A.23.4}$$

in which $k = $ the propagation constant $= \omega/c$.

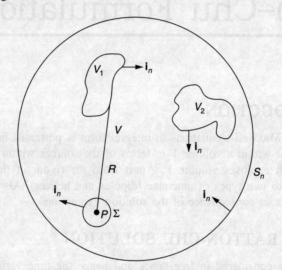

Figure A.23.1 Diagram for vector Green's theorem.

These two equations can be integrated by using a technique first suggested by Stratton and Chu, based on the vector formulation of Green's second identity (see Section 0.6.4).

A volume V is now considered (Figure A.23.1) bounded by the surfaces S_1, S_2, ..., S_n and contain the vectors $\mathbf{F}$ and $\mathbf{G}$ which are vector functions of position in this region which are continuous and have continuous first and second derivatives everywhere within V, and on the boundary surfaces S_i. Using the vector identity:

$$\nabla \cdot (\mathbf{A} \times \mathbf{B}) = \mathbf{B} \cdot \nabla \times \mathbf{A} - \mathbf{A} \cdot \nabla \times \mathbf{B}$$

and allowing $\mathbf{A} = \mathbf{F}$ and $\mathbf{B} = \nabla \times \mathbf{G}$, the identity becomes

$$\nabla \cdot (\mathbf{F} \times \nabla \times \mathbf{G}) = \nabla \times \mathbf{G} \cdot \nabla \times \mathbf{F} - \mathbf{F} \cdot \nabla \times \nabla \times \mathbf{G}$$

Interchanging $\mathbf{A} = \mathbf{G}$ and $\mathbf{B} = \nabla \times \mathbf{E}$, the identify changes to:

$$\nabla \cdot (\mathbf{G} \times \nabla \times \mathbf{F}) = \nabla \times \mathbf{F} \cdot \nabla \times \mathbf{G} - \mathbf{G} \cdot \nabla \times \nabla \times \mathbf{F}$$

Subtracting and then integrating the result over V,

$$\int_V (\mathbf{F} \cdot \nabla \times \nabla \times \mathbf{G} - \mathbf{G} \cdot \nabla \times \nabla \times \mathbf{F}) \, dV = \int_V \nabla \cdot (\mathbf{G} \times \nabla \times \mathbf{F} - \mathbf{F} \times \nabla \times \mathbf{G}) dV$$

If $\mathbf{i}_n$ is taken as the inward-drawn unit normal to any boundary surface S_i into the volume V, then by Gauss' Divergence theorem

$$\int_V (\mathbf{F} \cdot \nabla \times \nabla \times \mathbf{G} - \mathbf{G} \cdot \nabla \times \nabla \times \mathbf{F}) \, dV = - \int_{S_1, S_2 \dots S_n} (\mathbf{G} \times \nabla \times \mathbf{F} - \mathbf{F} \times \nabla \times \mathbf{G}) \, \mathbf{i}_n dS \qquad \text{(A.23.5)}$$

This result is the vector Green's theorem.

Let the fields $\mathbf{E}$ and $\mathbf{B}$ of Eqs (A.23.3) and (A.23.4) both satisfy the conditions which are satisfied by $\mathbf{F}$ in V, and let $\mathbf{G}$ be the vector Green's function defined by

$$\mathbf{G} = \frac{e^{jkR}}{R} \mathbf{a} \qquad \text{(A.23.6)}$$

where $\mathbf{a}$ = an arbitrary constant vector
   R = the distance from an arbitrary point P(x, y, z) with V to any point (ξ, η, ζ) with V or on S_i.

With this definition of G, it satisfies the conditions of the of the vector Green's theorem everywhere except at P.

$\therefore$ Surround P by a small sphere Σ of radius δ and consider that portion V' of V which is surrounded by the surface S_1, S_2, ..., S_n, Σ.

Now let $\mathbf{E} = \mathbf{F}$. Hence

$$\int_{V'} (\mathbf{E} \cdot \nabla_s \times \nabla_s \times \psi \mathbf{a} - \psi \mathbf{a} \cdot \nabla \times \nabla \times \mathbf{E}) \, dV$$

$$= - \int_{S_1 \dots S_n, \, \Sigma} (\psi \mathbf{a} \times \nabla_s \times \mathbf{E} - \mathbf{E} \times \nabla_s \times \psi \mathbf{a}\} \cdot \mathbf{i}_n dS \qquad \text{(A.23.7)}$$

in which, since ψ is a function of (x, y, z) as well as (ξ, η, ζ), it is necessary to distinguish between differentiation with respect to two sets of variables by using the subscript notations as regards the operators

$$\left. \begin{aligned} \nabla_s &= \mathbf{i}_x \frac{\partial}{\partial \xi} + \mathbf{i}_y \frac{\partial}{\partial \eta} + \mathbf{i}_z \frac{\partial}{\partial \zeta} \\[2mm] \nabla_F &= \mathbf{i}_x \frac{\partial}{\partial x} + \mathbf{i}_y \frac{\partial}{\partial y} + \mathbf{i}_z \frac{\partial}{\partial z} \end{aligned} \right\} \qquad \text{(A.23.8)}$$

and

It is possible to transform the Eq. (A.23.7) so that the constant vector $\mathbf{a}$ can be brought outside the integration sign, and the resulting equation becomes

$$\mathbf{a} \cdot \int_{V'} \left(j\omega\psi \frac{J}{\mu_0^{-1}} - \frac{\rho}{\varepsilon_0} \nabla_s \psi \right) dV - \mathbf{a} \cdot \int_{S_1, S_2 \dots S_n, \Sigma} (\mathbf{i}_n \times \mathbf{E}) \nabla_s \psi \, dS$$

$$= -\mathbf{a} \cdot \int_{S_1, S_2 \dots S_n, \, \Sigma} [j\omega\psi(\mathbf{i}_n \times \mathbf{B} - (\mathbf{i}_n \times \mathbf{E}) \times \nabla_s \psi] \, dS$$

Since $\mathbf{a}$ is arbitrary, the integrals on two sides of the above equation can be equated, which gives

$$\int_{V'} \left(j\omega\psi \frac{J}{\mu_0^{-1}} - \frac{\rho}{\varepsilon_0} \nabla_s \psi \right) dV - \int_{S_1 S_2 \dots S_n} [\mathbf{i}_n \cdot \mathbf{E})\nabla_s \psi + (\mathbf{i}_n \times \mathbf{E}) \times \nabla_s \psi - j\omega\psi(\mathbf{i}_n \times \mathbf{B})] dS$$

$$= \int_{\Sigma} [(\mathbf{i}_n \cdot \mathbf{E})\nabla_s \psi + (\mathbf{i}_n \times \mathbf{E}) \times \nabla_s \psi - j\omega\psi(\mathbf{i}_n \times \mathbf{B})] \, dS \qquad \text{(A.23.9)}$$

[Note that the surface integral over the sphere Σ is shown separately.]

It can be shown that the R.H.S. of the Eq. (A.23.9) reaches the limit $-4\pi E(x, y, z)$ with the (x, y, z)—the co-ordinates of point P, as Σ shrinks to zero. Hence the limiting value of Eq. (A.23.9) is

$$\mathbf{E}(x, y, z) = \frac{1}{4\pi} \int_V \left(\frac{P}{\varepsilon_0} \nabla_s \psi - j\omega\psi \frac{\mathbf{J}}{\mu_0^{-1}} \right) dV$$

$$+ \frac{1}{4\pi} \int_{S_1 S_2 \dots S_n} [(\mathbf{i}_n \cdot \mathbf{E})\nabla_s \psi + (\mathbf{i}_n \times \mathbf{E}) \times \nabla_s \psi - j\omega\psi(\mathbf{i}_n \times \mathbf{B})] dS \qquad \text{(A.23.10)}$$

This important formula gives $\mathbf{E}$ at any point in the volume V in terms of sources within V and field values on the surfaces which enclose V.

Now, let $\mathbf{B} = \mathbf{F}$ and a similar formula for $\mathbf{B}(x, y, z)$ can be deduced, by taking curl of the Eq. (A.23.10).

$$\mathbf{B}(x, y, z) = \frac{1}{4\pi} \int_V \frac{\mathbf{J}}{\mu_0^{-1}} \times \nabla_s \psi \, dV$$

$$+ \frac{1}{4\pi} \int_{S_1, S_2, \dots, S_n} \left[\frac{j\omega\psi}{c^2}(\mathbf{i}_n \times \mathbf{E}) + (\mathbf{i}_n \times \mathbf{B}) \times \nabla_s \psi + (\mathbf{i}_n \cdot \mathbf{B})\nabla_s \psi \right] dS \qquad \text{(A.23.11)}$$

If the volume V is totally unbounded, Eqs. (A.23.10) and (A.23.11) reduce to

$$\mathbf{E} = \int_V \frac{\rho\nabla_s \psi}{4\pi\varepsilon_0} \, dV - j\omega \int_V \frac{\mathbf{J}\psi}{4\pi\mu_0^{-1}} \, dV \qquad \text{(A.23.12)}$$

$$\mathbf{B} = \int_V \frac{\mathbf{J} \times \nabla_s \psi}{4\pi\mu_0^{-1}} \, dV \qquad \text{(A.23.13)}$$

Since $\nabla_F \psi = \nabla_s \psi$, and since $\mathbf{J}$ and the limits of integration are functions of (ξ, η, ζ) and not of x, y, z, the above results can be expressed as

$$\mathbf{E} = -\nabla_F \int_V \frac{\rho\psi}{4\pi\varepsilon_0} \, dV - j\omega \int \frac{\mathbf{J}\psi}{4\pi\mu_0^{-1}} \, dV \qquad \text{(A.23.14)}$$

$$\mathbf{B} = \nabla_F \times \int_V \frac{\mathbf{J}\psi}{4\pi\mu_0} \, dV \qquad \text{(A.23.15)}$$

The potential functions then are

$$\mathbf{A}(x, y, z, t) = \int_V \frac{\mathbf{J}(\xi, \eta, \zeta) \, e^{j(\omega t - kR)}}{4\pi\mu_0^{-1} R} \, dV$$

$$\phi(x, y, z, t) = \int_V \frac{\rho(\xi, \eta, \zeta) e^{j(\omega t - kR)}}{4\pi\varepsilon_0 R} \, dV$$

Note: Since $k = \dfrac{\omega}{c}, \, R = \dfrac{\omega R}{c}$.

Appendix 24

Frequency Spectrum for Wireless Communication

A.24.1 GENERAL CLASSIFICATION

1. Extremely Low Frequency (ELF)   Below 3 kHz
2. Very Low Frequency (VLF)   3 kHz to 30 kHz
   —Propagate between the earth's surface and the ionosphere, with low attenuation. Frequencies lower than 3 kHz (ELF) are effective for underwater communication channels and for mines and subterranean communication.
3. Low Frequencies (LF)   30 kHz to 300 kHz
4. Medium Frequencies (MF)   300 kHz to 3 MHz
   —They are useful for radio navigation of ships and air-crafts, and for broadcasting. Such radio waves propagate along the earth's surface by following the curvature of the earth— and are called 'surface waves', e.g. a 100 kHz wave has a wavelength of 3000 m and hence ground features, viz. buildings, hills trees, build-up topography, etc. do not affect significantly the radio propagation.
5. High Frequencies (HF)   3 MHz to 30 MHz
   —Signals in this spectrum propagate by reflection caused by the ionosphere. These are called 'sky waves'. This type of radio signal is used for long-distance land communication by broadcasting stations, i.e.—'short wave radio'.
6. Very High Frequencies (VHF)   30 MHz to 300 MHz
   —Used in a line-of-sight (LOS) mode for TV communications, long-range radar systems and radio-navigation systems.
7. Ultra High Frequencies (UHF)   300 MHz to 3 GHz
   (In some literature, its upper part 0.5 GHz to 3 GHz is also divided into P, L, S bands.) This frequency band is very effective for wireless microwave links for cellular systems (fixed and mobile), and for satellite communication channel.
   —Sometimes these are called 'Satellite waves'. In recent decades radio waves with frequencies higher than 3 GHz (C, X, K bands up to several hundred GHz-loosely described as microwaves) have begun to be used for constructing new kinds of wireless communication channels.

A.24.2 RADAR IEEE BAND DESIGNATIONS

1.	HF (High Frequency)	3–30 MHz
2.	VHF (Very High Frequency)	30–300 MHz
3.	UHF (Ultra High Frequences)	300–1000 MHz
4.	L-Band	1–2 GHz
5.	S-Band	2–4 GHz
6.	C-Band	4–8 GHz
7.	X-Band	8–12 GHz
8.	Ku-Band	12–18 GHz
9.	K-Band	18–27 GHz
10.	K_a-Band	27–40 GHz
11.	Millimetre Wave Band	40–300 GHz

Cellular Telephone

Land Mobile Systems
uplink (MS to BS) = Mobile station to Base station
Downlink (BS to MS) = Base station to Mobile station

	Uplink (MHz)	Downlink (MHz)
U.S. (IS 54)	869–894	824–849
Europe–Asia (GSM)	890–915	935–960
(Global System for Mobile communications)		
Japan (ATT)	870–855	925–940
Nippon Telegraph and Telephone corporation		

Cordless Telephone

U.S.A.	46–49 MHz
Digital European Cordless Communication (DECT)	1880–1.990 GHz

Radio

Amplitude Modulation (AM) Radio
No. of channels (107)—each with 10 kHz separation
Frequency range—535–1605 kHz
Frequency Modulation (FM) Radio
No. of channels (100) each with 200 kHz separation
Frequency Range 88–108 MHz.

Amatuer Bands

	Band	Frequency (MHz)	Band	Frequency (MHz)
1.	160 m	1.8–2.0	2 m	144.0–148.0
2.	80 m	3.5–4.0		220–225
3.	40 m	7.0–7.3		420–450
4.	20 m	14.0–14.35		1215–1300

5.	15 m	21.0–21.45		2300–2450
6.	10 m	28.0–29.7		3300–3500
7.	6 m	50.0–54.0		5650–5925

Television

VHF channels												
Channel no.	2	3	4	5	6	7	8	9	10	11	12	13

Channel no.	2	3	4	5	6	7	8	9	10	11	12	13

Frequency (MHz) 54↑60↑66↑72↑76↑82↑88↑174↑180↑186↑192↑198↑ 204↑ 210↑ 216↑

UHF Channels

Channel No   14   15   16   17   18   19   20   82   83

Frequency (MHz) 470↑476↑ 482↑ 488↑ 494↑ 500↑ 506↑ 512   878↑ 884↑ 890

For both VHF and UHF channels, each channel has a 6 MHz band width. For each channel the carrier frequency for the video part is equal to the lower frequency of the band width plus 1.25 MHz, while the carrier frequency for the audio part is equal to the upper frequency of the bandwidth minus 0.25 MHz.

Appendix 25

Some Electromagnetic Effects Associated with Other Forms of Energy

A.25.1 INTRODUCTION

There are a number of electromagnetic effects and also some effects associated with other forms of energy, i.e. thermal, chemical, and so on which have applications in various measurement devices. These measurements are not merely restricted to those of electric or magnetic or electromagnetic parameters, but also non-magnetic variables such as length, position etc. A number of such effects are described here. The present discussion is neither exhaustive nor very detailed. Only the salient points of some of these widely used effects have been mentioned here.

A.25.2 HALL EFFECT

This effect along with its important applications has been discussed in reasonable depth in Section 9.3.1 (Chapter 9) of Electromagnetism (Theory)—Volume 1 and hence here only some of the salient points will be stated.

This effect which is named after Edwin H. Hall (1855–1935) was discovered by him in 1879 and states that:

If an electric current flows in a wire or a strip placed in a strong transverse magnetic field, then a potential difference is developed across the wire, at right angles to both the magnetic field and the wire.

The Hall effect is a consequence of Lorentz force and can be expressed as

$$\mathbf{F} = e\mathbf{E} + e(\mathbf{v} \times \mathbf{B}) \tag{A.25.1}$$

and when the external electric field is expressed in terms of current density, then the Hall voltage is given by

$$\mathbf{E}_H = -R_H[\mathbf{J} \times \mathbf{B}] \tag{A.25.2}$$

where

$$R_H = \text{Hall coefficient} = \frac{1}{q \cdot n} \tag{A.25.3}$$

n = density of free-electrons
q = elementary charge

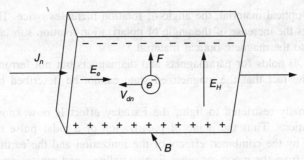

Figure A.25.1   Hall effect in long sample of *N* material: The magnetic forces push the electrons towards the upper boundary of the strip, so that a Hall voltage appears between the charged edges of the strip.

It should be noted that $\mathbf{E}_H$, $\mathbf{J}$ and $\mathbf{B}$ form a mutually orthogonal system, and so $\mathbf{B}$, while remaining perpendicular to both $\mathbf{J}$ and $\mathbf{E}_H$, can also be parallel to the flat face of the strip. This is the basic point which enables construction of 'vertical hall devices' which in turn permit a single chip to be used for 3-axis hall probes for more accurate magnetic field measurements.

A.25.3   FARADAY EFFECT (FARADAY ROTATION)

The phenomenon discovered by Faraday was: when linearly polarized light passes through a medium placed in a magnetic field and the direction of the magnetic field is parallel to that of the propagation of light, then the plane of polarization of light rotates.

Figure A.25.2 shows the scheme of a Faraday set-up. A linearly polarized light passes through magneto-optical material 3, analyser 4, and is collected by the photo receiver 5. The rotation of the plane of polarization, i.e. Faraday rotation by the signal of the photo-receiver is detected by means of the photo-receivers signal. The intensity of light transmitted by the analyser is proportional to the square of the cosine of the angle between the polarization of the incident light and the main plane of the analyser. Thus the direction of polarization of the emerging light (from the magneto-optical material) can be obtained.

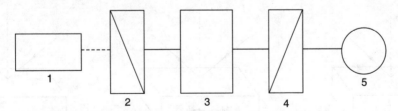

Figure A.25.2   Faraday rotation scheme.

Faraday's finding was that the angle of rotation was proportional to the magnetic intensity H and length of the magneto-optical material ($= l$) so that

$$F = VlH \tag{A.25.4}$$

where V is Verdet constant.

The Faraday effect represents an 'odd effect' with respect to the H direction. A change in the sign of H causes a change in the sense of Faraday rotation. So when light passes back and forth through the magneto-optical material, the angle of rotation increases twice. This non-reciprocity of Faraday effect enables the increase of the angle of polarization rotation substantially by passing the light back and forth to the magneto-optical material.

Equation (A.25.4) holds for paramagnets and diamagnets but not ferromagnets. The Faraday effect is related to the fact that the magnetized state cannot be described by a single refraction index.

Although originally restricted to light, the Faraday effect is now known to apply to other electromagnetic radiations. Thus the plane of polarization of a radar pulse travelling through the ionosphere is rotated by the combined effects of the ionization and the earth's magnetic field. By reflecting radar pulse from the moon, or other Earth satellites, and measuring the total rotation, the extent of ionization in the ionosphere can be calculated.

A.25.4 MAGNETO-OPTICAL KERR EFFECT

When 'plane-polarized' light is reflected from a highly polished pole of an electromagnet, the light becomes 'elliptically polarized'. Similarly, if a beam of light passes through a certain transparent liquid and solid to which a potential difference is applied, the plane of polarization of the light is rotated through an angle which depends upon the magnitude of the applied p.d. [named after John Kerr (1924–1907)].

This effect manifests itself in the change of the parameters of light reflected from a magnetic sample. That action of the sample on the light is a function of the mutual orientation of the plane of incidence of light, and of the direction of the magnetization of the sample. There are three basic types of the Kerr effect.

1. **The polar Kerr Effect:** The magnetization is perpendicular to the reflective surface and parallel to the plane of incidence [Figure A.25.3(a)].

2. **The Longitudinal (Meridional) Kerr Effect:** The magnetization is parallel to both the reflective surface and the plane of incidence [Figure A.25.3(b)].

3. **The transverse (Equatorial) Kerr Effect:** The magnetization is parallel to the reflective surface and perpendicular to the plane of incidence [Figure A.25.3(c)].

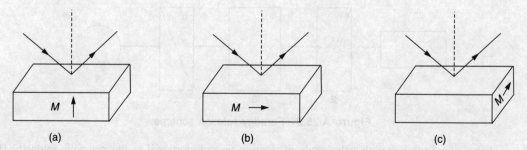

(a)   (b)   (c)

Figure A.25.3 Magneto-optical Kerr effect: (a) polar, (b) longitudinal, (c) transverse.

In polar Kerr effect, the linearly polarized light becomes elliptically polarized light, with the major axis of the polarization ellipse rotated w.r.t. the initial polarization direction. Similar changes also are observed in the longitudinal Kerr effect. A common feature of these two effects is that a component of the wave vector of light on the direction of the magnetization vector exists. This fact is responsible for the analogy of Kerr effect and the Faraday effect, and permits us to consider all those effect as longitudinal effects.

The transverse Kerr effect produces a change of intensity and in the phase shift of the reflected light. The phase shift is produced if the plane of polarization of the incident light is not either parallel or perpendicular to the plane of incidence.

A.25.5 PELTIER EFFECT

When an electric current flows across the junction between two different metals or semiconductors, a quantity of heat is evolved or absorbed, depending on the direction of the current. This quantity of heat is proportional to the total electric charge crossing the junction. This effect is due to the existence of an e.m.f. (= electromotive force) at the junction.

The discoverer of this effect was Jean Peltier (1785–1845).

A.25.6 SEEBECK EFFECT

When two wires of different metals are joined at their ends to form a circuit, and the two junctions are maintained at different temperatures, an electric current flows round the circuit.

This effect was discovered by T.J. Seebeck (1770–1831). It should be noted that the Peltier effect and the Seebeck effect are complimentary in nature.

A.25.7 NERNST EFFECT

When a temperature gradient is maintained across an electrical conductor (or semiconductor), which is placed in a transverse magnetic field, a potential difference will be produced across the conductor.

Walter Nernst (1864–1941) was the discoverer of this effect.

A.25.8 PIEZO-ELECTRIC EFFECT

This is a property of certain 'asymmetric crystals'. When such crystals are subjected to a pressure, +ve and –ve charges are produced on opposing faces. The signs of these charges get reversed if the pressure is replaced by tension. The inverse piezo-electric effect occurs when such crystals are subjected to an electric potential, whereby an alteration in the size of the crystal takes place.

This phenomenon in which a mechanical deformation produces an electric polarization is called piezo-electricity after the Greek word 'piezen' which means to 'press'. This effect was discovered by Pierre Curie; and is reciprocal; i.e. an electric field which produces polarization of the crystal, will also cause a contraction transverse to itself; and the electric field producing opposite polarization of the crystal will cause the crystal to elongate transverse to itself.

Out of 32 different classes of crystals, 20 lack a centre of symmetry and hence are possible piezo-electrics. Quartz and Rochelle salt are two common materials exhibiting this effect. Such crystals are important because they permit the conversion of mechanical energy to electrical energy and vice versa. Practical application are: the crystal pickup in a phonograph, stable frequency source, source of ultrasonic radiation, etc.

A.25.9 PINCH EFFECT

This can be summarized in two following statements:

1. The constriction of a liquid conductor (of finite cross-sectional area), e.g. mercury or molten metal-sodium-pottasium alloy, etc. which occurs when a substantial current passes through it.

2. The constriction of a plasma due to the magnetic field of a high current within the plasma.

Notes:

1. In thermo-nuclear reactions, the plasma is contained, i.e. separated from the walls of the containing vessel, either by use of externally applied magnetic field or by the magnetic field produced by the current flowing in the plasma itself.

2. For a simple mathematical analysis of pinch effect, see Problem 7.19, *Electromagnetisation: Problems and Solution* (3rd Edition); pp. 552–553.

Appendix 26

Energy, Forces and Torques in Electromechanical Systems
A Further Elaboration

A.26.1 ELECTROMECHANICAL COUPLING

An electromechanical device is a link between an electrical and a mechanical system.

The coupling between these two systems is through the medium of the fields of **electrical charges**.

These charges can be stationary or moving with constant velocity or accelerating. In general, both the electric and magnetic fields are present, and the energy stored in these fields is associated with the energy conversion. In the process of energy conversion, the energy in the coupling field may change or tend to change.

The electromechanical energy conversion process depends on the phenomena which interrelate the magnetic and the electric fields (on one hand) and the mechanical force (or torque) and the motion (linear and/or rotational) on the other. Now, in the system, at present under consideration, there are four important forces of electrical origin.

1. Force due to an electric field acting on a free charge
2. Force due to an electric field acting on a polarizable material
3. Force due to a magnetic field acting on a free moving charge (current)
4. Force due to a magnetic field acting on a magnetizable material

Note: Figures A.26.1(a) and A.26.2(a) show examples of a magnetic field electromechanical system and an electric field electromechanical system respectively; and Figures A.26.1(b) and A.26.2(b) show the schematic representation of these two systems respectively in terms of terminal parameters.

In both the cases, the coupling field does not include the mechanical energy storage and the electrical dissipative element.

Next, to analyse the energy conversion system, it is necessary to write the energy balance equation. But before this is done, since we are assuming a perfect coupling field with no intrinsic losses, the losses being incorporated at the terminals, we consider the behaviour of terminal parameters and variables. Also at this stage to keep the problem simple, a singly-connected system is being considered, i.e. the coupling field has one electrical terminal pair and one mechanical terminal pair. This simplification is no way constrains the capability of this method because when

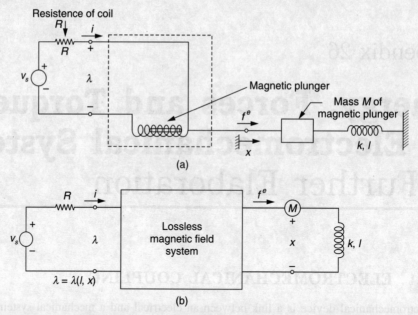

(a)

(b)

Figure A.26.1   (a) A magnetic field electromechanical system. (b) its representation in terms of terminal pairs. Note that the coupling network does not include mechanical energy storages or electrically dissipative elements (R).

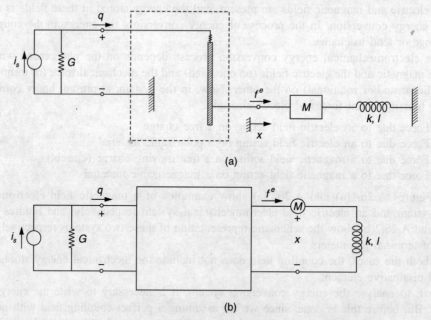

(a)

(b)

Figure A.26.2   (a) An electric field electromechanical system. (b) its representation in terms of terminal pairs. Note that the coupling network does not include mechanical energy storage element (M) or electrically dissipative elements G.

there are more than one pair of terminals on either side (i.e. multiply-connected system), the method can be extended to consider the complex situation by the **method of superposition**.

So starting with the simplest case of a singly-connected magnetic field coupling system, on the electrical side, the variables are current i and the flux-linkage λ; and on the mechanical side, the corresponding variables are force F_e and displacement x for linear motion (and for rotary motion, the corresponding variables are torque T_e and angular displacement θ). The electrical terminal variables are related and can be expressed in the form

$$\lambda = \lambda(i, x) \tag{A.26.1}$$

In physical terms, what this mathematical expression tells is that given the state (l, x) of the coupling magnetic field system, the value of λ—the flux-linkage is known.

At this stage an important assumption is being made, i.e. the mechanical force $\{= F_e\}$ of electrical origin, for a given value of the current i and a specified displacement, i.e position x {in rotational system x would be replaced by a value θ}, would have a **single value**

$$F_e = F_e(i, x) \tag{A.26.2}$$

$\{F_e$ is a single-valued function.$\}$

This assumption is reasonable and justifiable, if the coupling box contains **only those elements** that store energy in the magnetic field.

∴   All purely electrical elements (i.e. inductors not function of x, capacitors and resistors) and all purely mechanical elements (i.e. masses, springs and dampers) are connected to the terminals of the box externally.

Note: F_e is being defined as the force of electrical origin applied to the mechanical node in a direction which tends to increase the electrical displacement x, (i.e. also T_e tending to increase θ).

Now, Eq. (A.26.1) can also be solved to evaluate i, and so

$$i = i(\lambda, x) \tag{A.26.3}$$

∴   The force F_e can also be expressed as

$$F_e = F_e(\lambda, x) \tag{A.26.4}$$

At this stage, it should be carefully noted that the F_e function of Eq. (A.26.2) and of the Eq. (A.26.4) are not necessarily same, they are different functions, but for a given set of values i, λ and x, it will be seen that force F_e comes out to have the same numerical value irrespective of whether Eq. (A.26.2) or Eq. (A.26.4) has been used to evaluate F_e.

Similar arguments apply when the problem solved has a coupling electrical field, i.e.

$$F_e = F_e(q, x) \tag{A.26.5}$$

$$F_e = F_e(v, x) \tag{A.26.6}$$

Also, when the mechanical motion is rotational, the same ideas apply. All that is necessary is: F_e is replaced by T_e and x by θ. The process can also be generalized for a system with N electrical terminals and M mechanical terminals.

Question: How to evaluate F_e for a particular system?

i.e. solve the field problem—evaluate force densities—then volume integration to find the total force.

But solving the field problem is often difficult 2nd method, experimental—there are disadvantages. 3rd starting from electrical terminal relations.

Loss-less F_e from the coupling field can be evaluated analytically.

And electrical lumped parameters can be evaluated comparatively easily—is a more convenient way.

A.26.2   POTENTIAL ENERGY AND STORED ENERGY OF A SYSTEM

When the potential energy of a system is used for any mechanical work, out of the total energy taken, only one-half is used for the mechanical work, and the other half is stored in the (coupling) field.

Also the potential energy of the system is in the electrical sources.

To study and analyse the electromechanical energy conversion device or system, it becomes necessary to write **Energy Balance Equation**. Before that, it should be noted that at this stage, we are considering only, the quasi-static (i.e. low frequency) systems, in which the fields producing the forces in a particular element are either **electric** or **magnetic**, but **not both**.

We consider separately, either the forces due to the electric field or the forces due to the magnetic field.

So, start with coupling magnetic field energy storage system.

We, now, write energy balance equation. Hence, we consider some of the general properties of **loss-less** magnetic and electric field storage systems—these are functions of geometry.

Use of the 'principle of conservation of energy'

Consider the magnetic field storage system (coupling field of Figure A.26.1). The energy storage is affected by a function of both the electrical and mechanical variables. Coupling network is assumed to be loss-less. The energy fed into the system by the electrical and the mechanical terminal pairs gets stored in the magnetic field and is completely recoverable (through these terminals). Thus, it is a conservative system.

$$\therefore \qquad\qquad \text{loss-less} \equiv \text{conservative}$$

Now, energy input from electrical sources = Increase in the potential energy of the system

= Mechanical energy output + Increase in the energy stored in the coupling magnetic field

$$\downarrow \qquad\qquad\qquad\qquad \downarrow$$

$$+ \qquad\qquad\qquad\qquad +$$

(Friction and windage losses)   (Associated losses)

i.e.
$$dW_{elec} = dW_{mech} + dW_{fl} \tag{A.26.7}$$

The change in the potential energy, or the electrical energy input

$$= dW_{elec} = e.i\ dt \tag{A.26.8}$$

where

e = the time-rate of change of flux linked by the electrical circuit in the system,

i = the current in the system

If (as indicated before), λ-notation for flux-linkage, then

$$e\ dt = d\lambda$$

$$dW_{elec} = id\lambda \tag{A.26.9}$$

Next, to obtain the mechanical energy output, it is necessary to consider the mechanical force of electrical origin, i.e. $F_e(i, x)$ or $F_e(\lambda, x)$ and the displacement δx (using the already established convention for its sign).

$$dW_{\text{mech}} = F_e \, \delta x \quad \text{(for translatory motion)} \quad \text{(A.26.10)}$$

{The corresponding expression for rotary motion, would be

$$dW_{\text{mech}} = T_e \, \delta\theta\} \quad \text{(A.26.10a)}$$

The energy balance equation is

$$i \, \delta\lambda = F_e \, \delta x + dW_{\text{fld}}$$

Since the coupling field is magnetic $dW_{\text{fld}} = dW_{\text{in}}$

$$\therefore \qquad dW_m = i\delta\lambda - F_e\delta x \qquad (A.26.11)$$

The conservation of the power of the system can be expressed as

$$\frac{dW_m}{dt} = i\frac{d\lambda}{dt} - F_e\frac{dx}{dt} \qquad (A.26.12)$$

where $\dfrac{dW_m}{dt}$ = the time-rate of increase of the stored magnetic energy

$i\dfrac{d\lambda}{dt}$ = the electrical power input at the electrical terminals of the system

$-F_e\dfrac{dx}{dt}$ = power input at the mechanical-terminals

The –ve sign of the mechanical power is due to F_e has been defined to act on the mechanical node [Note before Eqs. (A.26.2) and (A.26.3)].

The energy Eq. (A.26.11) can be obtained by multiplying Eq. (A.26.12) by the time element δt and then taking the total differential.

At this stage, it should be noted that from Eqs. (A.26.3) and (A.26.4) (or Eqs. (A.26.1) and (A.26.2), of the four variables (i, λ, F_e, x), only two can be set independently, without violating the internal physics of the system. There are other constraints also, but at this stage, for simplifying, consider the 'coupling network' to be decoupled from both the electrical and the mechanical terminals; and let the independent variables be λ and x.

The reason for this choice is that the incremental changes in these variables are related to the incremental changes in the stored magnetic energy W_m.

The evaluation of the change in W_m when λ and/or x are varied by finite amounts = Line-integration through the variable space of λ and x.

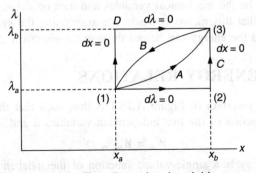

Figure A.26.3 Two-dimensional variable space.

{*Note:* The independence of the two variables is indicated by orthogonality of axes.}

To find the change in the stored energy when the independent variables are changed from (x_a, λ_a) to (x_b, λ_b).

To evaluate a line integral specify the path of integration.

Note: In a conservative system, the change in energy (stored) between any two points in variable space is independent of the path of integration.

Path C

$$W_m (\lambda_b, x_b) - W_m(\lambda_a, x_a)$$

$$= -\int_{x_a}^{x_b} F_e (\lambda_a, x) \, dx + \int_{\lambda_a}^{\lambda_b} i(\lambda, x_b) \, d\lambda \qquad (A.26.13)$$
$$\scriptstyle d\lambda=0 \qquad\qquad dx=0$$
$$\scriptstyle \text{for } 1-2 \qquad\qquad \text{for } 2-3$$

Path D

$$W_m(\lambda_b, x_b) - W_m(\lambda_a, x_a)$$

$$= \int_{\lambda_a}^{\lambda_b} i(\lambda, x_a) \, d\lambda - \int_{x_a}^{x_b} F_e (\lambda_b, x) \, dx \qquad (A.26.14)$$
$$\scriptstyle dx=0 \qquad\qquad d\lambda=0$$

The energy evaluated by both the equations must be the same.

A26.2.1   Physical Significance of the Integrations

The integrations in Eqs. (A.26.13) and (A.26.14) represent putting energy into the coupling network in two successive steps. In Eq. (A.26.13), the first integration at constant $\lambda(\lambda = \lambda_a)$, the work is being done against F_e, i.e. feeding energy into the mechanical terminals. In the 2nd integral, the energy is supplied by an electrical source which provides the excitation λ while keeping the position of the mechanical terminal fixed at x_b.

In Eq. (A.26.14), these steps have been reversed in order and the fixed parameters are suitably adjusted.

Note: When the electrical terminal variables are zero, i.e. in this case $\lambda_a = 0$, it means that there is no force of electrical origin. In this case, the difference between Eqs. (A.26.13) and (A.26.14) is that in Eq. (A.26.13), the contribution of F_e to the integration is zero {$F_e(0, x)$ = 0}. But in the second equation, F_e must be known to be able to carry out the integration, i.e. integrate first on the mechanical variables and then on the electrical variables to obtain W_m. Physically what this means is that while assembling the system, no force is required mechanically, and the energy can be put through the electrical terminal pairs.

A.26.3   FORCE–ENERGY RELATIONS

The magnetic field energy system of Figure A.26.1 is thus such that the magnetic stored energy can be expressed as a function of the two independent variables λ and x.

$\therefore$ $$W_m = W_m(\lambda, x) \qquad (A.26.15)$$

Conservative system energy is a single-valued function of the independent variables (λ, x) with finite second partial derivatives. The total differential of W_m is

$$dW_m = \frac{\partial W_m}{\partial \lambda} d\lambda + \frac{\partial W_m}{\partial x} dx \qquad (A.26.16)$$

Subtracting from Eq. (A.26.11)

$$0 = \left\{ i - \frac{\partial W_m}{\partial \lambda} \right\} d\lambda - \left\{ F_e + \frac{\partial W_m}{\partial x} \right\} dx \qquad (A.26.17)$$

Since λ and x are independent,

$$i = \frac{\partial W_m}{\partial \lambda} (\lambda, x) \qquad (A.26.18)$$

or

$$F_e = -\frac{\partial W}{\partial x} (\lambda, x) \qquad (A.26.19)$$

If the stored energy is known, the electrical and the mechanical terminal relations can be evaluated. The generalization to multiple terminals is by the method of superposition.

A.26.4   FORCE–CO-ENERGY RELATIONS

So far in the systems where magnetic field is the coupling network, the flux linkage λ has been used as the independent variable with the current i being described by the terminal relation, i.e.

$$dW_m = id\lambda - F_e dx \qquad (A.26.11)$$

and the corresponding equation for the electric field coupling has been

$$dW_e = vdq - F_e \, dx \qquad (A.26.11a)$$

where q (charge) is the independent variable and v (voltage) is described by terminal relation.

It is possible to use i as the independent variable for the magnetic field system and voltage v for the electric field system. Alternatively, sometimes it is convenient to use a hybrid set—current and flux linkage in the magnetic field system and voltage and charge in the electric field system.

Change of independent variable
For Eq. (A.26.11) shown above the electrical terminal relation is

$$\lambda = \lambda \, (i, x)$$

and the mechanical terminal relation is

$$F_e = F_e(i, x)$$

∴   To change the variable in Eq. (A.26.11), we use the total differential

$$d(\lambda i) = id\lambda + \lambda di \qquad (A.26.20a)$$

or

$$i\delta\lambda = d(\lambda i) - \lambda di \qquad (A.26.20b)$$

∴   The equation becomes

$$dW_m = \{ d(\lambda i) - \lambda di \} - F_e dx$$

or

$$d(\lambda i) - dW_m = \lambda di + F_e dx$$

or

$$dW'_m = \lambda di + F_e dx \qquad (A.26.21)$$

where

$$W'_m = \lambda i - W_m \qquad (A.26.22)$$

Now, Eq. (A.26.21) has the form in which the changes in the function W_m' are accounted for by the changes in the independent variables (i, x).

The function $W_m'(l, x)$ is called the co-energy of system and is defined in terms of the coupling energy $W_m(l, x)$ and the terminal relations $\lambda(i, x)$ by Eq. (A.26.22).

This above manipulation, which also represents 'conservation of energy' in terms of new independent variables is called a 'Legendre transformation' in classical mechanics and thermodynamics.

Equation (A.26.11) physically represents conservation of energy for the coupling network, and the form of this equation is similar to the equation and so by using similar arguments.

Since

$$W_m' = W_m'(i, x),$$

we get

$$dW_m' = \frac{\partial W_m'}{\partial i} di + \frac{\partial W_m'}{\partial x} dx \tag{A.26.23a}$$

Subtracting Eq. (A.26.23) from Eq. (A.26.21),

$$0 = \left\{ \lambda - \frac{\partial W_m'}{\partial i} \right\} di + \left\{ F_e - \frac{\partial W_m'}{\partial x} \right\} dx \tag{A.26.23b}$$

Since di and dx are independent,

$$\lambda = \frac{\partial W_m'}{\partial i}(i, x) \tag{A.26.24}$$

$$F_e = \frac{\partial W_m'}{\partial x}(l, x) \tag{A.26.25}$$

$\therefore$ If the stored energy is known (hence the co-energy as well), the electrical and the mechanical terminal relations can be evaluated.

Comparing Eq. (A.26.25) with Eq. (A.26.19), this shows the change in the form of the mechanical force expression when the independent variable is changed from λ to i,

Generalization

For a magnetic field coupling system, for N electrical terminal pairs and M translational mechanical terminal pairs, the energy equation

$$dW_m = \sum_{j=1}^{N} i_j d\lambda_j - \sum_{j=1}^{M} F_{ej} dx_j \tag{A.26.26}$$

and

$$\sum_{j=1}^{N} i_j d\lambda_j = \sum_{j=1}^{N} d(i_j, \lambda_j) - \sum_{j=1}^{N} \lambda_j di_j \tag{A.26.27}$$

$\therefore$

$$dW_m' = \sum_{j=1}^{N} X_j di_j + \sum_{j=1}^{M} F_{ej} dx_j \tag{A.26.28}$$

where

$$W_m' = \sum_{j=1}^{N} i_j \lambda_j - W_m \tag{A.26.29}$$

A.26.5 GRAPHICAL REPRESENTATION OF FLUX-MMF CHARACTERISTIC TO EXPLAIN THE ENERGY–CO-ENERGY RELATION

The relationship between (magnetic) energy and co-energy has been already established by Eq. (A.26.22), i.e.

$$W'_m = \lambda i - W_m \tag{A.26.22}$$

or generalizing for an n terminal coupling system,

$$W'_m = \sum_{i=1}^{n} \lambda_i l_i - W_m \tag{A.26.22a}$$

For the ith circuit, graphically it can be represented as in Figure A.26.4.

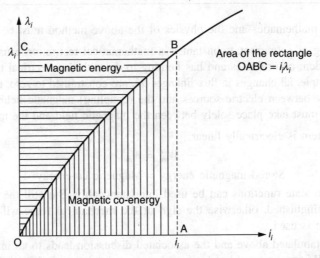

Figure A.26.4 Graphical relation between magnetic energy and co-energy.

The independent variables for the force–energy relations are λ-flux-linkage and x-displacement.
   The independent variables for the force co-energy relation are i-current and x-displacement.
Energy and co-energy are complementary in nature.

Stored magnetic energy $W_m = \int_{0...0}^{\lambda_1...\lambda_n} \sum_{i=1}^{n} i'_\lambda d\lambda'_i$

Magnetic co-energy $W'_m = \int_{0...0}^{i_1...i_n} \sum_{i=1}^{n} \lambda'_i \, di'_i$

Relation between energy and co-energy $W_m + W'_m = \sum_{i=1}^{n} i_i \lambda_i$

Conservation of energy during arbitrary displacement dx_k (loss-less)

$$= \sum_{i=1}^{n} i_i d\lambda_i = dW_m + (Fe)_k \, dx_k$$

The four expressions for $(F_e)_k$ given below are equivalent and will give the same force value identically, which is the true force for a given set of the system, i.e. i_i, λ_i, x_j.

The results of Table A.26.1 are completely general and independent of electrical source variation {for quasi-static problems}.

Table A.26.1   Mechanical Force Caused by Magnetic Coupling Field

Independent variables	Force evaluated from stored energy	Force evaluated from co-energy
Currents i_i co-ordinates x_j	$(F_e)_k = -\dfrac{\partial W_m}{\partial x_k} + \sum_{i=1}^{n} i_i \dfrac{\partial \lambda_i}{\partial x_k}$	$(F_e)_k = \dfrac{\partial W_m'}{\partial x_k}$
Flux linkages λ_i co-ordinates x_j	$(F_e)_k = \dfrac{\partial W_m'}{\partial x_k}$	$(F_e)_k = \dfrac{\partial W_m'}{\partial x_k} - \sum_{i=1}^{n} \lambda_i \dfrac{\partial i_i}{\partial x_k}$

However, the mathematics and the physics of the above method must be clearly understood.

1. The holding of i_s (currents) constant is a mathematical restriction caused by the selection of independent co-ordinates and has nothing to do with the electrical terminal constraints.

2. If, for example, all changes in flux linkages $d\lambda_i$ are constrained to zero, then there can be no energy flow between electric sources and the (coupling) magnetic fields; hence the energy conversion must take place solely between the magnetic field and the mechanical system.

When the system is electrically linear,

$$W_m' = W_m$$

then   Stored magnetic energy = Magnetic co-energy

In this case, the two state functions can be used interchangeably. But still the energy and the co-energy must be distinguished, otherwise the sign of the mechanical force will be in error, if the wrong state function is used.

Note: The results tabulated above and the associated discussion leads to an interpretation that the co-energy W_m' can be considered as a measure of the convertibility of the electrical energy from constant-current sources.

A.26.6   RECIPROCITY CONDITION

A conservative electromechanical coupling system, described mathematically must satisfy a 'reciprocity condition' which is a generalization of the reciprocity discussed in circuit theory.

Consider a magnetic field system, shown in Figure A.26.1 for which the terminal relations expressed in terms of the stored energy W_m in Eqs. (A.26.18) and (A.26.19) are:

$$i = \frac{\partial W_m}{\partial \lambda}(\lambda, x) \tag{A.26.18}$$

and

$$F_e = -\frac{\partial W_m}{\partial x}(\lambda, x) \tag{A.26.19}$$

Differentiating Eq. (A.26.18) w.r.t. x and Eq. (A.26.19) w.r.t. λ,

and $\because$ $$\frac{\partial^2 W_m(\lambda, x)}{\partial k \, \partial \lambda} = \frac{\partial^2 W_m(\lambda, x)}{\partial \lambda \, \partial x}$$

the reciprocity relation comes out to be

$$\frac{\partial i}{\partial x}(\lambda, x) = -\frac{\partial F_e}{\partial \lambda}(\lambda, x) \tag{A.26.30}$$

The above process shows that the reciprocity condition is necessary for the system to be conservative. It can also be shown that this condition is sufficient as well for the coupling system to be conservative. (It will be found in any good textbook on thermodynamics.)

This reciprocity condition can be generalized for a conservative system with any number of terminal pairs. Although the reciprocity conditions must always be satisfied for a conservative system, they are not very much used in the design and analysis of these systems. The usefulness of the conditions are due to:

(a) they provide a quick check to identify certain kinds of mathematical errors
(b) they provide a mathematical framework to find classes of non-linear functions for approximating the terminal relations of multi-terminal, electrical non-linear systems.

If the reciprocity conditions are not fulfilled, then the mathematical description implies the existence of energy sources and/or sinks which can be non-physical.

A.26.7 CONCLUSION: ENERGY CONVERSION

For any conservative coupling system, the conservation of energy can be expressed as

$$\boxed{\text{Electrical energy input}} + \boxed{\text{Mechanical energy input}} = \boxed{\text{Change in stored energy}} \tag{A.26.31}$$

For a cyclic process, the above equation becomes

$$\boxed{\begin{array}{c}\text{Net electrical energy} \\ \text{input for one cycle}\end{array}} + \boxed{\begin{array}{c}\text{Net mechanical energy} \\ \text{input for one cycle}\end{array}} = 0 \tag{A.26.32}$$

So it becomes necessary to calculate only one energy input to evaluate the net energy conversion between the two energy forms.

Example A.26.1 Figure A.26.5 shows the basic configuration which is used for tripping mechanism of circuit breakers, operating valves, etc. in which a large force has to be applied to a member which moves a relatively small distance. It consists of a fixed structure made of highly permeable magnetic material with an excitation winding of N turns. A movable plunger, also made of same highly permeable material (magnetic) is constrained to move in x-direction by using a non-magnetic sleeve of thickness g and rectangular cross-section. The thickness of the structure perpendicular to the plane of the paper is d {Figure A.26.5a).

(a) Evaluate the flux linkage λ at the electrical terminal pairs and the terminal voltage v for a specified time variation of the current i and the displacement x.
(b) In the actual system, let the winding resistance of the excitation coil and any additional series resistance be represented by R in the external circuit. A spring K is used to open the gap x to its maximum value when the current is zero. [The source $v_s(t)$ being either a +ve or –ve step.] The linear damper B represents the friction between the non-magnetic sleeve and the plunger.

Calculate the mechanical force of electrical origin and write down the complete equations of motion.

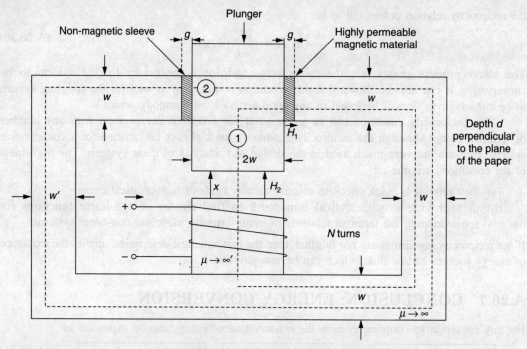

(a) Section of the magnetic field system, showing the basic configuration and the plunger. The $\oint H \cdot dl$ contours ① and ② are also indicated.

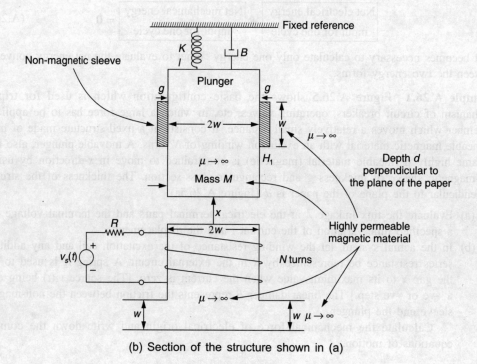

(b) Section of the structure shown in (a)

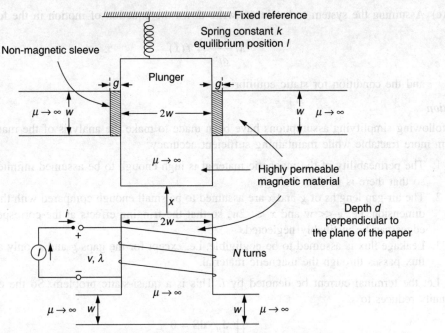

(c) Section of the structure shown in (a) {magnetic field transducer to explain the linearization techniques}

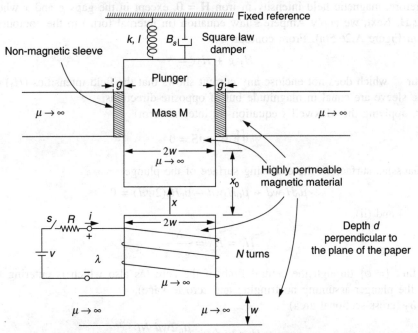

(d) Section of the structure shown in (a) {basic configuration of actuator for mechanically damped time-delay relay}.

Figure A.26.5 A magnetic field electromechanical system.

(c) Assuming the system to be linear, write down the equation of motion in the form

$$M \frac{d^2 x}{dt^2} = f(x)$$

and the condition for static equilibrium.

Solution

The following simplifying assumptions have been made to make the analysis of the magnetic field system more tractable while maintaining sufficient accuracy.

1. The permeability of the magnetic material is high enough to be assumed infinite ($\mu_r \to \infty$) so that there is no flux leakage.
2. The air-gap lengths of g and x are assumed to be small enough compared with the tranverse dimension, i.e. $g \ll w$ and $x \ll 2w$, so that the fringing effects at the corresponding gap edges can be justifiably neglected.
3. Leakage flux is assumed to be negligible, i.e. except for the gaps g and x, only appreciable flux passes through the magnetic material.

Let the terminal current be denoted by i. This is a quasi-static problem. So the equation of continuity reduces to

$$\oiint \mathbf{J}_n \cdot \mathbf{dS} = 0$$

and $\mathbf{B} = \mu \mathbf{H}$ in magnetic material $\mu \to \infty$.

Therefore, magnetic field intensity in iron $\mathbf{H} = 0$, except in the gaps g and x where $\mathbf{M} = 0$, and $\mathbf{B} = \mu_0 \mathbf{H}$. Next, we apply Ampere's law equation (in internal form) to the contours ① and ② as shown in Figure A.26.5(a). From contour ①,

$$H_1 g + H_2 x = Ni \tag{i}$$

The contour ② which does not enclose any current shows that the field intensities (H_1) on the two gaps of the sleeve are equal in magnitude but of opposite directions.

Next, applying the Maxwell's equation (in integral form)

$$\oiint \mathbf{B}_n \cdot \mathbf{dS} = 0$$

with the Gaussian surface as the enclosing surface of the plunger

$$\mu_0 H_1 wd + \mu_0 H_1 wd - \mu_0 H_2 (2wd) = 0 \tag{ii}$$

From Eqs. (i) and (ii),

$$H_1 = H_2 = \frac{N_i}{g + x} \tag{iii}$$

Next, the flux $\{= \phi\}$ through the central limb of the core (as also which is entering the bottom surface of the plunger-assuming no fringing and zero leakage),

$\phi = B_2$ (cross-sectional area)

$$= \mu_0 H_2 (2wd) = \frac{\mu_0 2wd \, Ni}{g + x} \tag{iv}$$

This flux is enclosed by the N-turn winding of the central limb, and hence the linked flux ($= \lambda$),

$$\lambda = N\phi = \frac{\mu_0 \, 2wdNiN}{g+x} = \frac{\mu_0 \, 2wdN^2 i}{g+x} \qquad \text{(v)}$$

Again, since the flux linkage (= λ) is a linear function of i —the system is electrically linear, it can be expressed as

$$\lambda = L(x)i \qquad \text{(vi)}$$

$L(x)$, being the self-inductance of the magnetic circuit, is given by

$$\therefore \qquad L(x) = \frac{2wd\mu_0 N^2}{g+x} \qquad \text{(vii)}$$

When it is assumed that the current and displacement are specified function of time, then the terminal voltage can be evaluated as

$$v = \underbrace{\frac{2wd\mu_0 N^2}{g+x} \frac{di}{dt}}_{\substack{\uparrow \\ \text{Transformer voltage} \\ \text{\{this part exists, if } x \text{ is fixed} \\ \text{and } i \text{ is varying\}}}} - \underbrace{\frac{2wd\mu_0 N^2 i}{(g+x)^2} \frac{dx}{dt}}_{\substack{\uparrow \\ \text{Speed voltage or motional voltage} \\ \text{\{this exists, if } i \text{ is constant and} \\ x \text{ is varying\}}}} \qquad \text{(viii)}$$

So far the flux-linkage and the inductance have been written in terms of the gaps in the infinitely permeable core, i.e.

$$\lambda(x) = \frac{\mu_0 \, 2wdN^2 i}{g+x} \quad \text{and} \quad L(x) = \frac{2wd\mu_0 N^2}{g+x}$$

For $x = 0$, i.e. the variable gap on the central limb has been closed, then denoting this value by L_0, we get

$$L_0 = \frac{2wd\mu_0 N^2}{g}, \text{ then } L = \frac{L_0}{1 + \dfrac{x}{g}} \text{ and } \lambda = \frac{L_0 i}{1 + \dfrac{x}{g}}$$

Then the terminal voltage of the coupling system [Eq. (viii)] can be expressed as

$$v_s(t) = \frac{L_0}{1 + \dfrac{x}{g}} \frac{di}{dt} - \frac{L_0 i}{g\left(1 + \dfrac{x}{g}\right)^2} \frac{dx}{dt} + iR \qquad \text{(ix)}$$

The third term comes in because as shown in Figure A.26.5(b), the supply to the excitation coil has now an internal resistance R which has to be shown external to the conservative coupling field.

For the equation of motion for the mechanical node, the force of electric origin has to be calculated. So the magnetic co-energy of the system has to be evaluated

i.e.

$$W'_m = \int_0^i \lambda(i, x) \, di'$$

$$= \frac{1}{2} \frac{L_0 i^2}{1 + x/g} \qquad \text{(x)}$$

$$\therefore \qquad\qquad F_e = \frac{\partial W_m'}{\partial x}$$

$$= -\frac{1}{2}\frac{L_0 l^2}{g(1 + x/g)^2} \qquad\qquad\qquad (xi)$$

$\therefore$ The equation of motion is

$$-\frac{1}{2}\frac{L_0 i^2}{g(1 + x/g)^2} = M\frac{d^2 x}{dt^2} + B\frac{dx}{dt} + K(x - l) \qquad\qquad (xii)$$

where K is the spring constant and the force is a linear function of the relative displacement of the two ends of the spring, e.g.

$$f = k(x_2 - x_1 - l) \qquad\qquad\qquad (xiii)$$

where l is value of the relative displacement for which the force is zero.

{Similar equation for the torque exists which is having relative angular displacements.}

The force at one end of the spring {$= F_s$} must always be balanced by an equal and opposite force at the other end. The fore is thus transmitted by the spring is in a manner like the current transmitted through an inductance. The applied force can be considered as a force source.

Damper (Mechanical):   This is analogous to electrical resistance in that it dissipates energy as heat. An ideal damper exhibits no mass or spring effect and exerts a force which is a function of the relative velocity between its two nodes. A linear damper {also called a viscous damper} is so constructed that the friction forces are due to the viscous drag of a fluid under laminar flow conditions. Force (F) {or torque T} is the force {or torque} that must be applied by an external agent to produce a positive relative velocity of the two nodes. For the linear motion damper, the terminal relation is

$$F = B\frac{d}{dt}(x_2 - x_1) \quad \text{or} \quad T = B\frac{d}{dt}(\theta_2 - \theta_1) \qquad\qquad (xiv)$$

It should be noted that B has different dimensions in these two above equations. Mechanical friction occurs under many different physical conditions—sometimes unwanted and sometimes desired. The final model of friction which has also to be considered is one resulting from the drag of a viscous fluid in turbulent flow. This type of friction is represented by a model which makes the force (or torque) proportional to the square of relative velocity (or relative angular velocity), i.e.

$$F = \pm B_s \left\{ \frac{d}{dt}(x_2 - x_1) \right\}^2 \qquad\qquad\qquad (xv)$$

Mass: The motion of a point which has associated with it a constant amount of mass M is described by Newton's second law:

$$\mathbf{F} = M\frac{d\mathbf{v}}{dt} \qquad\qquad\qquad (xvi)$$

where $\mathbf{F}$ is the force vector acting on the mass point and $\mathbf{v}$ is the vector velocity of the point. It should be clearly recognized that $\mathbf{v}$ must be measured in relation to a fixed or non-accelerating point or frame of reference (Such a reference system is called an inertial frame of reference). In motions occurring on the earth's surface, the earth is often approximated to an inertial reference frame, and $\mathbf{v}$ is measured in relation to the earth. But when dealing with the motion of long-range missiles, orbital vehicles, and spacecrafts, the earth cannot be considered as a non-accelerating reference, and the velocities are then measured w.r.t. fixed stars.

Note that Eqs. (ix) and (xii) are the equations of motion of the given system. Here the two dependent variables (the unknowns) are i and x. The source voltage $v_s(t)$ is the driving function. These equations can be solved completely, if $v_s(t)$ is specified completely and also the initial conditions are stated. The dynamic behaviour of the system can then be studied.

In the system under consideration, the electrical excitation is a current source, and so instead of considering the conditions at the pair of electrical terminals, the mechanical terminals are considered, and to linearize the system, damping is neglected. So the equation of motion for the mechanical node (x) is calculated as follows:

From Eq. (xii),

$$M\frac{d^2x}{dt^2} = -\frac{L_0 I^2}{2g(1 + x/g)^2} - K(x - l) \tag{xvii}$$

where the flux-linkage $\lambda = \dfrac{L_0 i}{1 + x/g}$

and $\qquad L_0 = \dfrac{\mu_0 N^2 (2wd)}{g}$ = inductance with the air-gap closed $(x = 0)$ $\qquad$ (xviii)

The force of the electric origin $(= F_e)$ has been obtained as

$$F_e = -\frac{L_0 I^2}{2g(1 + x/g)^2} \tag{xix}$$

Thus Eq. (xvii) has the form

$$M\frac{d^2x}{dt^2} = F(x) \tag{xx}$$

for which it can be said that mass M is in equilibrium at any point $x = X$ such that $f(X) = 0$.

Physically this means that at the point $x = X$, there is no external force to accelerate the mass, and hence it is possible that the mass can retain a static position (i.e. be in equilibrium) at this point

$\therefore \qquad\qquad F(x) = \dfrac{L_0 I^2}{2g(1 + x/g)^2} - K(x - l) = F_e(x) + F_s(x) \qquad$ (xxi)

For static equilibrium, this equation becomes

$$F(X) = \frac{L_0 I^2}{2g(1 + x/g)^2} - K(X - l) = 0 \tag{xxii}$$

This is a cubic equation where solution, though possible is not quite simple. It has three solutions. There are two values X_1 and X_2 at which the plunger experience no external forces and hence can be in static equilibrium. The third root of the cubic polynomial equation is less than zero and hence this is not physically achievable as then the plunger has to extend into the magnetic yoke.

Also for a given set of physical and geometrical parameters, all the three values of X can be determined uniquely. Here, instead of solving the problem formally mathematically, we will treat this problem in a qualitative manner. For the set of parameters under consideration, both $F_e(X)$ and $F_s(X)$ can be plotted over a range of values of X as shown in Figure A.26.6.

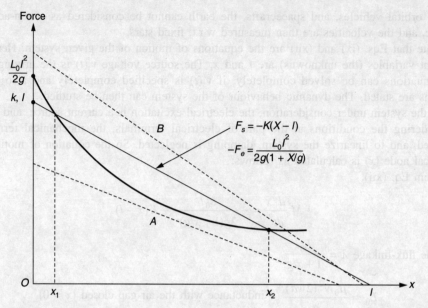

Figure A.26.6 Sketch to evaluate the equilibrium points of the system under consideration.

It is obvious that the relative values of the parameters can be such that there are no possible equilibrium points (curve A) or even only one equilibrium point (curve B), but when they exist, their values are for $x < l$.

From physical considerations, this is justifiable, as force F_e always tends to pull the plunger into the yoke. Lastly, to find the stability of the equilibrium points, the slopes of $\dfrac{dF_e}{dx}$ and $\dfrac{dF_s}{dx}$ have to be considered.

At $x = x_1$ $\dfrac{dF_e}{dx} > \dfrac{dF_s}{dx}$, and hence $\dfrac{dF}{dx}$ has the sign of $\dfrac{dF_e}{dx}$

$\therefore$
$$\frac{dF}{dx}(x_1) > 0 \qquad \text{(xxiii)}$$

$\therefore$ the equilibrium point is unstable.

On the other hand, at $x = x_2$, $\dfrac{dF_s}{dx} > \dfrac{dF_e}{dx}$

$\therefore$
$$\frac{dF}{dx}(x_2) < 0 \qquad \text{(xxiv)}$$

and the equilibrium point at x_2 is stable.

The basic device that has been studied so far, will now be made more realistic and considered as a non-linear problem. The device shown in Figure A.26.5(a) is now the basic actuator for a mechanically damped time-delay relay [section shown in Figure A.26.5(d)]. Its basic operation to be analysed is: Switch S is initially open and the spring pulls the plunger against a mechanical stop at $x = x_0$. On closing switch S, the current in the excitation coil produces a magnetic force which pulls the plunger against the stop at $x = 0$. This displacement either opens or closes the relay contacts. The motion of the plunger when driven by the magnetic force is affected or controlled by the mechanical dampers which here consist of a piston moving in a cylinder filled with oil and has a damping force proportional to the square of the velocity. Assuming the magnetic material to be infinitely permeable and neglecting the fringing, the electrical and the mechanical terminal relations have been obtained as:

$$\lambda = \frac{L_0 i}{1 + x/g}$$

$$F_e = -\frac{L_0 i^2}{2g(1 + x/g)^2}$$

where

$$L_0 = \frac{\mu_0 N^2 (2wd)}{g}$$

Now, with switch S closed and the plunger between the stops

$$0 < x < x_0$$

the equations of motion are

$$V = R_i + \frac{L_0}{1 + x/g} \frac{di}{dt} - \frac{L_0 i}{g(1 + x/g)^2} \frac{dx}{dt} \tag{xxv}$$

$$M \frac{d^2 x}{dt^2} \pm B_s \left(\frac{dx}{dt} \right)^2 + k(x - l) = -\frac{L_0 i^2}{2g(1 + x/g)^2} \tag{xxvi}$$

The +ve or −ve sign is so chosen as to make the damping force oppose the motion.

The transient condition to be analysed is what happens when switch S is closed at $t = 0$ with the initial conditions:

at $t = 0$, $i = 0$ and $x = x_0$

The damper controls the motion and slows the plunger and the closing down time becomes substantially longer (in minutes) so that $\dfrac{dx}{dt}$ term in Eq. (xxv) can be neglected. Hence the current equation is now

$$V = R_i + \frac{L_0}{1 + x/g} \frac{di}{dt} \tag{xxvii}$$

and the transient current is

$$i = \frac{V}{R} \{1 - e^{-t/\tau_e}\} \tag{xxviii}$$

where

$$\tau_e = \frac{L_0}{R(1 + x_0/g)}$$

$$= \text{Electrical time constant with the gap fully open}$$

Since for the mechanical motion, the damping force is most powerful and much greater than the accelerating force and the spring force (except for very short initial time), Eq. (xxvi) simplifiers to

$$-B_s \left(\frac{dx}{dt} \right)^2 = -\frac{L_0(V/R)^2}{2g(1 + x/g)^2} \qquad \text{(xxix)}$$

and the velocity comes out as:

$$\frac{dx}{dt} = -\frac{\sqrt{L_0/(2gB_s)}\ V/R}{1 + x/g} \qquad \text{(xxx)}$$

With the initial condition as specified earlier, by integrating the above equation, a quadratic in x is obtained from which the value of x comes out as

$$x = -g + \left\{ (g + x_0)^2 - \left(\frac{2L_0 g}{B_s} \right)^{1/2} \frac{V}{R} t \right\}^{1/2} \qquad \text{(xxxi)}$$

This expression satisfies the initial condition at $t = 0$, $x = x_0$.

Appendix 27

Maxwell's Stress Tensor

A.27.1 INTRODUCTION

Maxwell's stress have been discussed from physical considerations in Section 11.14 of Chapter 11 [Electromagnetism (Theory): Volume 1], with particular reference to magnetic fields. In that discussion it was seen that the "total force" between magnetic materials can be evaluated by considering a system of stresses on any closed surface round the magnetic bodies under consideration. The physical aspects of the method applied to magnetic field systems have been covered. However, it should be clearly understood that the method is equally applicable to electric field systems, and hence it can be said in general terms that electromechanical interactions involving the effects on the mechanical system from the electromagnetic fields, i.e. the mechanical forces of electrical origin, would be covered by this method.

Since the physical aspects of the method have already been discussed, what is proposed here is to set up the mathematical formalism of the method (and hence the derivation of the stress tensor). It should be noted that the forces, which define the electromagnetic field, are made of two parts (i) forces exerted on free charges by electric fields, (ii) forces exerted on free moving charges (i.e. free currents) by magnetic fields. The relative importance of these forces is a function of the type of system under consideration. As in magnetic field systems, the free current density J_f provides the important field excitation, and hence the important forces are due to the interactions of J_f with magnetic fields. Similarly, the significant forces in electric field systems are caused by the interactions of free charge density ρ_f with electric fields. There are also two other technically important electromagnetic forces which are the results of the interactions of polarization vector P with electric fields and the magnetization density vector M with magnetic fields. This method can be extended to account for force densities in polarized and/or magnetized media which are electrically linear, isotropic and homogeneous (LIH).

A.27.2 FORCES IN MAGNETIC FIELD SYSTEMS

The force considered at the initial stages is due to interaction of moving free charge (i.e. J_f) and a magnetic field which is given as the total magnetic force on a charge q moving with velocity v by Lorentz force as

$$\mathbf{f} = q\mathbf{v} \times \mathbf{B} \tag{A.27.1}$$

The force density $\mathbf{F}$ (N/m^3) can be derived from this expression as

$$F = \lim_{\delta V \to 0} \frac{\sum_i \mathbf{f}_i}{\delta V} = \lim_{dV \to 0} \frac{\sum_i q_i \mathbf{v}_i \times \mathbf{B}_i}{\delta V} \tag{A.27.2}$$

where $\mathbf{f}_i$, q_i, and $\mathbf{v}_i$ refer to all the particles in the volume element δV and $\mathbf{B}_i$ is the flux density experienced by the particle q_i. Since δV is 'Small' volume element, it can be argued that all the particles experience the same flux density $\mathbf{B}$, then using the definition of free currents density, Eq. (A.27.2) can be rewritten as

$$\mathbf{F} = \mathbf{J}_f \times \mathbf{B} \qquad (A.27.3)$$

Some important points to be noted in the above two equations are that Eq. (A.27.2) is the result of averaging of products and Eq. (A.27.3) is the product of averages. Furthermore for any two variables x and y, the result

$$[xy]_{av} = [x]_{av}\,[y]_{av}$$

is **not** generally true.

However, the force density given by Eq. (A.27.3) agrees with experimental results to a high degree of accuracy; and is valid because the volume element δV can be made as small as required to ensure a region of constant flux density in it, whilst still including many free charges. This equation is a preferred choice for the definition of $\mathbf{B}$ as both Biot and Savart and also Ampere did their experiments using free current density $\mathbf{J}_f$.

The force density as given in Eq. (A.27.3) has been expressed in terms of source and field quantities. However, it is useful to have the force expressed in terms of the field quantities alone because the field problems are often solved with evaluating the free current density. So at this stage, the Maxwell's Stress Tensor is being defined as a function of the field quantities from which the force density can be obtained by space differentiation. The Maxwell's Stress Tensor is particularly useful for a concise evaluation of electromechanical boundary conditions as well as the finding the total electromagnetic force on a body. So starting with a medium of constant permeability, i.e.

$$\mathbf{B} = \mu\mathbf{H} \qquad (A.27.4)$$

Using Ampere's law, Eq. (A.27.3) can be expressed as

$$\mathbf{F} = \mu(\nabla \times \mathbf{H}) \times \mathbf{H} \qquad (A.27.5)$$

By using a relevant vector identify, this equation becomes

$$\mathbf{F} = \mu(\mathbf{H} \cdot \nabla)\mathbf{H} - \frac{\mu}{2}\nabla(\mathbf{H} \cdot \mathbf{H}) \qquad (A.27.6)$$

This vector equation has three orthogonal components, which are separated out for specific requirements. A lot of manipulations become easier when the components of the vectors are considered separately. The expressions become simpler when 'index notation' is used.

Using a right-handed Cartesian system with co-ordinate directions x_1, x_2, x_3 (instead of x, y, z for easier manipulations), the force expression [Eq. (A.27.6)] is being used to establish the mathematical formalism.

The differential operator $\dfrac{\partial}{\partial x_n} \equiv \dfrac{\partial}{\partial x_1}$ or $\dfrac{\partial}{\partial x_2}$ or $\dfrac{\partial}{\partial x_3}$

and when the index is repeated in a single term, it means summation over the three values of the index, i.e.

$$\frac{\partial H_n}{\partial x_n} = \frac{\partial H_1}{\partial x_1} + \frac{\partial H_2}{\partial x_2} + \frac{\partial H_3}{\partial x_3} = \nabla \cdot \mathbf{H}$$

and
$$H_n \frac{\partial}{\partial x_n} = H_1 \frac{\partial}{\partial x_1} + H_2 \frac{\partial}{\partial x_2} + H_3 \frac{\partial}{\partial x_3} = \mathbf{H} \cdot \nabla$$

This explains 'the summation convention'.

$\dfrac{\partial H_n}{\partial x_n}$ represents any one of the nine possible derivatives of the components of $\mathbf{H}$ w.r.t. co-ordinates.

The Kronecker delta δ_{mn} (or sometimes denoted as δ_m^n) is defined such that

$$\delta_{mn} = \begin{cases} 1, & \text{when } m = n \\ 0, & \text{when } m \neq n \end{cases} \qquad \text{(A.27.7)}$$

Its properties are as follows:

$$\delta_{mn} H_n = H_m$$

and
$$\delta_{mn} \frac{\partial}{\partial x_n} = \frac{\partial}{\partial x_m}$$

With all these definitions, the mth component of Eq. (A.27.6) can be expressed as

$$F_m = \mu H_n \frac{\partial H_m}{\partial x_n} - \frac{\mu}{2} (H_k H_k) \qquad \text{(A.27.8)}$$

Using the property of Kronecker delta and some further manipulations, the above expression can be rewritten as

$$F_m = \frac{\partial}{\partial x_n} \left(\mu H_n H_m - \frac{\mu}{2} \delta_{mn} H_k H_k \right) - H_m \frac{\partial \mu H_n}{\partial x_n} \qquad \text{(A.27.9)}$$

The last term on the R.H.S. of the above equation is

$$H_m (\nabla \cdot \mu \mathbf{H}) = H_m (\nabla \cdot \mathbf{B}) = 0$$

Equation (A.27.9) can be written in the concise form as:

$$F_m = \frac{\partial T_{mn}}{\partial x_n} \qquad \text{(A.27.10)}$$

where the Maxwell's Stress Tensor T_{mn} is given by

$$T_{mn} = \mu H_n H_m - \frac{\mu}{2} \delta_{mn} H_k H_k \qquad \text{(A.27.11)}$$

Thus when the magnetic field intensity in a region of space is known, the components of the stress Tensor T_{mn} can be evaluated. It is necessary to calculate not more than 6 components because the stress tensor is symmetric, i.e.

$$T_{mn} = T_{nm} \qquad \text{(A.27.12)}$$

Next, to find the mth component of the total force $\mathbf{f}$ on the material enclosed within the volume V, the volume integration has to be performed:

$$f_m = \iiint_V F_m \, dV = \iiint_V \frac{\partial T_{mn}}{\partial x_m} \, dV \qquad \text{(A.27.13)}$$

The components of a vector $\mathbf{A}$ can be defined as
$$A_1 = T_{m1}, \ A_2 = T_{m2}, \ A_3 = T_{m3} \qquad \text{(A.27.14)}$$

then Eq. (A.27.13) can be expressed as

$$f_m = \iiint_V \frac{\partial A_n}{\partial x_n} \, dV = \iiint_V (\nabla \cdot \mathbf{A}) \, dV \qquad (A.27.15)$$

Using the divergence theorem to change the volume integral to a surface integral

$$f_m = \oiint_S \mathbf{A} \cdot \mathbf{n} \, dS = \oiint_S A_n n_n \, dS \qquad (A.27.16)$$

where n_n is the nth component of the outward-directed unit normal vector $\mathbf{n}$ to surface S which encloses volume V.

Substituting back from Eq. (A.27.14), the above equation becomes

$$f_m = \oiint_S T_{mn} n_n \, dS \qquad (A.27.17)$$

Thus the total force of magnetic origin on the matter in a volume V can be obtained by **knowing only the fields along the surface of the volume**.

A.27.3 THE STRESS TENSOR

So the Maxwell's Stress Tensor T_{mn} has now been introduced as an ordered array of nine functions of space and time, i.e. $T_{mn}(\mathbf{r}, t)$ from which magnetic force densities and total forces can be calculated. The concept of a tensor is quite useful for describing mechanical stresses and deformations in elastic and fluid media. Thus at this stage, some tensor concepts will now be developed.

Initially the stresses will be represented by tensor so as to show the physical significance of the components of a stress tensor. Next the mathematical techniques which are used with the stress tensor to evaluate the surface stresses (= Traction) and volume force densities will be discussed. Also some general mathematical properties of tensors will also be considered. These properties are so presented that physical interpretations of the solution can be made easily. It should be appreciated that tensor analysis is a mathematical formalism useful for analysing and solving quite a wide range of physical systems.

It has been stated earlier that the Maxwell's Stress Tensor is an ordered array of nine functions of space and time which can be written in matrix form as

$$T_{mn}(\mathbf{r}, t) = \begin{bmatrix} T_{11}(\mathbf{r}, t) & T_{12}(\mathbf{r}, t) & T_{13}(\mathbf{r}, t) \\ T_{21}(\mathbf{r}, t) & T_{22}(\mathbf{r}, t) & T_{23}(\mathbf{r}, t) \\ T_{31}(\mathbf{r}, t) & T_{32}(\mathbf{r}, t) & T_{33}(\mathbf{r}, t) \end{bmatrix} \qquad (A.27.18)$$

In this double index notation of the tensors, the first index denotes the row number, and the second index the column number of the location of the element. Equations (A.27.11) and (A.27.12) indicate that the Maxwell's stress tensor is symmetric, and the symmetry is about the main diagonal.

A.27.4 STRESS AND TRACTION

From Eq. (A.27.17), it follows that the stress tensor can be physically interpreted as the total force on the matter lying within volume V enclosed by closed surface S, to be related to an integral over surface S. The dimension of the integrand $T_{mn} n_n$ is that of a force per unit area and following the summation convention (of Einstein) with a repeated index, $T_{mn}n_n$ is the mth component of a vector. This vector whose components are $T_{mn}n_n$, has special significance and has been named as 'traction' and its symbol is τ (tau). Thus the mth component of the traction vector is expressed as

$$\tau_m = T_{mn}n_n = T_{m1}n_1 + T_{m2}n_2 + T_{m3}n_3 \qquad (A.27.19)$$

[*Note:* It is important to note that the subscript (m) on the traction τ_m is same as the first subscript on the stress tensor component T_{mn}. The order of the subscripts on T_{mn} is a matter of convention. The convention followed here is the one mostly used in literature, though the opposite one is also used. Hence it is important to check the convention by inspecting Eqs. (A.27.10) or (A.27.17).]

Next, it will be shown that the traction vector τ as defined by Eq. (A.27.17), is really the vector force per unit area applied to a surface of arbitrary orientation. At this stage, the Eq. (A.27.19) will be used to find some physical significance to the components of the stress vector.

Let the surface integral of the Eq. (A.27.18) be taken over a rectangular volume whose faces are orthogonal to the co-ordinate axes (x_1, x_2, x_3 corresponding to x, y, z respectively) shown in Figure A.27.1. Then the mth component of the total force **f**, which is f_m given by Eq. (A.27.17), can be obtained as the sum of the six integrals taken over the six plane faces of the rectangular volume as shown in the Figure A.27.1. First considered is the top face which has the outward directed normal vector,

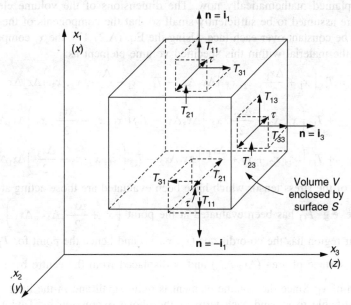

Figure A.27.1 A rectangular volume V acted on by T_{mn}.

The components of this normal vector are

$$n_1 = 1, \ n_2 = n_3 = 0.$$

$\therefore$ The three components of the traction vector on the top surface are

$$\tau_1 = T_{11}, \ \tau_2 = 21, \ \tau_3 = T_{31}$$

Similarly, for the bottom surface, the outward directed normal vector is

$$\mathbf{n} = -\mathbf{i}_1$$

whose components are

$$n_1 = -1, \ n_2 = n_3 = 0$$

Thus the three components of the traction vector on the bottom face are

$$\tau_1 = -T_{11}, \ \tau_2 = -T_{21}, \ \tau_3 = -T_{31}$$

These components of the stress tensor and the vector $\boldsymbol{\tau}$ are also shown in Figure A.27.1. The vector and the components for the stress tensor for the face with the outward directed normal vector $\mathbf{n} = \mathbf{i}_3$ (i.e. in the z-direction) are also shown in the same figure.

Thus, it has now been shown that **the component T_{mn} of the stress tensor can be physically interpreted as the mth component of the traction applied to R surface with a normal vector in the nth direction**; i.e. $T_{23}(= T_{yz})$ is the x_2-directed (y-direction) component of the traction applied to a surface whose normal vector is $\mathbf{i}_3 \ \{= \mathbf{i}_z\}$.

These ideas explained so far can now be extrapolated to construct all the components of the traction on all the six faces of the rectangular volume ($\Delta x_1 \ \Delta x_2 \ \Delta x_3$) (i.e. $\Delta x \ \Delta y \ \Delta z$) as shown in Figure A.27.2. The faces of this volume element are perpendicular to the co-ordinate axes, and the positions of these faces are properly defined. The corresponding stresses act in opposite directions on opposite faces. Hence, if such component of the stress tensor is a constant over the whole volume, the stresses oppose one another exactly and then no net force would be applied to the material inside the volume. Hence the stress tensor must vary with space to produce a net force.

This is explained mathematically now. The dimensions of the volume element (shown in Figure A.27.2) are assumed to be sufficiently small so that the components of the stress tensor can be considered to be constant over each face. Using the Eq. (A.27.17), the x_1 component of the total force applied to the material within this specified volume element as:

$$f_1 = T_{11}\left(x_1 + \frac{\Delta x_1}{2}, x_2, x_3\right)\Delta x_2 \Delta x_3 - T_{11}\left(x_1 - \frac{\Delta x_1}{2}, x_2, x_3\right)\Delta x_2 \Delta x_3$$

$$+ T_{12}\left(x_1, x_2 + \frac{\Delta x_2}{2}, x_3\right)\Delta x_3 \Delta x_1 - T_{12}\left(x_1, x_2 - \frac{\Delta x_2}{2}, x_3\right)\Delta x_3 \Delta x_1$$

$$+ T_{13}\left(x_1, x_2 + x_3 + \frac{\Delta x_3}{2}\right)\Delta x_1 \Delta x_2 - T_{13}\left(x_1, x_2, x_3 - \frac{\Delta x_3}{2}\right)\Delta x_1 \Delta x_2 \qquad \text{(A.27.20)}$$

The components of the stress tensor which have been evaluated are those acting at the centre of the enclosing surface, e.g. T_{11} has been evaluated at the point $\left(x_1 + \dfrac{\Delta x_1}{2}, \Delta x_2, \Delta x_3\right)$ whilst the centre of the rectangular region has the co-ordinates (x_1, x_2, x_3) and hence the point for T_{11} calculation lies on the bounding surface of area ($\Delta x_2 \ \Delta x_3$) and is displaced from the centre by a distance $\dfrac{\Delta x_1}{2}$ in the +ve direction of x_1. Since the volume element is quite small and in the limit this volume tends to zero, it is justifiable to expand each term of the above expression by Taylor's series and the higher degree terms can be justifiable neglected. Hence Eq. (A.27.20) can be simplified to

$$f_1 = \left\{T_{11} + \frac{\Delta x_1}{2}\frac{\partial T_{11}}{\partial x_1} - T_{11} + \frac{\Delta x_1}{2}\frac{\partial T_{11}}{\partial x_1}\right\} \Delta x_2 \ \Delta x_3$$

$$+ \left\{T_{12} + \frac{\Delta x_2}{2}\frac{\partial T_{12}}{\partial x_2} - T_{12} + \frac{\Delta x_2}{2}\frac{\partial T_{12}}{\partial x_2}\right\} \Delta x_3 \ \Delta x_1$$

$$+ \left\{T_{13} + \frac{\Delta x_3}{2}\frac{\partial T_{13}}{\partial x_3} - T_{13} + \frac{\Delta x_3}{2}\frac{\partial T_{13}}{\partial x_3}\right\} \Delta x_1 \ \Delta x_2$$

or $\qquad f_1 = \left\{ \dfrac{\partial T_{11}}{\partial x_1} + \dfrac{\partial T_{12}}{\partial x_2} + \dfrac{\partial T_{13}}{\partial x_3} \right\} \Delta x_1 \, \Delta x_2 \, \Delta x_3$ $\qquad$ (A.27.21)

All the terms in the above expressions are being evaluated at the centre of the volume element, i.e. the point (x_1, x_2, x_3) as shown in Figure A.27.2. The above expression shows that space-varying stress tensor components are **necessary** to obtain a net non-zero force.

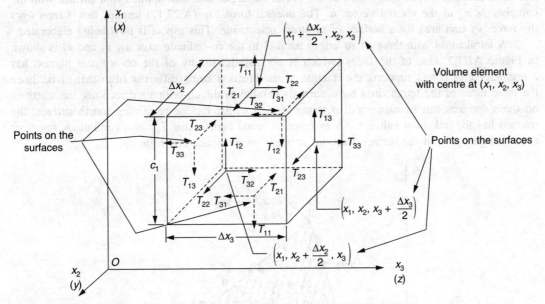

Figure A.27.2 Rectangular volume element (of volumes $\Delta x_1 \, \Delta x_2 \, \Delta x_3$) with centre at (x_1, x_2, x_3) {or (x, y, z)}. Showing all the six enclosing surfaces and the direction of the stresses T_{mn}.

From Eq. (A.27.21), the x_1 component of the force density **F** at the point (x_1, x_2, x_3) comes out as

$$F_1 = \lim_{\Delta x_1, \Delta x_2, \Delta x_3 \to 0} \frac{f_1}{\Delta x_1 \Delta x_2 \Delta x_3} = \frac{\partial T_{11}}{\partial x_1} + \frac{\partial T_{12}}{\partial x_2} + \frac{\partial T_{13}}{\partial x_3} \qquad \text{(A.27.22)}$$

The above result is exact as a consequence of the limiting process. Using Einstein's summation convention, the above result can be rewritten as

$$F_1 = \frac{\partial T_{1n}}{\partial x_n} \qquad \text{(A.27.23)}$$

Using similar process for the other two components of the force and force density at a point, the general expression is

$$F_m = \frac{\partial T_{mn}}{\partial x_n} \qquad (m\text{th component of the force density}) \qquad \text{(A.27.24)}$$

This is the same result as obtained in Eq. (A.27.10). What has been done here is that starting from the integral of Eq. (A.27.17), the derivative form of Eq. (A.27.24) has been obtained which is the reverse of the process of starting from Eq. (A.27.10) to obtain Eq. (A.27.17). This formalism discussed here is based on result of magnetic forces, though it should be appreciated that the stress tensor has more general significance, e.g. it can also be applied to a block of elastic material with mechanical stresses applied to the surfaces, etc.

In the Eq. (A.27.19), the mth component of the traction vector τ has been defined as

$$\tau_m = T_{mn}n_n \tag{A.27.25}$$

and the traction has been interpreted as the vector force per unit area applied to a surface with the components n_m of the normal vector **n**. The integral force Eq. (A.27.17) implies that τ represents the force per unit area for a surface of arbitrary orientation. This aspect is now being elaborated.

A tetrahedron with three of its edges parallel to the co-ordinate axes x_1, x_2 and x_3 is shown in Figure A.27.3. One of the faces (which is not parallel to any of the co-ordinate planes) has a normal vector **n** and supports the traction τ, its direction being different from that of **n**. Since the three faces of the tetrahedron have normals parallel to the co-ordinate directions, the tractions on these surfaces can be expressed in terms of T_{mn}, whilst for the remaining fourth surface, the traction has the unknown value τ. An assumption made here is that T_{mn} is a continuous function, even though T_{mn} (and the surface traction) depends on the space co-ordinates.

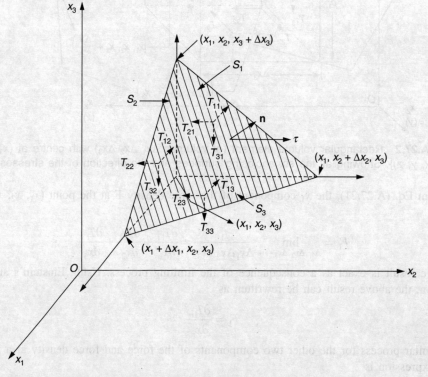

Figure A.27.3 A small tetrahedron used for evaluating the surface traction τ on a surface with the normal vector **n** in terms of the components of the stress tensor T_{mn}.

Therefore, as Δx_1, Δx_2, $\Delta x_3 \to 0$, the traction τ must balance the stresses on the –ve surfaces. It should be noted that the volume forces are proportional to the volume ($\Delta x_1 \Delta x_2 \Delta x_3$) and the surface tractions produce forces proportional to the areas $\Delta x_1 \Delta x_2$, $\Delta x_2 \Delta x_3$, and $\Delta x_3 \Delta x_1$. Hence in the limit as Δx_1, Δx_2, $\Delta x_3 \to 0$, the material of the tetrahedron would not be in force equilibrium unless the surface forces balance.

Let the surface with the normal **n** have area S and the –ve surfaces have areas S_{n1}, S_{n2}, S_{n3} and the continuity of the stresses acting in the x_1 direction will give the relationship

$$\tau_1 S \cong T_{11}S_{n1} + T_{12}S_{n2} + T_{13}S_{n3} \tag{A.27.26}$$

Note: A proof of this geometric relation is given by Gauss' theorem

$$\oiint_s \mathbf{A} \cdot \mathbf{n} = dS = \iiint_v (\nabla \cdot \mathbf{A})\,dV$$

with $\mathbf{A} = \mathbf{i}_1$.

This is to be repeated with $\mathbf{A} = \mathbf{i}_2$ and $\mathbf{A} = \mathbf{i}_3$.

In the limit as the dimensions of the tetrahedron become smaller, Eq. (A.27.26) becomes exact, and then Eq. (A.27.25) holds.

Example A.27.1 To derive the traction τ on the surface S shown in Figure A.27.4, given the stresses T_{11}, T_{12}, etc. It is assumed that **n** lies in the x_1–x_2 plane so that the normal vector is given by

$$\mathbf{n} = \mathbf{i}_1 \frac{\sqrt{3}}{2} + \mathbf{i}_2 \frac{1}{2}$$

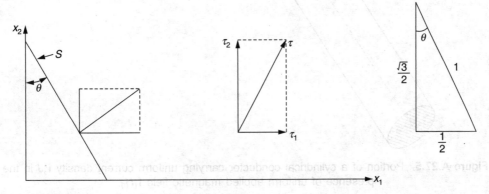

Figure A.27.4 Surface traction τ acting on a particular surface S.

It is to be noted that the components of **n** are **not** the unit vectors $\mathbf{i}_1$, $\mathbf{i}_2$, $\mathbf{i}_3$. According to Eq. (A.27.25) the components of τ acting on the surface S are:

$$\tau_1 = T_{11}\frac{\sqrt{3}}{2} + T_{12}\frac{1}{2}$$

$$\tau_2 = T_{21}\frac{\sqrt{3}}{2} + T_{22}\frac{1}{2}$$

$$\tau_3 = 0$$

where T_{31}, T_{32} and T_{33} are assumed to be zeroes, or that there is no component of the stress acting in the x_3 direction. The interpretation here is the stress components are the forces per unit area acting on surfaces which are perpendicular to the directions of co-ordinate axes.

A.27.4.1 A Current-carrying Cylindrical Conductor Placed in a Uniform Magnetic Field H_0

A cylindrical non-magnetic ($\mu = \mu_0$) conductor, with its axis coincident with x_3 axis (i.e. z-axis), carries a uniform current (constant) density

$$\mathbf{J} = \mathbf{i}_3 J \qquad \text{(i)}$$

An electromagnet (which is not shown in Figure A.27.5) produces a uniform magnetic field intensity

$$\mathbf{H}_0 = \mathbf{i}_1\, H_0 \qquad \text{(ii)}$$

over the whole region, when $J = 0$. There is no variation in the z-direction so that the problem can be treated as a two-dimensional one.

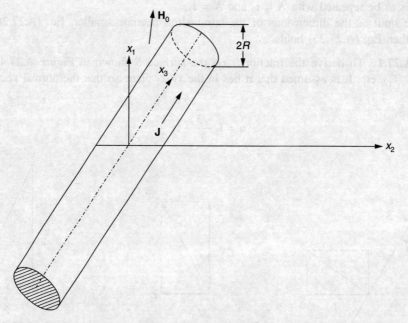

Figure A.27.5 Portion of a cylindrical conductor carrying uniform current density $\mathbf{i}_3 J$ in the presence of uniform applied magnetic field $\mathbf{i}_1 H_0$.

Since this is a linear field problem, it is justifiable to superimpose the field H_0 on the field produced by the current density J.

The current in the conductor (in the x_3 or z direction) would produce magnetic field normal to x_3 direction, i.e. H_1' and H_2' along x_1 and x_2 directions respectively. These can be obtained from the field values obtained directly in cylindrical co-ordinate system as shown in Figure A.27.6.

By using Ampere's law,

$$H_\theta = \frac{Jr}{2} \quad \text{for } r < R \qquad \text{(iii)}$$

and

$$H_\theta = \frac{JR^2}{2r} \quad \text{for } r > R \qquad \text{(iv)}$$

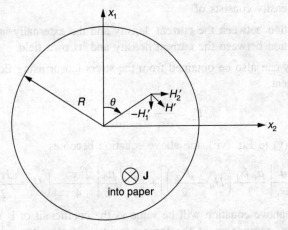

Figure A.27.6 Cylindrical co-ordinate system to evaluate the magnetic field produced by the conductor current.

The next step is to transform these expressions to Cartesian system (with coincident origin) and add the externally imposed field, i.e.

$$\left.\begin{array}{l} H_1 = H_0 - \dfrac{Jx_2}{2} \\[2mm] H_2 = \dfrac{Jx_1}{2} \end{array}\right\} \text{ for } x_1^2 + x_2^2 < R^2 \tag{v}$$

and

$$\left.\begin{array}{l} H_1 = H_0 - \dfrac{JR^2}{2}\left(\dfrac{x_2}{x_1^2 + x_2^2}\right) \\[3mm] H_2 = \dfrac{JR^2}{2}\left(\dfrac{x_1}{x_1^2 + x_2^2}\right) \end{array}\right\} \text{ for } x_1^2 + x_2^2 > R^2 \tag{vi}$$

In the above, the component $H_3 = 0$ for both the regions.

By using Eqs. (A.27.11) and (A.27.18), the stress tensor is obtained as

$$(T_{mn}) = \begin{bmatrix} \dfrac{\mu_0}{2}(H_1^2 - H_2^2) & \mu_0 H_1 H_2 & 0 \\[3mm] \mu_0 H_1 H_2 & \dfrac{\mu_0}{2}(H_2^2 - H_1^2) & 0 \\[3mm] 0 & 0 & -\dfrac{\mu_0}{2}(H_1^2 + H_2^2) \end{bmatrix} \tag{vii}$$

Equations (v) and (vi) can be used with the tensor matrix {Eq. (vii)} to evaluate the stress tensor both inside and outside the conductor.

Considering the inside first,

$$\mathbf{F} = \mathbf{J}_f \times \mathbf{B} = -\mathbf{i}_1 J \mu_0 H_2 + \mathbf{i}_2 J \mu_0 H_1$$

$$= -\mathbf{i}_1 \frac{\mu_0 J^2 x_1}{2} + \mathbf{i}_2 \mu_0 J \left\{ H_0 - \frac{Jx_2}{2} \right\} \tag{viii}$$

by using Eq. (A.27.3).

Thus the force density consists of

(a) due to interaction between the current density and the externally applied field, and
(b) due to interaction between the current density and its own field.

The same force density can also be obtained from the stress tensor using Eq. (A.27.10), and doing this for the x_2 component,

$$F_2 = \frac{\partial}{\partial x_1} T_{21} + \frac{\partial}{\partial x_2} T_{22} \tag{ix}$$

Substituting from Eq. (v) to Eq. (vii), the above equation becomes

$$F_2 = \frac{\partial}{\partial x_1} \left[\frac{\mu_0 J x_1}{2} \left(H_0 - \frac{J x_2}{2} \right) \right] + \frac{\partial}{\partial x_2} \left\{ \frac{\mu_0}{2} \left[\frac{J^2 x_1^2}{4} - \left(H_0 - \frac{J x_2}{2} \right)^2 \right] \right\} \tag{x}$$

On differentiating, the above equation will be same as the coefficient of $\mathbf{i}_2$ of Eq. (viii). A similar process will give the x_1 component of the force density, and also it can be checked that the x_3 component of the force density is zero.

Outside the conductor, the force density must be zero as the current density is zero. But Eqs. (vi) and (vii) show that the stress tensor has non-zero components in this region. However, it can be checked by writing the proper expression and completing the differentiation, that the correct zero value is obtained. The corresponding expression for F_2 is

$$F_2 = \frac{\partial}{\partial x_1} \left\{ \frac{\mu_0 J R^2}{2} \left(\frac{x_1}{x_1^2 + x_2^2} \right) \left[H_0 - \frac{J R^2}{2} \left(\frac{x_2}{x_1^2 + x_2^2} \right) \right] \right\}$$

$$+ \frac{\partial}{\partial x_2} \frac{\mu_0}{2} \left\{ \frac{J^2 R^4}{4} \left(\frac{x_1}{x_1^2 + x_2^2} \right)^2 - \left[H_0 - \frac{J R^2}{2} \left(\frac{x_2}{x_1^2 + x_2^2} \right) \right]^2 \right\} \tag{xi}$$

and on differentiating this comes out to be zero.

Similarly, F_1 and F_3 calculated from the stress tensor comes out to be zero.

The next step is to calculate the total magnetic force on a length l (in the axial direction) of the conductor. Hence the corresponding volume element dV is

$$dV = l \, dx_1 \, dx_2$$

and integrating (volume) the force density expression of Eq. (viii).

$$\mathbf{f} = \int_{-R}^{R} \int_{-\sqrt{(R^2 - x_1^2)}}^{\sqrt{(R^2 - x_1^2)}} \left[-\mathbf{i}_1 \frac{\mu_0 J^2 x_1}{2} + \mathbf{i}_2 \mu_0 J \left(H_0 - \frac{J x_2}{2} \right) \right] l \, dx_1 \, dx_2$$

Integrating this expression w.r.t. x_2 first with the limits and then w.r.t. x_1 within its limits, the answer comes out to be

$$\mathbf{f}_2 = \mathbf{i}_2 J \mu_0 H_0 \pi R^2 l \tag{xii}$$

The same result could be obtained by using the stress tensor and Eq. (A.27.17). The surface over which the integration has to be carried out is shown in Figure A.27.7, completely enclosing the conductor (or axial length l) and square cross-sectional area of $4R \times 4R$.

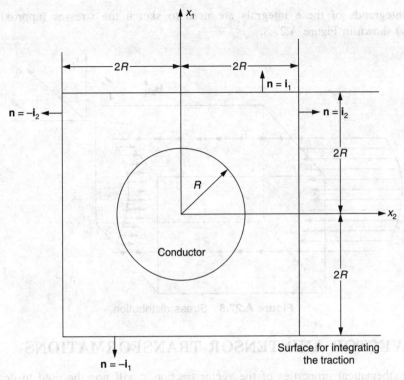

Figure A.27.7 Surface for integrating the traction.

Since this surface is completely outside the conductor, Eqs. (vi) and (vii) have to be used to calculate the components of the stress tensor. Since the problem is two-dimensional, the two ends perpendicular to x_3-axis contribute zero to the integral. The parallel lateral faces, i.e. $x_1 = \pm 2R$, $x_2 = \pm 2R$ are such that the only x_2 component of the total force is non-zero, and x_1 component is zero as shown by the Eq. (xii). Hence the f_2 component can be written and derived as

$$f_2 = \int_{-2R}^{2R} T_{21}(2R, x_2) l dx_2 - \int_{-2R}^{2R} T_{21}(-2R, x_2) l dx_2$$

$$+ \int_{-2R}^{2R} T_{22}(x_1, 2R) l dx_1 - \int_{-2R}^{2R} T_{22}(x_1, -2R) l dx_1 \qquad \text{(xiii)}$$

Substituting for T_{mn} from Eqs. (vii) and (vi), the result again comes out to be

$$f_2 = J\mu_0 H_0 \pi R^2 l$$

same as Eq. (xii).

Thus the total force on a current-carrying conductor material within a volume has been obtained by integrating the traction over a surface which encloses the volume. Thus it is seen that the first two integrals in the Eq. (xiii) involve the x_2-component of the traction applied to surfaces whose normal vectors are in the x_1 direction. Thus as these tractions are applied **along a surface**, they are referred to as '**shear stresses**'. The second two integrals deal with components of the traction which are perpendicular to the surfaces to which they applied and hence are called '**normal stresses**'.

The integrands of these integrals are used to sketch the stresses (approximately and qualitatively) shown in Figure A.27.8.

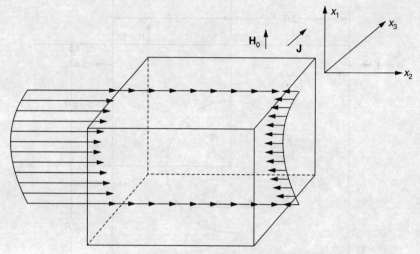

Figure A.27.8 Stress distribution.

A.27.5 VECTOR AND TENSOR TRANSFORMATIONS

Now, the mathematical properties of the vector traction τ will now be used to describe some mathematical properties of the stress tensor. The traction τ is a vector and its components would depend on the co-ordinate system that is being used for the vector. Given two co-ordinate systems (x_1, x_2, x_3) and (x_1', x_2', x_3'), the components of the vector τ in these two systems are related by the equations

$$\tau_p' = a_{pr}\tau_r \qquad (A.27.27)$$

where a_{pr} is the cosine of the angle between the x_p'-axis and the x_r-axis.

For this transformation relation to hold, it should be noted that both the co-ordinate systems are of Cartesian type with common origin and the primed system has been obtained by rotating the unprimed system through an angle θ. Also in this case there has been only rotary motion and no translational motion between the two co-ordinate systems.

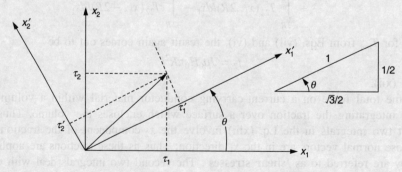

Figure A.27.9 Relationship between the primed and unprimed co-ordinate systems (obtained by rotation through $\theta = 30°$).

As an example, let the primed system (x_1', x_2', x_3') be obtained by rotating the unprimed system (x_1, x_2, x_3) through an angle $\theta = 30°$ in the anti-clockwise direction (Figure A.27.9).

From the geometry, the cosine of the angle between

$$x_1' \text{ and } x_1 = a_{11} = \frac{\sqrt{3}}{2} \qquad\qquad x_2' \text{ and } x_2 = a_{22} = \frac{\sqrt{3}}{2}$$

$$x_1' \text{ and } x_2 = a_{12} = \frac{1}{2} \qquad\qquad x_3' \text{ and } x_3 = a_{33} = 1$$

$$x_2' \text{ and } x_1 = a_{21} = -\frac{1}{2} \qquad\qquad \text{all others} = 0$$

$$\therefore \qquad [a_{mn}] = \begin{bmatrix} \dfrac{\sqrt{3}}{2} & -\dfrac{1}{2} & 0 \\[2mm] \dfrac{1}{2} & \dfrac{\sqrt{3}}{2} & 0 \\[2mm] 0 & 0 & 1 \end{bmatrix} \leftarrow \text{the rotation matrix}$$

Then Eq. (A.27.27) gives

$$\tau_1' = \frac{\sqrt{3}}{2}\,\tau_1 + \frac{1}{2}\tau_2$$

$$\tau_2' = -\frac{1}{2}\,\tau_1 + \frac{\sqrt{3}}{2}\,\tau_2$$

From this statement it can be argued that Eq. (A.27.27) is a simple statement of vector addition. The above results can also be deduced from Figure A.27.9 without the formalism of Eq. (A.27.27).

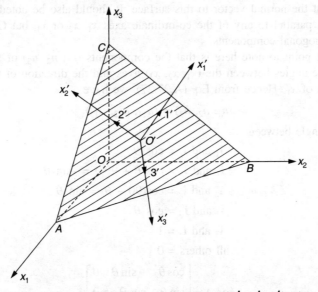

Figure A.27.10 Two co-ordinate systems (x_1, x_2, x_3) and (x_1', x_2', x_3') when x_1' is coincident with the normal vector **n** to the top surface of the tetrahedron having vertex at the origin of the co-ordinate system (x_1, x_2, x_3).

Equation (A.27.27) is the basis for determining the components of the stress tensor from one co-ordinate system to another.

According to Eq. (A.27.19), the components of τ are

$$\tau_r = T_{rs} n_s \tag{A.27.28}$$

Another Cartesian co-ordinate system (x_1', x_2', x_3') has been derived in such a manner that one of its co-ordinate axes (say x_1') coincides with the direction **n** shown in Figure A.27.10. It should be

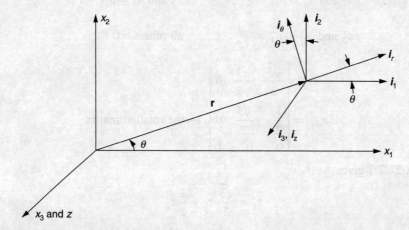

Figure A.27.11 Geometrical relationship between Cartesian and cylindrical co-ordinate systems.

noted that new co-ordinate system has been obtained by translating the origin of the original system (x_1, x_2, x_3) from point O to point O' which lies on the top face of the tetrahedron whose vertex is at O, and at O' co-ordinate system has been rotated till its x_1-axis (i.e. now x_1'-axis) coincides with the direction of the normal vector to this surface. It should also be noted that the translation distance OO' is not parallel to any of the co-ordinate axes x_1, x_2 or x_3, but OO' can be resolved into these three orthogonal components.

The important point to note here is that the components (n_1, n_2, n_3) of the normal vector n are the cosine of the angles between the (x_1, x_2, x_3) axes and the direction of the normal **n** which is also the direction of x_1'. Hence from Eq. (A.27.27), we have

$$(n_1, n_2, n_3) = (a_{11}, a_{12}, a_{13})$$

The cosine of the angle between

$$\mathbf{i}_1 \text{ and } \mathbf{i}_r = \cos\theta$$
$$\mathbf{i}_1 \text{ and } \mathbf{i}_\theta = \cos(\theta + 90°) = -\sin\theta$$
$$\mathbf{i}_2 \text{ and } \mathbf{i}_r = \cos(90 - \theta) = \sin\theta$$
$$\mathbf{i}_2 \text{ and } \mathbf{i}_\theta = \cos\theta$$
$$\mathbf{i}_3 \text{ and } \mathbf{i}_z = 1$$
$$\text{all others} = 0$$

$$\therefore \quad (a_{mn}) = \begin{bmatrix} \cos\theta & -\sin\theta & 0 \\ \sin\theta & \cos\theta & 0 \\ 0 & 0 & 1 \end{bmatrix}$$

The components of the stress are obtained directly by using Eq. (A.27.33).

$$T_{11} = T_{rr} \cos^2\theta - 2T_{r\theta} \sin\theta \cos\theta + T_{\theta\theta} \sin^2\theta$$

$$T_{12} = T_{rr} \sin\theta \cos\theta + T_{r\theta}(\cos^2\theta - \sin^2\theta) - T_{\theta\theta} \sin\theta \cos\theta$$

$$T_{13} = T_{rz} \cos\theta - T_{z\theta} \sin\theta$$

$$T_{22} = T_{rr} \sin^2\theta + 2T_{r\theta} \sin\theta \cos\theta + T_{\theta\theta} \cos^2\theta$$

$$T_{23} = T_{rz} \sin\theta + T_{z\theta} \cos\theta$$

$$T_{33} = T_{zz}$$

Usually a vector or first order tensor is defined as an array of three numbers which transforms according to an equation of the form of Eq. (A.27.27). Similarly, a second order tensor is defined as an array of number which transforms according to an equation in the form of Eq. (A.27.32).

Example A.27.2 In the two co-ordinate systems shown in Figure A.27.9, to express the stress component T_{11}' expressed in primed co-ordinate system to the components T_{mn} in unprimed system. Using Eq. (A.27.32), the result is

$$T_{11}' = a_{11}a_{11}T_{11} + a_{11}a_{12}T_{12} + a_{11}a_{13}T_{13}$$
$$+ a_{12}a_{11}T_{21} + a_{12}a_{12}T_{22} + a_{12}a_{13}T_{23}$$
$$+ a_{13}a_{11}T_{31} + a_{13}a_{12}T_{32} + a_{13}a_{13}T_{33}$$

For the numerical values given in that problem,

$$T_{11}' = \frac{\sqrt{3}}{2}\frac{\sqrt{3}}{2}T_{11} + \frac{\sqrt{3}}{2}\left(\frac{1}{2}\right)T_{12} + \left(\frac{1}{2}\right)\frac{\sqrt{3}}{2}T_{21} + \left(\frac{1}{2}\right)\left(\frac{1}{2}\right)T_{22}$$

Example A.27.3 The stress components T_{mn} expressed in a cylindrical co-ordinate system (r, θ, z) are given and to find the components of the stress tensor expressed in a Cartesian co-ordinate system with the axes x_1, x_2 and x_3 as shown in Figure A.27.11.

The relationship between the unit vectors is shown in Figure A.27.11. In the present example, the Cartesian co-ordinate system plays the role of the 'primed' system, and the cylindrical system is the unprimed system.

From Figure A.27.11, it is seen that Eq. (A.27.28) can also be written as

$$\tau_r = T_{rs} a_{15} \tag{A.27.29}$$

Since x_1' is perpendicular to this surface (ABC in Figure A.27.10) x_2' and x_3' must lie on this surface. Hence it is obvious that $(\tau_1', \tau_2', \tau_3')$ are just the components of the stress acting on a surface which has normal in the direction of x_1'.

$$\therefore \qquad \tau_p' = T_{p1}' \tag{A.27.30}$$

But, Eq. (A.27.27) can also be used to express T_p' as

$$\tau_p' = a_{pr}\tau_0 \tag{A.27.31}$$

which by Eq. (A.27.29) gives a relation for τ_p' in terms of stress components in the unprimed co-ordinates,

$$\tau_p' = a_{pr}(T_{rs}a_{15}) \tag{A.27.32}$$

$\therefore$ From Eq. (A.27.29),

$$T_{p1}' = a_{pr}a_{15}T_{rs} \tag{A.27.33}$$

Now, the designation of the normal direction by the x_1 axis has been arbitrarily chosen, and all these arguments can be justifiably repeated with 1 being replaced by 2, or 1 by 3. Thus it is seen that

$$T_{pq}' = a_{pr}a_{qs}T_{rs} \qquad (A.27.34)$$

Thus this above relation gives the rule for finding the stress in the primed co-ordinates when the components in the unprimed co-ordinates are known. Thus Eq. (A.27.34) serves the same purpose in dealing with tensors, which Eq. (A.27.27) does for the vectors.

Important points of note for tensor transformation:

1. When the components of a stress tensor are expressed in polar co-ordinate system or for that matter in any other **curvilinear** system, the space derivatives have to be carefully derived (this is because not all co-ordinate variables are lengths and the co-ordinate unit vectors are not all constant vectors).

2. The direction cosines a_{mn} which transformed the vector in Eq. (A.27.27) have been defined with the tacit assumption that all components of T were expressed in an **orthogonal** co-ordinate system. Hence there were implicit trigonometric relations between these direction cosines.

    Hence it is possible to extend the concept of a tensor to situations in which the transformations stated in Eqs. (A.27.27) and (A.27.34) are not of geometrical origin. Such relations can easily be established by using Eq. (A.27.27).

3. Equation (A.27.27) gives the transformation of the vector τ (traction) from an unprimed to a primed co-ordinate system. These two systems are totally arbitrarily chosen hence the transformation from a primed to the unprimed system can as well be defined

$$\tau_s = b_{sp}\tau_p' \qquad (A.27.35)$$

    where b_{sp} is the cosine of the angle between the x_s-axis and the x_p'-axis. But b_{sp}, from the definition as per Eq. (A.27.27), is also

$$b_{sp} \equiv a_{ps} \qquad (A.27.36)$$

    i.e. the transformation which reverses the transformation of Eq. (A.27.27) is

$$\tau_s = a_{ps}\tau_p' \qquad (A.27.37)$$

4. An important property of the direction cosine that is being established is that (a) the direction cosines a_{ps} transforming the vector τ to an arbitrary primed co-ordinate system, and then (b) transforming the components τ_m' back to the unprimed system in which these components must be the same as when started. Equation (A.27.27) provided the first transformation and Eq. (A.27.37) was the second transformation, i.e. Eq. (A.27.27) can be substituted into Eq. (A.27.37) to obtain the result

$$\tau_s = a_{ps}\, a_{pr}\tau_r \qquad (A.27.38)$$

In this above equation, considering the case of $s = 1$, the result comes out as

$$\tau_{11} = (a_{11}a_{11} + a_{21}a_{21} + a_{31}a_{31})\tau_1$$
$$+ (a_{11}a_{12} + a_{21}a_{22} + a_{31}a_{32})\tau_2$$
$$+ (a_{11}a_{13} + a_{21}a_{23} + a_{31}a_{33})\tau_3 \qquad (A.27.39)$$

This relation is quite general. Neither a_{ps} nor τ_m has been specified. Therefore, the terms in the second and third brackets must vanish and the first one must be unity. The result can then be expressed very concisely as

$$a_{ps}a_{pr} = \delta_{sr} \tag{A.27.40}$$

where δ_{sr} is the Kronecker delta.

Equation (A.27.38) reduces to the identity

$$\tau_s = \tau_s.$$

A.27.6 FORCES IN ELECTRICAL FIELD SYSTEMS

So far, only the magnetic field systems have been considered. The electric field systems can also be considered in a similar manner. For electric field problem, by using Lorentz force equation to find the force **f** on a charge of placed in an electric field **E**,

$$\mathbf{f} = q\mathbf{E} \tag{A.27.41}$$

The force density **F** can be found by taking the average of the above equation over a small volume

$$\mathbf{F} = \lim_{\delta V \to 0} \frac{\sum_i \mathbf{f}_i}{\delta V} = \lim_{\delta V \to 0} \frac{\sum_i q_i \mathbf{E}_i}{\delta V} \tag{A.27.42}$$

where q_i represents all the charges in the volume element δV, $\mathbf{E}_i$ is the electric field acting on the ith charge, and $\mathbf{f}_i$ is the force on the ith charge.

Experimentally it has been found that the free charge density is on the sparse side such that the microscopic field $\mathbf{E}_i$ as seen by a free charge can be justifiably approximated by the average macroscopic field **E** and all charges in the volume experience the same electric field **E**

$$\therefore \qquad\qquad \mathbf{F} = \rho_f \mathbf{E} \tag{A.27.43}$$

where

$$\rho_f = \lim_{\delta V \to 0} \frac{\sum_i q_i}{\delta V}$$

This is the force density on the charges, and like the magnetic force density, can be considered as the material force when each of the charge transmits its force to the medium.

The corresponding constitutive relation is

$$\mathbf{D} = \varepsilon \mathbf{E} \tag{A.27.44}$$

At present ε is assumed to be constant, though later this constant can be relaxed.

By using Gauss' theorem, the force Eq. (A.27.43) can be written in terms of the electric field as

$$\mathbf{F} = (\nabla \cdot \varepsilon \mathbf{E})\mathbf{E} \tag{A.27.45}$$

Expressing this equation as space derivative of a stress tensor by remembering that for electric field system $\nabla \times \mathbf{E} = 0$. Hence Eq. (A.27.45) can be written as

$$\mathbf{F} = (\nabla \cdot \varepsilon \mathbf{E})\mathbf{E} + (\nabla \times \mathbf{E}) \times \varepsilon \mathbf{E} \tag{A.27.46}$$

The last term in this equation is further modified by the vector identity given below

$$(\nabla \times \mathbf{A}) \times \mathbf{A} = (\mathbf{A} \cdot \nabla)\mathbf{A} - \frac{1}{2}\nabla(\mathbf{A} \cdot \mathbf{A})$$

F can now be expressed as:

$$\mathbf{F} = (\nabla \cdot \varepsilon\mathbf{E})\mathbf{E} + \varepsilon(\mathbf{E} \cdot \nabla)\mathbf{E} - \frac{1}{2}\varepsilon\nabla(\mathbf{E} \cdot \mathbf{E}) \qquad (A.27.47)$$

Using the index notation introduced earlier, combining the first two terms and writing the mth component of this equation as

$$F_m = \frac{\partial}{\partial x_n}(\varepsilon E_m E_n) - \frac{\varepsilon}{2}\frac{\partial}{\partial x_m}(E_k E_k) \qquad (A.27.48)$$

Using Kronecker delta to write

$$\frac{\partial}{\partial x_m} = \delta_{mn}\frac{\partial}{\partial x_n}$$

and putting Eq. (A.27.48) in the form for the tensor used earlier

$$F_m = \frac{\partial T_{mn}}{\partial x_n} \qquad (A.27.49)$$

where the Maxwell's stress tensor T_{mn} for the electric field systems is given by

$$T_{mn} = \varepsilon E_m E_n - \frac{\varepsilon}{2}\delta_{mn}E_k E_k \qquad (A.27.50)$$

It should be noted that this equation has the same form as Eq. (A.27.17) if ε is replaced by μ and **E** by **H**. The stress tensor here has all the properties discussed earlier in the section on vector and tensor transformation (Section A.27.5).

Both electric and magnetic forces are usually included in Maxwell's stress tensor. However, they have not been combined here because they do not occur simultaneously in appreciable amounts in the same quasi-static systems. The term Maxwell's stress tensor has been used here to denote that function from which electromagnetic force densities can be evaluated by differentiation.

A significant advantage of a formulation, which uses the stress tensor, is that the forces on the material within a volume can be determined without the knowledge of the details of the volume force distributions (i.e. distribution of currents or charges).

Appendix 28

Inversion of a Matrix
The Gaussian Elimination Method

A.28.1 INTRODUCTION

A simultaneous system of linear algebraic equations can be expressed in a compact matrix form as shown below, i.e.

$$Ax = b \qquad (A.28.1)$$

where A is a given matrix
      b is a given vector
      x is the unknown vector

This equation can be formally solved by premultiplying it by A^{-1}, and the solution is obtained as

$$x = A^{-1}b \qquad (A.28.2)$$

The matrix A^{-1} is called the 'reciprocal' or the 'inverse' of A, and any method by which A^{-1} can be evaluated is called 'the inversion of A'.

It is not always necessary to invert the matrix **A** for solving the linear Eq. (A.28.1), and it is dependent on the role of the known vector b. The matrix **A** is inherently associated with the given physical situation and the R.H.S. vector b has frequently the significance of a 'forcing function', and it may sometimes be necessary to obtain the response of a given structure to a variety of forcing functions. In such cases b may have to be changed freely whilst the L.H.S. of the equation remains unchanged. Hence evaluation of A^{-1} becomes necessary because knowing A^{-1}, it can be operated on b to obtain the solution of the problem.

A.28.2 THE GAUSSIAN ELIMINATION METHOD

This fundamental method of inverting a matrix was introduced by Gauss, and it works both for solving a set of linear equations and for inverting a matrix. Its underlying principle is quite simple, and its operational steps are easy to perform. Its numerical procedures make use of a large number of very simple operations, instead of a smaller number of more involved operations. Gradually the zero elements of the unit matrix get shifted over to the left side, and the right side gets filled with more and more elements. Finally the unit matrix is on the left side and the right side is completely full of elements which completes the job.

Considering a linear system with a given right side as shown in the Eqn. (A.28.1), and rewriting it as

$$Ax - b = 0 \qquad\qquad (A.28.2)$$

The system can be expressed symbolically (with the variables appearing at the top of the scheme)

$$
\begin{array}{cccccc}
x_1 & x_2 & \cdots & x_n & -1 \\
\end{array}
$$
$$
\begin{bmatrix}
a_{11} & a_{12} & \cdots & a_{1n} & b_1 \\
a_{21} & a_{22} & \cdots & a_{2n} & b_2 \\
\vdots & \vdots & \vdots & \vdots & \vdots \\
a_{n1} & a_{n2} & \cdots & a_{nn} & b_n
\end{bmatrix} = 0 \qquad (A.28.3)
$$

The elimination method is based on two fundamental operations which are as follows:

  (i) multiply any row of the above scheme by an arbitrary factor, and
  (ii) add it to any other row.

Reasons for these operations are that it is permissible to multiply any equation by an arbitrary factor and add it to any other row.

- Consider first the absolutely largest element of the matrix, i.e. (say) a_{ik}.
- Divide the entire row by a_{ik} so that a_{ik} is now replaced by 1.
- Next aim is to make all other elements of the kth column equal to zero, so that the kth column now consists of zeroes and one solitary 1.
- The zeroing of an element is done by multiplying the ith row by that particular element and then subtracting it from the row which that element occupies, e.g.

$$
\begin{array}{cccc}
x_1 & x_2 & x_3 & -1 \\
\end{array}
$$
$$
\begin{bmatrix}
33 & 16 & 72 & 359 \\
-24 & -10 & -57 & -281 \\
-8 & -4 & -17 & -85
\end{bmatrix} = 0 \qquad (A.28.4)
$$

The largest element of the matrix is 72, which is in the 1st row, and hence dividing the 1st row by 72, it reduces to:

$$
\begin{array}{cccc}
0.458333 & 0.222222 & 1 & 4.98611
\end{array} \qquad (A.28.5)
$$

Now 1 appears in the 3rd column. The remaining two elements of this column can be reduced to zero by multiplying the new first row [i.e. Eq. (A.28.5)] by +57 and then adding to the 2nd row of Eq. (A.28.4); and then again multiplying Eq. (A.28.5) by 17 and adding it to the 3rd row of Eq. (A.28.4). The matrix then becomes

$$
\begin{array}{cccc}
x_1 & x_2 & x_3 & -1 \\
\end{array} \qquad (A.28.6)
$$
$$
\begin{bmatrix}
0.458333 & 0.222222 & 1 & 4.98611 \\
2.12498 & 2.66665 & 0 & 3.20827 \\
-0.208339 & -0.222226 & 0 & -0.23613
\end{bmatrix}
$$

The variable x_3 is now eliminated as it has now been removed from the 2nd and 3rd equations.

The original 3×3 matrix (hence the original problem) has been reduced to a 2×2 problem.

Generalizing, the zeroing of one column reduces the original $n \times n$ problem to an $(n - 1) \times (n - 1)$ problem.

To continue with the process, the largest term now is $x_2 = 2.6665$ in the 2nd row. Hence dividing this 2nd row by this quantity (i.e. 2.66665), it becomes

$$0.796872 \quad 1 \quad 0 \quad 1.203108 \tag{A.28.7}$$

The 2nd column can now be zeroed in two stages, i.e. multiply the new 2nd row of Eq. (A.28.7) by 0.22222 and subtract it from the 1st row; and then again multiply the new 2nd row by -0.22226 and then subtract it from the 3rd row. Thus the new matrix now becomes

$$
\begin{matrix}
0.281250 & 0 & 1 & 4.71875 \\
0.796872 & 1 & 0 & 1.20311 \\
-0.031253 & 0 & 0 & 0.031232
\end{matrix}
\tag{A.28.8}
$$

Finally dividing the 3rd row by -0.031253, it becomes

$$1 \quad 0 \quad 0 \quad -1.00067 \tag{A.28.9}$$

The first column is now zeroed by multiplying the new 3rd row (i.e. A.28.9) by 0.281250 and 0.796872 successively and subtracting the multiplied rows from the 1st and 2nd row respectively. The result is now:

$$
\begin{bmatrix}
0 & 0 & 1 & 5.00019 \\
0 & 1 & 0 & 2.00052 \\
1 & 0 & 0 & -1.00067
\end{bmatrix}
\tag{A.28.10}
$$

The transformed set of equations are now

$$x_3 - 5.00019 = 0$$
$$x_2 - 2.00052 = 0$$
$$x_1 + 1.00067 = 0$$

Hence the solution

$$x_1 = -1.00067$$
$$x_2 = 2.00052$$
$$x_3 = 5.00019$$

The correct solution being $x_1 = -1$, $x_2 = 2$, $x_3 = 5$.

Appendix 29
Space-Charge Current

A.29.1 INTRODUCTION

A brief discussion of this type of current is given separately from the discussion in Appendix 13, because this current is produced by the movement of charges of one kind only, though under the influence of externally imposed electric field. Also this current is more important due to motion of positively charged particles and solved as a static problem.

A.29.2 SPACE-CHARGE CURRENT

So far currents in conductors have been considered to be due to movement of charges under the action of an electric field. The current constituted from the motion of –ve charges (i.e. electrons) in one direction and the +ve charges (i.e. rest of atom which is no longer electrically neutral but has now acquired a +ve charge due to separation of the electron from the outer most orbit of the atom. The consequence of such behaviour of the +ve and –ve charges is that at any part of the conductor volume, the net charge is zero.

A somewhat different situation would now be considered wherein the region under consideration has currents in which charges of one sign are present, so that the net charge in that region is **not zero**. An assumption is made here that the motion of the charges is so slow that the formulae of electrostatics are valid. (Ref: see Problem 1.31 from Electromagnetism 'M' Problems with solutions, 3rd edition, pp. 98–100, by A. PRAMANIK). Hence, in this region Poisson's equation must be satisfied, i.e.

$$\nabla^2 V = -\frac{\rho}{\varepsilon} \tag{A.29.1}$$

where V is the potential and ρ is the charge density. Here the charges are supposed to be similar and are associated with a mass m. Also their energy is acquired entirely from a superimposed electric field.

Hence, if their velocity is v (average value), and charge q, their energy at a point where their potential is V, will be

$$mv^2 = 2q(V_0 - V) \tag{A.29.2}$$

where V_0 = the potential of their point of origin.

Hence, the current density at any point is

$$\mathbf{J} = \rho \mathbf{v} \tag{A.29.3}$$

The simplest case to be considered first is one in which the charges are freed in unlimited quantity at the plane $x = 0$ and accelerated with a total potential of V_0 to a parallel plane at $x = b$. At the surface $x = 0$, charges will be freed until there is no longer an electric field to move them away so that the boundary condition on this plane is then (Fig. A.29.1)

$$\left(\frac{\partial V}{\partial x}\right)_{x=0} = 0 \tag{A.29.4}$$

Here all the velocities are in the x-direction so that, by eliminating ρ and $\mathbf{v}$ from the Eqs. (A.29.1), (A.29.2) and (A.29.3), the result comes out as:

$$\frac{\partial^2 V}{\partial x^2} = -\frac{J}{\varepsilon_0}\left\{\frac{m}{2q(V_0 - V)}\right\}^{1/2} \tag{A.29.5}$$

Multiplying Eq. (A.29.5) by $\dfrac{dV}{dx}$ and integrating from $V = V_0$ to V, and $\dfrac{dV}{dx} = 0$ to $\dfrac{dV}{dx}$, the result is

$$\left(\frac{dV}{dx}\right)^2 = \frac{4J}{\varepsilon_0}\left\{\frac{m(V_0 - V)}{2q}\right\}^{1/2} \tag{A.29.6}$$

Taking square-root of Eq. (A.29.6) and then integrating from $V = V_0$ at $x = 0$ to $V = 0$ at $x = b$, and then solving the equation for the current-density J, the expression for J comes out as

$$J = \frac{4\varepsilon_0}{9}\left(\frac{2q}{m}\right)^{1/2}\frac{V_0^{3/2}}{b^2} \tag{A.29.7}$$

The above equation is known as 'Child's equation'. It shows that with unlimited charge on one electrode plate, the current between the two plate electrodes, varies as the 3/2 power of the potential. Such a current is called **space-charge limited**. From Eq. (A.29.7), it is obvious that the space-charge limitation is much more serious for charged atoms than for electrons because of the greater mass of the charged atoms.

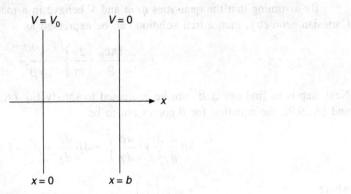

Figure A.29.1 Plane electrode system.

However, in practice, the emitting electrode is in the form of a small circular cylinder which accelerates charges to a larger concentric cylinder. The problem is now in cylindrical co-ordinate

system and if I is the total current per unit axial length of the cylinders, then Eq. (A.29.3) changes to

$$I = 2\pi r\, \rho v \qquad (A.29.8)$$

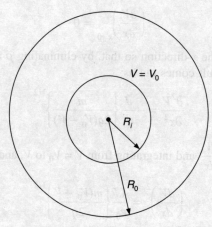

Figure A.29.2 Co-axial cylindrical electrode system.

Solving this problem in cylindrical co-ordinate system, the result comes out from the equivalent of Eq. (A.29.1) and eliminating ρ and v from Eqs. (A.29.2) and (A.29.8), and also writing V for $V_0 - V$, the resulting equation is obtained as:

$$r\frac{d^2V}{dr^2} + \frac{dV}{dr} = -\frac{I}{2\pi\varepsilon_0}\left\{\frac{m}{2qV}\right\}^{1/2} \qquad (A.29.9)$$

The direct solution of this equation in finite terms is a near impossibility. However a series solution can be obtained as follows:

By assuming that the quantities q, m and V behave in a manner similar to their behaviour in Cartesian geometry, then a trial solution can be expressed as

$$I = -\frac{8\pi\varepsilon_0}{9}\left\{\frac{2q}{m}\right\}^{1/2}\frac{V^{3/2}}{r\beta^2} \qquad (A.29.10)$$

Next step is to find out if β^2 can be evaluated to satisfy Eq. (A.29.9). Combining Eqs. (A.29.10) and (A.29.9), the equation for β comes out to be

$$3\beta\frac{d^2\beta}{d\gamma^2} + \left(\frac{d\beta}{d\gamma}\right)^2 + 4\beta\frac{d\beta}{d\gamma} + \beta^2 - 1 = 0 \qquad (A.29.11)$$

where

$$\gamma = \ln\left(\frac{r}{a}\right) \qquad (A.29.12)$$

Series solution for β comes out as:

$$\beta = \gamma - \frac{2}{5}\gamma^2 + \frac{11}{120}\gamma^3 - \frac{47}{3300}\gamma^4 + \cdots \qquad (A.29.13)$$

Langmuir has published tables of β as function of (r/a).

Note: Child–Langmuir law:

$$i = -KV_b^{3/2}$$

where

$$K = \frac{4}{9}\left\{\frac{2e}{m}\right\}^{1/2}\frac{\varepsilon_0}{l^2} = \frac{2.33\times 10^{-6}}{l^2}, \; l \text{ in metres}$$

for any geometry of cathode and plate.

K's dependence on geometry is not great.

Bibliography

Abraham, M. and Becker, R., *The Classical Theory of Electricity and Magnetism*, Blackie, London and Glasgow, 1937.

Abramowitz, M. and Stegun, I.A., *Handbook of Mathematical Functions*, Dover, New York, 1968.

Allen, D.N. de G., *Relaxation Methods*, McGraw-Hill, London and New York, 1954.

Ames, W.F., *Numerical Methods for Partial Differential Equations*, Nelson, 1969.

Askwith, E.H., *Analytical Geometry of the Conic Sections*, Adam and Charles Black, London, 1961

Attwood, S.S., *Electric and Magnetic Fields*, John Wiley & Sons, New York, 1949.

Balanis, C.A., *Advanced Engineering Electromagnetics*, John Wiley & Sons, Hoboken, NJ, 1989.

Bancroft, R., *Microstrip and Printed Antenna Design*, Prentice-Hall of India, New Delhi, 2006.

Bateman, H., *Partial Differential Equations of Mathematical Physics*, Dover, New York, 1944.

Bewley, L.V., *Two-dimensional Fields in Electrical Engineering*, Dover, New York, 1963.

_____, *Flux Linkages and Electromagnetic Induction*.

Binns, K.J. and Lawrenson, P.J., *Analysis and Computation of Electric and Magnetic Field Problems*, 2nd ed., Pergamon, Oxford, 1973.

Boast, W.B., *Vector Fields*, Harper & Row, New York.

Booker, H.G., *Energy in Electromagnetism*, Peter Prerengrinus, London, 1982.

Bozorth, R.M., *Ferromagnetism* (New Edition), IEEE Press, IEEE, New York.

Carter, G.W., *The Electromagnetic Field in Its Engineering Aspects*, Longmans, London, 1954.

Chalmers, B.J., *Electromagnetic Problems of A.C. Machines*, Chapman & Hall, London, 1965.

Churchill, R.V., *Fourier Series and Boundary Value Problems*, McGraw-Hill, New York, 1941.

Copson, E.T., *An Introduction to the Theory of Functions of a Complex Variable*, Clarendon Press, Oxford, 1935.

Coulson, C.A., *Electricity*, Oliver & Boyd, London, 1956.

Cullwick, E.G., *Electromagnetism and Relativity*, Longmans, London, 1961

Cullwick, E.G., *The Fundamentals of Electromagnetism*, Macmillan, New York, 1939.

Davies, E.J., Conduction and Induction Heating, *The Institution of Engineering and Technology*, London, 2007.

Duffin, W.J., *Advanced Electricity and Magnetism*, McGraw-Hill, London, 1968.

Duffin, W.J., *Electricity and Magnetism*, McGraw-Hill, London, 1964.

Dwight, H.B., *Tables of Integrals and Other Mathematical Data*, Macmillan, New York, 1934.

Edwards, J., *A Treatise on the Integral Calculus*, Macmillan, London, 1921.

Elliot, R.S., *Electromagnetics—History, Theory and Applications*, IEEE Press, Piscataway, NJ, 1993.

Fano, R.M., Chu, L.J., and Adler, R.B., *Electromagnetic Fields, Energy and Forces*, John Wiley, New York, 1960.

_____, *Electromagnetic Energy Transmission and Radiation*, John Wiley, New York, 1960.

Forsythe, G.E. and Wasow, W.R., *Finite Difference Methods for Partial Differential Equations*, John Wiley, New York, 1960.

Gibbs, W.J., *Conformal Transformations in Electrical Engineering*, Chapman & Hall, London, 1958.

Gradshteyn, I.S. and Ryzhik, I.W., *Table of Integrals, Series and Products*, Academic Press, London, 1965.

Graneau, P., and Graneau, N., *Newtonian Electrodynamics*, World Scientific Publishing, Singapur, 1996.

Großner, W. and Hofreiter, N., *Integraltafel*, Teil 2, Springer, Wein, 1958.

Großner, W., *Integraltafel*, Teil 1, Springer, Braunschweig, 1944.

Hague, B., *The Principles of Electromagnetism Applied to Electrical Machines*, Dovers, London, 1962.

_____, *Vector Analysis*, Methuen, London, 1955.

Hammond, P., *Energy Methods in Electromagnetism*, Clarendon Press, Oxford, 1986.

_____, *Applied Electromagnetism*, Pergamon, Oxford, 1971.

Hanselman, D., *Brushleso Permanent Magnet Motor Design*, 2nd ed., Magna Physics Publishing, Lebanon, Ohio, USA, 2003.

Haus, H.A. and Penhune, J.P., *Case Studies in Electromagnetism*, John Wiley, New York, 1960.

Hawes, M.A., *Electromagnetic Machines*, Vols. 1 and 2, Collins, London, 1972.

Irving, J. and Mullineux, N., *Mathematics in Physics and Engineering*, Academic Press, London.

Janke, E. and Emde, F., *Tables of Functions with Formulas and Curves*, Dover, New York, 1943.

Jeans, J., *The Mathematical Theory of Electricity and Magnetism*, University Press, Cambridge, 1951.

Jolley, L.B.W., *Summation of Series*, Dover, New York, 1961.

Jones, D.S., *The Theory of Electromagnetism*, Pergamon, Oxford, 1964.

Jordan, E.C. and Balmain, K.G., *Electromagnetic Waves and Radiating Systems*, Prentice-Hall of India, New Delhi, 1993.

Kantorovich, L.V. and Krylov, V.I., *Approximate Methods of Higher Analysis*, Groningen, 1958.

Kind, D. and Kärner, H., *High Voltage Insulation Technology,* Vieweg, Braunschweig, 1985.

Lammeraner, J. and Stafl, M., *Eddy Currents*, Iliffe, London, 1966.

Lanczos, C., *Applied Analysis*, Pitman, London, 1957.

Levi, E. and Panzer, M., *Electromechanical Power Conversion*, McGraw-Hill, New York, 1966.

Lorrain, P. and Corson, D., *Electromagnetic Fields and Waves*, Freeman, San Francisco, 1970.

Lukyanov, S. and Artsimovich, L.A., *Motion of Charged Particles in Electric and Magnetic Fields*, Mir, Moscow, 1980.

MacRobert, T.M., *Functions of a Complex Variable*, Macmillan, London, 1954.

Mason, M. and Weaver, W., *The Electromagnetic Field*, Chicago University Press, 1929.

Maxwell, J.C., *A Treatise on Electricity and Magnetism*, Clarendon Press, Oxford, 1892.

Moon, P. and Spencer, D.E., *Field Theory Handbook*, Springer-Verlag.

Moon, P. and Spencer, D.E., *Field Theory for Engineers*, van Nostrand, New York, 1961.

Moon, P. and Spencer, D.E., *Foundations of Electrodynamics*, van Nostrand, New York, 1961.

Morse, P.M. and Feshbach, H., *Methods of Theoretical Physics*, Vols. 1 and 2, McGraw-Hill, New York, 1953.

Moullin, E.B., *Principles of Electromagnetism*, University Press, Oxford, 1955.

Parker, R.J., and Studders, A.J., *Permanent Magnets and Their Applications*, John Wiley & Sons.

Pavel Ripka (Editor), *Magnetic Sensors and Magnetometers*, Artech House, London, 2000.

Petit Bois, G., *Tables of Indefinite Integrals*, Dover, New York, 1961.

Pierce, B.O., *A Short Table of Integrals*, Ginn & Co., Boston, 1956.

Pierpoint, J., *Functions of a Complex Variable*, Guin, Boston, 1914.

Popovic, B.D., *Introductory Engineering Electromagnetics*, Addison-Wesley, Reading, Mass., 1971.

Pyrtionen, B.J., Jokinen, T., Harabovcova, V., *Design of Rotating Electrical Machines*, John Wiley & Sons, London, 2007.

Romeiser, M., *Optical Fibers and RF*, Butterworths, Prentice-Hall of India, New Delhi, 2006.

Rosser, W.G.V., *Classical Electromagnetism via Relativity*, Butterworths, London, 1968.

Rothe, R., Ollendorff, F., and Pohlhausen, K., *Theory of Functions as Applied to Engineering Problems*, Technology Press, Cambridge, Mass., 1933.

Sadiku, M.N.O., *Elements of Electromagnetics*, Oxford University Press, 2005.

Sadiku, M.N.O., *Numerical Techniques in Electromagnetics*, CRC Press, London, 2000.

Shaw, F.S., *An Introduction to Relaxation Methods*, Dover, New York, 1953.

Sherchiff, J.A., *Vector Fields*, University Press, Cambridge, 1977.

Shevgaonkar, R.K., *Electromagnetic Waves*, Tata McGraw-Hill, New Delhi, 2005.

Silvester, P.P., and Ferrari, R.L., *Finite Elements for Electrical Engineers*, 2nd ed., Cambridge Universy, Press, Cambridge, 1990.

Simonyi, K., *Foundations of Electrical Engineering*, Pergamon Press, Oxford.

Smith, G.D., *Numerical Solutions of Partial Differential Equations*, Oxford University Press, London, 1965.

Smythe, W.R., *Static and Dynamic Electricity*, 3rd ed., McGraw-Hill, New York, 1968.

Sneddon, I.N., *Mixed Boundary-value Problem in Potential Theory*, North-Holland Publising Amsterdam, 1966.

Sokolonikoff, I.S., *Higher Mathematics for Engineers and Physicists*, McGraw-Hill, London, 1941.

Southwell, R.V., *Relaxation Methods in Theoretical Physics*, University Press, Oxford, 1946.

Stafl, M., *Electrodynamics of Electrical Machines,* Illife, London, 1967.

Stoll, R.L., *The Analysis of Eddy Currents*, Clarendon Press, Oxford, 1974.

Stratton, J.A., *Electromagnetic Theory*, McGraw-Hill, New York, 1941.

Todd, J., *Survey of Numerical Analysis*, McGraw-Hill, New York, 1968.

Varga, R.S., *Matrix Iterative Analysis*, Prentice-Hall, London, 1962.

Vitkovitch, D. (Ed.), *Field Analysis: Experimental and Computational Methods*, van Nostrand, London, 1966.

Wachspress, E.L., *Iterative Solutions of Elliptic Systems*, Prentice-Hall, London, 1966.

Walker, M., *The Schwarz-Christoffel Transformation Its Applications—A Simple Exposition*, Dover, New York.

Walsh, J., *Numerical Analysis: An Introduction*, Academic Press, London, 1966.

Weber, E., *Electromagnetic Fields*, Vol. 1, *Mapping of Fields*, Wiley, New York, 1960.

Whittaker, E.T. and Watson, G.N., *A Course of Modern Analysis*, University Press, Cambridge, 1920.

Woodson, H.H. and Melcher, J., *Electromechanical Dynamics*, Volumes 1–3, John Wiley & Sons, New York, 1968.

Index

Index

Volume 1